PREFACE

The British Catalogue of Music is a record of new music —with the exception of certain types of popular music— published in Great Britain. In addition, it records foreign music available in this country through a sole agent and books about music. It is based on the works deposited at the British Museum where copies of all new publications must be sent by law and is the most complete list of current British music available.

Hints for tracing information

The Catalogue is presented in three sections:
Classified Section
Composer and Title Index
Subject Index

The purpose of the Classified Section is to arrange works according to the various voices, instruments, and combinations for which they are written. It is not essential to understand the system of classification. To find information, first consult the Composer and Title Index, which makes it possible to find details of which the composer, title, arranger, or any similar fact, is known. The Subject Index provides an alphabetical index of instruments, musical forms, etc., appearing in the Classified Section.

Composer

When the composer or author of a work is known, look under his name in the Composer and Title Index. The information given here, including the publisher and price, will be adequate for most purposes. If, on the other hand, the fullest information about a work is required, turn to the entry in the Classified Section. This may be found by means of the class symbol (group of letters) at the end of the composer or author entry. In tracing class symbols which include ( ) "brackets" or / "stroke", it should be borne in mind that these signs precede letters in the arrangement.

Thus:

	A
is followed by	A(. . . .)
which is followed by	A/ . . . .
which is followed by	AA
which is followed by	AB
which is followed by	B, etc.

Titles, series, editors and arrangers

Entries are made in the Composer and Title Index under the titles of all works, so that, if you do not know the composer or author, a work can be found by looking up its title in the Composer and Title Index.

If you do not know either the composer or the title, it may still be possible to trace the work if the name of the editor or arranger is known and, in the case of vocal works, the author of the words.

Instrument, musical form and character

While the Classified Section displays the works systematically according to the instrument or combination for which a work is written, the Subject Index lists the principal musical forms and musical character and it shows by means of the class symbol where works having such forms or musical character are to be found in the Classified Section. For example, in the Subject Index under the word Sonatas the following entries may be found:

Sonatas: Arrangements for 2 pianos	QNUK/AE
Sonatas: Organ	RE
Sonatas: Piano duets, 4 hands	QNVE
Sonatas: Piano solos	QPE
Sonatas: Violin solos, Unaccompanied	SPME

It will be seen that this group of entries enables you to assemble all the works in sonata form no matter for what instrument the music is, or was originally, written.

Under the word Violin the following may be found:

Violin	S
Violin: Accompanying female voices: Choral works	FE/S
Violin: Books	AS
Violin & orchestra	MPS
Violin & string orchestra	RXMPS

This group directs you first to the place S in the Classified Section, where music for the violin is found, including works composed originally for other instruments and arranged for violin. It also directs you to works in which the violin figures in combination with other instruments.

It thus provides at one and the same time the link between an instrument and its place in the Classified Section and an exhaustive guide to all the works in which that particular instrument figures.

Musical literature

Books about music which normally appear in the *British National Bibliography* are also included in this catalogue. They occur in the sequences lettered A and B. They are indexed in exactly the same way as musical works in the Composer and Title Index and are designated by the qualification "Books" in the Subject Index. Thus, in the second group above, the entry Violin: Books, directing you to AS, indicates that books about the violin will be found at that place.

Prices

Prices given are those current at the time of the first recording of an entry in this catalogue. In a few cases prices of parts are not given but can be obtained on application to the publisher.

Abbreviations

Most of the abbreviations used in describing musical works are self-explanatory. The size of a musical work is indicated by one of the following conventional symbols: *8vo* for works up to 10½ in. in height, *4to* for works between 10½ and 12 in. in height, and *fol.* for works over 12 in. in height. The abbreviation *obl.* (oblong) is added to show when a work is of unusual proportions, and a single sheet is designated by the abbreviations *s.sh.* The abbreviations used for the description of books in the sections A and B are those in use in the *British National Bibliography*.

THE
BRITISH CATALOGUE
OF MUSIC
1975

THE
BRITISH CATALOGUE
OF MUSIC
1975

A record of music and books about music recently published in Great Britain, based upon the material deposited at the Copyright Receipt Office of the British Library, arranged according to a system of classification with a Composer and Title Index, a Subject Index, and a list of music publishers

LONDON
THE BRITISH LIBRARY

© 1976 The British Library

ISBN 0 900220 58 9

The British Catalogue of Music,
The British Library Bibliographic Services Division,
Store Street, London, WC1E 7DG
Telephone: 01–636 0755; Telex 22787

APRIL 1976

Printed in Great Britain by William Clowes & Sons, Limited, London, Beccles and Colchester

OUTLINE OF THE CLASSIFICATION

The following outline is given for general information only. Users are advised to consult the Subject Index to discover the exact location of required material in the Classified Section.

MUSICAL LITERATURE

A	General works
	Common sub-divisions
A(B)	Periodicals
A(C)	Encyclopaedias
A(D)	Composite works, symposia, essays by several writers
A(E)	Anecdotes, personal reminiscences
A(K)	Economics
A(M)	Persons in music
A(MM)	Musical profession
A(MN)	Music as a career
A(P)	Individuals
A(Q)	Organisations
A(QT)	Terminology
A(QU)	Notation
A(R)	Printing
A(S)	Publishing
A(T)	Bibliographies
A(U)	Libraries
A(V)	Musical education
A(X)	History of music
A(Y)	Music of particular localities
A/AM	Theory of music
A/CC	Aesthetics
A/CY	Technique of music
A/D	Composition
A/E	Performance
A/F	Recording
A/FY	Musical character
A/G	Folk music
A/GM	Music associated with particular occupations
A/H	Dance music
A/HM	Ballet music
A/J	Music accompanying drama
A/JR	Film music
A/KD	Music to accompany social customs
A/L	Religious music
A/LZ	Elements of music
A/R	Harmony
A/S	Forms of music
A/Y	Fugue
AB	Works on vocal music
AC	Works on opera
ACM	Works on musical plays
AD-AX	Works on music for particular vocal or instrumental performers, enumerated like D–X below
B	Works on individual composers (including libretti and other verbal texts of particular musical works)
BZ	Works on non-European music

MUSIC (SCORES AND PARTS)

C/AY	Collections not limited to work of particular composer, executant, form or character
C/AZ	Collections of a particular composer not otherwise limited
C/G-C/Y	Collections illustrating music of particular form, character, etc., enumerated like A/G-A/Y above
CB	Vocal music
CC	Opera. Vocal scores with keyboard
CM	Musical plays. Vocal scores with keyboard
D	Choral music
DC	Religious choral music
DF	Liturgical music
DH	Motets, Anthems, Hymns
DTZ	Secular choral music
DX	Cantatas
DW	Songs, etc.
E	Choral music with instruments other than keyboard
EZ	Choral music unaccompanied
F	Choral music. Female voices
G	Choral music. Male voices
J	Unison vocal works
K	Vocal solos
L	Instrumental music
M	Orchestral music
N	Chamber music
PVV	Music for individual instruments and instrumental groups
PW	Keyboard instruments
Q	Piano
R	Organ
RW	String instruments
S	Violin
SQ	Viola
SR	Cello
SS	Double bass
TQ	Harp
TS	Guitar
U	Wind instruments
V	Woodwind
VR	Flute
VS	Recorder
VT	Oboe
VU	Saxophone
VV	Clarinet
VW	Bassoon
W	Brass
WS	Trumpet
WT	Horn
WU	Trombone
WX	Bass tuba
X	Percussion instruments
Z	Non-European music

CORRIGENDA

The entries given below do not appear in their appropriate places in the Classified Section, and to ensure that they are not overlooked their correct places have been marked with a †.

ADW/G(YDL) — Folk songs. Scotland
Andrew Crawfurd's collection of ballads and songs / edited by E.B. Lyle.. — Edinburgh ([27 George Sq., Edinburgh EH8 9LD]) : The Scottish Text Society.
Vol.1. — 1975. — lvii,244p, : music, port ; 23cm. — (Scottish Text Society. Publications : 4th series ; 9)
Bibl.: p.xi-xii.
ISBN 0-9500245-4-6 : Unpriced

(B75-29319)

AKDW/HHW/E(P) — Holiday, Billie. Biographies
Chilton, John
Billie's blues : a survey of Billie Holiday's career, 1933-1959 / [by] John Chilton ; foreword by Buck Clayton. — London : Quartet Books, 1975. — [7],264p : facsims, ports ; 23cm.
Bibl.: p.239-259. — Index.
ISBN 0-7043-2091-6 : £3.95

(B75-19732)

APV/D — Electronic music. Composition
Dwyer, Terence
Making electronic music : a course for schools / [by] Terence Dwyer ; illustrated by Eric Tranter ; photographs by Kenneth Padley. — London : Oxford University Press.
Book 1. — 1975. — [4],53p : ill ; 25cm.
Index.
ISBN 0-19-321071-1 Sp : £1.50

(B75-24850)

AX/B(X) — Percussion instruments. History
Blades, James
Percussion instruments and their history / [by] James Blades. — New and revised ed. — London : Faber, 1975. — 3-509p,[72]p of plates : ill, music, ports ; 26cm.
Previous ed.: 1970. — Bibl. — Index.
ISBN 0-571-04832-3 : £15.00
ISBN 0-571-10360-x Pbk : £4.50

(B75-13738)

BHP(D) — Holst, Gustav. Essays
Rubbra, Edmund
Gustav Holst / [by] Edmund Rubbra ; collected essays edited by Stephen Lloyd and Edmund Rubbra ; with an introduction by Vernon Handley. — London (10E Prior Bolton St., N.1) : Triad Press, 1974. — 56p : music, port ; 19cm.
Limited ed. of 400 numbered copies.
ISBN 0-902070-12-6 Pbk : £2.40

(B75-00200)

CLASSIFIED SECTION

This section contains entries under subjects, executants and instruments according to a system of classification, a synopsis of which appears in the preliminary pages. The key to the classification and to this section is found in the Subject Index at the end of this volume, which is followed by a list of music publishers and their addresses.

The following are used in giving the sizes of musical works:—

8vo for works up to 10½" in height.
4to for works between 10½" and 12" in height.
fol. for works over 12" in height.
obl. indicates a work of unusual proportions.
s.sh. means a single sheet.

A — MUSICAL LITERATURE
Boulez, Pierre
Boulez on music today / [by] Pierre Boulez ; translated [from the French] by Susan Bradshaw and Richard Rodney Bennett. — London : Faber, 1975. — 144p : ill, music ; 20cm.
This translation originally published: 1971. — Translation of: 'Penser la musique aujourd'hui'. Paris : Gonthier, 1964. — Index.
ISBN 0-571-10587-4 Pbk : £0.80

(B75-06414)

Music / consulting editors Arthur Daniels, Lavern Wagner ; ... [contributors] Perry Williams [et al.]. — New York ; London [etc.] : Holt, Rinehart and Winston, 1975. — xv,512p : ill, music, ports ; 25cm.
Two gramophone records as inserts. — 'A Leogryph book'. — Bibl.: p.503-506. — Index.
ISBN 0-03-012681-9 : £7.00

(B75-29313)

A(D) — Essays
Schoenberg, Arnold
Style and idea : selected writings of Arnold Schoenberg / edited by Leonard Stein ; with translations [from the German] by Leo Black. — London : Faber, 1975. — 559p : music ; 26cm.
Bibl.: p.537-540. — Index.
ISBN 0-571-09722-7 : £17.50

(B75-11219)

A(DE) — Questions & answers
Butterworth, Neil
A music quiz / compiled by Neil Butterworth ; foreword by Joseph Cooper. — York (139 Holgate Rd, York) : Banks Music Publications, 1974. — [4],62p : music ; 19cm.
With answers.
ISBN 0-9503337-0-0 Sd : £0.45

(B75-27348)

Kinn, Maurice
The Armada pop quiz book / [by] Maurice Kinn ; illustrations by David Kemp ; crosswords compiled by Derek Johnson. — London : Armada Books, 1975. — [124]p,[4]p of plates : ill, ports ; 18cm.
With answers.
ISBN 0-00-690953-1 Pbk : £0.35

(B75-05789)

A(JC/K/YC/XM70) — Copyright. Economic aspects. Great Britain, 1905-74
Peacock, Alan
The composer in the market place / [by] Alan Peacock & Ronald Weir ; with a preface by Asa Briggs. — London : Faber, 1975. — 172p,[4]p of plates : ill, facsim, ports ; 23cm.
Index.
ISBN 0-571-10011-2 : £5.50

(B75-18726)

A(MN/YD) — Careers. Great Britain
Fortescue, Margaret
Careers with music ... / [written by Margaret Fortescue and Geoffrey Perrin]. — Norwich (Careers Centre, University of East Anglia, University Plain, Norwich NR4 7TJ) : University of East Anglia, 1975. — [2],28p ; 21cm. — (University of East Anglia. Careers information sheets)
Bibl.: p.19-20.
Sd : £0.15(£0.10 to university and polytechnic careers services)

(B75-15001)

A(N) — Biographies
Fanshawe, David
African Sanctus : a story of travel and music / [by] David Fanshawe. — London : Collins : Harvill Press, 1975. — 208p,[16] p of plates : ill(some col), facsims, col map(on lining papers), music, ports(some col) ; 24cm.
ISBN 0-00-262002-2 : £4.50

(B75-12857)

A(N/BC) — Biographies. Yearbooks. Directories
International who's who in music and musicians' directory. — Cambridge (Cambridge CB2 3QP) : International Who's Who in Music.
7th ed. : 1975 / edited by Ernest Kay. — 1975. — xxiv,1348p ; 26cm.
Previously published as: 'Who's who in music, and musicians' international directory.
ISBN 0-900332-31-x : £15.00
ISSN 0307-2894

(B75-27957)

A(QU/XPL25) — Notation, 1951-1975
Risatti, Howard
New music vocabulary : a guide to notational signs for contemporary music / [by] Howard Risatti. — Urbana [etc.] ; London : University of Illinois Press, 1975. — [16],219p : ill, music ; 26cm.
Bibl.: p.189-190. — Index.
ISBN 0-252-00406-x Pbk : £2.75

(B75-21069)

A(T) — Bibliographies
Duckles, Vincent
Music reference and research materials : an annotated bibliography / compiled by Vincent Duckles. — 3rd ed. — New York : Free Press ; London : Collier Macmillan, 1974. — xvii, 526p ; 24cm.
Previous ed.: 1967. — Index.
ISBN 0-02-907700-1 : £5.50

(B75-00957)

A(TD) — Thematic catalogues
Parsons, Denys
The directory of tunes and musical themes / [by] Denys Parsons ; introduction by Bernard Levin. — Cambridge : Spencer Brown, 1975. — 284p : music ; 24cm.
ISBN 0-904747-00-x : £6.00

(B75-13381)

A(UM) — Cataloguing
London and South Eastern Library Region
LASER manual for cataloguing monographs and music. — London (9 Alfred Place, WC1E 7EB) : L.A.S.E.R., 1975. — [1], 27 leaves ; 21x30cm.
ISBN 0-903764-04-0 Sp : £1.25

(B75-13384)

A(V) — Education
Bentley, Arnold
Music in education : a point of view / [by] Arnold Bentley. — Windsor : NFER, 1975. — 125p : ill ; 22cm.
Bibl.: p.123-125.
ISBN 0-85633-066-3 Pbk : £2.95

(B75-26085)

A(VC) — Teaching
Ingley, William Stevens
Music for today's children / by W. Stevens Ingley and Hilda Hunter ; [with foreword by Yehudi Menuhin]. — Warley (63 Highfield Rd, Rowley Regis, Warley, West Midlands) : H. Hunter, 1974. — [4],64p : music ; 30cm.
ISBN 0-9503936-0-6 Sp : £1.50

(B75-50000)

Lawrence, Ian
  Music and the teacher / [by] Ian Lawrence. — London [etc.] :
  Pitman, 1975. — x,84p ; 19cm. — (Pitman education library)
  Bibl. — Index.
  ISBN 0-273-00354-2 : £2.50
  ISBN 0-273-00355-0 Pbk : £1.25

(B75-19078)

A(VF) — Schools
Regelski, Thomas A
  Principles and problems of music education / [by] Thomas A.
  Regelski. — Englewood Cliffs ; London [etc.] : Prentice-Hall,
  1975. — xix,330p ; music ; 24cm.
  Bibl.: p.319-322. — Index.
  ISBN 0-13-709840-5 : £6.05
  ISBN 0-13-709832-4 Pbk : £3.85

(B75-20389)

A(X) — History
Alberti, Luciano
  Music through the ages / [by] Luciano Alberti ; translated from
  the Italian by Richard Pierce. — London : Cassell, 1974. —
  2-323p : ill(some col), music, ports(some col) ; 30cm.
  Translation of: 'Musica nei secoli'. Milano [Milan] : Mondadori, 1968. —
  Index.
  ISBN 0-304-29420-9 : £7.50

(B75-02995)

Baker, Richard, *b.1925*
  The magic of music / [by] Richard Baker. — London : Hamilton,
  1975. — 152p : ill(some col), music, ports(1 col) ; 25cm.
  Bibl.: p.146. — Index.
  ISBN 0-241-89194-9 : £3.95

(B75-11220)

Godwin, Joscelyn
  Schirmer scores : a repertory of Western music / by Joscelyn
  Godwin. — New York : Schirmer Books ; London : Collier
  Macmillan, 1975. — xiv,1101p : chiefly music ; 24cm.
  ISBN 0-02-870700-1 Pbk : £6.50

(B75-28635)

The **new** Oxford history of music. — London [etc.] : Oxford
University Press.
In 11 vols.
[Vol.5] : Opera and church music, 1630-1750 / edited by Anthony Lewis
and Nigel Fortune. — 1975. — xxii,869p,[1],vii leaves of plates : ill, facsims,
music, plan ; 26cm.
Bibl.: p.777-829. — Index.
ISBN 0-19-316305-5 : £12.50

(B75-29312)

Politoske, Daniel Theodore
  Music / [by] Daniel T. Politoske. — Englewood Cliffs ; London
  [etc.] : Prentice-Hall, 1974. — xiii,497p,[16]p of plates : ill,
  facsims, music, ports ; 25cm.
  Bibl.: p.479-487. — Index.
  ISBN 0-13-607465-0 : £5.10

(B75-02367)

A(XA1420) — History, up to 1420
Seay, Albert
  Music in the medieval world / [by] Albert Seay. — 2nd ed. —
  Englewood Cliffs ; London [etc.] : Prentice-Hall, 1975. — ix,
  182p : ill, facsims, music ; 23cm. — (Prentice-Hall history of
  music series)
  Previous ed.: 1965. — Bibl. — Index.
  ISBN 0-13-608133-9 : £5.50
  ISBN 0-13-608125-8 Pbk : £3.00

(B75-24232)

A(XCQ351) — History, 1400-1750
Blume, Friedrich
  Renaissance and Baroque music : a comprehensive survey / [by]
  Friedrich Blume ; translated [from the German] by M.D. Herter
  Norton. — London : Faber, 1975. — xi,180p ; 22cm.
  This translation originally published: New York : Norton, 1967 ; London :
  Faber, 1968. — Originally published: in 'Die Musik in Geschichte und
  Gegenwart'. Kassel : Bärenreiter, 1949. — Bibl.: p.167-170. — Index.
  ISBN 0-571-10719-2 Pbk : £1.25

(B75-08734)

A(XD251/D) — History, 1500-1750. Essays
Studies in Renaissance and baroque music in honour of Arthur
  Mendel / edited by Robert L. Marshall. — Kassel [etc.] ;
  [London] ([32 Great Titchfield St., W.1]) : Bärenreiter-Verlag
  [etc.], 1974. — 392p,[4]leaves of plates,[8]p of plates : ill, facsims,
  music, port ; 25cm.
  Bibl.: p.378-385. — Index.
  £20.70

A(XPE30) — History, 1945-1974
Brindle, Reginald Smith
  The new music : the avant-garde since 1945 / [by] Reginald Smith
  Brindle. — London [etc.] : Oxford University Press, 1975. — x,
  206p : ill, facsims, music ; 21cm.
  Index.
  ISBN 0-19-315424-2 Pbk : £3.95

(B75-27956)

A(Y) — MUSIC OF PARTICULAR LOCALITIES
A(YB/WE) — Europe. Festivals
Musical Europe : an illustrated guide to musical life in 18 European
  countries / edited by Marianne Adelmann. — New York ;
  London : Paddington Press, 1974. — 448p : ill, facsims, maps,
  ports ; 24cm.
  ISBN 0-8467-0031-x Pbk : £3.50

(B75-01174)

A(YB/XHN141) — Europe, 1833-1973
Abraham, Gerald
  A hundred years of music / by Gerald Abraham. — 4th ed. —
  London : Duckworth, 1974. — 333p : facsim ; 23cm.
  Previous ed.: 1964. — Bibl.: p.309-321. — Index.
  ISBN 0-7156-0703-0 : £6.95
  ISBN 0-7156-0704-9 Pbk : £2.50

(B75-12695)

A(YBU/D) — Jewish music. Essays
Yuval : studies of the Jewish Music Research Centre. — Jerusalem :
  Magnes Press ; [London] : Distributed by Oxford University Press.
  Vol.3 / edited by Israel Adler and Bathja Bayer. — 1974. — 291,[52]p : ill,
  facsims, music ; 25cm.
  English and Hebrew text with a contribution in French. — Second title page
  in Hebrew.
  ISBN 0-19-647920-7 : £10.25

(B75-08735)

A(YC/BC) — Great Britain. Yearbooks
British music yearbook : a survey and directory with statistics and
  reference articles. — London [etc.] : Bowker.
  1975 / edited by Arthur Jacobs. — 1975. — A26,xxi,801p : ill, ports ;
  23cm.
  Previously published: as 'The music yearbook'. — Index.
  ISBN 0-85935-024-x : £7.50
  ISSN 0306-5928

(B75-16403)

A(YC/Q/MM) — Great Britain. Incorporated Society of Musicians
Incorporated Society of Musicians
  Handbook and register of members / Incorporated Society of
  Musicians. — London (48 Gloucester Place, W1H 3HJ) : The
  Society.
  1974-75. — [1974]. — 318p ; 23cm.
  Index.
  ISBN 0-902900-06-4 : £4.00
  ISBN 0-902900-07-2 Pbk : £3.00

(B75-00738)

A(YDCGS/X) — Sheffield. History
Mackerness, Eric David
  Somewhere further north : a history of music in Sheffield / by
  E.D. Mackerness. — Sheffield : Northend, 1974. — xi,168p,leaf of
  plate,[4]p of plates : ill, facsims, port ; 22cm.
  Index.
  ISBN 0-901100-13-7 : £3.00

(B75-16404)

A(YDHDB/TC) — University of Bristol, Department of Music. Bibliography of scores
University of Bristol. *Department of Music*
  Composers' catalogue / University of Bristol, Department of
  Music. — Bristol (Royal Fort House, Bristol BS8 1UJ) : The
  Department, [1974]. — [1],28p ; 15x21cm.
  Amendment slips will be sent periodically.
  ISBN 0-904877-00-0 Sd : Free

(B75-12885)

A(YH/XEXK142/WJ) — France, 1650-1791. Exhibitions
French music and the Fitzwilliam : a collection of essays and a
  catalogue of an exhibition of French music in the Fitzwilliam
  Museum in May and June 1975 on the occasion of two concerts of
  French music. — Cambridge (Trumpington St., Cambridge) :
  Fitzwilliam Museum, 1975. — 55p,[4]p of plates : ill, facsim,
  ports ; 25cm.
  ISBN 0-904454-01-0 Pbk : £1.00

(B75-18363)

A(YK/X) — Spain. History
Livermore, Ann
  A short history of Spanish music / [by] Ann Livermore. —
  London : Duckworth, [1975]. — x,262p,[8]p of plates : ill, music,
  ports ; 22cm.
  Originally published: 1972. — Bibl.: p.254-255. — Index.
  ISBN 0-7156-0886-x Pbk : £2.95

(B75-21071)

A(YT) — United States
Pavlakis, Christopher
  The American music handbook / [by] Christopher Pavlakis. —
  New York : Free Press ; London : Collier Macmillan, 1974. —
  xxi,836p ; 26cm.
  Index.
  ISBN 0-02-925180-x : £10.00

(B75-11221)

A(Z) — MUSIC IN RELATION TO OTHER SUBJECTS
A(ZC/D) — Music - expounding socialist viewpoints. Essays
Cardew, Cornelius
Stockhausen serves imperialism, and other articles : with commentary and notes / [by] Cornelius Cardew. — London : Latimer New Dimensions, 1974. — 126p ; 23cm.
ISBN 0-901539-29-5 : £3.00

(B75-04503)

A(ZD) — Music - influencing literature
Fetzer, John F
Romantic Orpheus : profiles of Clemens Brentano / [by] John F. Fetzer. — Berkeley [etc.] ; London : University of California Press, 1974. — xi,313p : music ; 25cm.
Bibl.: p.297-304. — Index.
ISBN 0-520-02312-9 : £6.85

(B75-07422)

A(ZD) — Music - influencing medical therapy
Alvin, Juliette
Music therapy / [by] Juliette Alvin. — London : Hutchinson, 1975. — [10],181p,[8]p of plates : ill ; 23cm.
Index.
ISBN 0-09-120320-1 : £4.25

(B75-08620)

A/B — PHYSICS OF MUSIC
A/C — Appreciation
Bamberger, Jeanne Shapiro
The art of listening : developing musical perception / [by] Jeanne Shapiro Bamberger, Howard Brofsky ; with a foreword by Roger Sessions. — 3rd ed. — New York [etc.] ; London : Harper and Row, 1975. — xxviii,403p : ill, music, ports ; 24cm.
Previous ed.: New York : Harper and Row, 1972. — Bibl.: p.369-370. — Index.
ISBN 0-06-040948-7 Pbk : £3.85

(B75-21064)

Bernstein, Leonard
The joy of music / [by] Leonard Bernstein. — London [etc.] : White Lion Publishers, 1974. — 303p : ill, facsims, music ; 23cm.
Originally published: New York : Simon and Schuster, 1959 ; London : Weidenfeld and Nicolson, 1960.
ISBN 0-85617-717-2 : £3.25

(B75-04502)

A/C(VG) — Appreciation. Primary schools
Witham, June
Music workshop : an approach to music for the non-specialist teacher / [by] June Witham. — London [etc.] : Macmillan, 1974. — 1v. : ill(chiefly col) ; 26cm.
Forty-five cards (45 sides), sheet (2p.) and teachers' notes in plastic bag.
ISBN 0-333-14455-4 : £4.75

(B75-04501)

A/CC — AESTHETICS
A/CC(P) — Hanslick, Eduard
Deas, Stewart
In defence of Hanslick / by Stewart Deas. — Revised ed. ; with a new preface. — Farnborough, Hants. : Gregg, 1972. — [6],117p ; 20cm.
Previous ed.: London : Williams and Norgate, 1940. — Bibl.: p.113-114. — Index.
ISBN 0-576-28242-1 : £3.00

(B75-02991)

A/CS — PSYCHOLOGY
Buck, *Sir* Percy Carter
Psychology for musicians / by Percy C. Buck. — London [etc.] : Oxford University Press, 1974. — viii,115p : music ; 22cm.
Originally published: 1944. — Bibl.: p.112. — Index.
ISBN 0-19-311914-5 Pbk : £1.25

(B75-18003)

A/E — PERFORMANCE
A/EC — Conducting
Green, Elizabeth Adine Herkimer
The conductor and his score / [by] Elizabeth A.H. Green, Nicolai Malko. — Englewood Cliffs ; London [etc.] : Prentice-Hall, 1975. — xiii,191p : ill, music ; 24cm.
Bibl.: p.178-180. — Index.
ISBN 0-13-167312-2 : £4.40

(B75-16405)

A/EC(P) — Klemperer, Otto
Beavan, Peter
Klempererisms : a few of Dr Klemperer's lighter moments / [by] Peter Beavan. — London (15 Dungarvan Ave., S.W.15) : Cock Robin Press, [1975]. — [4],11p : port ; 19cm.
Limited ed. of 200 numbered copies. — Port. tipped in.
ISBN 0-9500594-2-0 Sd : Free

(B75-09268)

A/FD — RECORDED MUSIC
A/FD(BC) — Directories
'Music Week' industry yearbook. — London (7 Carnaby St., W1V 1PG) : Billboard Publications Ltd.
Previous control number B7512986.
No.6 : 1975-76 / compiled by Louise Fares. — [1975]. — 66p : ill ; 28cm.
ISBN 0-902285-01-7 Sd : £2.50
ISSN 0306-431x

(B75-12986)

A/FD(Q) — Sun Record Company. History
Escott, Colin
Catalyst : the Sun Records story / [by] Colin Escott and Martin Hawkins. — London : Aquarius Books ; Kings Langley (Station Rd, Kings Langley, Herts.) : Distributed by Argus Books, 1975. — 173p,[24]p of plates : ill, facsims, ports ; 21cm.
Bibl.: p.152-154. — Index.
ISBN 0-904619-00-1 Pbk : £2.90

(B75-21384)

A/FD(T/WT) — Bibliographies. Lists
Gramophone Company
'His Master's Voice' recordings, plum label 'C' series (12 inch) / the Gramophone Company Ltd ; [compiled] by Michael Smith and Frank Andrews. — [Blandford] ([Old School House, Tarrant Hinton, Blandford, Dorset]) : Oakwood Press, 1974. — xx,274p ; 21cm. — (Voices of the past ; vol.10)
Spine title: HMV plum label catalogue. — Index.
ISBN 0-85361-166-1 : £4.50

(B75-08384)

Numerical listing of Edison Bell 'Winner' / compiled by Karlo Adrian. — Bournemouth (19 Glendale Rd, Bournemouth BH6 4JA) : 'Talking Machine Review', [1975]. — 9v. : facsims, port ; 22cm.
Originally published: in parts as supplements to the 'Talking Machine Review'. 1969? - 1973.
ISBN 0-902338-17-x Sd : £2.00

(B75-19333)

A/FD(VK/WT) — Secondary schools. Lists
Tillman, June
Music as stimulus in secondary assembly and RE ... / by June Tillman. — London (2 Chester House, Pages La., N10 1PR) : Christian Education Movement, Religious Education Service, 1975. — [1],18p ; 30cm.
Previous control number B7515228.
ISBN 0-905022-00-9 Sd : £0.40

(B75-15228)

A/FD(WM) — Trade catalogues
Decca Group records & tapes, main catalogue (alphabetical & numerical. — London : Decca Record Co.
1975 : up to and including September 1974 ..). — 1975. — 692p in various pagings.
Index.
ISBN 0-901364-07-x : £5.00 yearly

(B75-09383)

A/FD(WM) — Trade catalogues, 1914-18
Gramophone Company
Gramophone records of the First World War : an HMV catalogue, 1914-1918 / introduced by Brian Rust. — Newton Abbot [etc.] : David and Charles, [1975]. — 480p in various pagings : ill, ports ; 20cm.
Facsimile reprint of: catalogues of gramophone records issued between 1914 and 1918 by the Gramophone Company Ltd of Hayes, Middlesex.
ISBN 0-7153-6842-7 : £5.25

(B75-12385)

A/FD(WT) — Recorded music. Lists
The **art** of record buying : a list of recommended microgroove recordings. — London : E.M.G.
1975. — [1975]. — [2],342p : map ; 23cm.
ISBN 0-900982-06-3 : £3.20

(B75-06145)

A/FD/E(P) — Spector, Phil. Biographies
Williams, Richard, *b.1947*
Out of his head : the sound of Phil Spector / [by] Richard Williams. — London : Abacus, 1974. — 156p,[12]p of plates : ill, ports ; 20cm.
Originally published: New York : Outerbridge and Lazard, 1972. — List of gramophone records : p.140-150.
ISBN 0-349-13723-4 Pbk : £0.65

(B75-22851)

A/FD/JT(P/X) — Desert Island Discs. History
Plomley, Roy
'Desert Island Discs' / [by] Roy Plomley. — London : Kimber, 1975. — 232p,[8]p of plates : ill, ports ; 23cm.
ISBN 0-7183-0024-6 : £2.95

(B75-50973)

A/FH — MECHANICAL MUSIC
Crowley, Terence Eldon
  Discovering mechanical music / [by] T.E. Crowley. — Aylesbury :
  Shire Publications, 1975. — 48p : ill, facsims ; 18cm. —
  (Discovering series ; no.200)
  Bibl.: p.45-46. — Index.
  ISBN 0-85263-257-6 Pbk : £0.35

(B75-08740)

A/FH/B(B) — Periodicals
Music Box Society
  News Letter / Music Box Society. — Bearsden (42 Dumgoyne
  Drive, Bearsden, Dunbartonshire) : The Society.
  No.1- ; Aug. 1974-. — 1974-. — ill ; 30cm.
  Six issues a year. — 16p. in issue no.5.
  Sd : Free to members

(B75-19736)

A/FY — MUSICAL CHARACTER
A/G(BC) — Folk music. Yearbooks. Directories
  The folk directory / [English Folk Dance and Song Society]. —
  London : The Society.
  1975 / edited by Mira S. Curtis. — 1975. — 188p : ill, map, ports ; 22cm.
  Index.
  ISBN 0-85418-107-5 Pbk : £2.00(£1.00 to members)
  ISBN 0-85418-106-7 Pbk : £1.00(£0.50 to members)

(B75-19082)

A/G(YC/B) — Folk music. Great Britain. Periodicals
Traditional Music. — London (90 St Julian's Farm Rd, SE27
  0RS) : Traditional Music.
  No.1- ; mid 1975-. — 1975-. — ill, music, ports ; 30cm.
  Three issues a year. — 30p. in 1st issue.
  Sd : £0.35(£1.20 yearly)
  ISSN 0306-7440

A/G(YDK) — Folk music. Wales
Williams, William Sidney Gwynn
  Welsh national music and dance / by W.S. Gwynn Williams. —
  4th ed. — Llangollen : Gwynn, 1971. — ix,165p,plate : facsim,
  music ; 22cm.
  Previous ed.: London : Curwen, 1953. — Bibl.: p.141-156. — Index.
  ISBN 0-900426-01-2 Pbk : £1.10

(B75-02368)

A/GB — Popular music
Top pop scene. — Maidenhead : Purnell.
  [1975]. — 1975. — 63p : chiefly ill(some col), ports(some col) ; 27cm.
  ISBN 0-361-03192-0 : £0.85

(B75-14332)

A/GB(YC/BC) — Popular music. Great Britain. Directories
Kemp's music & recording industry year book (international) : a
  comprehensive reference source and marketing guide to the music
  and recording industry in Great Britain & overseas. — London :
  Kemp's.
  1974-75 / executive editor F.J. Goodliffe. — [1974]. — [4],232p : ill, form ;
  22cm.
  ISBN 0-901268-76-3 : £3.75
  ISSN 0305-7100

(B75-02719)

A/GB/FD(B) — Popular music. Recorded music. Periodicals
Vintage Light Music : for the enthusiast of light music on 78 r.p.m.
  records. — West Wickham (c/o Hon. Secretary, 4 Harvest Bank
  Rd, West Wickham, Kent) : Vintage Light Music Society.
  No.1- ; Jan. 1975-. — 1975-. — ill, facsims, ports ; 22cm.
  Quarterly. — 22p. in 2nd issue.
  Sd : £0.25(£1.00 yearly)

(B75-15703)

A/GB/FD(X) — Popular music. Recorded music. History
Murrells, Joseph
  The book of golden discs / compiled by Joseph Murrells. —
  London : Barrie and Jenkins, 1974. — 503p : ports ; 26cm.
  Index.
  ISBN 0-214-20032-9 : £9.95

(B75-14337)

A/GB/JR(XPP21) — Popular music. Films, 1954-1974
Jenkinson, Philip
  Celluloid rock : twenty years of movie rock / [by] Philip
  Jenkinson and Alan Warner. — London : Lorrimer, 1974. —
  136p : ill(some col), facsims, ports ; 26cm.
  List of films: p.127-132. — Index.
  ISBN 0-85647-046-5 Pbk : £1.95

(B75-06416)

A/GB/L(XR5) — Popular music. Religious music, 1970-1974
Jasper, Tony
  Jesus in a pop culture / [by] Tony Jasper. — [London] : Fontana,
  1975. — 189p ; 19cm.
  Bibl.: p.183-184. — List of gramophone records: p.184-187. — Index.
  ISBN 0-00-215371-8 : £2.00
  ISBN 0-00-623748-7 Pbk : £0.40

(B75-06415)

A/GR(VG) — Activities. Primary schools
Chacksfield, Kathleen Merle
  Music and language with young children / [by] K.M. Chacksfield,
  P.A. Binns, V.M. Robins. — Oxford : Blackwell, 1975. — viii,
  182p : ill, music ; 23cm.
  Bibl.: p.179-180. — Index.
  ISBN 0-631-15330-6 : £4.50

(B75-22597)

Gilbert, Jean
  Musical activities with young children / [by] Jean Gilbert. —
  London : Ward Lock, 1975. — 96p : ill, music ; 20x25cm.
  Bibl.: p.71-74. — Index.
  ISBN 0-7062-3462-6 : £2.95

(B75-19508)

A/HK(ZF) — Rock 'n' roll - influenced by folk music
  The **electric** muse : the story of folk into rock / [by] Dave Laing ...
  [et al.]. — London : Eyre Methuen, 1975. — [6],182p,[18]p of
  plates : ill, ports ; 20cm.
  Index.
  ISBN 0-413-31860-5 Pbk : £1.70

(B75-21664)

A/LZ — ELEMENTS OF MUSIC
A/M — Rudiments
Hossack, Alfred
  From notes to rhythm / compiled by Alfred Hossack ; system by
  Mentor Textbooks. — Guildford : Lutterworth Press, 1975. —
  [50]p : ill, music ; 21cm. — (Mentor music books) (Music for
  beginners)
  Programmed text. — Index.
  ISBN 0-7188-2128-9 Sd : £0,75

(B75-25556)

A/PF — Tonality
Hossack, Alfred
  Major and minor scales / compiled by Alfred Hossack ; system by
  Mentor Textbooks. — Guildford : Lutterworth Press, 1975. —
  [50]p : ill, music ; 21cm. — (Mentor music books) (Music for
  beginners)
  Programmed text. — Index.
  ISBN 0-7188-2129-7 Sd : £0.75

(B75-25555)

A/PN — Twelve note music
Perle, George
  Serial composition and atonality : an introduction to the music of
  Schoenberg, Berg and Webern / by George Perle. — 2nd ed.
  revised and enlarged. — London : Faber, 1975. — ix,166p :
  music ; 24cm.
  Second ed. revised and enlarged originally published: 1968. — Index.
  ISBN 0-571-10700-1 Pbk : £2.60

(B75-13735)

A/PU — Timbre
Erickson, Robert
  Sound structure in music / [by] Robert Erickson. — Berkeley
  [etc.] ; London : University of California Press, 1975. — xi,205p :
  ill, music ; 26cm.
  Bibl.: p.195-202. — Index.
  ISBN 0-520-02376-5 : £6.00

(B75-27354)

A/R — Harmony
  The **Oxford** harmony. — London [etc.] : Oxford University Press.
  In 2 vols. — Originally published: 1946.
  Vol.1 / by R.O. Morris. — 1974. — vi,139p : music ; 22cm.
  ISBN 0-19-317315-8 Pbk : £1.20

(B75-12696)

Schenker, Heinrich
  Harmony / by Heinrich Schenker ; edited and annotated by
  Oswald Jonas ; translated [from the German] by Elisabeth Mann
  Borgese. — Cambridge, Mass, ; London : M.I.T. Press, 1973. —
  xxxii,361p : music ; 21cm.
  This translation originally published: Chicago : University of Chicago Press ;
  London : Cambridge University Press, 1954. — Translation of: 'Neue
  musikalische Theorien und Phantasien'. Bd.1. Stuttgart : Cotta'sche
  Buchhandlung Nachfolger, 1906. — Index.
  ISBN 0-262-69044-6 Pbk : £2.00

(B75-02996)

AB — MUSICAL LITERATURE. VOCAL MUSIC
AB/E — Singing
Caruso, Enrico
  Caruso and Tetrazzini on the art of singing / by Enrico Caruso
  and Luisa Tetrazzini. — New York : Dover Publications ;
  London : Constable, [1975]. — 71p,[4]p of plates : 2 ports ; 21cm.
  Originally published: New York : The Metropolitan Company, 1909.
  ISBN 0-486-23140-2 Pbk : £0.84

(B75-22212)

AC — MUSICAL LITERATURE. OPERA
Eaton, Quaintance
Opera production / [by] Quaintance Eaton. — Minneapolis :
University of Minnesota Press ; London [etc.] : Oxford University
Press.
2 : a handbook / with 'Production problems in Handel's operas' by
Randolph Mickelson. — 1974. — iii-xx,347p ; 24cm.
Index.
ISBN 0-8166-0689-7 : £7.25

(B75-26794)

AC/E(YC/QB) — Royal Opera House, Covent Garden
Goodwin, Noël
The story of the Royal Opera House, Covent Garden / [text by
Noël Goodwin ; photographs by Reg Wilson]. — [London] ([Head
Office, Poultry, EC2P 2BX]) : Midland Bank Ltd, 1973. — 12p :
col ill, ports(chiefly col) ; 22cm.
ISBN 0-9501576-2-7 Sd : Free

(B75-50001)

AC/E(YC/QB/X) — Handel Opera Society. History
Handel Opera Society
The story of the Handel Opera Society. — [London] ([Flat 3, 26
Medway St., S.W.1]) : The Society, [1975]. — 32p : ill, ports ;
24cm.
ISBN 0-901175-02-1 Sd : £0.75

(B75-08736)

ACM — MUSICAL LITERATURE. MUSICAL PLAYS
ACM/E(YT/X) — United States. History
Green, Stanley, *b.1923*
The world of musical comedy : the story of the American musical
stage as told through the careers of its foremost composers and
lyricists / [by] Stanley Green ; foreword by Deems Taylor. — 3rd
ed. revised and enlarged. — South Brunswick ; New York :
Barnes ; London : Yoseloff, 1974. — xvii,556p : ill, ports ; 26cm.
Previous ed.: 1968. — Lists of records. — Index.
ISBN 0-498-01409-6 : £7.00

(B75-29315)

AD — MUSICAL LITERATURE. CHORAL MUSIC
AD/E(QB/YDHWC/X) — Gresley Male Voice Choir. History
Gresley Male Voice Choir : 70 years of music making, 1904-1974.
— Burton-on-Trent (14 Vale Rd, Midway, Burton-on-Trent,
Staffs.) : J. Mason, [1974]. — 49p : ill, facsims, ports ; 22cm.
ISBN 0-9504178-0-7 Sd : £0.25

(B75-16406)

AD/E(YDJGH/QB) — Huddersfield Glee and Madrigal Society
Huddersfield Glee and Madrigal Society
Huddersfield Glee & Madrigal Society, 1875-1975 / [written] by
Sidney H. Crowther. — Huddersfield (Princess Alexandra Walk,
Huddersfield HD1 2SU) : Kirklees Libraries and Museums
Service, 1974. — 32p : 1 ill, port ; 21cm.
ISBN 0-9502568-1-1 Sd : £0.50

(B75-07343)

AD/LD(YD/D) — Church music. England. Essays
English church music : a collection of essays. — Croydon
(Addington Palace, Croydon CR9 5AD) : Royal School of Church
Music.
1975. — [1975]. — 58p,2 leaves of plates : ports ; 22cm.
ISBN 0-85402-060-8 Pbk : £1.00

(B75-21074)

AD/LD(YE/X) — Church music. Germany. History
Traditionen und Reforman in der Kirchenmusik : Festschrift für
Konrad Ameln zum 75. Geburstag am 6, Juli 1974 /
herausgegeben von Gerhard Schuhmacher. — Kassel [etc.] ;
London ([32 Great Titchfield St., W.1]) : Bärenreiter-Verlag, 1974.
— 251p : 4 ill, music ; 24cm.
Bibl.: p.234-245. — Index.
Pbk : £13.80
ISBN 3-7618-0501-2

ADW/G(YC) — Folk songs. Great Britain
Folksongs of Britain and Ireland : a guidebook to the living
tradition of folksinging in the British Isles and Ireland, containing
360 folksongs from field recordings sung in English, Lowland
Scots, Scottish Gaelic, Irish Gaelic and Manx Gaelic, Welsh,
Cornish, Channel Islands French, Romany and Tinkers' Cant,
etc. / edited by Peter Kennedy, assisted by ... [others] ; musical
transcriptions and guitar chords by Raymond Parfrey. —
London : Cassell, 1975. — xvi,824p : map(on lining papers),
music, ports ; 29cm.
Bibl. — Index.
ISBN 0-304-93754-1 : £15.00

(B75-50974)

ADW/G(YD) — Folk songs. England
Lloyd, Albert Lancaster
Folk song in England / [by] A.L. Lloyd. — St Albans : Paladin,
1975. — 413p : music ; 20cm.
Originally published: London : Lawrence and Wishart, 1967. — Bibl.:
p.391-394. — Index.
ISBN 0-586-08210-7 Pbk : £1.50

(B75-10254)

ADW/GB — Popular songs
Rock file. — St Albans : Panther. — (Panther rock series)
3 / edited by Charlie Gillett and Simon Frith. — 1975. — 224p,[16]p of
plates : ill, ports ; 18cm.
ISBN 0-586-04261-x Pbk : £0.75

(B75-21065)

ADW/GB(XQ14) — Popular songs, 1960-1973
Sarlin, Bob
Turn it up! (I can't hear the words) / [by] Bob Sarlin. —
London : Coronet, 1975. — 239p,[4]p of plates : ports ; 18cm.
Originally published: New York : Simon and Schuster, 1973.
ISBN 0-340-17848-5 Pbk : £0.50

(B75-07793)

ADW/GB(XU7) — Popular songs, 1939-45
Great songs of World War II : with the Home Front in pictures /
written and edited by Michael Leitch ... ; music compilation by
Peter Foss and Ann Munday. — London [etc.] : Wise
Publications ; London (78 Newman St., W.1) : Distributed by
Music Sales Ltd, 1975. — 181p : chiefly ill, music, ports ; 28cm.
Cover title: World War II songs.
ISBN 0-86001-041-4 Pbk : £3.95

(B75-22844)

ADW/GB(YC/XMA14) — Popular songs. Great Britain, 1901-1914
Pearsall, Ronald
Edwardian popular music / [by] Ronald Pearsall. — Newton
Abbot [etc.] : David and Charles, 1975. — 207p : ill, facsims,
ports ; 23cm.
Bibl.: p.199-201. — Index.
ISBN 0-7153-6814-1 : £4.95

(B75-11753)

ADW/GB(YT/XM51) — Popular songs. United States, 1945-50
Wilder, Alec
American popular song : the great innovators, 1900-1950 / [by]
Alec Wilder ; edited and with an introduction by James T. Maher.
— London [etc.] : Oxford University Press, 1975. — xxxix,536p :
music ; 23cm.
Originally published: New York : Oxford University Press, 1972. — Index.
ISBN 0-19-284009-6 Pbk : £3.25

(B75-18368)

ADW/GB/FD(YT/X) — Popular songs. Recorded music. United States. History
Gillett, Charlie
Making tracks : Atlantic Records and the growth of a
multi-billion-dollar industry / [by] Charlie Gillett. — London :
W.H. Allen, 1975. — [7],305p : ill, ports ; 22cm.
Bibl.: p.287-288. — Index.
ISBN 0-491-01152-0 : £3.50

(B75-06240)

ADW/GMC(YUH) — Shanties. West Indies
Abrahams, Roger David
Deep the water, shallow the shore : three essays on shantying in
the West Indies / [by] Roger D. Abrahams ; music transcribed by
Linda Sobin. — Austin ; London : University of Texas Press for
the American Folklore Society, 1974. — xiv,125p : music ; 23cm.
— (American Folklore Society. Memoir series ; vol.60)
Bibl.: p.123-125.
ISBN 0-292-71502-1 : £3.80

(B75-00739)

ADW/KG(YC/XNU7) — Military songs. Great Britain, 1939-45
Kiss me goodnight, Sergeant Major : the songs and ballads of
World War II / edited by Martin Page ; illustrated by Bill Tidy ;
introduction by Spike Milligan. — St Albans : Panther, 1975. —
235p : ill ; 18cm.
This collection originally published: London : Hart-Davis MacGibbon, 1973.
— Index.
ISBN 0-586-04152-4 Pbk : £0.60

(B75-29320)

AK — MUSICAL LITERATURE. VOCAL SOLOS
AKDW/GB/E(M) — Popular songs. Singers
Jasper, Tony
Simply pop / by Tony Jasper. — London : Queen Anne Press,
1975. — 80p : ill, map, ports ; 24cm.
With answers.
ISBN 0-362-00247-9 : £0.95

(B75-27955)

Pop today / [editor and designer Gavin Petrie]. — London [etc.] :
Hamlyn, 1974. — 128p : ill, ports(some col) ; 29cm. — ([A 'Disc'
special])
ISBN 0-600-37080-1 : £1.95

(B75-02994)

AKDW/GB/E(P) — Bay City Rollers. Biographies
Paton, Tam
The Bay City Rollers / [by] Tam Paton with Michael Wale. —
London : Everest, 1975. — 2-154p,[16]p of plates : ports ; 18cm.
ISBN 0-903925-60-5 Pbk : £0.45

(B75-29316)

AKDW/GB/E(P) — Beatles, The. Biographies
The **Beatles** : the fabulous story of John, Paul, George and Ringo /
[material compiled by Robert Burt]. — London : Octopus Books,
1975. — 5-82p : chiefly col ill, facsim, ports(some col) ; 31cm.
Col. ports on lining papers.
ISBN 0-7064-0446-7 : £1.99
(B75-21666)

Carr, Roy
The **Beatles** : an illustrated record / [by] Roy Carr & Tony Tyler.
— London : New English Library, 1975. — 128p : ill(some col),
facsims, ports(some col) ; 30cm.
ISBN 0-450-02626-4 Pbk : £1.95
(B75-13736)

AKDW/GB/E(P) — Coasters, The. Biographies
Millar, Bill
The **Coasters** / by Bill Millar. — London (44 Hill St., W1X
8LB) : Star Books, 1975. — 206p,[8]p of plates : ill, ports ; 19cm.
List of gramophone records: p.189-204.
ISBN 0-352-30020-5 Pbk : £0.60
(B75-04508)

AKDW/GB/E(P) — Crosby, Bing. Biographies
Thompson, Charles
Bing : the authorised biography / [by] Charles Thompson. —
London : W.H. Allen, 1975. — vi,249p,[32]p of plates : ports ;
23cm.
Index.
ISBN 0-491-01715-4 : £3.95
(B75-25558)

AKDW/GB/E(P) — Dylan, Bob
Gray, Michael, *b.1946*
Song and dance man : the art of Bob Dylan / [by] Michael Gray.
— London : Abacus, 1973. — 332p,[4]p of plates : ports ; 20cm.
Originally published: London : Hart-Davis MacGibbon, 1972. — List of
recordings : p.307-322. — Index.
ISBN 0-349-11540-0 Pbk : £0.75
(B75-18369)

AKDW/GB/E(P) — Formby, George. Biographies
Randall, Alan
George Formby : a biography / by Alan Randall and Ray Seaton.
— London : W.H. Allen, 1974. — 192p,[32]p of plates : ill,
facsims, ports ; 23cm.
List of films: p.184-186. — List of gramophone records: p.187-192.
ISBN 0-491-01771-5 : £2.50
(B75-01176)

AKDW/GB/E(P) — Garland, Judy. Biographies
Frank, Gerold
Judy / [by] Gerold Frank. — London : W.H. Allen, 1975. —
xviii,654p,[32]p of plates : ports ; 24cm.
Also published: New York : Harper and Row, 1975. — Index.
ISBN 0-491-01735-9 : £5.00
(B75-24858)

Smith, Lorna
Judy, with love : the story of 'Miss Show Business' / [by] Lorna
Smith. — London : Hale, 1975. — 208p,[16]p of plates : ports ;
23cm.
List of films: p.199-201. — Index.
ISBN 0-7091-5257-4 : £3.80
(B75-24859)

AKDW/GB/E(P) — Glitter, Garry. Biographies
Tremlett, George
The **Gary** Glitter story / [by] George Tremlett. — London :
Futura Publications, 1974. — 144p,[16]p of plates : ill, ports ;
18cm.
ISBN 0-86007-094-8 Pbk : £0.40
(B75-01177)

AKDW/GB/E(P) — Jagger, Mick. Biographies
Marks, J.
Mick Jagger : the singer, not the song / [by] J. Marks. —
London : Abacus, 1974. — 156p,[32]p of plates : ill, ports ; 20cm.
Originally published: New York : Curtis Books, 1973.
ISBN 0-349-12288-1 Pbk : £0.60
(B75-02369)

AKDW/GB/E(P) — John, Elton. Biographies
Stein, Cathi
Elton John / [by] Cathi Stein. — [London] : Futura Publications,
1975. — 3-144p,[16]p of plates : ill, ports ; 18cm.
List of records: p.143-144.
ISBN 0-86007-201-0 Pbk : £0.45
(B75-19733)

AKDW/GB/E(P) — Jolson, Al. Biographies
Jay, Dave
Jolsonography : the world's greatest reference work on the world's
greatest entertainer / written, compiled & annotated by Dave Jay.
— 2nd ed. — Bournemouth (70 Southcote Rd, Bournemouth,
Hants.) : Barrie Anderton, 1974. — [1],284p : ill, facsims, ports ;
26cm.
Ill., facsims and ports tipped in. — Limited ed. of 250 numbered copies. —
Bibl.: p.246-264.
ISBN 0-9501412-1-6 : £15.00
(B75-03647)

AKDW/GB/E(P) — Joplin, Janis. Biographies
Caserta, Peggy
Going down with Janis / [by] Peggy Caserta; as told to Dan
Knapp. — London : Talmy Franklin, 1975. — 271p, : port ;
19cm.
Also published: Secaucus, New Jersey : Lyle Stuart, 1975?.
ISBN 0-900735-40-6 : £1.95
(B75-29317)

AKDW/GB/E(P) — McCartney, Paul. Biographies
Tremlett, George
The **Paul** McCartney story / [by] George Tremlett. — London :
Futura Publications, 1975. — 192p,[16]p of plates : ill, ports ;
18cm.
ISBN 0-86007-200-2 Pbk : £0.50
(B75-19734)

AKDW/GB/E(P) — Richard, Cliff. Biographies
Tremlett, George
The **Cliff** Richard story / [by] George Tremlett. — London :
Futura Publications, 1975. — 156p,[16]p of Plates : ill, ports ;
18cm.
ISBN 0-86007-232-0 Pbk : £0.50
(B75-29318)

AKDW/GB/E(P) — Slade. Biographies
Tremlett, George
The **Slade** story / [by] George Tremlett. — London : Futura
Publications, 1975. — 3-128p,[16]p of plates : ports ; 18cm.
ISBN 0-86007-193-6 Pbk : £0.40
(B75-13167)

AKDW/GB/E(P) — Who, The. Biographies
Tremlett, George
The **Who** / [by] George Tremlett. — London : Futura
Publications, 1975. — 125p,[16]p of plates : ill, ports ; 18cm.
ISBN 0-86007-069-7 Pbk : £0.40
(B75-13168)

AKDW/GB/E(P/XPU4) — Beatles, The, 1959-1962
Williams, Allan
The **man** who gave the Beatles away / [by] Allan Williams and
William Marshall. — London : Elm Tree Books, 1975. — 236p,
[16]p of plates : ill, ports ; 22cm.
ISBN 0-241-89204-x : £3.50
(B75-16094)

AKDW/GB/E(YTLD/M) — Popular songs. Afro-American singers
Black music / [editor and designer Gavin Petrie]. — London [etc.] :
Hamlyn, 1974. — 128p : ill, ports(some col) ; 28cm.
ISBN 0-600-31343-3 : £1.95
(B75-03641)

The **soul** book / [by] Ian Hoare ... [et al.] ; edited by Ian Hoare. —
London : Eyre Methuen, 1975. — ix,206p,[16]p of plates : 1 ill,
ports ; 20cm.
Index.
ISBN 0-413-32150-9 Pbk : £1.50
(B75-29984)

AKDW/GB/E)P/XQM) — Rolling Stones, The. Biographies, 1972
Greenfield, Robert
A **journey** through America with the Rolling Stones / [by] Robert
Greenfield. — St Albans : Panther, 1975. — 287p,[16]p of plates :
ill, ports ; 18cm.
Originally published: as 'STP : a journey through America with the Rolling
Stones', New York : Saturday Press ; and as 'Stones Touring Party : a
journey through America with the Rolling Stones', London : Joseph, 1974.
ISBN 0-586-04195-8 Pbk : £0.75
(B75-24849)

AKDW/GC/E(M) — Country music. Singers
Gray, Andy
Great country music stars / [by] Andy Gray. — London [etc.] :
Hamlyn, 1975. — 176p : facsim, ports(some col) ; 31cm.
Bibl.: p.174. — Index.
ISBN 0-600-33979-3 : £2.95
(B75-50975)

AKDW/HHR(YTRN/XPF28) — Rhythm 'n' blues. New Orleans, 1946-1973
Broven, John
Walking to New Orleans : the story of New Orleans rhythm & blues / [by] John Broven. — Bexhill-on-Sea (38a Sackville Rd, Bexhill-on-Sea, Sussex) : Blues Unlimited, 1974. — xxv,249p,[52]p of plates : ill, facsims, map, ports ; 23cm.
Bibl.: p.221-223. — Index.
ISBN 0-9500229-3-4 : £3.75
ISBN 0-9500229-2-6 Pbk : £2.25
(B75-00201)

AKDW/HHW(X) — Blues. History
Cook, Bruce
Listen to the blues / by Bruce Cook. — London : Robson Books, 1975. — [8],263p,[16]p of plates : ill, ports ; 24cm.
Originally published: New York : Scribner, 1973. — Index.
ISBN 0-903895-47-1 : £4.35
(B75-21070)

AKDW/HHW(YTKC/XNK43) — Blues. Chicago, 1930-1972
Rowe, Mike
Chicago breakdown / [by] Mike Rowe. — London (2 Greycoat Place, S.W.1) : Eddison Press Ltd, 1973. — 226p : ill, facsims, 2 maps, ports ; 23cm. — (Eddison blues books ; [1])
Bibl.: p.215. — List of gramophone records: p.219-222. — Index.
ISBN 0-85649-015-6 : £2.50
(B75-03645)

AKDW/HHW/E(M) — Blues. Musicians
Charters, Samuel Barclay
The legacy of the blues : a glimpse into the art and the lives of twelve great bluesmen : an informal study / [by] Samuel Charters. — London : Calder and Boyars, 1975. — 192p : ill, maps, ports ; 21cm.
Bibl.: p.187-188. — List of gramophone records: p.189-192.
ISBN 0-7145-1098-x : £3.95
ISBN 0-7145-1099-8 Pbk : £1.50
(B75-50976)

AKDW/HHW/FD(WT/XPC18) — Blues. Recorded music. Lists, 1943-1966
Leadbitter, Mike
Blues records, January, 1943 to December, 1966 / [by] Mike Leadbitter and Neil Slaven]. — London [etc.] (Music Sales Ltd, 78 Newman St., W.1) : Oakwood Publications, [1975?]. — 381p ; 23cm.
Originally published: London : Hanover Books, 1968.
ISBN 0-86001-089-9 Pbk : Unpriced
(B75-50977)

AKDW/HK/E(M) — Rock 'n' roll singers
Rock life / [editor and designer Gavin Petrie]. — London [etc.] : Hamlyn, 1974. — 128p : ports(some col) ; 29cm. — (['Melody Maker' special])
ISBN 0-600-38708-9 : £1.95
(B75-03642)

AKDW/K/G/KDX(XHK11) — Bawdy songs, 1830-1840
Bawdy songs of the early music hall / selected, with an introduction, by George Speaight. — Newton Abbot [etc.] : David and Charles, 1975. — 96p : ill, music ; 26cm.
Facsimile reprints of selections from various song-books originally published by William West of London.
ISBN 0-7153-7013-8 : £3.95
(B75-31191)

AKGGC/E(M) — Castrato voice. Singers
Heriot, Angus
The castrati in opera / [by] Angus Heriot. — London : Calder and Boyars, 1975. — 243p,[7] leaves of plates : ill, ports ; 22cm. — (Opera library)
Originally published: London : Secker and Warburg, 1956. — Bibl.: p.229-232. — Index.
ISBN 0-7145-0153-0 : £5.75
(B75-26087)

AKGH/E(P) — Kelly, Michael. Biographies
Kelly, Michael, *b.1762*
Reminiscences [of] Michael Kelly. — [2nd ed. reprinted with corrections] / edited with an introduction by Roger Fiske. — London [etc.] : Oxford University Press, 1975. — xxxiv,396p,[12]p of plates : ill, facsim, music, ports ; 25cm. — (Oxford English memoirs and travels)
Second ed. originally published: London : Henry Colburn, 1826. — Bibl.: p.xvi. — Index.
ISBN 0-19-255417-4 : £7.50
(B75-20392)

AL — MUSICAL LITERATURE. INSTRUMENTAL MUSIC
AL/B — Instruments
Ingman, Nicholas
What instrument shall I play? / text by Nicholas Ingman ; illustrations by Bernard Brett. — London : Ward Lock, 1975. — 128p : ill(some col), ports(1 col) ; 29cm.
Index.
ISBN 0-7063-1988-5 : £2.95
(B75-29314)

AL/B(YC/XF101) — Instruments. Great Britain, 1700-1800
Thibault, G
Eighteenth century musical instruments, France and Britain = Les Instruments de musique au XVIIIe Siecle, France et Grande-Bretagne : [catalogue of an exhibition] / [exhibition designed and catalogue written by] G. Thibault (Mme de Chambure), Jean Jenkins, Josiane Bran-Ricci ; [exhibition organised by the Circulation Department, Victoria and Albert Museum]. — London : Victoria and Albert Museum, 1973. — [2], xxx,229p : chiefly ill(some col), maps ; 28cm.
Parallel English and French texts. — '- more than one hundred musical instruments drawn from the collections of the Conservatoire National Supérieur de Musique in Paris and of the Victoria and Albert Museum and of the Horniman Museum in London ... planned as a travelling exhibition ...' - Foreword.
ISBN 0-901486-71-x Pbk : £2.50
Primary classification AL/B(YH/XF101)
(B75-03646)

AL/B(YH/XF101) — Instruments. France, 1700-1800
Thibault, G
Eighteenth century musical instruments, France and Britain = Les Instruments de musique au XVIIIe Siecle, France et Grande-Bretagne : [catalogue of an exhibition] / [exhibition designed and catalogue written by] G. Thibault (Mme de Chambure), Jean Jenkins, Josiane Bran-Ricci ; [exhibition organised by the Circulation Department, Victoria and Albert Museum]. — London : Victoria and Albert Museum, 1973. — [2], xxx,229p : chiefly ill(some col), maps ; 28cm.
Parallel English and French texts. — '- more than one hundred musical instruments drawn from the collections of the Conservatoire National Supérieur de Musique in Paris and of the Victoria and Albert Museum and of the Horniman Museum in London ... planned as a travelling exhibition ...' - Foreword.
ISBN 0-901486-71-x Pbk : £2.50
Also classified at AL/B(YC/XF101)
(B75-03646)

AL/BC — Instrument making
Brune, John A.
Resonant rubbish / by John A. Brune ; illustrated by Lilla Fox. — London (2 Regent's Park Rd, NW1 7AY) : English Folk Dance and Song Society, [1975]. — 48p : ill ; 22cm. — (The folk shop instrumental series)
Index.
ISBN 0-85418-097-4 Sd : Unpriced
(B75-08293)

AM — MUSICAL LITERATURE. ORCHESTRAL MUSIC
AM(W) — Concerts
Mann, Peter Henry
The audience for orchestral concerts : a report on surveys in Birmingham, Bournemouth, Glasgow, Liverpool and Manchester / by Peter H. Mann ; prepared for the Arts Council of Great Britain. — [London] : [Arts Council of Great Britain], [1975]. — [3],54p ; 21x30cm.
ISBN 0-7287-0059-x Sp : £0.50
(B75-13446)

AMT — MUSICAL LITERATURE. JAZZ
AMT(M) — Jazz musicians. Biographies
Feather, Leonard
From Satchmo to Miles / [by] Leonard Feather. — London : Quartet Books, 1975. — 258p : ports ; 20cm.
Originally published: New York : Stein and Day, 1972 ; London : Quartet Books, 1974.
ISBN 0-7043-1223-9 Pbk : £1.50
(B75-10770)

AMT(P) — Collins, Lee. Biographies
Collins, Lee
Oh, didn't he ramble : the life story of Lee Collins / as told to Mary Collins ; edited by Frank J. Gillis and John W. Miner. — Urbana [etc.] ; London : University of Illinois Press, 1974. — xv, 159p,[16]p of plates : ill, ports ; 26cm. — (Music in American life)
33 1/3 rpm disc as insert. — Bibl.: p.149-150. — List of records: p.141-147. — Index.
ISBN 0-252-00234-2 : £5.50
(B75-01179)

AMT(P) — Miller, Glenn. Biographies
Simon, George Thomas
Glenn Miller and his Orchestra / by George T. Simon. — London : W.H. Allen, 1974. — xv,473p : ill, facsims, ports ; 24cm.
Ill. on lining papers. — Also published: New York : Crowell, 1974. — List of gramophone records: p.451-456. — Index.
ISBN 0-491-01501-1 : £4.95
(B75-00202)

AMT/FD(XPE26) — Recorded music, 1945-1970
Modern jazz, the essential records : a critical selection / by Max Harrison ... [et al.]. — London : Aquarius Books ; Kings Langley (Station Rd, Kings Langley, Herts.) : Distributed by Argus Books, 1975. — [8],140p ; 22cm.
Index.
ISBN 0-904619-01-x Pbk : £2.90
(B75-21669)

AP — MUSICAL LITERATURE. INDIVIDUAL INSTRUMENTS & INSTRUMENTAL GROUPS

APV — Electronic music
The **development** and practice of electronic music / editors Jon H. Appleton, Ronald C. Perera ; authors Otto Luening ... [et al.]. — Englewood Cliffs ; London [etc.] : Prentice-Hall, 1975. — xi, 384p : ill ; 24cm.
Bibl.: p.336-343. — List of gramophone records: p.344-366. — Index.
ISBN 0-13-207605-5 : £8.80

(B75-15702)

APV/B — Electronic instruments
Brown, Robert, *b.1943*
Experimenting with electronic music / [by] Robert Brown and Mark Olson [i.e. Olsen] ; with a specially written chapter for the guidance of the English reader by W. Oliver. — Slough : Foulsham-Tab, 1974. — viii,5-180p : ill ; 22cm.
Originally published: Blue Ridge Summit : Tab Books, 1974. — Index.
ISBN 0-7042-0129-1 Pbk : £1.50

(B75-05798)

Crowhurst, Norman Herbert
Electronic musical instruments / [by] Norman H. Crowhurst ; with a specially written chapter for the guidance of the English reader by W. Oliver. — Slough : Foulsham-Tab, 1975. — viii, 3-191p : ill ; 22cm.
Originally published: Blue Ridge Summit : Tab Books, 1971. — Index.
ISBN 0-7042-0144-5 Pbk : £1.80

(B75-50978)

Howe, Hubert S
Electronic music synthesis : concepts, facilities, techniques / [by] Hubert S. Howe, Jr. — London : Dent, 1975. — xv,272p : ill, music ; 24cm.
Originally published: New York : Norton, 1975. — Bibl.: p.263-266. — Index.
ISBN 0-460-04251-3 : £6.50

(B75-07344)

APV/D — Electronic music. Composition
Dwyer, Terence
Making electronic music : a course for schools / [by] Terence Dwyer ; illustrated by Eric Tranter ; photographs by Kenneth Padley. — London : Oxford University Press.
Book 2. — 1975. — [4],41p : ill ; 25cm.
Index.
ISBN 0-19-321072-x Sp : £1.50

(B75-24851)

Teacher's book. — 1975. — v,39p : ill ; 25cm.
Bibl.: p.36-37. — Index.
ISBN 0-19-321070-3 Sp : £2.50

(B75-24852)

APW — MUSICAL LITERATURE. KEYBOARD INSTRUMENTS

APW/B(X) — Instruments. History
Hollis, Helen Rice
The piano : a pictorial account of its ancestry and development / [by] Helen Rice Hollis. — Newton Abbot [etc.] : David and Charles, 1975. — 120p : ill, music, ports ; 25cm.
Bibl.: p.117-118. — Index.
ISBN 0-7153-6559-2 : £4.50

(B75-13169)

APW/E(XCX601) — Performance, 1300-1900
Ferguson, Howard
Keyboard interpretation from the 14th to the 19th century : an introduction / [by] Howard Ferguson. — London : Oxford University Press, 1975. — ix,211p : music ; 21cm.
Bibl.: p.177-198. — Index.
ISBN 0-19-318419-2 Pbk : £2.95

(B75-21076)

AQ/B(K/X) — Piano. Economics. Instruments. History
Wainwright, David, *b.1929*
The piano makers / [by] David Wainwright. — London : Hutchinson, 1975. — 192p,leaf of plate,[56]p of plates : ill(1 col), facsim, ports ; 25cm.
Ill. on lining papers. — Bibl.: p.182-183. — List of records: p.183-184. — Index.
ISBN 0-09-122950-2 : £6.00

(B75-50979)

AQ/BC — Piano making
White, William Braid
Theory and practice of piano construction, with a detailed practical method for tuning / [by] William B. White. — New York : Dover Publications [etc.] ; London : Constable, 1975. — 160p : ill ; 22cm.
Facsimile reprint of: 'Theory and practice of pianoforte building'. New York : E.L. Bill, 1906.
ISBN 0-486-23139-9 Pbk : £1.40

(B75-19735)

Wolfenden, Samuel
A treatise on the art of pianoforte construction / by Samuel Wolfenden. — Old Woking (The Gresham Press, Old Woking, Surrey) : Union Bros Ltd, 1975. — [15],274,[10]p,4p of plates : ill, port ; 24cm.
Facsimile reprint of: 1st ed., London : Unwin Bros, 1916. — Index. — Includes supplement first published 1927.
ISBN 0-9502121-3-x Pbk : £5.85

(B75-18372)

AQ/E(P) — Liberace. Biographies
Liberace
Liberace : an autobiography. — London (44 Hill St., W1X 8LB) : Star Books, 1974. — xii,307p,[16]p of plates : ill, ports ; 18cm.
Originally published: New York : Putnam ; London : W.H. Allen, 1973.
ISBN 0-352-30010-8 Pbk : £0.60

(B75-02999)

AQPHX/E — Piano. Jazz. Performance
Harvey, Eddie
Jazz piano / [by] Eddie Harvey. — London : English Universities Press, 1974. — ix,163p : 1 ill, music ; 20x21cm. — (Teach yourself books)
Bibl.: p.162-163.
ISBN 0-340-12456-3 Pbk : £0.95

(B75-09744)

AR(YC/VP/Q) — Organists. Great Britain. Royal College of Organists. Yearbooks
Royal College of Organists
Year book / Royal College of Organists. — London (Kensington Gore, SW7 2QS) : The College.
1974-1975. — [1975]. — [1],viii,167p : ill, port ; 21cm.
Cover title.
ISBN 0-902462-05-9 Pbk : £0.75
ISSN 0080-4320

(B75-05797)

AR/B(XCL431) — Organs. Instruments, 1320-1750
Klotz, Hans
Über die Orgelkunst der Gotik, der Renaissance und des Barock : Musik, Disposition, Mixturen, Mensuren, Registrierung, Gebrauch der Klaviere / [von] Hans Klotz. — 2., völlig neubearb. Aufl. — Kassel [etc.] ; London ([32 Great Titchfield St., W.1]) : Bärenreiter, 1975. — xx,427p : ill ; 27cm.
Previous ed.: Kassel : Bärenreiter, 1934. — Bibl.: p.394-405. — Index.
£31.50
ISBN 3-7618-0170-x

AR/B(YC/XPQ20) — Organs. Instruments, 1955-74
Rowntree, John Pickering
The classical organ in Britain, 1955-1974 / [by] John P. Rowntree and John F. Brennan ; [illustrations by John Brennan]. — Oxford (130 Southfield Rd, Oxford OX4 1PA) : Positif Press, 1975. — 144p : ill ; 22cm.
Bibl.: p.144. — Index.
ISBN 0-9503892-1-8 : £2.95
ISBN 0-9503892-0-x Pbk : £2.25

(B75-13170)

AR/B(YDDB) — Organs. St Andrew's Church, Boreham
Smith, William Joseph Thomas
The organ & organists / [by] William J.T. Smith. — [Chelmsford] ([Boreham Vicarage, Chelmsford, Essex CM3 3EG]) : The author, 1975. — 32p : ill ; 26cm. — (Boreham histories ; no.4)
Bibl.: p.32.
ISBN 0-9504312-0-6 Pbk : £0.25

(B75-21667)

AR/B(YDFGWB) — Organs. Wells Cathedral
Bowers, Roger
The organs and organists of Wells Cathedral / [by Roger Bowers and Anthony Crossland]. — [Wells] ([22 Vicars' Close, Wells, Somerset BA5 2UJ]) : The Friends of Wells Cathedral, 1974. — [2],24p,[8]p of plates : ill ; 22cm.
Based on: 'A brief history of the organs of Wells Cathedral' / by L.S. Colchester. 5th ed. 1970.
ISBN 0-902321-12-9 Sd : £0.20

(B75-00741)

AR/B(YT/X) — Organs. United States. History
Ochse, Orpha
The history of the organ in the United States / [by] Orpha Ochse. — Bloomington ; London : Indiana University Press, 1975. — xv, 494p : ill, music ; 24cm.
Bibl.: p.440-463. — Index.
ISBN 0-253-32830-6 : £11.25

(B75-17690)

AR/BC(Q/YDJGS) — Brindley and Foster, Sheffield
Knott, Joshua Robert
A study of Brindley and Foster, organ builders of Sheffield, 1854-1939 / by J.R. Knott. — Bognor Regis (101 Highcroft Cres., Bognor Regis, Sussex PO22 8DT) : The author, 1974. — [2],82p, [4] leaves of plates ; 26cm.
Cover title: Brindley & Foster, organ builders, Sheffield, 1854-1939.
ISBN 0-9503869-0-1 Sd : £1.15

(B75-50002)

AR/BC(XCRR420) — Organs. Instrument making, 1436-1855
Martini, Ulrich
Die Orgeldispositionssammlungen bis zur Mitte des 19.
Jahrhunderts / [von] Unrich Martini. — Kassel [etc.] ; London
([32 Great Titchfield St., W.1]) : Bärenreiter, [1975]. — [3],ix,
198p : maps ; 27cm. — (Orgenwissenschaftliche Forschungsstelle,
Westfälische Wilhelmsuniversität. Veröffentlichungen ; nr.6)
Bibl.: p.159-161. — Index.
Pbk : £7.36

AR/BPPG — Organs. Pipes. Scaling
Mahrenholz, Christhard
The calculation of organ pipe scales from the middle ages to the
mid-nineteenth century / [by] Christhard Mahrenholz ; translated
[from the German] by Andrew H. Williams. — Oxford (130
Southfield Rd, Oxford OX4 1PA) : Positif Press, 1975. — 87p :
ill ; 22cm.
Limited ed. of 1000 copies. — Translation of: 'Die Berechnung der
Orgelpfeifenmensuren vom Mittelalter bis zur Mitte des 19. Jahrhunderts'.
Kassel : Bärenreiter, 1968.
ISBN 0-9503892-2-6 Pbk : £2.50

(B75-31193)

ARPV/JR(X) — Cinema organs. History
Wyatt, Geoffrey
At the mighty organ / [by] Geoffrey Wyatt. — Oxford : Oxford
Illustrated Press, 1974. — [6],98p : ill, facsim, ports ; 24cm.
ISBN 0-902280-22-8 : £3.75

(B75-12698)

ARW — MUSICAL LITERATURE. STRING INSTRUMENTS
ARXN(TC) — String ensembles. Bibliographies of scores
Farish, Margaret K
String music in print / [by] Margaret K. Farish. — 2nd ed. —
New York ; London : Bowker, 1973. — xv,464p ; 27cm.
Previous ed.: 1965. — Bibl.: p.408-410. — Index.
ISBN 0-8352-0596-7 : £18.00

(B75-25110)

ARXT/BC(P/WJ) — Retford centenary exhibition
The **Retford** centenary exhibition. — London ([4 Station Parade,
Uxbridge Rd, W5 3LD]) : Ealing Strings, 1975. — 64p,leaf of
plate,100p of plates : ill, facsims, ports ; 26cm.
ISBN 0-9504357-0-8 : £12.50

(B75-22849)

ASR — Cello
Cowling, Elizabeth
The cello / [by] Elizabeth Cowling. — London [etc.] : Batsford,
1975. — 224p,[32]p of plates : ill, geneal tables, music ; 23cm.
Bibl.: p.215-217. — Index.
ISBN 0-7134-2879-1 : £6.50

(B75-13737)

ASR/E(P) — Casals, Pablo. Biographies
Kirk, H L
Pablo Casals : a biography / by H.L. Kirk. — London :
Hutchinson, 1974. — xi,692p : ill, facsim, ports ; 25cm.
Originally published: New York : Holt, Rinehart and Winston, 1974. —
Bibl.: p.657-666. — List of gramophone records: p.568-625. — Index.
ISBN 0-09-122230-3 : £5.50

(B75-13171)

ASR/E(VC) — Cello. Teaching
Horsfall, Jean
Teaching the cello to groups / [by] Jean Horsfall. — London
[etc.] : Oxford University Press, 1974. — [3],108p,[8]p of plates :
ill, music ; 20cm.
ISBN 0-19-318510-5 : £2.75

(B75-01178)

**AT — MUSICAL LITERATURE. PLUCKED STRING
INSTRUMENTS**
ATS/B — Guitar. Instruments
Wheeler, Tom
The guitar book : a handbook for electric and acoustic guitarists /
[by] Tom Wheeler. — London : Macdonald and Jane's, 1975. —
xvii,269p : ill, ports ; 29cm.
Originally published: New York : Harper and Row, 1974. — Index.
ISBN 0-356-08322-5 : £5.50

(B75-25560)

ATS/E — Guitar. Performance
Fradd, Dale
The guitar / [by] Dale Fradd. — London : Teach Yourself Books,
1975. — 126p : ill, music ; 21cm. — (Teach yourself books)
Bibl.
ISBN 0-340-16197-3 Pbk : £1.50

(B75-18373)

Stevens, Susan
Help yourself to play the guitar / by Susan Stevens ; illustrated by
Elizabeth Wall. — London : Girl Guides Association, 1975. — [1]
,32p : ill(some col), music ; 15x21cm.
ISBN 0-85260-002-x Sd : £0.35

(B75-10255)

ATSX/BT — Sitar. Maintenance
Gupta, Punita
Maintenance of the sitar / [by] Punita Gupta ; illustrated by John
Lyall. — [Southall] ([9 Ranelagh Rd, Southall, Middx]) : [The
author], [1975]. — [4]p : ill ; 30cm.
ISBN 0-9504319-0-7 Sd : Free

(B75-20395)

AU — MUSICAL LITERATURE. WIND INSTRUMENTS
AUMM — Military band
Mays, Spike
The band rats / [by] Spike Mays. — London : P. Davies, 1975. —
xiii,184p,8p of plates : ill, music, ports ; 22cm.
ISBN 0-432-09230-7 : £4.50

(B75-24238)

AVS/B — Recorder. Instruments
Thomson, John Mansfield
Your book of the recorder / [by] John M. Thomson. — 2nd ed.
— London : Faber, 1974. — 3-75p,[8]p of plates : ill, music,
ports ; 22cm.
Previous ed.: 1968. — Bibl.: p.70-71.
ISBN 0-571-04873-0 : £1.25

(B75-08738)

AVS/E — Recorder. Performance
Etkin, Ruth
Playing & composing on the recorder / by Ruth Etkin. — New
York : Sterling [etc.] ; London : Distributed by Ward Lock, 1975.
— 72p : ill, music ; 22cm.
Index.
ISBN 0-7061-2080-9 : £1.95

(B75-28638)

AVY — Bagpipes
Seton, Sir Bruce Gordon, bart
The pipes of war : a record of the achievements of pipers of
Scottish and overseas regiments in the war, 1914-1918 / by Sir
Bruce Seton, bart, and John Grant. — [1st ed. reprinted] ; with a
new introduction by Frank Richardson. — Wakefield : EP
Publishing [etc.], 1974. — x,v-xi,291p,[8]leaves of plates : ill,
music, ports ; 25cm.
Originally published: Glasgow : Maclehose, Jackson, 1920.
ISBN 0-7158-1089-8 : £5.00

(B75-15172)

AVY/B(X) — Bagpipes. Instruments. History
Collinson, Francis
The bagpipe : the history of a musical instrument / [by] Francis
Collinson. — London [etc.] : Routledge and Kegan Paul, 1975. —
xx,257p,[16]p of plates : ill ; 24cm.
Bibl.: p.242-249. — Index.
ISBN 0-7100-7913-3 : £7.50

(B75-04509)

AVY/T(QU) — Bagpipes. Pibroch. Notation
Thomason, Charles Simson
Ceol mor notation : a new and abbreviated system of musical
notation for the piobaireachd as played on the Highland bagpipe,
with examples / by C.S. Thomason. — Wakefield : EP Publishing
[etc.], 1975. — [280]p : chiefly music ; 27cm.
Facsimile reprint of: 1st ed., Dehra Dun : C.S. Thomason, 1893. — 'For
completeness, the publishers have included both versions of pages where the
second edition [1905] varied from the first edition'. — title page verso. —
Index.
ISBN 0-7158-1114-2 : £6.75

(B75-22850)

**AX — MUSICAL LITERATURE. PERCUSSION
INSTRUMENTS**
AXSR — Church bells
Camp, John
Discovering bells and bellringing / [by] John Camp. — 2nd ed. —
Aylesbury : Shire Publications, 1975. — 47p : ill ; 18cm. —
(Discovering series ; no.29)
Previous ed.: Tring : Shire Publications, 1968. — Index.
ISBN 0-85263-290-8 Pbk : £0.35

(B75-08739)

AXSR/E(X) — Change ringing. History
Morris, Ernest
The history and art of change ringing / by Ernest Morris ; with a
foreword by G.F. Coleridge. — [1st ed. reprinted] ; new
introduction by Cyril A. Wratten. — Wakefield : EP Publishing,
1974. — [4],xviii,673p,[40]p of plates,[44] leaves of plates : ill,
music, ports ; 22cm.
Facsimile reprint of: 1st ed., London : Chapman and Hall, 1931. — Index.
ISBN 0-85409-995-6 : £8.00

(B75-18374)

AY/B — Other instruments
New/rediscovered musical instruments. — London ([15 Bayonne
Rd, W.6]) : Mirliton Publications.
Vol.1 / [by] Hugh Davies ... [et al.]. — 1974. — 26p : ill, ports ; 23cm.
ISBN 0-904414-03-5 Sd : £0.75

(B75-04507)

AY/BC — Other instruments. Manufacture
Education Development Center
    The musical instrument recipe book / [Education Development
    Center]. — Harmondsworth [etc.] : Penguin Education, 1974. —
    85p : ill ; 19cm. — (Extensions) (Penguin education)
    Originally published: St Louis : Webster Division, McGraw-Hill, 1968.
    ISBN 0-14-081185-0 Pbk : £0.50
                                                                        (B75-08294)

B — INDIVIDUAL COMPOSERS
BBC(N) — Bach, Johann Sebastian. Biographies
    Johann Sebastian Bach : Leben und Werk in Dokumenten. —
    Kassel [etc.] ; London ([32 Great Titchfield St., W.1) :
    Bärenreiter-Verlag [etc.], 1975. — 206p : facsim, music ; 18cm.
    Index.
    Pbk : £1.56

BBCB(N) — Bach family. Biographies
Bizony, Celia
    The family of Bach : a brief history / by Celia Bizony. —
    Horsham : Artemis Press, 1975. — 47p : geneal table ; 24cm.
    ISBN 0-85141-281-5 Pbk : £0.90
                                                                        (B75-13733)

BBGAM — Bartók, Béla. Orchestral music
McCabe, John
    Bartók orchestral music / [by] John McCabe. — London : British
    Broadcasting Corporation, 1974. — 64p : music ; 20cm. —
    (British Broadcasting Corporation. Music guides)
    Index.
    ISBN 0-563-12674-4 Pbk : £0.55
                                                                        (B75-02998)

BBJ — Beethoven, Ludwig van
    Beethoven : a documentary study / compiled and edited by H.C.
    Robbins Landon ; [translated from the German by Richard
    Wadleigh and Eugene Hartzell]. — Abridged ed. — London :
    Thames and Hudson, 1974. — 216p : ill(some col), music,
    ports(some col) ; 22cm.
    Previous ed.: i.e. Full ed. of this translation, 1970. — Translation of:
    'Beethoven : sein Leben und seine Welt in zeitgenössischen Bildern und
    Texten'. Zürich : Universal Edition, 1970. — Bibl.: p.22. — Index.
    ISBN 0-500-18146-2 : £3.00
    ISBN 0-500-20140-4 Pbk : £1.95
                                                                        (B75-03644)

BBJ/D — Beethoven, Ludwig van. Composition
Mies, Paul
    Beethoven's sketches : an analysis of his style based on a study of
    his sketch-books / by Paul Mies ; translated [from the German]
    by Doris L. MacKinnon. — New York : Dover Publications
    [etc.] ; London : Constable, 1975. — [8],198p : music ; 22cm.
    Facsimile reprint of: 1st ed. of this translation, London : Oxford University
    Press, 1929. — Translation of: 'Die Bedeutung des Skizzen Beethovens zur
    Erkenntnis seines Stiles'. Leipzig : Breitkopf und Härtel, 1925. — Bibl.:
    p.189-190. — Index.
    ISBN 0-486-23042-2 Pbk : £1.40
                                                                        (B75-25553)

BBJARXNS — Beethoven, Ludwig van. String quartets
Lam, Basil
    Beethoven string quartets / [by] Basil Lam. — London : British
    Broadcasting Corporation. — (British Broadcasting Corporation.
    Music guides)
    In 2 vols.
    1. — 1975. — 68p : music ; 20cm.
    ISBN 0-563-10166-0 Pbk : £0.70
                                                                        (B75-30569)

    2. — 1975. — 72p : music ; 20cm.
    ISBN 0-563-12675-2 Pbk : £0.70
                                                                        (B75-30570)

BBKR — Berg, Alban
Carner, Mosco
    Alban Berg : the man and his work / [by] Mosco Carner. —
    London : Duckworth, 1975. — xv,255p,leaf of plate,[6]p of
    plates : ill, facsims, music, ports ; 24cm.
    List of works: p.243-245. — Bibl.: p.246-247. — Index.
    ISBN 0-7156-0769-3 : £12.00
                                                                        (B75-28636)

BBNS — Billings, William
McKay, David Phares
    William Billings of Boston : eighteenth-century composer / by
    David P. McKay and Richard Crawford. — Princeton ; London :
    Princeton University Press, 1975. — xii,303p : ill, facsims, map,
    music ; 24cm.
    Bibl.: p.279-290. — Index.
    ISBN 0-691-09118-8 : £8.40
                                                                        (B75-50980)

BBSL — Boyle, Ina
Maconchy, Elizabeth
    Ina Boyle : an appreciation : with a select list of her music / by
    Elizabeth Maconchy. — Dublin : Trinity College Dublin, Library,
    1974. — [16]p,plate : port ; 22cm.
    Limited ed. of 300 copies. — List of music: p.[10]-[16].
    ISBN 0-904720-00-4 Sd : Unpriced
                                                                        (B75-50003)

BBT — Brahms, Johannes
Latham, Peter, *b.1894*
    Brahms / by Peter Latham. — Revised [ed.]. — London : Dent,
    1975. — x,230p,[8]p of plates : ill, facsims, music, ports ; 20cm.
    — (The master musicians series)
    Previous ed.: 1966. — Bibl.: p.221-223. — Catalogue of works: p.193-216. —
    Index.
    ISBN 0-460-03158-9 : £2.95
    ISBN 0-460-02156-7 Pbk : £1.60
                                                                        (B75-27352)

BBT(N) — Brahms, Johannes. Biographies
Gál, Hans
    Johannes Brahms : his work and personality / [by] Hans Gál ;
    translated from the German by Joseph Stein. — London : Severn
    House, 1975. — ix,245,iv p,[8]p of plates : ill, music, ports ; 21cm.
    This translation originally published: London : Weidenfeld and Nicolson,
    1964. — Translation of: 'Johannes Brahms'. Frankfurt am Main : Fischer
    Bücherei, 1961. — Bibl.: p.239. — List of composition: p.241-245. — Index.
    ISBN 0-7278-0078-7 : £4.50
                                                                        (B75-30567)

BBUE — Bruckner, Anton
Watson, Derek
    Bruckner / by Derek Watson. — London : Dent, 1975. — ix,
    174p,[8]p of plates : ill, music, ports ; 20cm. — (The master
    musicians series)
    Bibl.: p.167-169. — Index.
    ISBN 0-460-03144-9 : £2.95
                                                                        (B75-21066)

BBVM(N) — Busoni, Ferrucio. Biographies
Dent, Edward Joseph
    Ferruccio Busoni : a biography / by Edward J. Dent. — London
    (48 Great Marlborough St., W.1) : Eulenberg Books, 1974. — xv,
    368p,XXIIIp of plates : ill, music, ports ; 22cm.
    Originally published: London : Oxford University Press, 1933. — List of
    music: p.337-352. — Index.
    ISBN 0-903873-15-x : £3.75
    ISBN 0-903873-02-8 Pbk : £2.00
                                                                        (B75-24235)

BBX(N) — Byrd, William. Biographies
Sharp, Geoffrey Brinsley
    Byrd ; &, Victoria / [by] Geoffrey B. Sharp. — Sevenoaks :
    Novello, 1974. — 20p ; 19cm. — (Novello short biographies)
    ISBN 0-85360-060-0 Sd : £0.20
    Also classified at BVI(N)
                                                                        (B75-03643)

BCMTADW — Cotton, Reynell. Cricket song for the Hambleden
            Club
Knight, Ronald David
    The Hambledon cricket song of the Rev Reynell Cotton / edited
    and annotated by Ronald D. Knight. — Weymouth (40A
    Abbotsbury Rd, Weymouth, Dorset DT4 0AE) : R.D. Knight,
    1975. — [1],25 leaves ; 21cm. — (Hambledon's cricket glory ;
    vol.6)
    Song on fold. sheet ([3]p.; music) as insert. — Bibl.: leaf 25.
    ISBN 0-903769-00-x Pbk : £0.30
                                                                        (B75-12697)

BCT(N) — Crotch, William. Biographies
Rennert, Jonathan
    William Crotch, 1775-1847 : composer, artist, teacher / by
    Jonathan Rennert. — Lavenham : Dalton, 1975. — 116p,[16]p of
    plates : ill, facsims, music, ports ; 23cm.
    Bibl.: p.109-111. — Index.
    ISBN 0-900963-61-1 : £3.20
                                                                        (B75-20390)

BDJAM — Debussy, Claude. Orchestral music
Cox, David, *b.1916*
    Debussy orchestral music / [by] David Cox. — London : British
    Broadcasting Corporation, 1974. — 64p : music ; 20cm. —
    (British Broadcasting Corporation. Music guides)
    ISBN 0-563-12678-7 Pbk : £0.55
                                                                        (B75-50004)

BDL(N) — Delius, Frederick. Biographies
Beecham, *Sir* **Thomas,** *bart*
    Frederick Delius / [by] Sir Thomas Beecham. — Revised ed. ;
    with new material and discography ; introduction [by] Felix
    Aprahamian ; discography [compiled by] Malcolm Walker. —
    [London] : Severn House, 1975. — [2],243,[12]p of plates : ill,
    ports ; 21cm.
    Previous ed.: London : Hutchinson, 1959. — List of records: p.231-243. —
    Index.
    ISBN 0-7278-0073-6 : £5.25
    ISBN 0-7278-0099-x Pbk : £4.75
                                                                        (B75-27351)

BDL(TE) — Delius, Frederic. Bibliographies of manuscripts
Delius Trust
Frederick Delius 1862-1934, a catalogue of the Music Archive of
the Delius Trust, London / [compiled by] Rachel Lowe. —
London : Delius Trust : Distributed by Boosey and Hawkes, 1974.
— 182p : ill, coat of arms, facsims, music ; 26cm.
Limited ed. of 500 numbered copies.
ISBN 0-85162-023-x : £7.50

(B75-08382)

BDRAC — Donizetti, Gaetano. Opera
Allitt, John
Donizetti and the tradition of romantic love : (a collection of
essays on a theme) / by John Allitt. — London (56 Harbut Rd,
SW11 2RB) : Donizetti Society, 1975. — 287p : ill, facsims,
music, ports ; 23cm.
Limited ed. of 500 numbered copies. — Bibl.: p.282-287.
ISBN 0-9503333-1-x Pbk : £5.00

(B75-08295)

BEP(N/XM21) — Elgar, Sir Edward. Biographies, 1914-1934
Moore, Jerrold Northrop
Elgar on record : the composer and the gramophone / [by] Jerrold
Northrop Moore. — London [etc.] : Oxford University Press,
1974. — viii,244p,leaf of plate,[12]p of plates : ill, facsim, music,
ports ; 25cm.
Pbk version available with a set of records (HMV RLS713). — Index.
ISBN 0-19-315434-x : £5.00

(B75-06901)

BFS(N) — Foulds, John. Biographies
MacDonald, Malcolm, *b.1948*
John Foulds : his life in music : with a detailed catalogue of his
works, a discography, a bibliographical note, and with music
examples and illustrations / by Malcolm MacDonald. —
Rickmansworth (22 Pheasants Way, Rickmansworth, Herts.) :
Triad Press, 1975. — 2-112p : music, port ; 30cm. — (Triad Press
bibliographical series ; no.3)
Index.
ISBN 0-902070-15-0 Sp : £4.75

(B75-28637)

BG — Gabrieli, Giovanni
Arnold, Denis
Giovanni Gabrieli / [by] Denis Arnold. — London [etc.] : Oxford
University Press, 1974. — 70p : music ; 22cm. — (Oxford studies
of composers ; 12)
ISBN 0-19-315231-2 Pbk : £1.80

(B75-07792)

BHC — Handel, George Frideric
Young, Percy Marshall
Handel / by Percy M. Young. — [Revised ed.]. — London :
Dent, 1975. — x,244p,[8]p of plates : ill, music, ports ; 20cm. —
(The master musicians series)
Previous ed.: 1947. — Bibl.: p.221-223. — Index.
ISBN 0-460-03161-9 : £3.95
ISBN 0-460-02165-6 Pbk : £2.25

(B75-13734)

BHC(N/XEZE28) — Handel, George Frideric, 1685-1712
Bell, Arnold Craig
Handel before England / by A. Craig Bell. — Darley (Darley,
Harrogate, N. Yorkshire) : Grian-Aig Press, 1975. — [4],60p :
music, ports ; 22cm.
Index.
ISBN 0-9500714-5-5 Pbk : £4.10

(B75-31189)

BHE — Haydn, Joseph
Hughes, Rosemary
Haydn / by Rosemary Hughes. — Revised ed. — London : Dent,
1974. — xiii,271p,[8]p of plates : 1 ill, facsims, music, ports ;
20cm. — (The master musicians series)
Previous ed.: 1970. — Bibl.: p.253-259. — Index.
ISBN 0-460-03160-0 : £2.95
ISBN 0-460-02160-5 Pbk : £1.65

(B75-01175)

BHM(N) — Hindemith, Paul. Biographies
Skelton, Geoffrey
Paul Hindemith : the man behind the music : a biography / by
Geoffrey Skelton. — London : Gollancz, 1975. — 319p,[8]p of
plates : ill, facsims, music, ports ; 23cm.
Bibl.: p.297-298. — List of musical works : p.299-308. — List of
gramophone records : p.308-310. — Index.
ISBN 0-575-01988-3 : £6.00

(B75-22841)

BHO(N) — Holmbee, Vagn
Rapoport, Paul
Vagn Holmboe : a catalogue of his music, discography,
bibliography, essays / compiled and [essays] translated [from the
Danish] by Paul Rapoport. — London (10E Prior Bolton St.,
N.1) : Triad Press, 1974. — 3-78p ; 30cm. — (Triad Press
bibliographical series ; no.2)
Bibl.: p.77-78. — Index. — Includes 3 essays by Vagn Holmboe.
ISBN 0-902070-13-4 Sp : £2.50

(B75-04505)

†

BHP(T) — Holst, Gustav. Bibliographies
Short, Michael
Gustav Holst (1874-1934) : a centenary documentation / [by]
Michael Short. — London [etc.] : White Lion Publishers, 1974. —
[3],iv,285p ; 26cm.
Bibl.: p.206-233. — Index.
ISBN 0-7285-0000-0 : £15.00

(B75-07086)

BIV(N) — Ives, Charles. Biographies
Perlis, Vivian
Charles Ives remembered : an oral history / by Vivian Perlis. —
New Haven ; London : Yale University Press, 1974. — xviii,
237p : ill, facsims, music, ports ; 26cm.
Index.
ISBN 0-300-01758-8 : £6.25

(B75-05791)

Wooldridge, David
Charles Ives : a portrait / by David Wooldridge. — London :
Faber, 1975. — [12],342,x p,[8]p of plates : ill, ports ; 24cm.
Originally published: as 'From the steeples and mountains'. New York :
Knopf, 1974. — List of gramophone records: p.330-342. — Index.
ISBN 0-571-10687-0 : £6.00

(B75-15003)

BIVUMM — Ives, Charles. Military band music
Elkus, Jonathan
Charles Ives and the American band tradition : a centennial
tribute / by Jonathan Elkus. — Exeter : American Arts
Documentation Centre, University of Exeter, 1974. — 32p,4p of
plates : music ; 21cm. — (University of Exeter. American Arts
Documentation Centre. American arts pamphlets ; no.4)
Bibl.: p.32.
ISBN 0-85989-005-8 Sd : £0.60

(B75-05796)

BJRP — Joplin, Scott
Gammond, Peter
Scott Joplin and the ragtime era / [by] Peter Gammond. —
London [etc.] : Angus and Robertson, 1975. — 223p,[32]p of
plates : ill, facsims, ports ; 21cm.
ISBN 0-207-95648-0 : £3.00

(B75-18371)

BLJ(N) — Liszt, Franz. Biographies
Perényi, Eleanor
Liszt / [by] Elaenor Perényi. — London : Weidenfeld and
Nicolson, [1975]. — [11],466p,leaf of plate,[16]p of plates : ill,
ports ; 24cm.
Originally published: Boston, Mass. : Little, Brown, 1974. — Bibl.:
p.423-429. — Index.
ISBN 0-297-76910-3 : £8.50

(B75-11755)

Wilkinson, Anthony
Liszt / [by] Anthony Wilkinson. — London : Macmillan, 1975. —
112p : ill(incl 1 col), facsims, music, ports(some col) ; 27cm. —
(The musicians)
Bibl.: p.108-109. — List of works: p.109-111. — Index.
ISBN 0-333-15064-3 : £3.75

(B75-14335)

BME — Mahler, Gustav
Holbrook, David
Gustav Mahler and the courage to be / by David Holbrook. —
London : Vision Press, 1975. — 270p : music ; 25cm. —
(Holbrook, David. Studies in the psychology of culture)
Bibl.: p.263-264. — Index.
ISBN 0-85478-243-5 : £7.95

(B75-27350)

Mitchell, Donald
Gustav Mahler / by Donald Mitchell. — London : Faber.
The Wunderhorn years : chronicles and commentaries. — 1975. — 3-461p,
[4]p of plates : ill, facsims, music, ports ; 26cm.
Facsims on lining papers. — Bibl.: p.432-437. — Index.
ISBN 0-571-10674-9 : £15.00

(B75-30566)

Walter, Bruno
Gustav Mahler / [by] Bruno Walter ; translated from the German by James Galston. — London : Severn House : [Distributed by Hutchinson], 1975. — ix,160p,plate : port ; 21cm.
This translation originally published: London : Kegan Paul, 1937. — Translation of: 'Gustav Mahler'. Wien : Reichner, 1936.
ISBN 0-7278-0075-2 : £3.75
(B75-27349)

BME(N) — Mahler, Gustav. Biographies
Raynor, Henry
Mahler / [by] Henry Raynor. — London [etc.] : Macmillan, 1975. — 112p : ill(some col), facsims, ports(some col) ; 27cm. — (The musicians)
Bibl.: p.110. — Index.
ISBN 0-333-18137-9 : £3.75
(B75-14333)

BMFMN(N) — Martinu, Bohuslav. Biographies
Large, Brian
Martinu / [by] Brian Large. — London : Duckworth, 1975. — xiv,198p,leaf of plate,[24]p of plates : ill, facsims, ports ; 24cm.
Bibl.: p.189. — Catalogue of works : p.157-186. — Index.
ISBN 0-7156-0770-7 : £9.50
(B75-22839)

BMKS — Messiaen, Olivier
Johnson, Robert Sherlaw
Messiaen / [by] Robert Sherlaw Johnson. — London : Dent, 1975. — 221p : ill, music ; 26cm.
Bibl.: p.211-212. — Index.
ISBN 0-460-04198-3 : £6.95
(B75-17689)

Nichols, Roger
Messiaen / [by] Roger Nichols. — London [etc.] : Oxford University Press, 1975. — 79p : music ; 22cm. — (Oxford studies of composers ; 13)
Bibl.: p.79.
ISBN 0-19-315428-5 Pbk : £2.50
(B75-15004)

BMN — Monteverdi, Claudio
Arnold, Denis
Monteverdi / by Denis Arnold. — Revised ed. — London : Dent, 1975. — ix,212p,[8]p of plates : ill, facsims, music, ports ; 20cm. — (The master musicians series)
Previous ed.: 1963. — Bibl.: p.200-201. — Catalogue of works: p.178-194. — Index.
ISBN 0-460-03155-4 : £3.95
ISBN 0-460-02153-2 Pbk : £2.25
(B75-27353)

BMS — Mozart, Wolfgang Amadeus
Blom, Eric
Mozart / by Eric Blom. — Revised ed. — London : Dent, 1974. — xi,388p,[8]p of plates : ill, facsims, music, ports ; 20cm. — (The master musicians series)
Previous ed.: 1935. — Bibl.: p.361-363. — Index.
ISBN 0-460-03157-0 : £3.15
ISBN 0-460-02155-9 Pbk : £1.50
(B75-04504)

BNO(N) — Novello, Ivor. Biographies
Noble, Peter
Ivor Novello : man of the theatre / by Peter Noble ; with a foreword by Noel Coward. — London [etc.] : White Lion Publishers, 1975. — 306p,[1] leaf of plate,[20]p of plates : ill, ports ; 23cm.
Originally published: London : Falcon Press, 1951. — Index.
ISBN 0-85617-769-5 : £3.75
(B75-19084)

Rose, Richard, *b.1902*
Perchance to dream : the world of Ivor Novello / [by] Richard Rose. — London : Frewin, 1974. — 199p : ill, ports ; 26cm.
Ill. on lining papers.
ISBN 0-85632-120-6 : £4.95
(B75-50005)

BOFACF — Offenbach, Jacques. La Périchole. Librettos
Grimsey, John
La Périchole : operetta in three acts / libretto by John Grimsey & Phil Park ; original libretto by H. Meilhac & L. Halévy ; music by Jacques Offenbach ; adapted & arranged by Ronald Hanmer. — London (10 Rathbone St., W1P 2BJ) : Josef Weinberger Ltd, 1974. — [2],vii,105p : plans ; 20cm.
ISBN 0-902136-36-4 Sd : £0.80
(B75-19083)

BOFGACN/L — O'Gorman, Denis. Advent to Easter. Librettos
O'Gorman, Denis
Advent to Easter : short musical plays for junior and middle schools / [by] Denis O'Gorman ; accompaniment Jim Brand ; music calligraphy Ann Dawson. — Pinner : Grail Publications, [1975]. — 72p : music ; 25cm.
ISBN 0-901829-25-0 Sd : £1.00
(B75-18364)

BPIACM — Pippin, Don. Fashion. Librettos
Mowatt, Anna Cora
Fashion : a musical comedy / by Anna Cora Mowatt ; adapted by Anthony Stimac ; music by Don Pippin ; lyrics by Steve Brown. — New York ; London [etc.] : French, [1975]. — 64p : plans ; 22cm. — (French's musical library)
Three men, 7 women.
ISBN 0-573-68065-5 Sd : £1.10
(B75-20393)

BPU(N) — Puccini, Giacomo. Biographies
Puccini, Giacomo
Letters of Giacomo Puccini : mainly connected with the composition and production of his operas / edited by Giuseppe Adami ; translated [from the Italian] by Ena Makin. — New ed. / revised and introduced by Mosco Carner. — London : Harrap, 1974. — 341p,leaf of plate,[6]p of plates : ill, facsims, music, ports ; 23cm.
Previous ed. of this translated collection: 1931. — Index.
ISBN 0-245-52422-3 : £4.00
(B75-05793)

BPV — Purcell, Henry
Westrup, *Sir* **Jack Allan**
Purcell / by J.A. Westrup. — [7th ed.]. — London : Dent, 1975. — xi,323p,[8]p of plates : ill, facsims, music, ports ; 20cm. — (The master musicians series)
Previous ed.: 1968. — Bibl.: p.298-301. — Catalogue of works : p.271-288. — Index.
ISBN 0-460-03150-3 : £3.60
ISBN 0-460-02139-7 Pbk : £1.80
(B75-24233)

BRI(N) — Rimsky-Korsakoff, Nikolai
Rimsky-Korsakoff, Nikolai
My musical life / [by] Nikolay Andreyevich Rimsky-Korsakoff ; translated from the fifth revised Russian edition by Judah A. Joffe ; edited with an introduction by Carl Van Vechten. — London (48 Great Marlborough St., W.1) : Ernst Eulenberg Ltd, 1974. — [2],xliv,480,xxii p,[16]leaves of plates : music, ports ; 23cm.
This translation originally published: New York : A.A. Knopf, 1942. — Translation of: 'Letopis' moei muzykal'noi zhizni, 1844-1906'. 5th ed. Moscow : Gosudarstvennoe muzykalnoe izdatelstvo, 1935. — Index.
ISBN 0-903873-13-3 Pbk : £6.25
(B75-24236)

BSCT(N) — Satie, Erik. Biographies
Harding, James
Erik Satie / [by] James Harding. — London : Secker and Warburg, 1975. — xiii,269p,[8]p of plates : ill, facsims, ports ; 23cm.
List of compositions : p.245-255. — Bibl.: p.257-262. — Index.
ISBN 0-436-19106-7 : £5.75
(B75-24234)

BSFADW — Schubert, Franz. Songs, etc
Moore, Gerald, *b.1899*
The Schubert song cycles : with thoughts on performance / by Gerald Moore. — London : Hamilton, 1975. — xvi,240p : ill, music ; 25cm.
Index.
ISBN 0-241-89082-9 : £6.95
(B75-07794)

BSGP(N) — Shaw, Martin. Biographies
Routley, Erik
Martin Shaw : a centenary appreciation / by Erik Routley. — London (77 Archway St., SW13 0AN) : E.M. Campbell, 1975. — [27]p : ill, coat of arms, ports ; 21x20cm.
Bibl.: p.[14]-[26].
ISBN 0-9504306-0-9 Sd : £0.45
(B75-21068)

BSIM/FD — Smetana, Bedrich. Recorded music
Bennett, John Reginald
Smetana on 3000 records / [by] John R. Bennett. — [Blandford] : Oakwood Press, 1974. — 466p,[2]p of plates : ill, music, port ; 23cm.
Index.
ISBN 0-85361-158-0 : £8.75
(B75-14334)

BSNK — Stockhausen, Karlheinz
Harvey, Jonathan
The music of Stockhausen : an introduction / by Jonathan Harvey. — London : Faber, 1975. — 144p : ill, music, port ; 26cm.
Bibl.: p.133-135. — List of gramophone records: p.136-139. — List of music: p.140-141. — Index.
ISBN 0-571-10251-4 : £6.50
(B75-11222)

BSQ(N) — Strauss, Johann, b.1825. Biographies
Gartenberg, Egon
Johann Strauss : the end of an era / [by] Egon Gartenberg. —
University Park ; London : Pennsylvania State University Press,
[1975]. — xiii,360p : ill, ports ; 23cm.
Bibl.: p.345-349. — Index.
ISBN 0-271-01131-9 : £7.00

(B75-21067)

BSU(N) — Strauss, Richard. Biographies
Jefferson, Alan
Richard Strauss / [by] Alan Jefferson. — London [etc.] :
Macmillan, 1975. — 112p : ill(some col), facsims, music,
ports(some col) ; 27cm. — (The musicians)
Bibl.: p.111. — Index.
ISBN 0-333-14649-2 : £3.75

(B75-15005)

BSUAC — Strauss, Richard. Ariadne auf Naxos. Librettos
Hofmannsthal, Hugo von
Ariadne auf Naxos : opera in one act with a prelude / by Hugo
von Hofmannsthal ; English version [translated from the German]
by Alfred Kalisch ; music by Richard Strauss. — London [etc.] :
Boosey and Hawkes, [1975]. — 63p ; 27cm.
Parallel German and English libretti.
ISBN 0-85162-026-4 Sd : £1.50

(B75-08737)

BSV — Stravinsky, Igor
Routh, Francis
Stravinsky / by Francis Routh. — London : Dent, 1975. — ix,
202p,[8]p of plates : music, ports ; 20cm. — (The master
musicians series)
Bibl.: p.188-191. — Index.
ISBN 0-460-03138-4 : £4.50

(B75-24847)

BSV(N) — Stravinsky, Igor. Biographies
Stravinsky, Igor
An autobiography / [by] Igor Stravinsky ; [translated from the
French]. — London : Calder and Boyars, 1975. — xi,180p,4p of
plates : ports ; 21cm.
This translation originally published: as 'Chronicle of my life'. London :
Gollancz, 1936. — Translation of: 'Chroniques de ma vie'. Paris : Denoël et
Steel, 1935. — Index.
ISBN 0-7145-1063-7 : £5.95

(B75-25554)

BSW(N) — Sullivan, Sir Arthur Seymour. Biographies
Brahms, Caryl
Gilbert and Sullivan : lost chords and discords / [by] Caryl
Brahms. — London : Weidenfeld and Nicolson, 1975. — 264p :
ill(some col), facsims, music, ports(some col) ; 26cm.
Index.
ISBN 0-297-76936-7 : £5.25

(B75-26088)

BSWACF(C) — Sullivan, Sir Arthur Seymour. Encyclopaedias
Ayre, Leslie
The Gilbert and Sullivan companion / [by] Leslie Ayre ; foreword
by Martyn Green ; illustrated from the Raymond Mander and Joe
Mitchenson Theatre Collection. — London [etc.] : Pan Books,
1974. — [12],499p : ill ; 20cm.
Originally published: London : W.H. Allen, 1972.
ISBN 0-330-24138-9 Pbk : £1.50

(B75-01796)

BSWACF(N) — Sullivan, Sir Arthur Seymour
Pearson, Hesketh
Gilbert and Sullivan : a biography / [by] Hesketh Pearson ;
introduction by Malcolm Muggeridge. — London : Macdonald
and Jane's, 1975. — 319p,[8]p of plates : ill, ports ; 21cm.
Originally published: London : Hamilton, 1935. — Index.
ISBN 0-356-08034-x : £3.95

(B75-27958)

BTD(N) — Tchaikovsky, Peter. Biographies
Volkoff, Vladimir
Tchaikovsky : a self portrait / [by] Vladimir Volkoff. — Boston
[Mass.] : Crescendo Publishing Co. ; London : Hale, 1975. —
348p,[12]p of plates : ill, coat of arms, facsims, geneal table,
music, ports ; 23cm.
Bibl.: p.337-338. — Index.
ISBN 0-7091-4976-x : £5.50
ISBN 0-87597-088-5

(B75-21665)

BTDALF — Tchaikovsky, Peter. Concertos
Warrack, John
Tchaikovsky symphonies and concertos / [by] John Warrack. —
2nd ed. — London : British Broadcasting Corporation, 1974. —
64p : music ; 20cm. — (British Broadcasting Corporation. Music
guides)
Previous ed.: 1969. — Index.
ISBN 0-563-12773-2 Pbk : £0.45
Primary classification BTDAMME

(B75-00740)

BTDAMME — Tchaikovsky, Peter. Symphonies
Warrack, John
Tchaikovsky symphonies and concertos / [by] John Warrack. —
2nd ed. — London : British Broadcasting Corporation, 1974. —
64p : music ; 20cm. — (British Broadcasting Corporation. Music
guides)
Previous ed.: 1969. — Index.
ISBN 0-563-12773-2 Pbk : £0.45
Also classified at BTDALF

(B75-00740)

BVEAC — Verdi, Giuseppe. Opera
Godefroy, Vincent
The dramatic genius of Verdi : studies of selected operas / by
Vincent Godefroy. — London : Gollancz.
In 2 vols.
Vol.1 / with an introduction by Charles Osborne. — 1975. — 287p : music ;
23cm.
ISBN 0-575-01979-4 : £6.00

(B75-19731)

BVI(N) — Victoria, Tomás Luis de. Biographies
Sharp, Geoffrey Brinsley
Byrd ; &, Victoria / [by] Geoffrey B. Sharp. — Sevenoaks :
Novello, 1974. — 20p ; 19cm. — (Novello short biographies)
ISBN 0-85360-060-0 Sd : £0.20
Primary classification BBX(N)

(B75-03643)

BWC(N) — Wagner, Richard. Biographies
Wagner : a documentary study / compiled and edited by Herbert
Barth, Dietrich Mack, Egon Voss ; [documents translated from
the German by P.R.J. Ford and Mary Whittall] ; preface by
Pierre Boulez. — London : Thames and Hudson, 1975. — 256p :
ill(some col), facsims, music, ports(some col) ; 31cm.
Translation of: 'Wagner : sein Leben und seine Welt in zeitgenössischen
Bildern und Texten'. Vienna : Universal Edition, 1975. — Index.
ISBN 0-500-01137-0 : £12.00

(B75-30568)

BWNTM(N) — Wilson, Sandy. Biographies
Wilson, Sandy
I could be happy : an autobiography / [by] Sandy Wilson. —
London : Joseph, 1975. — 283p,[8]p of plates : ill, ports ; 24cm.
Index.
ISBN 0-7181-1370-5 : £6.00

(B75-50389)

BWNVAPV — Wishart, Trevor. Journey into space
Wishart, Trevor
Journey into space travelogue : an antiscore / [by] Trevor
Wishart. — [London] ([2 Fareham St., W.1]) : [Distributed by
Alfred A. Kalmus], 1975. — [28]p : ill, music ; 21x30cm.
ISBN 0-9504561-0-1 Sd : Unpriced

(B75-31194)

BZ — LITERATURE ON NON-EUROPEAN MUSIC
BZCAL/B — Turkey. Instruments
Picken, Laurence
Folk musical instruments of Turkey / [by] Laurence Picken. —
London [etc.] : Oxford University Press, 1975. — xl,685p,46p of
plates,[4]leaves of plates(3 fold) : ill(1 col), maps, music ; 26cm.
Bibl.: p.613-626. — Index.
ISBN 0-19-318102-9 : £38.50

(B75-25557)

BZFLAXQ/AC — North India. Percussion instruments. Tabla. Tutors
Baily, John
Krishna Govinda's rudiments of tabla playing / by John Baily. —
Carmarthen (Llan-fynydd, Carmarthen, Dyfed SA32 7TT) :
Unicorn Bookshop, 1974. — [2],xi,89p : ill, music ; 28cm.
'... published in conjunction with a 40 minute instructional tape ...' - Preface.
ISBN 0-85659-018-5 Sp : £2.50

(B75-04510)

BZK — Africa
Bebey, Francis
African music : a people's art / [by] Francis Bebey ; translated
[from the French] by Josephine Bennett. — London : Harrap,
1975. — viii,184p : ill, music ; 24cm.
Translation of: 'Musique de l'Afrique'. Paris : Horizons de France, 1969. —
List of records: p.150-176.
ISBN 0-245-52735-4 : £4.50

(B75-20391)

Nketia, Joseph Hanson Kwabena
The music of Africa / [by] J.H. Kwabena Nketia. — London :
Gollancz, 1975. — x,278p : ill, maps, music ; 22cm.
Bibl.: p.263-271. — Index.
ISBN 0-575-01842-9 : £4.00

(B75-05792)

BZNCWAL/B — East Africa. Instruments
Musical instruments of East Africa. — Nairobi ; London [etc.] :
Nelson.
1 : Kenya / notes by Graham Hyslop. — 1975. — viii,64p : ill, map, ports,
music ; 21cm.
ISBN 0-17-511250-9 Pbk : £0.80
(B75-26086)

BZNNALN(P) — Malawi. Kachamba Brother's Band
Kubik, Gerhard
The Kachamba Brothers' Band : a study of neo-traditional music
in Malawi / by Gerhard Kubik. — Manchester : Manchester
University Press for University of Zambia Institute for African
Studies, [1975]. — x,75p,8p of plates : ill, facsim, music, ports ;
23cm. — (Zambian papers ; no.2 ISSN 0084-5124)
Bibl.: p.72-75.
ISBN 0-7190-1408-5 Pbk : £2.25
(B75-15002)

BZWYADW/GR — New Zealand. Action songs
Maori action songs / compiled by Alan Armstrong and Reupena
Ngata. — Wellington ; London : Reed, 1973. — 113p ; 8vo.
With glossary.
ISBN 0-589-00777-7 : £3.45
(B75-50981)

C/AY — GENERAL COLLECTIONS
C/AYD — England
Musica Britannica : a national collection of music. — 2nd revised
ed. — London : Stainer and Bell.
Vol.22 : Consort songs / transcribed and edited by Philip Brett. — 1974. —
xxi,193p ; fol.
Unpriced
Also classified at KE/STNSDW/AYD
(B75-50006)

Musica Britannica : a national collection of music. — London :
Stainer and Bell.
Vol.36 : Early Tudor songs and carols; transcribed and edited by John
Stevens. — 1975. — xxvii,170p ; fol.
Unpriced
Also classified at CB/AYD
(B75-50982)

C/AZ — Collected works of individual composers
Liszt, Franz
Liszt Society publications. — London : Schott.
Vol.6 : Selected songs. — 1975. — [8],73p ; 4to. —
Unpriced
(B75-50390)

Purcell, Henry
[Works]. The works of Henry Purcell. — 2nd ed. — Sevenoaks :
Novello.
Vol.2 : Timon of Athens originally edited by Frederick Arthur Gore
Ouseley ; revised by Jack Westrup ; words by Thomas Shadwell. — 1974. —
xix,60p ; 8vo.
£3.00
(B75-50007)

Romano, Eustachio
Musica duorum, Rome, 1521 / [by] Eustachio Romano ; edited
from the literary estate of Hans T. David by Howard Mayer
Brown and Edward E. Lowinsky. — Chicago ; London : Chicago
University Press, 1975. — xviii,182p ; fol.
Also included in an appendix are frottole by Eustachio Romano and his
contemporary Eustachius de Monte Regali Gallus. The addition of
Romano's extant vocal works make this edition an opera omnia.
ISBN 0-226-22646-8 : Unpriced
(B75-50983)

CB — VOCAL MUSIC
CB/AFH — Vocalises
Gabus, Monique
Vocalise / [par] Monique Gabus. — Paris ; [London] : Chappell.
No.1. — 1972. — 2p ; fol. —
Unpriced
(B75-50391)

No.2. — 1972. — 2p ; fol. —
Unpriced
(B75-50392)

No.3. — 1972. — 2p ; fol. —
Unpriced
(B75-50393)

CB/AYD — Collections. England
Musica Britannica : a national collection of music. — London :
Stainer and Bell.
Vol.36 : Early Tudor songs and carols; transcribed and edited by John
Stevens. — 1975. — xxvii,170p ; fol.
Unpriced
Primary classification C/AYD

CB/AYDFR — Collections. Cornwall
The **Cornish** song book = Lyver canow Kernewek / compiled by
Ralph Dunstan. — Padstow : Lodenek Press ; London :
Ascherberg Hopwood and Crew.
Previous ed.: 1929.
Part 1. — 1974. — 75p ; 4to.
ISBN 0-902899-32-5 : £1.50
(B75-50984)

Part 2 : Carols and sacred music. — 1974. — 55p ; 4to.
ISBN 0-902899-34-1 : £1.20
(B75-50985)

CB/J — Stage music
Rands, Bernard
Ballad 2 : music/theatre piece for voice and piano / [by] Bernard
Rands ; text by Gilbert Sorrentino. — London : Universal, 1974.
— ix,8p ; 4to.
Unpriced
(B75-50986)

CB/LF/AY — Christmas. Collections
A **book** of Christmas music / selected and arranged by John
Horton. — London : Schott, 1975. — 121p ; 8vo.
ISBN 0-901938-56-4 : Unpriced
(B75-50987)

CC — OPERA. VOCAL SCORES
Britten, Benjamin
[Death in Venice. *Vocal score*]. Death in Venice. Op.88 : an opera
in two acts / music by Benjamin Britten ; libretto by Myfanwy
Piper ; based on the short story by Thomas Mann ; German
translation by Claus Henneberg and Hans Keller ; piano reduction
by Colin Matthews. — London : Faber Music, 1975. — 265p ;
4to.
Text in English and German.
Unpriced
(B75-50988)

Cavalli, Francesco
[La Calisto. *Vocal score*]. La Calisto : opera in two acts with a
prologue / [by] Francesco Cavalli ; performing edition realized by
Raymond Leppard ; libretto by Giovanni Faustini ; English
translation by Geoffrey Dunn ; German translation by Karl
Robert Marz. — London : Faber Music, 1975. — 191p ; 4to.
Text in Italian, English and German.
Unpriced
(B75-50989)

Hoddinott, Alun
[The beach of Falesa. *Vocal score*]. The beach of Falesa : opera in
three acts / [by] Alun Hoddinott ; libretto by Glyn Jones ; based
on a short story by R.L. Stevenson. — London : Oxford
University Press, 1974. — 240p ; 4to.
£8.50
(B75-50394)

Hurd, Michael
[The widow of Ephesus. *Vocal score*]. The widow of Ephesus :
chamber opera in one act / [by] Michael Hurd ; libretto by David
Hughes and Michael Hurd. — Sevenoaks : Novello, 1975. —
76p ; 4to.
Duration 45 min.
£2.10
(B75-50395)

Mozart, Wolfgang Amadeus
[Don Giovanni. K 527. *Vocal score*]. Don Giovanni. KV 527 /
Dramma giocoso in zwei Akten ; [von] Wolfgang Amadeus
Mozart ; text von Lorenzo da Ponte ; deutsche Übersetzung von
Walther Durr ; Klavierauszug von Heinz Moehn. — London :
Cassel : Bärenreiter, 1975. — vi,412p ; 8vo.
Italian and German text.
Unpriced
(B75-50396)

CF — OPERETTAS. VOCAL SCORES
Lopez, Francis
[Viva Napoli. *Vocal score*]. Viva Napoli : operette à grand
spectacle en 2 actes et 12 tableaux / [par] Francis Lopez ; airs
additionels de Anja Lopez, dialogues de René Jolivet, lyrics de
Francis Lopez et Daniel Ringold, adaptation musicale de Paul
Bonneau. — Paris ; [London] : Chappell, 1971. — 205p ; 4to.
Unpriced
(B75-50990)

Sullivan, *Sir* Arthur Seymour
[The zoo. *Vocal score*]. The zoo : a musical folly / music by
Arthur Sullivan ; words by B.C. Stephenson ('Bolton Rowe') ;
vocal score arranged by Roderick Spencer ; with a note on the
libretto by Terence Rees. — London : Cramer, 1975. — 92p ; 4to.
Unpriced
(B75-50397)

CM — MUSICAL PLAYS. VOCAL SCORES
Loewe, Frederick
[Gigi. *Vocal score*]. Lerner and Loewe's Gigi / music by
Frederick Loewe ; book and lyrics by Alan Jay Lerner ; piano
reduction by Trude Rittmann. — New York ; [London] :
Chappell, 1975. — 199p ; 4to.
Unpriced

(B75-50398)

CM/L — Religious musical plays. Vocal scores
Warren, Norman
Mary Jones : a musical play for young people / music by Norman
Warren ; words by Elspeth Stephenson. — Leamington Spa :
Maplewell Press, 1975. — 29p ; 4to.
ISBN 0-9504473-0-7 : Unpriced

(B75-50991)

Webber, Andrew Lloyd
[Joseph and the amazing technicolour dreamcoat. *Vocal score*].
Joseph and the amazing technicolour dreamcoat / [by] Andrew
Lloyd Webber ; words by Tim Rice. — Revised and enlarged ed.
— Sevenoaks : Novello, 1975. — 125p ; 8vo.
£2.00

(B75-50399)

CM/LN — Religious musical plays. Whitsun. Vocal scores
Larsson, John
[Spirit!. *Vocal score*]. Spirit! : a musical / music John Larsson ;
lyrics John Gowans ; script John Gowans and John Larsson. —
London : Salvationist Publishing and Supplies, 1975. — iv,143p ;
4to.
Unpriced

(B75-50400)

CN — Children's musical plays. Vocal scores
Kay, Peter
[The snowman of Kashmir. *Vocal score*]. The snowman of
Kashmir : a workshop opera for children / music by Peter Kay ;
words by Stefan Janski. — London : Universal, 1975. — 13p ;
8vo.
Unpriced

(B75-50401)

Kelly, Bryan
[The spider monkey uncle king. *Vocal score*]. The spider monkey
uncle king : an opera pantomime for children / music by Bryan
Kelly ; libretto by John Fuller. — Sevenoaks : Novello, 1975. —
70p ; 8vo.
£1.10

(B75-50008)

Long, Robert
[The fire maid. *Vocal score*]. The fire maid : an opera for
schools / music by Robert Long ; story adapted and lyrics by
Dorothy Gulliver from a story in 'The malachite casket' by Pavel
Petrovich Bazhov. — London : Oxford University Press, 1975. —
69p ; 8vo.
ISBN 0-19-337374-2 : £2.50

(B75-50402)

Paynter, John
[A temporary diversion. *Vocal score*]. A temporary diversion : (or
the monumental photographic and zoological umbrella show) /
music, John Paynter ; text, Paul Townsend. — London :
Universal, 1975. — 40p ; 8vo.
Unpriced

(B75-50992)

Shaw, Francis
[The selfish giant. *Vocal score*]. The selfish giant : an opera for
young people / adapted from a story by Oscar Wilde ; music
Francis Shaw ; libretto Michael Ffinch. — London : Chester :
Hansen, 1974. — 58p ; 4to.
Duration 55 min.
Unpriced

(B75-50009)

CPF — MASQUES. VOCAL SCORES
Detweiler, Alan
[David and Goliath. *Vocal score*]. David and Goliath : a masque,
for soloists, SATB chorus and instrumental ensemble, and optional
narrator / [by] Alan Detweiler ; words selected from the Bible. —
Sevenoaks : Novello, 1975. — 135p ; 8vo.
Duration: mimed version 60 min; concert version 50 min.
£2.50

(B75-50403)

CQC — OPERA. FULL SCORES
Berlioz, Hector
Les Troyens / by Hector Berlioz ; edited with a foreword by
Hugh Macdonald. — London : Eulenburg, 1974. — xix,751p ;
8vo.
Miniature score. — From 'Hector Berlioz New edition of the complete
works' volumes 2a and 2b.
Unpriced

(B75-50010)

Gazzaniga, Guiseppe
[Don Giovanni]. Don Giovanni o sai Il Convitato di pietra :
dramma giocoso in un atto di Giovanni Bertati / [music by]
Giuseppe Gazzaniga ; herausgegeben von Stefan Kunze. —
Cassel ; London : Bärenreiter, 1974. — xii,228p ; fol.
Unpriced

(B75-50404)

Mussorgsky, Modest
Boris Godunov : opera in four acts with a prologue / [by] Modest
Mussorgsky ; libretto by the composer based on Pushkin's
historical tragedy of the same name and Karamazin's 'History of
the Russian state' : the complete original texts of Mussorgsky's
'initial' (1869) and 'definitive' (1872) versions with additional
variants and fragments newly edited from the autograph
manuscripts by David Lloyd-Jones, critical commentary and
musical appendices edited by David Lloyd-Jones, deutsche
Übersetzung von Max Hube. — London : Oxford University
Press, 1975. — 2v. ; 4to.
Text in English, German and Russian. — In slip case.
ISBN 0-19-337699-7 : Unpriced

(B75-50993)

CQM — MUSICAL PLAYS. FULL SCORES
CQN — Children's musical plays. Full scores
Arch, Gwyn
The discontented man : musical play for voices, piano and
percussion / [by] Gwyn Arch ; lyrics by Pat Rooke. — London :
British and Continental Music : EMI Music, 1975. — 32p ; 8vo.
Unpriced

(B75-50011)

Arch, Gwyn
My friend Androcles : musical play for voices, piano and
percussion / by Gwyn Arch ; words by Pat Rooke. — London :
British and Continental Music : EMI Music, 1974. — 35p ; 8vo.
Unpriced

(B75-50012)

Berio, Luciano
Opus number zoo : children's play for wind quintet (1951, rev.
1970) / [by] Luciano Berio ; text by Rhoda Levine ; German
version, Friedl Hofbauer ; Italian version, Vittoria Ottolenghi. —
London : Universal, 1975. — 16p ; fol.
Text in English, German and Italian.
Unpriced

(B75-50994)

Kay, Peter
The snowman of Kashmir : a workshop opera for children /
music by Peter Kay ; words by Stefan Janski. — London :
Universal, 1975. — 22p ; 8vo.
Unpriced

(B75-50995)

DAC — OPERATIC CHORAL WORKS. CHORAL SCORES
DACB/JM — Vocal music. Choral scores. Incidental music
Purcell, Henry
[King Arthur. *Choral score*]. King Arthur / [by] Henry Purcell ;
an entirely new version of the opera by John Dryden, edited and
adapted by Colin Graham, realised by Philip Ledger, deutsche
Übersetzung von Karl Robert Marz. — London : Faber Music,
1974. — 77p ; 4to.
English & German texts.
Unpriced

(B75-50996)

DACF — OPERETTA. CHORAL WORKS. CHORAL SCORES
Sullivan, *Sir* **Arthur Seymour**
[The Mikado. *Choral score : arr*]. The Mikado, or, The Town of
Titipu / [by] Arthur Sullivan ; words by W. Gilbert ; arranged for
school performance by Christopher le Fleming. — London :
Cramer, 1975. — 105p ; 8vo.
£1.20

(B75-50405)

DACM — MUSICAL PLAYS. CHORAL WORKS. CHORAL SCORES
DADD — Oratorios. Choral scores
Handel, George Frideric
[Messiah. *Selections*]. Messiah ornamented : an ornamented
edition of the solos from the oratorio / by Handel ; edited by
Peter Wishart. — London : Stainer and Bell, 1974. — 44p ; 8vo.
ISBN 0-85249-318-5 : Unpriced

(B75-50013)

DADX — SECULAR CANTATAS. CHORAL SCORES
Bedford, David
[Twelve hours of sunset. *Choral score*]. Twelve hours of sunset /
[by] David Bedford. — London : Universal, 1975. — 36p ; 4to.
Unpriced

(B75-50406)

Spinner, Leopold
[Cantata on German folksong texts. Op. 20. *Choral score]*.
Cantata on German folksong texts. Op. 20 : for mezzo-soprano
solo, chorus and chamber orchestra / [by] Leopold Spinner. —
London : Boosey and Hawkes, 1975. — 25p ; 8vo.
Duration 18 min.
£1.50

(B75-50014)

DE — RELIGIOUS CANTATAS WITH KEYBOARD ACCOMPANIMENT
Bliss, *Sir* **Arthur**
Shield of faith : cantata for soprano and baritone soli, SATB and
organ / by Arthur Bliss. — Seveonoaks : Novello, 1975. — 24p ;
8vo.
Duration 30 min.
£1.00

(B75-50407)

Drayton, Paul
[Templa quam dilecta. *Vocal score]*. Templa quam dilecta :
cantata for SATB and orchestra / [by] Paul Drayton ; words from
Psalm 84. — Sevenoaks : Novello, 1975. — 57p ; 8vo.
Duration 21 min.
£0.95

(B75-50997)

Mathias, William
[This worlde's joie. *Vocal score]*. This worlde's joie : a cantata for
soprano, tenor and baritone soloists, mixed chorus, boys' (or girls')
choir, and orchestra / [by] William Mathias. — London : Oxford
University Press, 1975. — 110p ; 8vo.
ISBN 0-19-337437-4 : £3.95

(B75-50408)

Paynter, John
[God's grandeur. *Vocal score]*. God's grandeur : for mixed chorus,
brass and organ (or chorus and organ) / by John Paynter ; text by
George Herbert and Gerard Manley Hopkins. — London : Oxford
University Press, 1975. — 37p ; 8vo.
ISBN 0-19-337781-0 : Unpriced

(B75-50998)

DE/LF — Christmas
Ryba, Jakub Jan
[Czech Christmas mass. *Vocal score]*. Ceska mse vanocni =
Böhmische Hirtenmesse = Czech Christmas Mass / [by] Jakub
Jan Ryba ; piano accompaniment by Josef Hercl ; German text,
Helmut Fritsch ; English text, John Clapham. — Prague :
Supraphon ; [London] : [Achauer], 1974. — 82p ; 4to.
Text in Czech, German and English.
£5.60

(B75-50999)

DF/LP — Liturgical music. Harvest
The **providence** of God : a sequence of readings, hymns and
anthems to celebrate the harvest / music selected or composed by
Desmond Ratcliffe ; words by Richard Tatlock. — Sevenoaks :
Novello, 1975. — 39p ; 8vo.
£0.60

(B75-50409)

DFF — ROMAN LITURGY
DG — Ordinary of the Mass
Genzmer, Harald
Deutsche Messe : für gemischten Chor und Orgel / [von] Harald
Genzmer. — Frankfurt : Litolff ; London : Peters, 1973. — 35p ;
8vo.
Unpriced

(B75-50015)

Janacek, Leos
[Mass in E flat major]. Mass, E flat major (unfinished Mass) /
[by] Leos Janacek ; adapted and compiled by Vilem Petrzelka. —
Cassel ; London : Bärenreiter, 1972. — 34p ; 8vo.
Duration 8 min. — Comprises Kyrie, Credo, Agnus Dei.
£2.10

(B75-50016)

MacDermot, Galt
[Mass in F. *Vocal score]*. Mass in F for choir with instrumental
accompaniment / [by] Galt MacDermot. — New York ;
[London] : Chappell, 1971. — 39p ; 8vo.
Unpriced

(B75-50017)

Mozart, Wolfgang Amadeus
[Mass, no.12, in C major. K.258. *Vocal score]*. Piccolomini mass.
(Missa brevis in C) : mixed chorus / [by] Wolfgang Amadeus
Mozart ; edited with piano or organ accompaniment by H.C.
Robbins Landon. — New York ; London : Schirmer, 1974. — iv,
60p ; 8vo.
Unpriced

(B75-50410)

Mozart, Wolfgang Amadeus
[Mass, no.13, in C major. K.259. *Vocal score]*. Organ solo mass.
(Missa brevis in C) : mixed chorus / [by] Wolfgang Amadeus
Mozart ; edited with piano or organ accompaniment by H.C.
Robbins Landon. — New York ; London : Schirmer, 1974. — iv,
56p ; 8vo.
Unpriced

(B75-50411)

DGKAV — Requiems. Vocal scores
Fauré, Gabriel
[Requiem. Opus 48. *Vocal score: arr]*. Requiem. Opus 48 / [by]
Gabriel Fauré ; arranged for soprano and baritone (or
mezzo-soprano) soli, SSA and orchestra by Desmond Ratcliffe. —
Sevenoaks : Novello, 1975. — 56p ; 8vo.
Latin and English text.
£1.00
Also classified at FDGKAV

(B75-51000)

Fauré, Gabriel
[Requiem. Op.48. *Vocal score]*. Requiem. Op.48 : for four-part
chorus of mixed voices with soprano and baritone soli / [by]
Gabriel Fauré ; piano reduction by Bruce Howden. — New
York ; London : Schirmer, 1975. — 76p ; 8vo.
Unpriced

(B75-51001)

Fauré, Gabriel
[Requiem. Op.48. *Vocal score]*. Requiem. Opus 48 : for soprano
and baritone soli, SATB and orchestra / [by] Gabriel Fauré ;
edited with piano accompaniment by Desmond Ratcliffe. —
Sevenoaks : Novello, 1975. — 52p ; 8vo.
Duration 40 min.
£0.75

(B75-50018)

Patterson, Paul
[Requiem. *Vocal score]*. Requiem for chorus and orchestra / [by]
Paul Patterson. — London : Weinberger, 1975. — 72p ; 4to.
Duration 40 min.
Unpriced

(B75-50019)

DGM — ANGLICAN LITURGY
DGMS — Salvator mundi
Ashfield, Robert
Salvator mundi : SATB / [by] Robert Ashfield. — York : Banks,
1973. — 4p ; 8vo.
Salvator mundi is used in Alternative Services, Second Series Revised,
Morning and Evening Prayer.
Unpriced

(B75-50412)

DGNQ — Morning Prayer. Te Deum
Maw, Nicholas
Te Deum : treble and tenor soli, chorus, congregation and organ /
[by] Nicholas Maw. — London : Boosey and Hawkes, 1975. —
32p ; 8vo.
The choir sing in Latin, the congregation in English.
£2.00

(B75-51002)

DGNT — Morning Prayer. Jubilate
Ives, Grayston
Jubilate = (O be joyful in the Lord) : anthem for SATB and
organ / [by] Grayston Ives. — Sevenoaks : Novello, 1975. —
16p ; 8vo.
£0.25

(B75-50413)

DGNV — Morning Prayer. Venite
Nelson, Ron
Psalm 95 - Come let us praise Yaweh : for mixed chorus and
organ with optional instrumental accompaniment / [by] Roy
Nelson ; text, Jerusalem Bible. — New York ; [London] : Boosey
and Hawkes, 1975. — 23p ; 8vo.
Unpriced
Primary classification DR

(B75-50434)

DGPP — Evening Prayer. Canticles
Walmisley, Thomas Attwood
[Cathedral music. Morning and Evening Service in D major].
Magnificat and Nunc dimittis : for SATB and organ / [by] T.A.
Walmisley ; edited by Watkins Shaw. — London : Oxford
University Press, 1975. — 23p ; 8vo.
ISBN 0-19-395316-1 : £0.50

(B75-50414)

Wills, Arthur
Evening service (with verses) : SATB / by Arthur Wills. —
London : Oxford University Press, 1974. — 16p ; 8vo.
ISBN 0-19-351648-9 : £0.35

(B75-50020)

DGSKAD — Communion. Sentences
Aston, Peter
Seasonal sentences from Series 3 / [by] Peter Aston. — Croydon : Royal School of Church Music, 1975. — 12p ; 8vo.
Unpriced
(B75-50415)

Kelly, Bryan
Seasonal sentences suitable for the Series 3 communion service or as independent anthems. — London : Oxford University Press, 1975. — 32p ; 8vo.
ISBN 0-19-395242-4 : £0.90
(B75-50416)

DH — MOTETS, ANTHEMS, HYMNS, ETC.
Artman, Ruth
Lord, walk with me : for SATB chorus and piano / words and music by Ruth Artman. — New York : Warner ; [London] : [Blossom], 1973. — 7p ; 8vo.
Unpriced
(B75-50417)

Bliss, *Sir* Arthur
Sing mortals! : a sonnet for the festival of St Cecilia, for SATB and organ / by Arthur Bliss ; words by Richard Tydeman. — Sevenoaks : Novello, 1974. — 10p ; 8vo.
Unpriced
(B75-50021)

Britten, Benjamin
A hymn of St Columba (Regis regum rectissimi) : SATB and organ / [by] Benjamin Britten. — London : Boosey and Hawkes, 1975. — 12p ; 8vo.
£0.20
(B75-50418)

Chadwick, George Whitfield
[Judith. God. Jehovah]. God, Jehovah : mixed chorus and keyboard / [by] George W. Chadwick ; edited by Leonard van Camp. — New York : Galaxy ; [London] : [Galliard], 1975. — 4p ; 8vo.
Unpriced
(B75-51003)

Ives, Charles
Crossing the bar : anthem for solo quartet or mixed choir and organ / [by] Charles Ives ; edited by John Kirkpatrick ; poem by Alfred, Lord Tennyson. — New York ; London : Associated Music, 1975. — 8p ; 8vo.
Unpriced
(B75-50419)

Nelson, Ron
Prayer of St. Francis of Assisi : for S.A.T.B. chorus and organ or piano / [by] Ron Nelson. — New York ; [London] : Boosey and Hawkes, 1975. — 11p ; 8vo.
£0.30
(B75-51004)

Roe, Betty
Like as the hart : soprano solo and mixed chorus / [by] Betty Roe. — London : Thames, 1975. — 15p ; 8vo.
Unpriced
(B75-51005)

Rutter, John
Thy perfect love : SATB / [by] John Rutter ; words: 15th century. — London : Oxford University Press, 1975. — 4p ; 8vo.
ISBN 0-19-351122-3 : £0.10
(B75-50420)

Schweizer, Rolf
Lobet den Namen des Herrn : vierstimmiger gemischter Chor und Orgel / [von] Rolf Schweizer ; Psalm 135 : 1. — Cassel ; London : Bärenreiter, 1974. — 4p ; 8vo.
£0.20
(B75-50022)

Thomas, Paul Lindsley
Shout the glad tidings. Op.12 : for mixed choir and organ, with optional instruments / [by] Paul Lindsley Thomas ; [text by] William Augustus Muhlenberg. — New York ; [London] : Oxford University Press, 1975. — 12p ; 8vo.
Unpriced
(B75-51006)

Wills, Arthur
I hunger and I thirst : anthem for SATB with divisions and organ / [by] Arthur Wills ; words by J.S.B. Monsell. — Sevenoaks : Novello, 1975. — 12p ; 8vo.
Unpriced
(B75-50421)

Wilson, Don
Rejoice ye pure in heart : for mixed chorus and keyboard, based on a hymn by Arthur Messiter / by Don Wilson ; words by Edward H. Plumtre. — New York : Galaxy ; London : Galliard, 1971. — 6p ; 8vo.
Unpriced
(B75-50023)

DH/AY — Collections
Royal School of Church Music
Five anthems for today : SATB. — Croydon : Royal School of Church Music, 1974. — 30p ; 8vo.
Contents: I will lift up mine eyes: Alan Gibbs - Blessing and glory: Francis Jackson - Ah, my dear angry Lord: Arthur Wills - Thee we adore: Colin Mawby - It is a good thing to give thanks: Michael Hurd.
Unpriced
(B75-50024)

Twelve easy anthems / anthems 1 to 10 edited and arranged by Anthony Greening. — Croydon : Royal School of Church Music, 1975. — 38p ; 8vo.
Unpriced
(B75-51007)

DH/AYT — Collections. United States
Christmas music from Colonial America : an anthology of Christmas psalms and anthems from the revolutionary and federal eras : for mixed chorus, organ and optional instruments / compiled, edited and arranged by Leonard Van Camp. — New York : Galaxy ; [London] : [Galliard], 1975. — 45p ; 8vo.
Unpriced
Primary classification EZDH/AYT
(B75-50463)

Early American anthem book : anthem tunes and verses from the colonial period in new settings / arranged for mixed chorus and keyboard by Katherine K. Davis. — New York : Galaxy ; [London] : [Galliard], 1975. — 36p ; 8vo.
Unpriced
(B75-50422)

Psalm of joy of the congregation in Salem, for the peace celebration, July 4, 1783 : the music of the first organized Independence Day celebration, for soli, chorus of mixed voices and organ music / compiled by Johann Friedrich Peter, prepared for modern performance by Marilyn P. Gombrosi with a preface by Karl Kroeger. — New York ; [London] : Boosey and Hawkes, 1975. — 64p ; 8vo.
Unpriced
(B75-51008)

DJ — MOTETS
Dering, Richard
Cantica sacra, 1618 / [by] Richard Dering ; transcribed and edited by Peter Platt. — London : Stainer & Bell, 1974. — xiii,201p ; 8vo.
Unpriced
(B75-50025)

Najera, Edmund
Exultate Deo : for four-part chorus of mixed voices with piano accompaniment / [by] Edmund Najera. — New York ; London : Schirmer, 1974. — 8p ; 8vo.
Unpriced
(B75-50423)

DK — ANTHEMS
Barnes, Norman J
The Spirit of the Lord : SATB / [by] Norman J. Barnes ; text from St Luke 4. — York : Banks, 1973. — 4p ; 8vo.
Unpriced
(B75-50424)

Gibbons, Orlando
Lord we beseech thee = The collect for the Annunciation of the Blessed Virgin Mary : verse anthem for alto and chorus (SAATB) with accompaniment for viols or organ / [by] Orlando Gibbons ; reconstructed by Paul Vining. — Sevenoaks : Novello, 1975. — 10p ; 8vo.
£0.20
Primary classification ESTNRDK
(B75-50040)

McClelland-Young, Thomas
Bow down thine ear : short anthem for baritone or bass solo, SATB and organ, suitable for Lent or general use / [by] Thomas McClelland-Young ; text from Psalm 86. — Sevenoaks : Novello, 1975. — 6p ; 8vo.
£0.15
(B75-50425)

Mueller, Carl Frank
An anthem of faith 'Lord increase our faith' : for four-part chorus
of mixed voices with piano or organ accompaniment / [by] Carl
F. Mueller ; text from Luke II or 5 Heb II. — New York ;
London : Associated Music, 1974. — 8p ; 8vo.
Unpriced

(B75-50426)

Mundy, John
Sing joyfully : SSATB and strings (or organ) with verses for bass
solo / [by] John Mundy ; edited by Edmund H. Fellowes, text
from Ps.81. — Revised ed. / by David Scott. — London : Oxford
University Press, 1975. — 16p ; 8vo.
ISBN 0-19-352184-9 : £0.40
Primary classification ERXNRDK

(B75-50453)

Purcell, Henry
[Praise the Lord, O Jerusalem. *Vocal score*]. Praise the Lord, O
Jerusalem : verse anthem for five-part chorus of mixed voices and
optional solo group / [by] Henry Purcell ; edited and with
keyboard reduction by William Herrmann, text from Psalms 147,
48, 21 and Isaiah 49. — New York ; [London] : Schirmer, 1975.
— iv,19p ; 8vo.
Unpriced

(B75-51009)

Wilson-Dickson, Andrew
The word : SATB / [by] Andrew Wilson-Dickson ; [text from] I
St John I. — York : Banks, 1973. — 3p ; 8vo.
Unpriced

(B75-50427)

Wise, Michael
The Lord is my shepherd : anthem for two sopranos, chorus and
organ / [by] Michael Wise ; edited by Michael J. Smith. —
Sevenoaks : Novello, 1975. — 10p ; 8vo.
£0.20

(B75-51010)

DK/LP — Harvest
Ferguson, Barry
Praise the Lord, O my soul : anthem for unison voices or SATB
and organ, suitable for Rogation, Harvest or general use / music
by Barry Ferguson ; text from Psalm 104. — Sevenoaks : Novello,
1975. — 4p ; 8vo.
£0.10
Primary classification JDK/LP

(B75-50523)

DM — HYMNS
DM/LSG/AY — United Reform Church. Collections
New church praise / compiled by Erik Routley, Peter Cutts, David
Gardner. — Edinburgh : Saint Andrew Press, 1975. — viii,223p ;
8vo.
ISBN 0-7152-0311-8 : Unpriced

(B75-50428)

DP — CAROLS
Carter, Sydney
[Nine carols or ballads. Lord of the dance. *arr*]. Lord of the
dance / [by] Sydney Carter ; arranged for four-part mixed chorus
and keyboard, with optional percussion accompanied choral
adaptation by Donald Waxman. — New York : Galaxy ;
[London] : [Galliard], 1971. — 8p ; 8vo.
Unpriced

(B75-50429)

DP/LF — Christmas
Hurford, Peter
Sunny bank : carol, SATB / [by] Peter Hurford ; traditional
words. — London : Oxford University Press, 1975. — 4p ; 8vo.
ISBN 0-19-343051-7 : £0.10

(B75-50430)

Madden, John
Make we joy now in this feast : SATB / [by] John Madden ; 15
th century words. — London : Oxford University Press, 1975. —
8p ; 8vo.
ISBN 0-19-343054-1 : Unpriced

(B75-51011)

Rocherolle, Eugenie R
How can it be? : for unison, SA or SAB chorus and piano /
words and music by Eugenie R. Rocherolle. — New York :
Warner ; London : Blossom, 1975. — 8p ; 8vo.
Duration 2 1/2 min.
Unpriced
Also classified at FDP/LF; JDP/LF

(B75-51012)

Wichmann, Russell G
Bell carol : based on the tune 'Puer nobis', for junior choir, mixed
choir, and organ, with optional bells / [by] Russell G.
Wichmann ; Christmas words, Charles Coffin (1736), translated by
John Chandler ; Easter words, Latin hymn 5th century, translated
by John Mason Neale. — New York ; [London] : Oxford
University Press, 1972. — 8p ; 8vo.
Unpriced
Also classified at DP/LL

(B75-51013)

Willcocks, David
Birthday carol : SATB / words and music by David Willcocks. —
London : Oxford University Press, 1974. — 4p ; 8vo.
ISBN 0-19-343050-9 : £0.08

(B75-50026)

Wills, Arthur
Welcome Yule : a Christmas fanfare, SATB / [by] Arthur Wills ;
15th-century words. — London : Oxford University Press, 1975.
— 8p ; 8vo.
ISBN 0-19-343052-5 : Unpriced

(B75-51014)

DP/LF/AY — Christmas. Collections
Behold your King : a devotion for choir and congregation devised
by Erik Routley. — Croydon : Royal School of Church Music,
1974. — 32p ; 8vo.
ISBN 0-85402-059-4 : Unpriced

(B75-51015)

Six carols with descants / arranged for mixed voices and organ by
Philip Ledger. — London : Oxford University Press, 1975. —
16p ; 8vo.
ISBN 0-19-353244-1 : Unpriced

(B75-51016)

DP/LFP — Epiphany
Graves, Richard
Three journeys : a carol / words and music by Richard Graves.
— Sevenoaks : Novello, 1975. — 4p ; 8vo.
£0.10
Primary classification JDP/LFP

(B75-50526)

Hill, Anthony Herschel
The magi : carol for SATB, piano and double bass (optional) /
[by] Anthony Herschel Hill ; words by William Kean Seymour. —
London : Thames, 1975. — 7p ; 8vo.
Unpriced

(B75-50431)

DP/LL — Easter
Wichmann, Russell G
Bell carol : based on the tune 'Puer nobis', for junior choir, mixed
choir, and organ, with optional bells / [by] Russell G.
Wichmann ; Christmas words, Charles Coffin (1736), translated by
John Chandler ; Easter words, Latin hymn 5th century, translated
by John Mason Neale. — New York ; [London] : Oxford
University Press, 1972. — 8p ; 8vo.
Unpriced
Primary classification DP/LF

DR — PSALMS
Binkerd, Gordon
Psalm 23 : mixed voices, tenor solo and organ / [by] Gordon
Binkerd ; text from the New English Bible. — New York ;
[London] : Boosey and Hawkes, 1972. — 15p ; 8vo.
Unpriced

(B75-50432)

Carissimi, Giacomo
Beatus vir, Psalm 112 : SATB / [by] G. Carissimi ; edited by
Peter Seymour. — London : Oxford University Press, 1975. —
12p ; 8vo.
ISBN 0-19-350351-4 : Unpriced

(B75-50433)

Nelson, Ron
Psalm 95 - Come let us praise Yaweh : for mixed chorus and
organ with optional instrumental accompaniment / [by] Roy
Nelson ; text, Jerusalem Bible. — New York ; [London] : Boosey
and Hawkes, 1975. — 23p ; 8vo.
Unpriced
Also classified at DGNV

(B75-50434)

Schweizer, Rolf
Zehn Psalmspruche : für drei und vierstimmigen gemischten Chor
und Orgel / [von] Rolf Schweizer. — Cassel ; London :
Bärenreiter, 1974. — 38p ; 8vo.
£2.00

(B75-50027)

DS/LDB — Litanies. Roman Catholic Church
  Mozart, Wolfgang Amadeus
    [Litaniae Lauretanae. K.109. *Vocal score*]. Litaniae Lauretanae.
    K.109 (Marien [sic] litany) : for four-part chorus of mixed voices
    and soprano, alto, tenor and bass solos / [by] Wolfgang Amadeus
    Mozart ; edited and with English text adapted by Maynard
    Klein ; keyboard reduction by Byron Hanson. — New York ;
    London : Schirmer, 1974. — 37p ; 8vo.
    Unpriced

(B75-50435)

DW — SONGS, ETC.
  Atkinson, Condit
    Four things a man must learn to do : for mixed chorus and piano
    with optional bass and guitar / by Condit Atkinson ; words by
    Henry Van Dyke. — New York : Galaxy ; London : Galliard,
    1975. — 8vo.
    Score (8p.) & part.
    Unpriced

(B75-50436)

Berlioz, Hector
    [Les Troyens. Gloire, gloire à Didon. *Vocal score*]. Hail all hail to
    the queen : SATB / [by] Hector Berlioz ; piano reduction of the
    orchestral accompaniment by Herbert Sumsion ; words by E.J.
    Dent. — London : Oxford University Press, 1974. — 4p ; 8vo.
    ISBN 0-19-343046-0 : £0.08

(B75-50028)

Cassey, Charles R
    Blossom's a possum : for mixed chorus, SATB / [by] Charles R.
    Cassey ; lyrics by William J. Powers. — New York ; [London] :
    Chappell, 1971. — 7p ; 8vo.
    Unpriced

(B75-50437)

Davis, Katherine Kennicot
    Come along, sweet Liza Jane : SATB and piano / by Katherine
    K. Davis ; text Appalachian. — New York : Warner ; [London] :
    [Blossom], 1975. — 8p ; 8vo.
    Unpriced

(B75-50438)

Deale, Edgar Martin
    The lark in the clear air : Irish air / arr. SATB by Edgar Deale ;
    words by Sir Samuel Ferguson. — York : Banks, 1973. — 4p ;
    8vo.
    Unpriced

(B75-50439)

Dello Joio, Norman
    The poet's song : for four-part chorus of mixed voices with piano
    accompaniment / [by] Norman dello Joio ; based on a poem by
    Alfred, Lord Tennyson. — New York ; London : Associated
    Music, 1974. — 11p ; 8vo.
    £0.25

(B75-51017)

Foster, Stephen Collins
    Some folks : for four-part chorus of mixed voices with guitar or
    piano accompaniment / by Stephen C. Foster ; Foster's guitar part
    edited by David Starobin ; edited by Gregg Smith. — New York ;
    London : Schirmer, 1974. — 4to.
    Score (6p.) & part.
    Unpriced
    Primary classification ETSDW

(B75-50455)

Hawthorne, Alice
    Listen to the mocking bird : for four-part chorus of mixed voices
    with optional tenor and bass solos and optional flute or violin and
    piano accompaniment / [by] Alice Hawthorne ; edited by Gregg
    Smith. — New York ; London : Schirmer, 1974. — 8p ; 8vo.
    Unpriced

(B75-50440)

Hays, Will Shakespeare
    Put the right man at the wheel : for four-part chorus of mixed
    voices with piano accompaniment / by Will S. Hays ; edited by
    Gregg Smith. — New York ; London : Schirmer, 1974. — 4p ;
    8vo.
    Unpriced

(B75-50441)

Hutchinson Family
    The horticultural wife : (written by a celebrated English gardener
    after disappointment in love) : for four-part chorus of mixed
    voices with tenor (or baritone) solo and piano accompaniment /
    by the Hutchinsons ; edited by Gregg Smith. — New York ;
    London : Schirmer, 1974. — 8p ; 8vo.
    Unpriced

(B75-50442)

King, Jeffrey
    A wind has blown the rain away : SATB and piano / [by] Jeffrey
    King ; poem by E.E. Cummings. — New York ; [London] :
    Boosey and Hawkes, 1971. — 20p ; 8vo.
    Unpriced

(B75-51018)

Kittredge, Walter
    Tenting on the old camp ground : for four-part mixed voices with
    piano or guitar (and optional oboe, flute, or violin) / by Walter
    Kittredge ; guitar accompaniment by David Starobin ; edited by
    Gregg Smith. — New York ; London : Schirmer, 1974. — 8vo.
    Score (6p.) & part.
    Unpriced

(B75-50443)

Loesser, Frank
    ['Hans Christian Andersen'. Anywhere I wander. *arr*]. Anywhere I
    wander : for mixed chorus (SATB) and piano with optional
    rhythm guitar, bass guitar and drums / [by] Frank Loesser ;
    arranged by Howard Cable. — Boston ; [London] : Frank Music,
    1972. — 8p ; 8vo.
    Unpriced

(B75-51019)

Loesser, Frank
    ['Hans Christian Andersen'. The inch worm. *arr*]. The inch
    worm : for mixed chorus (SATB) and piano with optional rhythm
    guitar, bass guitar and drums / [by] Frank Loesser ; arranged by
    Howard Cable. — Boston ; [London] : Frank Music, 1972. —
    11p ; 8vo.
    Unpriced

(B75-51020)

Lombardo, Mario
    [Sounds I prefer. *arr*]. Sounds I prefer : for mixed chorus
    (SATB) / [by] Mario Lombardo ; arranged by Chuck Cassey,
    lyrics by Bill Margaretten. — New York ; [London] : Chappell,
    1972. — 8p ; 8vo.
    Unpriced

(B75-51021)

Rutter, John
    [When icicles hang. *Vocal score*]. When icicles hang : a cycle of
    choral settings (SATB) with small orchestra / [by] John Rutter.
    — London : Oxford University Press, 1975. — 47p ; 8vo.
    Duration 18 1/2 min.
    ISBN 0-19-338073-0 : £1.50

(B75-50444)

Sullivan, *Sir* Arthur Seymour
    [Operettas. *Selections*]. The best of Gilbert and Sullivan : SATB.
    — London : Chappell, 1975. — 48p ; 8vo.
    Unpriced

(B75-50445)

Zimmerman, Heinz Werner
    Vier Collagen : für Klavier und Kammerchor nach Inventionen
    von J.S. Bach und Epigrammen von A.G. Kastner, J.W.L. Gleim,
    Fr. von Hagedorn und J.J. Ewald / [von] Heinz Werner
    Zimmerman. — Cassel ; London : Bärenreiter, 1974. — 16p ; fol.
    £2.40

(B75-50030)

DW/AY — Collections
  London Welsh Male Voice Choir
    Take me home : [part-songs]. — London : Chappell, 1975. —
    88p ; 8vo.
    Unpriced

(B75-51022)

DW/LC — Spirituals
  Cumming, Richard
    Lonesome valley : spiritual, SATB / arranged by Richard
    Cumming. — New York ; [London] : Boosey and Hawkes, 1972.
    — 6p ; 8vo.
    Unpriced

(B75-50446)

Rutter, John
    Down by the riverside : American traditional song / arranged
    S.A.T.B. by John Rutter. — London : Oxford University Press,
    1975. — 16p ; 8vo.
    Duration 4 min.
    ISBN 0-19-343049-5 : Unpriced

(B75-51023)

DW/LC/AY — Spirituals. Collections
    A **heritage** of spirituals : a collection of American spirituals, for
    mixed chorus and piano or organ / arranged by John W. Work,
    James Miller, Fred Fox. — New York : Galaxy ; [London] :
    [Galliard], 1975. — 62p ; 8vo.
    Unpriced

(B75-50447)

DW/LF — Christmas
Dittersdorf, Carl Ditters von
[Concerto for harpsichord in A major. Rondeau. *arr*]. Christmas is coming / from the music of Dittersdorf ; adapted and arranged, four-part SATB, by John Mitri Habash ; original text by John Mitri Habash. — New York ; [London] : Robbins, 1971. — 9p ; 8vo.
Unpriced

(B75-50031)

Van Dresar, Mary
[Christmas magic. *arr*]. Christmas magic / words and music by Mary van Dresar ; arranged for SATB chorus and piano by Elliott Shay. — New York : Warner ; [London] : [Blossom], 1975. — 6p ; 8vo.
Unpriced

(B75-51024)

DX — SECULAR CANTATAS
Bennett, Richard Rodney
[Spells. *Vocal score*]. Spells : soprano solo, mixed chorus & orchestra / [by] Richard Rodney Bennett ; words by Kathleen Raine. — Sevenoaks : Novello, 1975. — 64p ; 8vo.
Duration 36 min.
£1.00

(B75-50448)

Hoddinott, Alun
The silver swimmer. Opus 84 : for mixed chorus, [SATB] and piano duet / by Alun Hoddinott ; words by Jon Manchip White. — London : Oxford University Press, 1975. — 23p ; 8vo.
ISBN 0-19-336840-4 : £1.20

(B75-50032)

Janacek, Leos
[Festival chorus]. Slavnostní sbor = Festlicher Chor = Festival chorus : for four male voices, women's and men's chorus and piano / [by] Leos Janacek ; edited by Jan Trojan ; words by Karel Kucera ; German translation, Kurt Honolka. — Cassel ; London : Bärenreiter, 1972. — 16p ; 8vo.
£1.20

(B75-50033)

Kagel, Mauricio
Gegenstimmen : für gemischten Chor und obligates Cembalo / [von] Mauricio Kagel. — London : Universal, 1975. — 43p ; 4to.
One of the parts is spoken ; the conductor also speaks.
Unpriced

(B75-50449)

Purcell, Henry
[Ode on St Cecilia's day, 1692. Z.328. *Vocal score*]. Ode on St Cecilia's day, 1692 : Hail! bright Cecilia : for soprano, two altos, tenor and two basses soli, SSAATB and instruments / [by] Henry Purcell ; edited by Peter Dennison, words by Nicholas Brady. — Sevenoaks : Novello, 1975. — 86p ; 8vo.
£1.20

(B75-51025)

E — CHORAL WORKS WITH ACCOMPANIMENT OTHER THAN KEYBOARD
EMDD/LK — With orchestra. Oratorios. Good Friday
Bach, Johann Sebastian
[St Matthew passion S.244]. Matthaus-Passion = St Matthew Passion / [by] Johann Sebastian Bach ; edited by Alfred Durr ; using preliminary work by Max Schneider. — Cassel ; London : Bärenreiter, 1973. — x,309p ; 8vo.
Miniature score.
£4.40

(B75-50034)

EMDE — With orchestra. Religious cantatas
Huber, Klaus
' - inwending voller figur - ' : for chorus, loudspeakers, tape and large orchestra (1970/71) / by Klaus Huber ; choice and compilation of the texts by the composer. — Mainz : Ars Viva ; [London] : Schott, 1974. — 65p ; fol.
Study score. — Duration 24 min.
£6.00

(B75-50035)

EMDX — With orchestra. Secular cantatas
Bennett, Richard Rodney
The Bermudas : for chorus and orchestra / [by] Richard Rodney Bennett ; poem by Andrew Marvell. — London : Universal, 1975. — 39p ; 4to.
Duration 10 min.
Unpriced

(B75-51026)

Husa, Karel
Apotheosis of this earth : for orchestra and chorus / [by] Karel Husa. — New York ; London : Associated Music, 1974. — 124p ; 4to.
Unpriced

(B75-50450)

ENVSNRDW/LF — With recorder & string quintet. Songs. Christmas
Bune, Robert
Tell me what month : an American Christmas folk song / arranged for SATB with guitars, 2 recorders, string bass (or piano) by Robert Bune ; piano accompaniment by Val Johnson. — New York : Warner ; [London] : [Blossom], 1975. — 12p ; 8vo.
Pages 11 and 12 contain the instrumental accompaniment printed in score.
Unpriced

(B75-50451)

ENYLDW — With keyboard & percussion. Songs, etc
Orff, Carl
Von der Freundlichkeit der Welt = The world's welcome (1930/1973) : choral settings on texts by Bert Brecht for mixed chorus, three pianos and percussion instruments / [by] Carl Orff ; English translation by Norman Platt. — Mainz ; London : Schott, 1975. — 23p ; 4to.
Unpriced

(B75-51027)

Sansom, Clive A
Tick-tock song : for SATB (or SA, SSA, TTB) with instrumental accompaniment / words and music by Clive A. Sansom. — London : Paterson, 1974. — 7p ; 8vo.
Duration 3 min.
Unpriced
Also classified at FE/NYLDW; GE/NYLDW

(B75-50036)

ENYLDX — With keyboard & percussion. Secular cantatas
Mathias, William
Ceremony after a fire raid. Op.63 : for mixed voices (SATB Bar B), piano and percussion / [by] William Mathias ; poem by Dylan Thomas. — London : Oxford University Press, 1975. — 38p ; 4to.
ISBN 0-19-337434-x : £1.50

(B75-50452)

ENYLNTDW — With keyboard & percussion trio. Songs, etc
Paviour, Paul
The Congo jive : for choir, percussion and piano / music by Paul Paviour ; words by Vachel Lindsay. — London : Boosey and Hawkes, 1974. — 8vo & 4to.
Score (38p.), Chorus score (11p.) & 3 parts.
£3.60

(B75-50037)

EPVDX — With electronic instruments. Secular cantatas
Stockhausen, Karlheinz
Nr 17 = Mikrophonie 2 : für Chor, Hammondorgel und 4 Ringmodulatoren / [von] Karlheinz Stockhausen ; Text 'Einfache grammatische Meditationem' von Helmut Heissenbuttel. — London : Universal, 1974. — 17ff ; obl.fol.
Printed on one side of the leaf only. — German edition. — Instructions provided in German, English and French.
Unpriced

(B75-50038)

ERXNRDK — With string quintet. Anthems
Mundy, John
Sing joyfully : SSATB and strings (or organ) with verses for bass solo / [by] John Mundy ; edited by Edmund H. Fellowes, text from Ps.81. — Revised ed. / by David Scott. — London : Oxford University Press, 1975. — 16p ; 8vo.
ISBN 0-19-352184-9 : £0.40
Also classified at DK

(B75-50453)

ESDW — With violin. Songs, etc
Avshalomov, Jacob
I saw a stranger yester'en : for mixed chorus and violin or piano / [by] Jacob Avshalomov ; words old Gaelic rune. — New York : Galaxy ; London : Galliard, 1975. — 12p ; 8vo.
Unpriced

(B75-50454)

ESNTPWDH — With two violins & keyboard. Motets, Anthems, Hymns, etc
Capricornus, Samuel
Mein Gott und Herr : concerto for two sopranos and bass, (chorus or soloists), two violins and basso continuo / [by] Samuel Capricornus ; edited by Ebbe Selen. — Cassel ; London : Bärenreiter, 1973. — 4to.
Score (21p.) & 3 parts. — Duration 9 min.
£2.40

(B75-50039)

ESTNRDK — With viol quintet. Anthems
Gibbons, Orlando
Lord we beseech thee = The collect for the Annunciation of the Blessed Virgin Mary : verse anthem for alto and chorus (SAATB) with accompaniment for viols or organ / [by] Orlando Gibbons ; reconstructed by Paul Vining. — Sevenoaks : Novello, 1975. — 10p ; 8vo.
£0.20
Also classified at DK

(B75-50040)

ETSDW — With guitar. Songs, etc
Foster, Stephen Collins
Some folks : for four-part chorus of mixed voices with guitar or
piano accompaniment / by Stephen C. Foster ; Foster's guitar part
edited by David Starobin ; edited by Gregg Smith. — New York ;
London : Schirmer, 1974. — 4to.
Score (6p.) & part.
Unpriced
Also classified at DW

(B75-50455)

ETSPDW — With guitar & piano. Songs, etc
De Cormier, Robert
The whistling gypsy : Irish folk song, for four-part chorus of
mixed voices with baritone solo, piano and guitar
accompaniment / arranged by Robert de Cormier. — Wendover :
Roberton, 1974. — 11p ; 8vo.
£0.16

(B75-50456)

ETWNUDU — With two lutes. Madrigals
Striggio, Alessandro
Ecco ch'io lass'il core : SSATTB (unacc. or with lutes) / [by]
Alessandro Striggio ; edited by M.E.C. Bartlet ; lute parts from
Emanuel Adriensen's 'Pratum musicum'. — London : Oxford
University Press, 1975. — 15p ; 8vo.
ISBN 0-19-341221-7 : Unpriced
Also classified at EZDU

(B75-50457)

EUMDK — With wind band. Anthems
Vaughan Williams, Ralph
[O how amiable. *arr*]. O how amiable : anthem for mixed chorus
(SATB) and band or organ / [by] Ralph Vaughan Williams ;
adapted by Carl A. Rosenthal. — New York ; [London] : Oxford
University Press, 1972. — 14p ; 4to.
Unpriced

(B75-51028)

EUMDX — With wind band. Secular cantatas
Heider, Werner
Stundenbuch : für 12 Stimmen und 12 Bläser / [von] Werner
Heider ; text von Eugen Gomringer. — Frankfurt : Litolff ;
London : Peters, 1974. — 54p ; 4to.
Study score. — Duration 16-17 min. — With a separate leaf headed
'Stundenbuch Vorbmerkung' inserted.
Unpriced

(B75-50041)

Washburn, Robert
We hold these truths : bicentennial ode, for chorus and symphonic
band with optional strings / [by] Robert Washburn ; text adapted
from writings of Thomas Jefferson. — New York ; [London] :
Boosey and Hawkes, 1975. — 4to & 8vo.
Score (24p.) & 76 parts. — Duration 7 min.
£15.00

(B75-51029)

EWMDR — With brass band. Psalms
Wenzel, Eberhard
Psalm-Tripychon : für gemischten Chor und Bläserchor / [von]
Eberhard Wenzel. — Cassel ; London : Bärenreiter, 1973. — 19p ;
8vo.
Duration 8 min. — Contents: 1: Psalm 130 : Aus tiefer Not schrei ich zu
dir - 2: Psalm 103 : Nun ob mein Seel den Herren - 3: Psalm 67 : Es wolle
Gott uns gnadig sein.
£2.40

(B75-50042)

EWNPDW — With brass septet. Songs, etc
Washburn, Robert
[Earth song. *Vocal score*]. Earth song : mixed voices with brass
accompaniment and timpani, trumpets 1 and 2 in B flat, horns 1
and 2 in F, trombones 1 and 2, tuba, timpani (optional) / words
and music by Robert Washburn. — New York ; [London] :
Boosey and Hawkes, 1974. — 8vo.
Vocal score (12p.) & 8 parts.
Unpriced

(B75-50043)

**EWSNSRDH — With brass trio & organ. Motets, Anthems, Hymns,
etc**
Gardonyi, Zoltan
Davids Danklied : für Bariton, vierstimmigen gemischten Chor,
Bläser und Orgel / [von] Zsolt Gardonyi ; nach 2. Samuel 22 in
der Ubersetzung von Martin Buber. — Cassel ; London :
Bärenreiter, 1973. — 24p ; 8vo.
Duration 6 min.
£3.20

(B75-50044)

EXTPRPDW — With chime bars & piano. Songs, etc
Jenni, Donald
Death, be not proud : for four-part chorus of mixed voices with
chimes and piano accompaniment / [by] Donald Jenni ; words by
John Donne. — New York ; London : Associated Music, 1974. —
8p ; 8vo.
Unpriced

(B75-50458)

EZ — UNACCOMPANIED CHORAL WORKS
EZDE/LF — Religious cantatas. Christmas
Roe, Betty
Merry be man : a Christmas sequence / [by] Betty Roe ; words by
Jacqueline Froom. — London : Thames, 1974. — 11p ; 8vo.
Unpriced
Primary classification FEZDE/LF

(B75-50499)

EZDG — Roman liturgy. Ordinary of the mass
Camilleri, Charles
Missa brevis : for full chorus of mixed voices, unaccompanied / by
Charles Camilleri. — Wendover : Roberton, 1975. — 22p ; 8vo.
£0.30

(B75-51030)

EZDGC — Roman liturgy. Ordinary of the Mass. Gloria
Argento, Dominick
[The masque of angels. Gloria. *arr*]. Gloria : [unaccompanied
mixed chorus] / [by] Dominick Argento. — New York ;
[London] : Boosey and Hawkes, 1975. — 16p ; 8vo.
£0.40
Primary classification EZDH

EZDGKADD/LK — Stabat mater
Palestrina, Giovanni Pierluigi da
Stabat mater : for double choir / by G.P. da Palestrina ; foreword
by Denis Arnold. — London : Eulenburg, 1974. — vii,16p ; 8vo.
Unpriced

(B75-50045)

**EZDGKH/LL — Roman liturgy. Divine Office. Matins.
Easter**
Taverner, John
Dum transisset Sabbatum : S.A.T. Bar. B. unacc. / [by] John
Taverner ; edited by Philip Brett. — London : Oxford University
Press, 1975. — 7p ; 8vo.
ISBN 0-19-350350-6 : Unpriced

(B75-51031)

EZDGKHL — Roman liturgy. Divine Office. Sext
Handl, Jacob
[Quartus tomus musici operis. In nomine Jesu]. In nomine Jesu :
motet for five voices, SAATB, for the Feast of the Holy Name
and general use / [by] Jacob Handl ; edited by Anthony G. Petti.
— London : Chester, 1975. — 6p ; 8vo.
Duration 2 1/2 min.
Unpriced

(B75-51032)

EZDGKJ — Roman liturgy. Divine Office. Vespers
Philips, Peter
[Cantiones sacrae. Alma redemptoris]. Alma redemptoris :
antiphon of the Blessed Virgin, for five voices, S.S.A.T.B. / [by]
Peter Philips ; edited by Anthony G. Petti. — London : Chester,
1975. — 11p ; 8vo.
Duration 4 1/4 min.
Unpriced

(B75-51033)

EZDGMM — Anglican liturgy. Preces and responses
Lloyd, Richard
Preces and responses : for SATB with divisions (unaccompanied) /
by Richard Lloyd. — Sevenoaks : Novello, 1975. — 8p ; 8vo.
£0.15

(B75-50046)

EZDGS — Anglican liturgy. Communion
Wright, John
Missa brevis : for unaccompanied voices / [by] John Wright. —
Chipping Norton (35 West St., Chipping Norton) : Gray Jewitt
Pritchard, 1975. — 8p ; 4to.
Unpriced

(B75-50047)

**EZDGTC/LH/AYM — Orthodox Eastern Church. Holy Week.
Collections. Russia**
Orthodox Holy Week Music : SATB a cappella / [compiled by]
Alexei Haieff ; English text by Martin Cooper. — London :
Boosey and Hawkes, 1975. — 31p ; 8vo.
£1.75

(B75-50459)

EZDH — Motets, Anthems, Hymns, etc
Argento, Dominick
[The masque of angels. Gloria. *arr]*. Gloria : [unaccompanied
mixed chorus] / [by] Dominick Argento. — New York ;
[London] : Boosey and Hawkes, 1975. — 16p ; 8vo.
£0.40
Also classified at EZDGC

(B75-51034)

Binkerd, Gordon
O sweet Jesu : SATB / by Gordon Binkerd ; poem by Christina
Rossetti. — New York ; [London] : Boosey and Hawkes, 1974. —
18p ; 8vo.
Unpriced

(B75-50048)

Herzogenberg, Heinrich von
Vier Choral-Motetten = Four chorale motets. Op.102 : for
unaccompanied four-part chorus / [by] Heinrich von
Herzogenberg ; edited by Wilhelm Ehmann. — Cassel ; London :
Bärenreiter, 1973. — 32p ; 8vo.
£1.20

(B75-50049)

Hufschmidt, Wolfgang
Der barmherzige Samariter : für gemischten Chor und Sprecher /
[von] Wolfgang Hufschmidt. — Cassel ; London : Bärenreiter,
1974. — 12p ; 8vo.
£1.00

(B75-50050)

Parker, Horatio
[Hora novissima. Urbs Syon unica]. City of high renown = Urbs
Syon unica : unaccompanied mixed chorus / [by] Horatio Parker ;
edited by Leonard van Camp, Latin text by Bernard de Morlaix ;
English translation by Isabella G. Parker. — New York : Galaxy ;
[London] : [Galliard], 1975. — 14p ; 8vo.
Unpriced

(B75-51035)

Radcliffe, Philip
God be in my head : SSAATTBB (unacc.) / [by] Philip
Radcliffe ; words from Sarum Primer. — London : Oxford
University Press, 1975. — 4p ; 8vo.
ISBN 0-19-350354-9 : Unpriced

(B75-50460)

Rorem, Ned
Canticle of the Lamb : SATB unaccompanied / [by] Ned Rorem.
— New York ; [London] : Boosey and Hawkes, 1972. — 4p ; 8vo.
Unpriced

(B75-51036)

Rose, Bernard
Feast song for Saint Cecilia : for SATB with divisions
(unaccompanied) / music by Bernard Rose ; words by Gregory
Rose. — Sevenoaks : Novello, 1975. — 11p ; 8vo.
£0.20

(B75-51037)

Schwarz-Schilling, Reinhard
Der Herr, der ewige Gott und Vater unser : für gemischten
Chor / [von] Reinhard Schwarz-Schilling. — Cassel ; London :
Bärenreiter, 1974. — 13p ; 8vo.
It is possible to use either of the alternative English texts in the Lord's
Prayer and also the Latin text.
£1.20
Also classified at EZDTF

(B75-50051)

Schweizer, Rolf
Die Seligpreisungen : dreistimmiger gemischter Chor und
Gemeinde (mit Tasteninstrument ad libitum) / [von] Rolf
Schweizer. — Cassel ; London : Bärenreiter, 1973. — 4p ; 8vo.
£0.20

(B75-50052)

Tunnard, Thomas
Maker of man : plainsong melody, faburden verses SATB / [by]
Thomas Tunnard. — York : Banks, 1974. — 2p ; 8vo.
Unpriced

(B75-50461)

Williams, Grace
Ave maris stella : for unaccompanied mixed voices / [by] Grace
Williams ; Latin text. — London : Oxford University Press, 1975.
— 15p ; 8vo.
Duration 9 1/2 min.
ISBN 0-19-338755-7 : £0.50

(B75-50462)

Wolf, Hugo
Sechs geistliche Lieder = Six sacred songs : for four-part chorus
of mixed voices / by Hugo Wolf ; edited by Clifford G. Richter ;
poems by Joseph von Eichendorff ; English version by Dora
Linley. — Cassel ; London : Bärenreiter, 1973. — 28p ; 8vo.
£1.60

(B75-50053)

EZDH/AYT — Motets, Anthems, Hymns, etc. Collections. United
States
Christmas music from Colonial America : an anthology of
Christmas psalms and anthems from the revolutionary and federal
eras : for mixed chorus, organ and optional instruments /
compiled, edited and arranged by Leonard Van Camp. — New
York : Galaxy ; [London] : [Galliard], 1975. — 45p ; 8vo.
Unpriced
Also classified at DH/AYT

(B75-50463)

EZDH/LEZ — Motets, Anthems, Hymns, etc. Advent
Jenni, Donald
Ad te levavi : for full chorus of mixed voices a cappella / [by]
Donald Jenni ; text from Psalm 24, [freely adapted by the
composer]. — New York ; London : Associated Music, 1974. —
7p ; 8vo.
Unpriced

(B75-50464)

EZDH/LK — Motets, Anthems, Hymns, etc. Good Friday
Nelson, Havelock
O King of the Friday : SATB unacc. / [by] Havelock Nelson ;
words by Douglas Hyde (from the Gaelic). — York : Banks, 1975.
— 4p ; 8vo.
Unpriced

(B75-51038)

EZDJ — Motets
Dalby, Martin
Ad flumina Babyloniae : for mixed voices (unaccompanied
minimum 3333) / music by Martin Dalby ; words from Psalm
137. — Sevenoaks : Novello, 1975. — 16p ; 8vo.
£0.25

(B75-51039)

Schütz, Heinrich
Jesu dulcissime : motet for six voices / [by] Heinrich Schütz ;
edited by Werner Brieg. — First edition. — Cassel ; London :
Bärenreiter, 1974. — 23p ; 8vo.
Attributed to Schütz.
£1.40

(B75-50054)

Schwarz-Schilling, Reinhard
Exaudi Domine vocem meam : vier Psalm-Motetten, für
gemischten Chor / [von] Reinhard Schwarz-Schilling. — Cassel ;
London : Bärenreiter, 1974. — 12p ; 8vo.
£1.20

(B75-50055)

EZDJ/AYE — Motets. Collections. Germany
[Biblische Motetten für das Kirchenjahr. Band 2: Darstellung des
Herrn bis Trinitas. *Selections]*. Spruchmotten / herausgegeben von
Konrad Ameln und Harald Kummerling. — Cassel ; London :
Bärenreiter.
3 : Motetten. — 1974. — 32p ; 8vo.
£1.40

(B75-50056)

EZDJ/LFP — Motets. Epiphany
Palestrina, Giovanni Pierluigi da
Surge, illuminare Jerusalem : a motet for two four-part choirs
(SATB SATB for the feast of the Epiphany) / [by] G.P. da
Palestrina] ; edited by Anthony G. Petti. — London : Chester,
1975. — 16p ; 8vo.
Duration 4 min.
Unpriced

(B75-51040)

EZDK — Anthems
Kroeger, Karl
Hear my prayer, O Lord : SATB / [by] Karl Kroeger ; text from
Psalm 55. — New York ; [London] : Boosey and Hawkes, 1974.
— 17p ; 8vo.
Unpriced

(B75-50057)

Two short Elizabethan anthems : for SATB unaccompanied or with
organ / edited by Watkins Shaw. — Sevenoaks : Novello, 1975. —
3p ; 8vo.
Contents: 1: Teach me thy way, O Lord / words from Psalm 86 by William
Fox - 2: Hide not thou thy face / words based on Psalm 27 by Richard
Farrant.
Unpriced

(B75-50465)

EZDM — Hymns

Beechey, Gwilym
An Easter introit : SATB / [by] Gwilym Beechey ; words by Isaac Watts. — York : Banks, 1974. — s,sh ; 8vo.
Unpriced
(B75-50466)

Belcher, Supply
[Harmony of Maine. *Selections*]. Deep North Spirituals, 1794 : mixed or male voices in three and four parts / [by] Supply Belcher ; revised and edited by Oliver Daniel. — New York ; London : Peters, 1973. — 23p ; 8vo.
Unpriced
Also classified at GEZDM
(B75-50058)

Davis, Katherine Kennicott
Choristers of light : for mixed voices / [by] Katherine K. Davis ; words by K.K.D. — New York : Galaxy ; London : Galliard, 1971. — 3p ; 8vo.
Unpriced
(B75-50059)

EZDM/AYT — Hymns. Collections. United States

Five American hymn tunes : for men's or mixed voices unaccompanied / edited by Charles Edward Lindsley. — New York ; [London] : Oxford University Press, 1975. — 11p ; 8vo.
Unpriced
Primary classification GEZDM/AYT
(B75-50512)

EZDP/LF — Carols. Christmas

Agricola, Martin
[Her ich verkund euch neue Mar]. Weihnachtsgesang : for four-part mixed choir / by Martin Agricola ; edited by Heinz Funck. — Cassel ; London : Bärenreiter, 1974. — 7p ; 8vo.
£0.60
(B75-50060)

Copley, Ian Alfred
The holy son of God : carol for SATB / [by] I.A. Copley ; words by Henry More. — London : Thames, 1975. — 2p ; 8vo.
Unpriced
(B75-50467)

Dinham, Kenneth J
Jesus, Jesus, rest your head : Southern Appalachian carol / arr. SATB by K.J. Dinham. — York : Banks, 1975. — 2p ; 8vo.
Unpriced
(B75-51041)

Gruber, Franz
[Stille Nacht. *arr*]. Stille Nacht = Silent night / [by] Franz Gruber ; arranged SATB unacc. by Donald Cashmore, words by Joseph Mohr, trans. David Willcocks. — London : Oxford University Press, 1975. — 3p ; 8vo.
German & English text.
ISBN 0-19-343053-3 : Unpriced
(B75-51042)

Hill, Anthony Herschel
Child in the manger : carol for SATB / [by] Anthony Herschel Hill ; words by Mary Macdonald. — London : Thames, 1975. — 2p ; 8vo.
Unpriced
(B75-50468)

Inness, Peter
Balulalow : carol for SAATB with divisions unaccompanied / [by] Peter Inness ; words by James, John and Robert Wedderburn. — Sevenoaks : Novello, 1975. — 4p ; 8vo.
£0.10
(B75-50061)

Najera, Edmund
In dulci jubilo : for four-part chorus of mixed voices a cappella / [by] Edmund Najera. — New York ; London : Schirmer, 1974. — 11p ; 8vo.
Unpriced
(B75-50469)

Parfrey, Raymond
Here on a bed of straw : carol for unison voices, SAB or SATB / [by] Raymond Parfrey ; words by Mary Dawson. — London : Thames, 1975. — 2p ; 8vo.
Unpriced
Primary classification JFDP/LF
(B75-50533)

Philips, Peter
[Les Rossignols spirituels. *Selections*]. Eleven Christmas carols / by Peter Phillips [sic] ; edited and translated for mixed voices (four-part or two-part) by Lionel Pike. — London : Oxford University Press, 1975. — 25p ; 4to.
ISBN 0-19-353346-4 : Unpriced
(B75-51043)

EZDP/LF/AY — Carols. Christmas. Collections

Four Victorian carols : SATB unacc. / arranged and edited by Richard Graves. — York : Banks, 1975. — 4p ; 8vo.
Contents: 1: The shepherd's song / anon - 2: Glory to God / by R.F. Smith - 3: Come ye lofty / by Archer Gurney - 4: Merry Christmas / by J.H. Leslie.
Unpriced
(B75-51044)

A garland of carols : SATB a cappella settings. — London : Chappell, 1975. — 68p ; 8vo.
Carols by Richard Blackford, Herbert Chappell, Adrian Cruft, Stephen Dodgson, John Hall, Anthony Hedges, John Lambert, Elizabeth Maconchy, Colin Mawby, Alan Ridout, Thomas Wilson.
Unpriced
(B75-50470)

EZDTF — Lord's Prayer

Bates, Tom
The Lord's Prayer : SATB with alternative version for unison voices / [by] Tom Bates. — York : Banks, 1975. — 2p ; 8vo.
Unpriced
Also classified at JDTF
(B75-50471)

Rose, Gregory
The Camrose Lord's Prayer : SATB with optional accompaniment / [by] Gregory Rose. — London : Boosey and Hawkes, 1975. — 8vo.
Score (3p.) & congregational card.
£0.10
Also classified at JEZDTF
(B75-50472)

Schwarz-Schilling, Reinhard
Der Herr, der ewige Gott und Vater unser : für gemischten Chor / [von] Reinhard Schwarz-Schilling. — Cassel ; London : Bärenreiter, 1974. — 13p ; 8vo.
It is possible to use either of the alternative English texts in the Lord's Prayer and also the Latin text.
£1.20
Primary classification EZDH
(B75-50051)

EZDU — Madrigals

Arcadelt, Jacques
[Il primo libro di madrigali. *Selections*]. Three madrigals : for 4 voices or instruments / [by] Jacques Arcadelt ; edited by Iain Fenlon. — Lustleigh : Antico, 1975. — 9p ; 4to.
Unpriced
Also classified at LNS
(B75-50473)

Hassler, Hans Leo
[Canzonette. Hor va canzona mia]. Hor va canzona mia = How freely flies my song : SATB a cappella / [by] Hans Leo Hassler ; English translation by Gloria Mainero, edited by Eugene Guettler. — New York : Warner ; [London] : [Blossom], 1972. — 4p ; 8vo.
Text in Italian & English.
Unpriced
(B75-51045)

Striggio, Alessandro
Ecco ch'io lass'il core : SSATTB (unacc. or with lutes) / [by] Alessandro Striggio ; edited by M.E.C. Bartlet ; lute parts from Emanuel Adriensen's 'Pratum musicum'. — London : Oxford University Press, 1975. — 15p ; 8vo.
ISBN 0-19-341221-7 : Unpriced
Primary classification ETWNUDU
(B75-50457)

Thomas, Bernard
Two chansons for flutes / edited by Bernard Thomas ; pub. Pierre Attaingnant (1533). — London : Oxford University Press, 1975. — 7p ; 8vo.
Contents: 1 Si bon amour, by Jacotin - 2 Parle qui veult, by Claudin de Sermisy.
ISBN 0-19-341220-9 : £0.12
Also classified at VRNS
(B75-50062)

EZDU/AYJ — Madrigals. Collections. Italy

The Penguin book of Italian madrigals for four voices / edited by Jerome Roche. — Harmondsworth : Penguin Books, 1974. — 176p ; 8vo.
ISBN 0-14-070843-x : £1.00
(B75-50063)

EZDW — Songs, etc

Baksa, Robert F
And will you leave me so? : SATB unaccompanied / by Robert F. Baksa ; text adapted from a poem by Sir Thomas Wyatt. — London : Boosey and Hawkes, 1972. — 8p ; 8vo.
Unpriced
(B75-50474)

Binkerd, Gordon
Tomorrow the fox will come to town : mixed chorus, SATB /
[by] Gordon Binkerd ; words anon., 16th century. — New York ;
[London] : Boosey and Hawkes, 1974. — 32p ; 8vo.
Unpriced
(B75-50064)

Brydson, John Collis
And wilt thou leave me thus? : SATB / music by John C.
Brydson ; words by Sir Thomas Wyatt. — London : Cramer,
1975. — 7p ; 8vo.
£0.12
(B75-50475)

Dale, Mervyn
Thou wert my purer mind : unaccompanied part song for SATB /
music by Mervyn Dale ; words by Percy Bysshe Shelley. —
London : Ashdown, 1975. — 8p ; 8vo.
Duration 3 min.
£0.15
(B75-50476)

Ekwueme, Laz
Hombe : Kenya (Luo) folk song, for 4-part mixed choir and
contralto solo unaccompanied / arranged by Laz Ekwueme. —
Wendover : Roberton, 1975. — 10p ; 8vo.
Unpriced
(B75-50477)

Erb, James
Shenandoah : American folk song, for full chorus of mixed voices
unaccompanied / arranged by James Erb. — Wendover :
Roberton, 1975. — 8p ; 8vo.
£0.12
(B75-50478)

Foster, Stephen Collins
Come where my love lies dreaming : for four-part chorus of mixed
voices a cappella / by Stephen Foster ; edited by Gregg Smith. —
New York ; London : Schirmer, 1974. — 12p ; 8vo.
Unpriced
(B75-50479)

Furman, James
Four little foxes : for unaccompanied mixed chorus / [by] James
Furman ; poems by Lew Sarett. — New York ; [London] : Oxford
University Press, 1971. — 11p ; 8vo.
Unpriced
(B75-50065)

Furman, James
Four little foxes : for unaccompanied mixed chorus / [by] James
Furman ; poems by Lew Sarett. — New York : Oxford University
Press, 1971. — 11p ; 8vo.
Unpriced
(B75-50480)

Gardner, Ward
Bo-peep : based on the traditional air and a fugue by Pachelbel /
arr. SATB unacc. by Ward Gardner. — York : Banks, 1975. —
4p ; 8vo.
Unpriced
(B75-51046)

Horovitz, Joseph
Three choral songs from 'As you like it' : SATB / music by
Joseph Horovitz ; words by William Shapespeare. — Sevenoaks :
Novello, 1975. — 18p ; 8vo.
£0.50
(B75-51047)

Jenni, Donald
Early spring : for four part chorus of mixed voices a cappella /
[by] D. Jenni ; text based on an anonymous 14th century English
poem. — New York ; London : Associated Music, 1975. — 6p ;
8vo.
£0.20
(B75-51048)

Josquin des Prés
Qui belles amours : ATTB / [by] Josquin des Prés ; edited by
William Prizer. — London : Oxford University Press, 1975. —
8p ; 8vo.
ISBN 0-19-341222-5 : Unpriced
(B75-51049)

Kelterborn, Rudolf
Drei Fragmente : für Chor, [SATB] 1973 / [von] Rudolf
Kelterborn. — Cassel ; London : Bärenreiter, 1974. — 22p ; fol.
£3.00
(B75-50066)

Nelson, Havelock
Oh! I am come to the Low Countrie : traditional melody /
arranged for SATB unaccompanied by Havelock Nelson ; words
by Robert Burns. — Sevenoaks : Elkin, 1975. — 8p ; 8vo.
£0.15
(B75-50481)

Terzakis, Dimitri
[Ikos]. Ikos : für zwei Soprane, zwei Alte, zwei Tenore, zwei
Basse, [with] Katawassia : für zwei Soprane, Alt, zwei Tenore,
Bariton / [von] Dimitri Terzakis. — Cassel ; London :
Bärenreiter, 1974. — 20p ; 8vo.
Unpriced
(B75-50482)

EZDW/AY — Songs, etc. Collections
Five folk-songs / arranged for unaccompanied mixed voices by
David Willcocks. — London : Oxford University Press, 1975. —
25p ; 8vo.
ISBN 0-19-343836-4 : £0.75
(B75-50483)

Invitation to the partsong. — London : Stainer and Bell.
No.2 : Part songs for SATB : a selection of four-part works / newly
transcribed and edited by Geoffrey Bush and Michael Hurd. — 1974. —
47p ; 8vo.
ISBN 0-85249-288-x : Unpriced
(B75-50067)

EZDW/XC — Songs, etc. Rounds
Benoy, Arthur William
Two rounds for voices / words and music by A.W. Benoy. —
London : Oxford University Press, 1975. — 5p ; 8vo.
Contents: 1: The restless rambler - 2: The yodelling round.
ISBN 0-19-343509-8 : Unpriced
(B75-51050)

EZDX — Secular cantatas
Jergenson, Dale
Bric-a-Bach (constructed from five different compositions by J.S.
Bach) : for full chorus of mixed voices with optional guitar, bass
and drums accompaniment / [by] Dale Jergenson. — New York ;
London : Schirmer, 1974. — 25p ; 8vo.
Unpriced
(B75-50484)

Schnebel, Dieter
Für Stimmen (... missa est) dt 31, 6 : Fassung für grossen Chor /
[von] Dieter Schnebel. — Mainz ; London : Schott, 1975. — 16p ;
fol.
Unpriced
(B75-51051)

F — FEMALE VOICES, CHILDREN'S VOICES
FDE — Religious cantatas
Kagel, Mauricio
Vom Hönensagen : für Frauenstimmen und obligates
Harmonium / [von] Mauricio Kagel ; text aus Wolfram von
Eschenbach's 'Parzival'. — London : Universal, 1975. — 25p ;
4to.
Unpriced
(B75-50485)

FDE/LF — Religious cantatas. Christmas
Sansom, Clive A
The donkey : the Christmas story portrayed by the animals /
words and music by Clive A. Sansom. — London : Studio Music,
1974. — 43p ; 8vo.
Unpriced
(B75-50068)

FDGKAV — Roman liturgy. Requiems
Fauré, Gabriel
[Requiem. Opus 48. *Vocal score: arr*]. Requiem. Opus 48 / [by]
Gabriel Fauré ; arranged for soprano and baritone (or
mezzo-soprano) soli, SSA and orchestra by Desmond Ratcliffe. —
Sevenoaks : Novello, 1975. — 56p ; 8vo.
Latin and English text.
£1.00
Primary classification DGKAV

FDP/LF — Carols. Christmas
Mario of the Cross, *Sister*
Blessed be that maid Mary : Christmas carol, SATB and organ /
tune from Ballet's lute book arranged by Sister Maria of the
Cross, text from an old English carol modernized by G.R.
Woodward. — New York ; [London] : Oxford University Press,
1972. — 8p ; 8vo.
Unpriced
(B75-51052)

Rocherolle, Eugenie R
How can it be? : for unison, SA or SAB chorus and piano /
words and music by Eugenie R. Rocherolle. — New York :
Warner ; London : Blossom, 1975. — 8p ; 8vo.
Duration 2 1/2 min.
Unpriced
Primary classification DP/LF

Rutter, John
Donkey carol : two-part / words and music by John Rutter. —
London : Oxford University Press, 1975. — 11p ; 8vo.
ISBN 0-19-341511-9 : £0.20
(B75-50486)

Toplis, Gloria
Now the holly bears a berry : unison song with descant /
arranged by Gloria Toplis ; words, traditional. — Chesham :
Ricordi, 1975. — 4p ; 8vo.
Unpriced
(B75-51053)

Walters, Edmund
The bells : a carol for S.S.A. and piano / [by] Edmund Walters ;
words by Peter Kennerley. — London : Boosey and Hawkes,
1975. — 7p ; 8vo.
£0.15
(B75-51054)

Walters, Edmund
Born in Bethlehem : a carol for treble voices with optional S.A. or
S.A.T.B. chorus / music, based on a XVI th century English
melody, by Edmund Walters ; words by Peter Kennerley. —
London : Boosey and Hawkes, 1975. — 4p ; 8vo.
£0.10
(B75-51055)

FDR — Psalms
Coombes, Douglas
I was glad when they said unto me : a paraphrase of Psalm 122,
for two equal voices / music by Douglas Coombes ; words by Ivor
Bryant. — Clifton (28 Knolls Way, Clifton, Beds.) : Lindsay
Music, 1972. — 5p ; 8vo.
£0.12
(B75-50487)

Harper, John
Psalm 150 : two-part / [by] John Harper. — London : Oxford
University Press, 1974. — 3p ; 8vo.
ISBN 0-19-351120-7 : £0.08
(B75-50069)

FDW — Songs, etc
Artman, Ruth
I can't sing pretty! (But I shore sing loud!) : for unison or SA
chorus and piano / words and music by Ruth Artman. — New
York : Warner ; [London] : [Blossom], 1973. — 7p ; 8vo.
Unpriced
(B75-50488)

Bacon, Ernst
Of a feather : five songs for high and low voices and piano / [by]
Ernst Bacon ; words by Marie de L. Welch. — Sevenoaks :
Novello, 1975. — 16p ; 8vo.
Unpriced
(B75-50489)

Crawford, John
The mad maid's song : for SSAA and piano / [by] John
Crawford ; words by Robert Herrick. — New York ; [London] :
Oxford University Press, 1971. — 12p ; 8vo.
Unpriced
(B75-50070)

Dale, Mervyn
Three more songs for two-part choir / music by Mervyn Dale ;
words by Joan Lane. — London : Ashdown, 1974. — 8p ; 8vo.
Contents: The little red squirrel - Make believing - My red balloon.
£0.15
(B75-50071)

Joplin, Scott
[The entertainer. arr]. The entertainer : two-part song / music by
Scott Joplin, words and arrangement by Richard Graves. —
London : Ashdown, 1975. — 7p ; 8vo.
£0.12
(B75-51056)

Kelly, Bryan
Boys in a pie : two-part song with piano / music by Bryan Kelly ;
words by John Fuller. — Wendover : Roberton, 1975. — 8p ;
8vo.
£0.12
(B75-50490)

Miller, Carl
The Eddystone light / arranged for two-part chorus by Carl
Miller. — New York ; [London] : Chappell, 1975. — 5p ; 8vo.
Unpriced
(B75-50491)

Miller, Carl
Lolly too dum / arranged for two-part chorus by Carl Miller. —
New York ; [London] : Chappell, 1975. — 5p ; 8vo.
Unpriced
(B75-50492)

Miller, Carl
Simple gifts : traditional Shaker song / arranged for two-part
chorus by Carl Miller. — New York ; [London] : Chappell, 1975.
— 8p ; 8vo.
Unpriced
(B75-50493)

Miller, Carl
The willow song / arranged for two-part chorus by Carl Miller.
— New York ; [London] : Chappell, 1975. — 6p ; 8vo.
Unpriced
(B75-50494)

Platts, Kenneth
A midnight carol. Op.21 : two-part / [by] Kenneth Platts ; text by
Leonard Clark. — London : Ashdown, 1975. — 4p ; 8vo.
Unpriced
(B75-50495)

Rota, Nino
[The godfather, part 2. Love said goodbye. arr]. Love said
goodbye : music by Nino Rota / lyric by Larry Kusik ; arranged
by Harry Simeone. — New York : Famous Music ; [London] :
[Chappell], 1974. — 8vo.
S.A., (8p.), S.S.A., (8p.).
Unpriced
(B75-50072)

Tate, Phyllis
To words by Joseph Beaumont : three songs for soprano and alto
voices (SSA) and piano / [by] Phyllis Tate. — London : Oxford
University Press, 1974. — 28p ; 8vo.
Duration 9 min. — Contents: 1: When love - 2: The gnat - 3: House and
home.
ISBN 0-19-338382-9 : £0.90
(B75-50496)

Thiman, Eric Harding
The thrush in spring : two-part song / music by Eric H. Thiman ;
words by K.M. Warburton. — Wendover : Roberton, 1975. —
7p ; 8vo.
Staff and tonic sol fa notation. — Duration 2 1/2 min.
£0.12
(B75-50497)

FDW/LC — Spirituals
Arch, Gwyn
Four negro spirituals : SSA and piano / arranged by Gwyn Arch.
— London : Boosey and Hawkes, 1974. — 28p ; 8vo.
£1.00
(B75-50073)

FDX — Secular cantatas
Hurd, Michael
Hip-hip Horatio : an 'oratorio' for narrator (tenor), chorus (high
and low voices) and piano / music by Michael Hurd ; words by
Michael Blom. — Sevenoaks : Novello, 1975. — 66p ; 8vo.
Duration 30 min.
£0.90
(B75-50498)

Williamson, Malcolm
[The glitter gang. Vocal score]. The glitter gang : a cassation for
audience and orchestra (piano) / by Malcolm Williamson ; words
by the composer. — London : Weinberger, 1975. — 4to.
Vocal score (13p.) & audience part (7p.).
Unpriced
(B75-50074)

FE/NYERNQDH — With flute, strings & percussion sextet. Motets,
Anthems, Hymns, etc
Stout, Alan
O altitudo : soprano solo, flute solo, violin, violoncello, harp,
celesta, percussion, women's chorus / by Alan Stout. — New
York ; London : Peters, 1974. — 4to.
Score (18p.) & 6 parts.
Unpriced
(B75-50075)

FE/NYFPNTDP/LF — With woodwind, keyboard & percussion trio.
Carols. Christmas
Roe, Betty
Rocking : for two voices, woodwind, keyboard and percussion /
music by Betty Roe. — London : Thames, 1975. — 4p ; 8vo.
Unpriced
(B75-51057)

FE/NYLDW — With keyboard & percussion. Songs, etc
Sansom, Clive A
Tick-tock song : for SATB (or SA, SSA, TTB) with instrumental
accompaniment / words and music by Clive A. Sansom. —
London : Paterson, 1974. — 7p ; 8vo.
Duration 3 min.
Unpriced
Primary classification ENYLDW
(B75-50036)

FE/XDP/LF — With percussion. Carols. Christmas
Toplis, Gloria
Somerset wassail / arranged for S.A. with percussion by Gloria
Toplis; words, traditional. — Chesham : Ricordi, 1975. — 4p ;
8vo.
Unpriced

(B75-51058)

FEZDE/LF — Unaccompanied voices. Religious cantatas. Christmas
Roe, Betty
Merry be man : a Christmas sequence / [by] Betty Roe ; words by
Jacqueline Froom. — London : Thames, 1974. — 11p ; 8vo.
Unpriced
Also classified at GEZDE/LF; EZDE/LF

(B75-50499)

FEZDJ — Unaccompanied voices. Motets
Poos, Heinrich
Das ist ein kestlich Ding, dem Herren danken : Motette für vier
gleiche Stimmen und zweistimmige Kinderchor / [von] Heinrich
Poos ; Psalm 92, 2, 3, 5. — Cassel ; London : Bärenreiter, 1974.
— 4p ; 8vo.
£0.20

(B75-50076)

FEZDK — Unaccompanied voices. Anthems
Diemer, Emma Lou
The prophecy : SSAA unaccompanied / [by] Emma Lou Diemer ;
words from Isaiah 11-12. — New York ; [London] : Boosey and
Hawkes, 1974. — 19p ; 8vo.
Unpriced

(B75-50077)

FEZDP/LF — Unaccompanied voices. Carols. Christmas
Beaumont, Adrian
Long long ago : for four-part female chorus, unaccompanied /
music by Adrian Beaumont ; words traditional. — Wendover :
Roberton, 1974. — 4p ; 4to.
£0.08

(B75-51059)

Copley, Ian Alfred
Two lullaby carols : for 4-part female voices unaccompanied /
music by I.A. Copley. — Wendover : Roberton, 1975. — 4p ; 8vo.
Contents: 1: Dormi Jesu (trans. Coleridge) - 2: Sweet was the song the
Virgin sang (Ballet).
£0.10

(B75-51060)

Lane, Philip
A babe is born : SSA unacc. / [by] Philip Lane ; words, 15th
century. — York : Banks, 1975. — 2p ; 8vo.
Unpriced

(B75-51061)

Lane, Philip
A spotless rose : S.A. unacc. / [by] Philip Lane ; words 15th
century. — York : Banks, 1975. — 2p ; 8vo.
Unpriced

(B75-51062)

Toplis, Gloria
The angel Gabriel : for S.S.A. / arranged by Cloria Toplis; words,
traditional. — Chesham : Ricordi, 1975. — 3p ; 8vo.
Unpriced

(B75-51063)

FEZDW — Unaccompanied voices. Songs, etc
Benger, Richard
October songs : SSA unacc. / [by] Richard Benger ; words by
Mary Dawson. — York : Banks, 1975. — 8p ; 8vo.
Contents: 1: Midland autumn - 2: Magpies - 3: October.
Unpriced

(B75-50500)

Benger, Richard
Winter fragments : SSA unacc. / words and music by Richard
Benger. — York : Banks Music, 1975. — 4p ; 8vo.
Contents: 1: Invocation - 2: Snowflake - 3: Tree - 4: Fireside.
Unpriced

(B75-50501)

Burtch, Mervyn
The lantern festival : S.S.A. unacc. / [by] Mervyn Burtch ; poems
by Chiang K'uei, translated [from the Chinese] by Clara M.
Candlin. — York : Banks, 1975. — 6p ; 8vo.
Contents: 1: Remember yesteryear - 2: The dream - 3: The lanterns.
Unpriced

(B75-51064)

Kennedy, John Brodbin
The look, the kiss and joy : three madrigals with coda, SSA
unaccompanied / by John Brodbin Kennedy ; words by Sara
Teasdale. — New York ; [London] : Boosey and Hawkes, 1972.
— 8p ; 8vo.
Unpriced

(B75-51065)

Nelson, Havelock
The enchanted valley : traditional Irish air / arranged for
three-part female voice choir and soprano solo by Havelock
Nelson. — Wendover : Roberton, 1975. — 7p ; 8vo.
£0.12

(B75-50502)

Short, Michael
Song's eternity : part-song for unaccompanied female voices
(SSA) / [by] Michael Short ; words by John Clare. — Wendover :
Roberton, 1975. — 8p ; 8vo.
Duration 4 3/4 min.
£0.14

(B75-50503)

FEZDW/G/AY — Unaccompanied voices. Folk songs. Collections
Blüh nur mein Sommerkorn : [songs] aus der klingenden Saat / von
Walther Hensel ; herausgegeben von Walther Sturm. — Cassel ;
London : Bärenreiter, 1973. — vi,221p ; 8vo.
£3.20

(B75-50078)

FEZDW/G/AYULD — Unaccompanied voices. Folk songs.
Collections. Jamaica
Beeny Bud : 12 Jamaican folk-songs for children / collected and
arranged for schools by Olive Lewin. — London : Oxford
University Press, 1975. — 24p ; obl.8vo.
ISBN 0-19-330543-7 : Unpriced

(B75-51066)

Dandy Shandy : 12 Jamaican folk-songs for children / collected and
arranged for schools by Olive Lewin. — London : Oxford
University Press, 1975. — 20p ; obl.4to.
ISBN 0-19-330545-3 : £0.40

(B75-50504)

FEZDW/XC — Unaccompanied voices. Rounds
Beeson, Jack
The model housekeeper : nine rounds and canons for women's
voices / [by] Jack Beeson ; receipts by Elizabeth W. Smith. —
New York ; [London] : Boosey and Hawkes, 1972. — 28p ; 8vo.
Unpriced

(B75-50505)

FLDK — Treble voices. Anthems
Hilty, Everett Jay
You are the temple of God : for treble choir in two parts and
organ / by Everett Jay Hilty ; words adapted from 1. Corinthians
10, 11, 16 and 17. — New York ; [London] : Oxford University
Press, 1975. — 4p ; 8vo.
Unpriced

(B75-50079)

FLDP — Treble voices. Carols
Carter, Sydney
[Nine carols or ballads. Lord of the dance. *arr*]. Lord of the
dance / [by] Sydney Carter ; arranged for two-part treble chorus
and keyboard with optional percussion, accompanied choral
adaptation by Donald Waxman. — New York : Galaxy ;
[London] : [Galliard], 1971. — 8p ; 8vo.
Unpriced

(B75-50506)

FLDP/LF — Treble voices. Carols. Christmas
Liddell, Claire
A Scottish carol : for 3-part treble voices with optional solo /
music by Claire Liddell, words by J.C.M. — Wendover :
Roberton, 1975. — 4p ; 8vo.
£0.10

(B75-51067)

Wills, Arthur
I sing of a Maiden : two-part / [by] Arthur Wills ; words anon.
15th century. — London : Oxford University Press, 1975. — 4p ;
4to.
Duration 3 1/2 min.
ISBN 0-19-341510-0 : £0.10

(B75-50507)

FLDR — Treble voices. Psalms
Hedges, Anthony
[Psalm 104. Op.52. *Vocal score*]. Psalm 104. Opus 52 : for S.S.S.S.
and piano / [by] Anthony Hedges. — London : Chappell, 1974.
— 4to.
Vocal score (31p.) & 4 choral score.
Unpriced

(B75-50080)

FLDW — Treble voices. Songs, etc
Loesser, Frank
['Hans Christian Andersen'. The ugly duckling. *arr*]. The ugly
duckling : for two-part chorus of treble voices with piano / [by]
Frank Loesser ; arranged by Howard Cable. — Boston ;
[London] : Frank Music, 1972. — 10p ; 8vo.
Unpriced

(B75-51068)

Loesser, Frank
['Hans Christian Andersen'. Wonderful Copenhagen. *arr].*
Wonderful Copenhagen : for two-part chorus of treble voices with
piano / [by] Frank Loesser ; arranged by Howard Cable. —
Boston ; [London] : Frank Music, 1972. — 7p ; 8vo.
Unpriced

(B75-51069)

Williams, Patrick
Mr Squirrel : SSA / music by Patrick Williams ; words by V.M.
Julian. — London : Bosworth, 1974. — 4p ; 8vo.
Staff & tonic sol-fa notation.
Unpriced

(B75-50081)

Williams, Phyllis
[Friends, relatives, parents. *arr].* Friends, relatives, parents : a
program opener for two-part chorus of treble voices with piano
and optional guitar / [by] Phyllis Williams ; arranged by Walter
Ehret. — New York ; [London] : Frank Music, 1972. — 10p ;
8vo.
Unpriced

(B75-51070)

Williams, Phyllis
[How do you open a show without a curtain?. *arr].* How do you
open a show without a curtain? : a program opener, for two-part
chorus of treble voices with piano and optional guitar / [by]
Phyllis Williams ; arranged by Walter Ehret. — Boston ;
[London] : Frank Music, 1972. — 11p ; 8vo.
Unpriced

(B75-51071)

Williams, Phyllis
[That's a very good sign. *arr].* That's a very good sign : for
two-part chorus of treble voices and piano / [by] Phyllis
Williams ; arranged by Walter Ehret. — Boston ; [London] :
Frank Music, 1972. — 7p ; 8vo.
Unpriced

(B75-51072)

FLDX — Treble voices. Secular cantatas
Young, Douglas
[The listeners. *Vocal score].* The listeners : a dramatic cantata for
soprano solo, male speaker and small soprano chorus, with
chamber orchestra / [by] Douglas Young ; based on two poems by
Walter de la Mare. — London : Faber Music, 1975. — 22p ; 4to.
Duration 12 1/2 min.
Unpriced

(B75-51073)

G — MALE VOICES
GDR — Psalms
Crawford, John
Psalm 98 : for men's chorus (TBB), accompanied by brass quintet
and piano, or by organ and piano alone / [by] John Crawford. —
New York ; [London] : Oxford University Press, 1971. — 15p ;
8vo.
Unpriced
Primary classification GE/NWXPNQDR

(B75-50083)

GDW — Songs, etc
Noble, Harold
A Welshman can't help singing = Mae'r Cymro'n canu heunydd :
chorus for male voices (TTBB) and piano / original English words
and music by Harold Noble ; y trosiad Cymraeg gan Urien
Wiliam. — London : Bosworth, 1975. — 8p ; 8vo.
Duration 2 1/2 min.
Unpriced

(B75-50508)

Rota, Nino
[The godfather, part 2. Love said goodbye. *arr].* Love said
goodbye / music by Nino Rota ; lyric by Larry Kusik ; arranged,
TTBB, by Harry Simeone. — New York : Famous Music ;
[London] : [Chappell], 1974. — 8p ; 8vo.
Unpriced

(B75-50082)

Sansom, Clive A
He's got the whole world / arranged for two-part singing by Clive
A. Sansom. — London : Studio Music, 1975. — 4p ; 8vo.
Unpriced

(B75-50509)

GDW/G/AYDK — Folk songs. Collections. Wales
Four Welsh songs / arranged for male voices and piano (or
orchestra) by Alun Hoddinott ; English versions by Rhiannon
Hoddinott. — London : Oxford University Press, 1975. — 22p ;
8vo.
Duration 10 min.
ISBN 0-19-343653-1 : £0.60

(B75-50510)

GE/NWXPNQDR — With brass & keyboard sextet. Psalms
Crawford, John
Psalm 98 : for men's chorus (TBB), accompanied by brass quintet
and piano, or by organ and piano alone / [by] John Crawford. —
New York ; [London] : Oxford University Press, 1971. — 15p ;
8vo.
Unpriced
Also classified at GDR

(B75-50083)

GE/NYLDW — With keyboard & percussion. Songs, etc
Sansom, Clive A
Tick-tock song : for SATB (or SA, SSA, TTB) with instrumental
accompaniment / words and music by Clive A. Sansom. —
London : Paterson, 1974. — 7p ; 8vo.
Duration 3 min.
Unpriced
Primary classification ENYLDW

(B75-50036)

GE/WNPDE — With trumpet septet. Religious cantatas
Lübeck, Vincent
Gott, wie dein Name, so ist auch dein Ruhm : Kantate für
dreistimmigen Männerchor, drei Trompeten und Basso continuo,
(Bläsersatz), Pauken (ad lib.) / [von] Vincent Lubeck ; aussetzung
des Basso continuo von Heinrich Ehmann. — Cassel ; London :
Bärenreiter, 1975. — 32p ; 8vo.
Unpriced

(B75-50511)

GEZDE/LF — Unaccompanied voices. Religious cantatas. Christmas
Roe, Betty
Merry be man : a Christmas sequence / [by] Betty Roe ; words by
Jacqueline Froom. — London : Thames, 1974. — 11p ; 8vo.
Unpriced
Primary classification FEZDE/LF

(B75-50499)

GEZDM — Unaccompanied voices. Hymns
Belcher, Supply
[Harmony of Maine. *Selections].* Deep North Spirituals, 1794 :
mixed or male voices in three and four parts / [by] Supply
Belcher ; revised and edited by Oliver Daniel. — New York ;
London : Peters, 1973. — 23p ; 8vo.
Unpriced
Primary classification EZDM

(B75-50058)

**GEZDM/AYT — Unaccompanied voices. Hymns. Collections. United
States**
Five American hymn tunes : for men's or mixed voices
unaccompanied / edited by Charles Edward Lindsley. — New
York ; [London] : Oxford University Press, 1975. — 11p ; 8vo.
Unpriced
Also classified at EZDM/AYT

(B75-50512)

GEZDP/LF — Unaccompanied voices. Carols. Christmas
Dinham, Kenneth J
Jesus, Jesus, rest your head : Southern Appalachian carol / arr.
[male voices] K.J. Dinham. — York : Banks, 1975. — 2p ; 8vo.
Unpriced

(B75-51074)

GEZDW — Unaccompanied voices. Songs, etc
Binkerd, Gordon
There is a garden in her face : TTB, unaccompanied / [by]
Gordon Binkerd ; words by Thomas Campion. — New York ;
[London] : Boosey and Hawkes, 1972. — 8p ; 8vo.
Unpriced

(B75-50513)

Clements, John
A young man's song : TTBB unacc. / music by John Clements ;
words by William Bell. — London : Oxford University Press,
1975. — 4p ; 8vo.
ISBN 0-19-341020-6 : £0.10

(B75-50514)

Nelson, Havelock
Peggy, my love : Uist boat song, traditional Scottish melody /
arranged for TTBB unaccompanied by Havelock Nelson ; words
by Sydney Bell from the Gaelic. — Sevenoaks : Elkin, 1975. —
8p ; 8vo.
£0.15

(B75-51075)

Noble, Harold
Heart's music : TTBB (unacc.) / [by] Harold Noble ; words from
Campion's 'Book of Ayres'. — York : Banks, 1973. — 4p ; 8vo.
Unpriced

(B75-50515)

Schubert, Franz
[Part-songs for men's voices. Selections]. Unaccompanied
part-songs for men's voices / by Franz Schubert ; edited by
Dietrich Berke. — Cassel ; London : Bärenreiter, 1973. — 32p ;
8vo.
£1.70
(B75-50084)

Zelter, Carl
Four songs for male voices / [by] Carl Zelter ; translation by Carl
Zytowski. — New York ; [London] : Boosey and Hawkes.
1 : Saint Paul ; text from I Timothy 5. — 1975. — 8p ; 8vo.
Unpriced
(B75-50516)
2 : Ephiphanias / poem by J.W. Goethe. — 1975. — 12p ; 8vo.
Unpriced
(B75-50517)

Zelter, Carl
Four songs for male voices / by Carl Zelter. — New York ;
[London] : Boosey and Hawkes.
3 & 4 : Master and journeyman ; and, Song of the flea / text by J.K.
Grubel and J.W. Goethe respectively. — 1975. — 6p ; 8vo.
Unpriced
(B75-50518)

GEZDW/G/AYFS — Unaccompanied voices. Folk songs. Collections.
Slovakia
Drei slowakische Volkslieder : für Männerchor / [von] Jan Cikker ;
deutsche Übersetzung, Kurt Honulka. — Cassel ; London :
Bärenreiter, 1974. — 24p ; 8vo.
£2.00
(B75-50085)

GEZDW/XC — Unaccompanied voices. Rounds
Beeson, Jack
Everyman's handyman : nine rounds and canons for men's
voices / [by] Jack Beeson ; receipts by Elizabeth W. Smith. —
New York ; [London] : Boosey and Hawkes, 1972. — 20p ; 8vo.
Unpriced
(B75-50519)

HY — SPEAKING CHORUS
HYE/M — With orchestra
Nono, Luigi
Epitaffio no. 1, 2 & 3 / [di] Luigi Nono. — Mainz : Ars Viva ;
[London] : [Schott], 1974. — 16p ; 4to.
Study score. — Contents: No.1: Espana en el corazon : studi per soprano
solo, baritono solo, coro parlato e strumenti su testi/ di Federico Garcia
Lorca e Pablo Neruda - No.2: Y su sangre ya viene cantando per flauto e
piccola orchestra (1952/53) - No.3: Memento : romance de la guardia civil
espanola, per voce recitante, cor parlato ed orchestra festo/ di Federico
Garcia Lorca (1952/53).
£11.60
(B75-50086)

HYE/NYDNQ — Speaker with wind, string, keyboard & percussion
sextets
Regner, Hermann
'Mit Musik'. 5 Gedichte von Ernst Jandl : für einen Sprecher und
Instrumente, (2 Trompeten in C-oder Klarinetten, Flöten,
Blockflöten-, Violoncello, Kontrabass, Schlagzeug und Klavier) /
[von] Hermann Regner. — Mainz ; London : Schott, 1975. — obl.
8vo.
Score (27p.) & 5 parts.
£3.50
(B75-51076)

HYE/QP — Speaker with piano
Wilcock, Frank
Six monologues for boys / with music by Frank Wilcock ; written
by Robert Rutherford. — Glasgow : Brown, Son and Ferguson,
1975. — 24p ; 4to.
Unpriced
(B75-50520)

J — VOICES IN UNISON
JDG/AY — Ordinary of the Mass. Collections
Sing the Mass : a new source-book of liturgical music for cantor,
choir and congregation / editorial board : Nicholas Kenyon, Colin
Atkinson, Michael Dawrey, Kevin Donovan, Gerard Fitzpatrick,
Jeremiah Threadgold, Harold Winstone. — London : Chapman,
1975. — xiii,229p ; 8vo.
ISBN 0-225-65984-0 : Unpriced
Also classified at JDGK/AY
(B75-50521)

JDGK/AY — Proper of the Mass. Collections
Sing the Mass : a new source-book of liturgical music for cantor,
choir and congregation / editorial board : Nicholas Kenyon, Colin
Atkinson, Michael Dawrey, Kevin Donovan, Gerard Fitzpatrick,
Jeremiah Threadgold, Harold Winstone. — London : Chapman,
1975. — xiii,229p ; 8vo.
ISBN 0-225-65984-0 : Unpriced
Primary classification JDG/AY
(B75-50521)

JDGS — Anglican liturgy. Communion
Shaw, Martin
[Anglican folk mass]. An Anglican folk mass : [unison] / [by]
Martin Shaw ; adapted to the text of Series 3 by Richard Graves.
— Wendover : Roberton, 1975. — 8vo.
Score (11p.) & congregational part. — The music for the Acclamations has
been freely adapted from the original 'Alternative Kyrie' for which Series 3
makes no call.
£0.30
(B75-51077)

JDH — Motets, Anthems, Hymns, etc
Clarke, Jeremiah
[Prince of Denmark's march. arr]. Let the earth resound ('Lobt
den Herrn der Welt') / [by Jeremiah Clarke] ; arranged as a
unison song with descant ad lib. and piano (or organ)
accompaniment by Willy Trapp ; adapted by Richard Graves ;
English words by Richard Graves ; based on German text by
Willy Trapp. — London : Bosworth, 1975. — 6p ; 8vo.
The music in this publication is here attributed to Henry Purcell ('... set to
Purcell's Trumpet Voluntary').
Unpriced
(B75-50522)

JDK/LP — Anthems. Harvest
Ferguson, Barry
Praise the Lord, O my soul : anthem for unison voices or SATB
and organ, suitable for Rogation, Harvest or general use / music
by Barry Ferguson ; text from Psalm 104. — Sevenoaks : Novello,
1975. — 4p ; 8vo.
£0.10
Also classified at DK/LP
(B75-50523)

JDM — Hymns
Schneider, Martin Gotthard
[Der Weg der Barmherzigkeit]. There's a road (which leads from
Jerusalem) : hymn / original words and music : Martin G.
Schneider ; English words : M.A. Baughen. — London :
Bosworth, 1975. — 3p ; 8vo.
Unpriced
(B75-50524)

JDM/AY — Hymns. Collections
Christ in competition / music by Edward Hughes ; words by Peter
Westmore ; additional music and lyrics by Russ David, Harry
Fisher and Will Reed ; songs selected and edited by Peter
Westmore and Will Reed. — London : Edwardian Music, 1975.
— 63p ; 8vo.
ISBN 0-551-05530-8 : Unpriced
(B75-51078)

From the beginning : [a collection of hymns]. — London : Galliard,
1975. — 34p ; 8vo.
ISBN 0-85249-306-1 : Unpriced
(B75-51079)

JDM/JS/AY — Hymns. Television. Collections
New hymns for young people : twelve hymns chosen from the
Southern Television network competition. — London :
Weinberger, 1975. — 20p ; 8vo.
£0.60
(B75-50087)

Sing a new song : twenty-three hymns and songs from Southern
Television Hymn Contest, 1975 / arrangements by Nigel Brooks.
— London : Weinberger, 1975. — 44p ; 8vo.
£0.85
(B75-50525)

JDP/AY — Carols. Collections
Carter, Sydney
Green print for song : a book of carols / by Sydney Carter ; with
illuminations by Robert Reid. — London : Galliard, 1974. —
90p : ill ; 8vo.
ISBN 0-85249-284-7 : Unpriced
(B75-50088)

JDP/LF — Carols. Christmas
Ager, Laurence
Mary and Joseph : a Christmas calypso, [unison] / [by] Laurence
Ager ; words by Kenneth Allen. — London : Ashdown, 1975. —
4p ; 8vo.
£0.08
(B75-51080)

Graves, Richard
Twentieth century carol : unison with optional 2nd part / words
and music by Richard Graves. — London : Bosworth, 1975. —
7p ; 8vo.
Unpriced
(B75-51081)

Rocherolle, Eugenie R
How can it be? : for unison, SA or SAB chorus and piano / words and music by Eugenie R. Rocherolle. — New York : Warner ; London : Blossom, 1975. — 8p ; 8vo.
Duration 2 1/2 min.
Unpriced
Primary classification DP/LF

JDP/LF/AY — Carols. Christmas. Collections
Chappell, Herbert
Carols for today : two-part / [by] Herbert Chappell. — London : Chappell, 1974. — 55p ; 8vo.
A few of the carols are for voices in two parts.
Unpriced

(B75-50089)

JDP/LFP — Carols. Epiphany
Graves, Richard
Three journeys : a carol / words and music by Richard Graves. — Sevenoaks : Novello, 1975. — 4p ; 8vo.
£0.10
Also classified at DP/LFP

(B75-50526)

JDP/LL — Carols. Easter
Davis, Katherine Kennacott
A wonderful thing : Easter carol, unison, piano (flute hand bells optional) / words and music by Katherine K. Davis. — New York : Warner ; [London] : Blossom, 1972. — 8p ; 8vo.
Unpriced

(B75-50090)

JDR — Psalms
Mann, Michael A
Two psalms : unison / [by] Michael A. Mann. — Sydney ; London : Chappell, 1971. — 4p ; 8vo.
Unpriced

(B75-51082)

Walker, Christopher
Cry out with joy : unison / [by] Christopher Walker ; text : Psalm 99. — London : Oxford University Press, 1975. — 7p ; 8vo.
ISBN 0-19-351121-5 : Unpriced

(B75-51083)

JDTF — Lord's Prayer
Bates, Tom
The Lord's Prayer : SATB with alternative version for unison voices / [by] Tom Bates. — York : Banks, 1975. — 2p ; 8vo.
Unpriced
Primary classification EZDTF

(B75-50471)

Merbecke, John
[The Booke of Common Praier noted. The Lord's Praier. *arr*]. The Lord's Prayer : for unison choir or solo voice and piano or organ / [by] John Merbecke ; arranged by Everett Jay Hilty. — New York ; [London] : Oxford University Press, 1971. — 3p ; 8vo.
Unpriced

(B75-51084)

JDW — Songs, etc
Fraser, Shena
[Full fathom five. Sea Lullaby]. Sea lullaby : unison or soprano solo / [by] Shena Fraser ; words by Eugene Field. — London : Thames, 1975. — 4p ; 8vo.
Unpriced
Also classified at KFLDW

(B75-50527)

JDW/AY — Songs, etc. Collections
Liedermagazin : für die Sekundarstufen / zusammengestellt und kommentiert von Werner Breckoff ... [et al.]. — London : Cassel : Bärenreiter, 1975. — 255p ; 8vo.
Unpriced

(B75-50528)

Sociable songs / compiled by Anne Mendoza and Pat Shaw. — London : Oxford University Press.
Book 3, part 1 : for unison or part-singing with optional instrumental parts. — 1975. — 4to & 8vo.
Full ed. (2,29p.) & melody ed. (20p.).
ISBN 0-19-330590-9 : Unpriced

(B75-51085)

Book 3, part 2 : for unison or part-singing with optional instrumental parts. — 1975. — 4to & 8vo.
Full ed. (2,29p.) & melody ed. (20p.).
ISBN 0-19-330592-5 : Unpriced

(B75-51086)

JDW/KM/AY — National songs. Collections
National anthems of the world / edited by Martin Shaw, Henry Coleman and T.M. Cartledge. — 4th and revised ed. — Poole : Blandford Press, 1975. — viii,477p ; 4to.
Includes a list of national days.
ISBN 0-7137-0679-1 : £5.80

(B75-50529)

JDX — Secular cantatas
Wakeman, Rick
[The myths and legends of King Arthur and the Knights of the Round Table. *Vocal score*]. The myths and legends of King Arthur and the Knights of the Round Table : cantata / music and lyrics by Rick Wakeman ; transcribed for pianoforte by Jeff Muston. — London : Rondor Music, 1975. — 68p ; 4to.
Unpriced

(B75-51087)

JE/TSDW/G/AY — With guitar. Folk songs. Collections
[**Jon** Raven, nos 1-8]. Contemporary life : eight folk-songs for voices and guitar / from the collection compiled by Jon Raven. — London : Oxford University Press, 1974. — 19p ; 8vo.
ISBN 0-19-330627-1 : £0.35

(B75-50091)

Sounds like folk. — London : E.F.D.S.
No.4 : Victorian tear jerkers / music arranged by Karen Harris. — 1974. — 29p ; 8vo.
Unpriced

(B75-50092)

Sounds like folk. — London : EFDS.
No.5 : Songs of faith and feeling. — 1974. — 24p ; 8vo. — Unpriced

(B75-50093)

[**Turpin** hero, nos. 9-16]. Flight, fight and romance : eight folk songs for voices and guitar / from the collection compiled by Jon Raven. — London : Oxford University Press, 1974. — 19p ; 8vo.
ISBN 0-19-330628-x : £0.35

(B75-50094)

[**Turpin** hero, nos. 17-21]. Good earth : five folk songs for voices and guitar / from the collection compiled by Jon Raven. — London : Oxford University Press, 1974. — 15p ; 8vo.
ISBN 0-19-330629-8 : £0.35

(B75-50095)

[**Turpin** hero, nos. 22-30]. Bravado and travellers all : nine folk songs for voices and guitar / from the collection compiled by Jon Raven. — London : Oxford University Press, 1974. — 19p ; 8vo.
ISBN 0-19-330630-1 : £0.35

(B75-50096)

JE/TSDW/G/AYD — With guitar. Folk songs. Collections. England
The **crystal** spring : English folk songs / collected by Cecil Sharp ; edited by Maud Karpeles. — London : Oxford University Press.
Book 1. — 1975. — [8],77p ; 8vo.
ISBN 0-19-330516-x : Unpriced

(B75-51088)

Book 2. — 1975. — 79p ; 8vo.
ISBN 0-19-330517-8 : Unpriced

(B75-51089)

JE/TSDW/GM/AYD — With guitar. Working songs. Collections. England
The **iron** man : English occupational songs / edited by Michael Dawney. — London : Galliard : Stainer and Bell, 1974. — 42p ; obl. 8vo.
ISBN 0-85249-294-4 : Unpriced

(B75-50097)

JE/UMDX — With wind band. Secular cantatas
Mailman, Martin
Shouts, hymns and praises. Op.52 : for wind band with vocal part for the audience / [by] Martin Mailman ; text by Richard B. Sale. — Oceanside ; [London] : Boosey and Hawkes, 1975. — 4to.
Score (44p.) & 75 parts. — Duration 12 min.
Unpriced

(B75-51090)

JEZDTF — Unaccompanied voices. Lord's Prayer
Rose, Gregory
The Camrose Lord's Prayer : SATB with optional accompaniment / [by] Gregory Rose. — London : Boosey and Hawkes, 1975. — 8vo.
Score (3p.) & congregational card.
£0.10
Primary classification EZDTF

(B75-50472)

JFDM — Female voices, Children's voices. Hymns
Binkerd, Gordon
Song of praise and prayer : children's hymn, unison, with organ or piano accompaniment / [by] Gordon Binkerd ; poem by William Cowper. — New York ; [London] : Boosey and Hawkes, 1972. — 6p ; 8vo.
Unpriced

(B75-50530)

JFDM/AY — Female voices, Children's voices, Hymns. Collections
Sing it in the morning : [hymns] / selected by Geoffrey Clifton. — Teachers' ed. — London : Nelson, 1975. — 112p ; 8vo.
ISBN 0-17-428009-2 : Unpriced

(B75-50531)

Sing hosanna : hymns / selected and compiled by Harold Clarke,
[et al.]. — Edinburgh : Holmes McDougall, 1974. — 4to & 8vo.
Music ed. (138p.) & Melody ed. (109p.). — The music ed. contains a 7 inch
33 1/3 r.p.m. record of selected hymns sung by the school children of a
primary school in Sunderland.
ISBN 0-7157-0934-8 : £3.80

(B75-51091)

JFDP — Female voices, Children's voices. Carols
Coombes, Douglas
Carols of the elements : for unison voices, optional 2 part melodic
instruments, percussion, and piano / music by Douglas Coombes ;
words by John Emlyn Edwards. — Clifton (28 Knolls Way,
Clifton, Beds.) : Lindsay Music, 1973. — 11p ; 8vo.
ISBN 0-85957-004-5 : £0.25

(B75-50532)

JFDP/LF — Female voices, Children's voices. Carols. Christmas
Parfrey, Raymond
Here on a bed of straw : carol for unison voices, SAB or SATB /
[by] Raymond Parfrey ; words by Mary Dawson. — London :
Thames, 1975. — 2p ; 8vo.
Unpriced
Also classified at EZDP/LF

(B75-50533)

JFDW — Female voices, Children's voices. Songs, etc
Davies, Laurence Hector
Lovely Scouse song : unison modern comedy folk song, with
chorus, words and music / by Laurence H. Davies. — London :
Ashdown, 1975. — 4p ; 8vo.
£0.07

(B75-50534)

Deacon, Helen
Rabbits : unison song / music by Helen Deacon, words anon. —
Wendover : Roberton, 1975. — 3p ; 8vo.
£0.10

(B75-51092)

Gillies, Douglas
Tinga layo : West Indian song / arranged and adapted, unison
and piano, with optional recorder and percussion by Douglas
Gillies ; words by D.G. — London : Oxford University Press,
1975. — 8p ; 8vo.
ISBN 0-19-342051-1 : Unpriced

(B75-51093)

Parke, Dorothy
By winding roads : fifteen unison songs of the Irish countryside /
music by Dorothy Parke ; words by John Irvine. — Wendover :
Roberton, 1975. — 24p ; 8vo.
£1.00

(B75-51094)

JFDW — Female voices. Children's voices. Songs, etc
Reaks, Brian
As fit as a fiddle / by Brian Reaks. — London : British and
Continental.
Book 2 : Six health education songs for younger children. — 1974. — 9p ;
4to. —
Unpriced

(B75-50098)

**JFDW/AY — Female voices, Children's voices. Songs, etc.
Collections**
Sing, children, sing : songs, dances and singing games of many
lands and peoples / compiled, edited and arranged by Carl S.
Miller ; introduction by Leonard Bernstein. — New York ;
[London] : Chappell, 1972. — 72p ; 4to.
Unpriced

(B75-51095)

**JFDW/G/AYDK — Female voices, Children's voices. Folk songs.
Collections. Wales**
Hei dyma ni : a chaneuon eraill i'r plant lleiaf / wedi eu trefnu gan
E. Olwen Jones. — Llandybie : Christopher Davies, 1975. — 48p ;
obl.8vo.
Unpriced

(B75-50535)

JFDW/GR — Female voices, Children's voices. Songs, etc. Activities
Gray, Vera
Knives and forks and spoons : 20 songs with rhymes / by Vera
Gray. — Potton (24 Royston St., Potton) : Lindsay Music, 1975.
— 17p ; 4to.
ISBN 0-85957-006-1 : £0.55

(B75-50536)

**JFE/LNRPXDW — Female voices, Children's voices. With four
instruments & percussion. Songs, etc**
Pehkonen, Elis
Who killed Lawless Lean? : for voices, 4 melody instruments,
percussion and piano / music, Elis Pehkonen ; text, Stevie Smith.
— London : Universal, 1975. — 9p ; obl.8vo.
Unpriced

(B75-51096)

**JFE/NYDSDX — Female voices, Children's voices. With recorder,
strings, keyboard & percussion. Secular cantatas**
A festival for autumn : for dramatic presentation or concert
performance, for voices, recorder, guitar, piano and percussion /
music compiled by Anne Mendoza. — Sevenoaks : Novello, 1975.
— 24p ; 4to.
£0.50

(B75-50537)

**JFE/NYEDX — Female voices, Children's voices. With wind, strings
& percussion. Secular cantatas**
Blyton, Carey
Konrad of the mountains : a pageant for voice and instruments /
music by Carey Blyton ; libretto by Peter Porter. — Croydon :
Belwin-Mills, 1975. — 33p ; 8vo.
Unpriced

(B75-50538)

**JFE/NYFSDW — Female voices, Children's voices. With recorders,
keyboard & percussion. Songs, etc**
Bonsor, Brian
Hurry, little pony : Spanish traditional song / arranged for unison
voices, recorders, percussion and piano, with optional violin and
optional cello by Brian Bonsor ; words by Elizabeth Barnard. —
London : Oxford University Press, 1975. — 4to.
Score (8p.) & 4 parts. — The first and second descant recorder and treble
recorder parts, the soprano and alto glockenspiel, chime bar and sleigh bell
parts, and the violin and cello parts are printed severally in score.
ISBN 0-19-344836-x : Unpriced

(B75-51097)

**JFE/NYFSRDW — Female voices, Children's voices with descant
recorder, keyboard & percussion. Songs, etc**
Burnett, Michael
Songs for Naomi : unison voices, glockenspiel and/or chime bars,
xylophone, descant recorder, triangle, tambourine, wood blocks,
piano (one stave) / music Michael Burnett ; words R.C. Scriven.
— Chesham : Ricordi, 1974. — 16p ; 4to.
Unpriced

(B75-50099)

**JFE/NYHDP/LF/AYB — Female voices, Children's voices, with
wind & percussion. Carols. Christmas. Collections.
Europe**
Six Christmas carols : six easy carols from five countries, for easy
wind and percussion / arranged by Sybil Bell. — Chesham :
Ricordi, 1975. — 11p ; 8vo.
Unpriced

(B75-51098)

**JFE/NYJDW/AY — Female voices, Children's voices. With strings
& percussion. Songs, etc. Collections**
Apusskidu : songs for children, with piano accompaniments, with
chords for guitar and with parts for descant recorders,
glockenspiel, chime bars and percussion / songs chosen by
Beatrice Harrop. — London : Black, 1975. — 96p ; obl. 4to.
ISBN 0-7136-1553-2 : Unpriced

(B75-50539)

**JFE/NYLDE/LF — Female voices, Children's voices. With keyboard
& percussion. Religious cantatas. Christmas**
Coombes, Douglas
Zalzabar : a Christmas cantata for children, music [for voices,
melodic instrument, percussion & piano] / by Douglas Coombes ;
libretto by John Emlyn Edwards. — Clifton (28 Knolls Way,
Clifton, Beds.) : Lindsay Music, 1972. — obl.4to & 4to.
Pupils' book (16p.) & teachers' book (15p.).
£0.49

(B75-50540)

**JFE/NYLDW — Female voices, Children's voices. With keyboard &
percussion. Songs, etc**
Coombes, Douglas
Seven space songs : music [for voices, melodic instruments,
percussion and piano] / by Douglas Coombes ; words by John
Emlyn Edwards. — Clifton (28 Knolls Way, Clifton, Beds.) :
Lindsay Music, 1973. — 15p ; 4to.
£0.58

(B75-50541)

JFE/NYLDX — Female voices, Children's voices. With keyboard & percussion. Secular cantatas
Tomlinson, Geoffrey
Creature conforts : a fantasy for voices and percussion / music by Geoffrey Tomlinson ; words by E.V. Rieu. — London : Boosey and Hawkes, 1975. — 4to.
Score (16p.) Vocal score (12p.) & 7 parts.
2.50
(B75-50542)

JFE/TSDW/AY — Female voices, Children's voices with guitar. Songs. Collections
Our chalet song book. — Adelboden : Our Chalet Committee, 1974. — 95p ; 8vo.
The Our Chalet Committee is associated with the Girl Guide movement.
Unpriced
(B75-50100)

JFE/XMDW/AY — Female voices, Children's voices. With percussion band. Songs, etc. Collections
Tommy Thumb : ten songs for young singers and players, for unison voices with tuned and untuned percussion (and guitar symbols) / arranged by Jean Maughan. — London : Oxford University Press, 1974. — 21p ; obl.8vo.
ISBN 0-19-330558-5 : £0.65
(B75-50101)

JFE/YBPN — Female voices, Children's voices. With balloon & pin ensemble
Bedford, David
Balloonmusic 1 : for any number of players from 2 to 1000 each with 2 balloons, a pin and their voices / [by] David Bedford. — London : Universal, 1975. — s.sh.fol ; 8vo.
Duration 4 1/2 min.
Unpriced
(B75-50543)

JFEZDW/JS — Unaccompanied female voices, children's voices. Television songs
Huw Jones, Sheila
Caneuon Lili Lon / [gan] Sheila Huw Jones [a] Maimie Noel Jones. — Abertawe : Christopher Davies, 1975. — [9],56p ; 4to.
ISBN 0-7154-0167-x : £0.90
(B75-51099)

JFLDP/LF — Treble voices. Carols. Christmas
Walters, Edmund
The cuckoo carol : a traditional Czech carol / arranged for treble voices and piano by Edmund Walters; words translated from the Czech by Percy Dearmer. — London : Boosey and Hawkes, 1975. — 4p ; 8vo.
£0.10
(B75-51100)

JGHE/WNQDH — Tenor voices. With brass sextet. Motets, Anthems, Hymns, etc
Hammerschmidt, Andreas
[Kirchen - und Tafelmusik, no.21]. Gelobet seist du, Jesu Christ : Choralkonzert für Tenor (einstimmigen Chor), zwei Trompeten, vier Posaunen und Basso continuo (ad lib) / [von] Andreas Hammerschmidt ; aussetzung des Basso continuo, Heinrich Ehmann. — Cassel ; London : Bärenreiter, 1974. — 12p ; 8vo.
Unpriced
(B75-50544)

JN — SINGLE VOICES IN COMBINATION
JNCE/MDX — Vocal quartet. With orchestra. Secular cantatas
Miroglio, Francis
Tremplins : voices and orchestra / [by] Francis Miroglio ; text by Jacques Dupin. — London : Universal, 1975. — xiii,2-71p ; fol.
Unpriced
(B75-50545)

JNEDH — Vocal duets. Motets, Anthems, Hymns, etc
Schein, Johann Hermann
[Opella nova. Tl. 1,2. Selections]. Sechs Choral konzerte : für zwei gleiche Stimmen und Basso continuo / von Johann Hermann Schein ; herausgegeben von Ludwig Doormann. — Cassel ; London : Bärenreiter, 1974. — 4to.
Score (24p.) & part.
£2.00
(B75-50102)

JNFEDW — Female voice, Child's voice duets. Songs, etc
Berthold, G
Duetto buffo di due gatti = Comic duet for two cats / attributed to Rossini ; edited by Douglas Coombes. — Clifton (28 Knolls Way, Clifton, Beds.) : Lindsay Music, 1974. — 6p ; 8vo.
Sometimes attributed to Rossini, but probably the work of Robert Lucas Pearsall, published under the name of G. Berthold in 1823.
ISBN 0-85957-005-3 : £0.15
(B75-50546)

JNFVEDH/LF — Middle voice duets. Motets, Anthems, Hymns, etc. Christmas
Grimm, Heinrich
[Prodromus musicae ecclesiasticae. Selections]. Hosianna dem Sohne David, und, Wohlauf wohlauf zu dieser Frist : zwei kleine Weihnachtskonzert, für zwei mittlere Stimmen und Basso continuo / [von] Heinrich Grimm ; herausgegeben von Hermann Lorenzen. — Cassel ; London : Bärenreiter, 1974. — 4to.
Score (12p.) & part.
£1.20
(B75-50103)

JNGHE/MDW — Tenor voice duet with orchestra. Songs, etc
Fortner, Wolfgang
Machaut-Balladen : für Gesang und Orchester / [von] Wolfgang Fortner ; [text von] Guillaume de Marchaut. — Mainz ; London : Schott, 1975. — 69p ; 4to.
Study score.
£7.30
Also classified at KGHE/MDW
(B75-51101)

K — VOCAL SOLOS
K/AFH — Vocalises
Vaccai, Nicolo
[Metodo practico di canto italiano]. Practical method of Italian singing / [by] Nicola Vaccai ; edited with introduction, translation and notes by John Glenn Paton. — New ed. — New York ; London : Schirmer, 1975. — 8vo.
For soprano or tenor (42p.), for mezzo-soprano (alto) or baritone (42p.), for high soprano (42p.).
Unpriced
(B75-50547)

KDW — SONGS, ETC. SOLOS
Antoniou, Theodore
[Klima tis apussias. Vocal score].
[Klimatis apussias. Vocal score]. Klima tis apussias = Stimmung der Abwesenheit = Sense of absence : for voice and piano / by Theodore Antoniou ; poem by Odysseas Elytis. — Cassel ; London : Bärenreiter, 1973. — 7p ; fol.
Duration 10 min.
£2.40
(B75-50104)

Arne, Thomas Augustine
[Songs. Selections : arr]. Selected songs / [by] Thomas Augustine Arne ; arranged and edited by Robert Barclay Wilson. — London : Cramer, 1975. — 32p ; 4to.
The editor has also included two songs by Michael Arne.
Unpriced
(B75-50548)

Berlin, Irving
[Songs. Selections : arr]. The golden years of Irving Berlin : songs. — London : Chappell, 1975. — 128p ; 4to.
Unpriced
(B75-51102)

Bernstein, Leonard
[Songs. Selections]. An album of songs / [by] Leonard Bernstein. — New York ; London : Schirmer, 1974. — 105p ; 4to.
Unpriced
(B75-50549)

Bernstein, Leonard
[Candide. Selections: arr]. Candide : vocal selections / music by Leonard Bernstein ; lyrics by Richard Wilbur; with additional lyrics by Stephen Sondheim and John Latouche. — New York ; London : Schirmer, 1974. — 44p ; 4to.
Unpriced
(B75-50550)

Bridge, Frank
[Songs. Selections]. Four songs / by Frank Bridge ; with an introduction by Peter Pirie. — London : Galliard : Stainer and Bell, 1974. — iv,28p ; 8vo.
Contents: Day after day (Tagore) - Speak to me my love! (Tagore) - Dweller in my deathless dreams (Tagore) - Journey's end (Wolfe).
ISBN 0-85249-319-3 : Unpriced
(B75-50105)

Butterworth, George
[Songs. Selections]. Folk songs from Sussex and other songs / by George Butterworth ; with an introduction by Peter Pirie. — London : Galliard, 1974. — iii,46p ; 8vo.
ISBN 0-85249-332-0 : Unpriced
Also classified at KDW/G/AYDCR
(B75-50551)

Butterworth, George
Eleven songs from 'A Shropshire Lad' / by George Butterworth ; with an introduction by Peter Pirie. — London : Galliard, 1974. — iii,46p ; 8vo.
ISBN 0-85249-333-9 : Unpriced
(B75-50552)

Carter, Elliott
Three poems of Robert Frost : for voice and piano / [by] Elliott Carter. — New York ; London : Associated Music, 1975. — 12p ; 4to.
Contents: Dust of snow - The rose family - The line-gang.
£1.30
                                                                                                    (B75-51103)

Chappell, Herbert
[The adventures of Paddington Bear. Paddington Bear. *arr*].
Paddington Bear : song / music by Herbert Chappell ; words by Brenda Johnson. — London : Music Sales, 1974. — 4p ; 4to.
£0.25
                                                                                                    (B75-50106)

Florilegium cantionum latinarum : melodiae veteres ad cantum clavibus / a Jan Novak ; Fasc. 2. — Padua : Zanibon ; [London] : [Hinrichsen].
With a separate leaflet bearing the words of the songs.
Carmina profana. — 1974. — 2,19p ; 4to.
Unpriced
                                                                                                    (B75-50107)

Foster, Stephen
[Songs. *Selections*]. Stephen Foster song book : original sheet music of 40 songs / selected with introduction and notes by Richard Jackson. — New York : Dover ; [London] : [Constable], 1974. — ix,181p ; 4to.
£2.40
                                                                                                    (B75-50553)

Ireland, John
[Songs. *Selections*]. The land of lost content and other songs / [by] John Ireland ; with an introduction by John Longmire. — London : Stainer and Bell, 1975. — v,40p ; 8vo.
ISBN 0-85249-320-7 : Unpriced
                                                                                                    (B75-51104)

Joplin, Scott
[Treemonisha. *Selections: arr*]. Treemonisha / [by] Scott Joplin ; vocal selection edited by Vera Brodsky Lawrence. — New York : Fanfare Press : Chappell ; [London] : [Chappell], 1975. — 95p : ill, port ; 4to.
Unpriced
                                                                                                    (B75-51105)

Kennedy, John Brodbin
April and May : two songs / by John Brodbin Kennedy ; poem by Samuel Menashe. — New York ; London : Boosey and Hawkes, 1972. — 8p ; 4to.
Unpriced
                                                                                                    (B75-51106)

Kern, Jerome
[Songs. *Selections*]. The best of Jerome Kern. — London : Chappell, 1975. — 83p ; 4to.
Unpriced
                                                                                                    (B75-50554)

Loesser, Frank
[Hans Christian Andersen. *Selections: arr*]. Hans Andersen : souvenir song book / words and music by Frank Loesser. — London : Edwin H. Morris, 1975. — 40p ; 4to.
                                                                                                    (B75-50108)

Newley, Anthony
[Quilp. *Selections : arr*]. Quilp : a musical adaptation of Charles Dickens 'The old curiosity shop' / music and lyrics of seven selected songs by Anthony Newley. — New York ; [London] : Edwin H. Morris, 1975. — 7 no ; 4to.
The songs enclosed separately in a cover. — Contents: Quilp - Somewhere - Happiness pie - The sport of kings - Every dog has his day - When a felon needs a friend - Love has the longest memory.
Unpriced
                                                                                                    (B75-51107)

Noble, Harold
The road of evening : song with piano accompaniment / music by Harold Noble ; words by Walter de la Mare. — South Croydon : Lengnick, 1975. — 5p ; 4to.
£0.35
                                                                                                    (B75-50555)

Novak, Jan
[Schola cantans. *Vocal score*]. Schola cantans : graves auctores latini, leviter decantandi, cantus ad claves / [de] Jan Novak. — Padua : Zanibon ; [london] : [Hinrichsen], 1974. — 47p ; 4to.
Unpriced
                                                                                                    (B75-50109)

Plumstead, Mary
Ha'nacker Mill : song / [by] Mary Plumstead ; words by Hilaire Belloc. — Wendover : Roberton, 1975. — 7p ; 4to.
Unpriced
                                                                                                    (B75-50556)

Purcell, Henry
If music be the food of love (3rd setting). Z.379C / [by] Henry Purcell ; edited by Gwilym Beechey ; words by Henry Heveningham. — London : Oxford University Press, 1974. — 8p ; 4to.
Duration 5 min.
ISBN 0-19-345707-5 : £0.50
                                                                                                    (B75-50557)

Rodgers, Richard
[Musical plays. *Selections: arr*]. Rogers and Hammerstein showtime. — London : Williamson Music.
Vol.4. — 1975. — 72p ; 4to. —
Unpriced
                                                                                                    (B75-50110)

Rodgers, Richard
[Musical plays. *Selections: arr*]. Rogers and Hammerstein 'Showtime'. — London : Williamson.
M784.3061.
Vol.2. — 1975. — 72p : ill ; 4to.
Unpriced
                                                                                                    (B75-50111)

Rodgers, Richard
[Musical plays. *Selections: arr*].
[Musical plays. Selections. *arr*]. Rogers and Hammerstein 'Showtime'. — London : Williamson.
M784.3061.
Vol.1. — 1975. — 72p : ill ; 4to.
Unpriced
                                                                                                    (B75-50112)

Rorem, Ned
[Songs. *Selections*]. 14 songs on American poetry : voice and piano / [by] Ned Rorem. — New York ; London : Peters, 1975. — 37p ; 4to.
Unpriced
                                                                                                    (B75-50558)

Rorem, Ned
Absalom / [by] Ned Rorem ; text by Paul Goodman. — New York ; [London] : Boosey and Hawkes, 1972. — 4p ; 4to.
Unpriced
                                                                                                    (B75-51108)

Rorem, Ned
Jack L'Eventreur / [by] Ned Rorem ; text by Mary Laure. — New York ; [London] : Boosey and Hawkes, 1972. — 4p ; 4to.
Unpriced
                                                                                                    (B75-51109)

Rorem, Ned
Love in a life / [by] Ned Rorem ; text by Robert Browning. — New York ; [London] : Boosey and Hawkes, 1972. — 5p ; 4to.
Unpriced
                                                                                                    (B75-51110)

Rorem, Ned
To a young girl / [by] Ned Rorem ; poem by W.B. Yeats. — New York ; [London] : Boosey and Hawkes, 1972. — 4p ; 4to.
Unpriced
                                                                                                    (B75-51111)

Rota, Nino
[The godfather, part 2. *Selections: arr*]. The godfather, part 2 / [by] Nino Rota ; souvenir song album, revisedu, including 3 songs and photos. — New York : Charles Hansen ; [London] : [Chappell], 1974. — 64p : ill. ; 4to.
Unpriced
                                                                                                    (B75-50113)

Rubbra, Edmund
Fly, envious time. Op.148 : song with piano accompaniment / [by] Edmund Rubbra ; words by Milton. — South Croydon : Lengnick, 1975. — 4p ; 4to.
£0.35
                                                                                                    (B75-51112)

Sondheim, Stephen
[A little night music. *Selections : arr*]. A little night music : souvenir song folio / music and lyrics by Stephen Sondheim. — London : Chappell, 1975. — 49p ; 4to.
Unpriced
                                                                                                    (B75-50559)

Strauss, Johann, b.1825
[Operettas. *Selections : arr*]. The Johann Strauss song book : containing twelve songs for solo voice and piano / lyrics by Geoffrey Dunn and others, new piano arrangements by Ronald Hanmer. — London : Weinberger, 1975. — 56p ; 4to.
Unpriced
                                                                                                    (B75-51113)

Swann, Donald
[Songs. *Selections*]. The Michael Flanders and Donald Swann song book / music by Donald Swann ; words by Michael Flanders. — London : Chappell, 1974. — 59p ; 4to.
Unpriced

(B75-50114)

KDW/AY — Songs, etc. Collections
Songs from the golden years of Gracie Fields. — London : Chappell, 1975. — 51p ; 4to.
Unpriced

(B75-51114)

KDW/G/AYDCR — Folk songs. Collections. Sussex
Butterworth, George
[Songs. *Selections*]. Folk songs from Sussex and other songs / by George Butterworth ; with an introduction by Peter Pirie. — London : Galliard, 1974. — iii,46p ; 8vo.
ISBN 0-85249-332-0 : Unpriced
Primary classification KDW

(B75-50551)

KDW/GB/AY — Popular songs. Collections
Tin Pan Alley : a pictorial history (1919-1939) with complete words and music of forty songs / selected and edited by Ian Whitcomb. — London : EMI Music, 1975. — 251p ; 4to.
£2.95

(B75-50560)

KDW/GB/AY(XHS64) — Popular songs. Collections, 1837-1901
Just a song at twilight : the second parlour song book / edited and introduced by Michael R. Turner and Antony Miall. — London : Michael Joseph, 1975. — 288p ; 8vo.
ISBN 0-7181-1339-x : £8.50

(B75-51115)

KDW/GB/AYC(XMP5) — Popular songs. Collections. Great Britain, 1914-1918
Mud songs and Blighty : a scarpbook of the first World War / compiled by Colin Walsh. — London : Hutchinson : EMI, 1975. — 176p ; 4to.
ISBN 0-09-124421-8 : £3.50

(B75-51116)

KDW/GB/AYT(XKF41) — Popular songs. United States. Collections, 1866-1906
Show songs from 'The black crook' to 'The red mill' : original sheet music for 60 songs from 50 shows, 1866-1906 / edited by Stanley Appelbaum. — New York : Dover ; London : Constable, 1974. — li,279p ; 4to.
£4.20

(B75-51117)

KDW/JR — Songs, etc. Films
Loewe, Frederick
[The little prince. Little prince. *arr*]. Little prince : song / music by Frederick Loewe ; words by Alan Jay Lerner. — London : Famous Chappell, 1974. — 5p ; 4to.
Unpriced

(B75-51118)

KDW/JR/AY — Film songs. Collections
That's entertainment : a musical and pictorial history of the MGM musical. — London : Chappell, 1974. — 164p ; 4to.
Unpriced

(B75-50115)

KDW/JS — Songs. Television
Batt, Mike
[Songs. *Selections: arr*]. The giant Wombles music book : containing words and music of 32 compositions / by Mike Batt. — London : Chappell, 1975. — 120p ; 4to.
The Wombles is a BBC TV series.
Unpriced

(B75-50561)

KDW/JS/AY — Songs, etc. Television. Collections
Twenty great TV themes / arranged for piano solo, including six songs with piano accompaniment. — London : Essex Music, 1975. — 76p ; 4to.
Unpriced
Primary classification QPK/JS/AY

(B75-50721)

KDW/JV/AY — Songs, etc. Music hall. Collections
Music hall song book : a collection of 45 of the best songs from 1890-1920 / edited and introduced by Peter Gammond. — Newton Abbott : David & Charles ; London : EMI, 1975. — 160p ; 8vo.
With bibliography and discography of recordings by original artists available on LP.
ISBN 0-7153-7115-0 : £4.50

(B75-51119)

KDW/LC — Spirituals
Burt, James
Swing low, sweet chariot / arr. James Burt. — London : Chappell, 1975. — 4p ; 4to.
Unpriced

(B75-50562)

KDW/LF — Songs, etc. Christmas
Parker, Jim
[Follow the star. *Selections: arr*]. Follow the star : song album from a new musical for Christmas / music by Jim Parker ; book and lyrics by Wally K. Daly. — London : Chappell, 1975. — 40p ; 4to.
Unpriced

(B75-51120)

KDW/LF/AY — Songs, etc. Christmas. Collections
Christmas presentation album : [songs]. — London : Chappell, 1975. — 144p ; 4to.
Unpriced

(B75-51121)

KE — VOCAL SOLOS WITH ACCOMPANIMENT OTHER THAN KEYBOARD
KE/MRDW — With chamber orchestra. Songs, etc
Antoniou, Theodore
Klima tis apussias = Stimmung der Abwesenheit = Sense of absence : for voice and chamber orchestra / by Theodore Antoniou ; poem by Odysseas Elytis. — Cassel ; London : Bärenreiter, 1973. — 24p ; 4to.
Duration 10 min. — Study score.
£2.40

(B75-50116)

KE/STNSDW/AYD — With viol quartet. Songs, etc. Collections. England
Musica Britannica : a national collection of music. — 2nd revised ed. — London : Stainer and Bell.
Vol.22 : Consort songs / transcribed and edited by Philip Brett. — 1974. — xxi,193p ; fol.
Unpriced
Primary classification C/AYD

(B75-50006)

KE/TSDW/AY — With guitar. Songs, etc. Collections
Four centuries of song, from the troubadour to the Elizabethan age : for voice and guitar / transcribed from the original lute tablatures and manuscripts with arrangements and editing by Joseph Iadone ; text underlay by Norma Verrilli Iadone ; English text edited by Hans Tischler ; English version of the French, German and Italian texts by Hans Tischler ; English version of the Spanish texts by Juan Orrego-Salas. — New York ; London : Associated Music, 1974. — iii,43p ; 4to.
Unpriced

(B75-50563)

KE/TSDW/AYDB — With guitar. Songs, etc. Collections. London
Cockney ding dong / chosen and illustrated by Charles Keeping. — Harmondsworth : Kestrel Books ; London : EMI, 1975. — 190p ; 29cm.
ISBN 0-7226-5061-2 : £3.95

(B75-51122)

KE/TSDW/G/AY — With guitar. Folk songs. Collections
Jerry Silverman's folk song encyclopaedia : with over 1,000 favorite songs arranged for voice and guitar / edited by Beverley Tillett. — New York ; [London] : Chappell.
Vol.1. — 1975. — 431p ; 4to.
Unpriced

(B75-50564)

Vol.2. — 1975. — 431p ; 4to.
Unpriced

(B75-50565)

KE/TSDW/G/AYH — With guitar. Folk songs. Collections. France
Trois chansons tristes, from the late 19th century collection of old French songs by Theodore Botrel / arranged for voice and guitar by Phyllis Tate. — London : Oxford University Press, 1974. — 10p ; 4to.
ISBN 0-19-345828-4 : £0.90

(B75-50566)

KE/TSPDW — With guitar & piano. Songs, etc
Huscroft, John
And when I am entombed : for voices, guitar & piano / music by John Huscroft ; words by Ralph Waldo Emerson. — Chelmsford (27 Donald Way, Chelmsford) : John Huscroft, 1975. — 4p ; 4to.
Unpriced

(B75-50567)

KE/TWDW/AZ — With lute. Songs, etc. Collected works of individual composers
Johnson, Robert, *b.1582*
[Songs. *Collections*]. Ayres, songs and dialogues / [by] Robert Johnson ; transcribed and edited by Ian Spink. — 2nd revised ed. — London : Stainer and Bell, 1974. — iv,80p ; 8vo.
Unpriced
(B75-51123)

KE/XDW — With percussion. Songs, etc
Gerhard, Roberto
The Akond of Swat : for voice and percussion / [by] Roberto Gerhard ; words by Edward Lear. — London : Oxford University Press, 1975. — 13p ; 4to.
ISBN 0-19-345361-4 : Unpriced
(B75-50568)

KF — FEMALE VOICE, CHILD'S VOICE
KFDM — Hymns
Binkerd, Gordon
Song of praise and prayer : children's hymn / [by] Gordon Binkerd ; poem by William Cowper. — New York ; [London] : Boosey and Hawkes, 1972. — 6p ; 4to.
Unpriced
(B75-50569)

KFE/VSPDW — With recorder & piano. Songs, etc
Owen, Elfed
Morys y Gwyat : can ddwy-ran ar gyfer ysgolion cynradd gyda chyfeiliant piano a recorder / gan Eldred Owen ; geiriau gan I.D. Hooson. — Cardiff : University of Wales Press, 1975. — 9p ; 4to.
Unpriced
(B75-50570)

KFLDW — Soprano voice. Songs, etc
Fraser, Shena
[Full fathom five. Sea Lullaby]. Sea lullaby : unison or soprano solo / [by] Shena Fraser ; words by Eugene Field. — London : Thames, 1975. — 4p ; 8vo.
Unpriced
Primary classification JDW
(B75-50527)

Spinner, Leopold
Drei Lieder. Op.16 : für Sopran und Klavier / [von] Rainer Maria Rilke. — London : Boosey and Hawkes, 1975. — 12p ; 4to.
£1.50
(B75-50571)

KFLDX — Soprano voice. Secular cantatas
Scarlatti, Domenico
Selve caverne e monti : cantata for soprano and basso continuo / [by] Domenico Scarlatti ; edited by Loek Hautus ; German words, Walther Dürr. — 1st ed. — Cassel ; London : Bärenreiter, 1973. — 4to.
Score (10p.) & 2 parts.
£1.80
(B75-50117)

KFLE/MDW — Soprano voice. With orchestra. Songs, etc
Berio, Luciano
[Opera. Air]. Air : for soprano and orchestra / [by] Luciano Berio ; words by Alessandro Striggio. — London : Universal, 1975. — 30p ; fol.
Duration 7 min.
Unpriced
(B75-50572)

KFLE/MPWTDX — Soprano voice. With French horn & orchestra. Secular cantatas
Del Tredici, David
Syzygy : for soprano, French horn and chamber orchestra / by David del Tredici ; text by James Joyce. — New York ; London : Boosey and Hawkes, 1974. — vii,153p ; 8vo.
Miniature score. — Duration 26 min. — Contents: Ecce puer - Nightpiece.
£9.00
(B75-50118)

KFLE/NUNQDX — Soprano voice. With wind string & keyboard sextet. Secular cantatas
Lumsdaine, David
Annotations of Auschwitz : soprano, flute (bass flute), trumpet, horn, violin, cello, piano / [by] David Lumsdaine ; text by Peter Porter. — Sydney ; [London] : Universal, 1975. — 35p ; obl.4to.
Duration 15 min.
Unpriced
(B75-51124)

KFLE/NVVQNTDW — Soprano voice with clarinet (A) & string trio. Songs, etc
Riley, Dennis
Five songs on Japanese haiku : soprano, clarinet, in A, violin, violoncello / [by] Dennis Riley ; haiku translated by Harold Stewart. — New York ; London : Peters, 1971. — 5p ; 4to.
(B75-51125)

KFLE/NXNSDW — Soprano voice. With string & keyboard quartet. Songs, etc
Berio, Luciano
[Opera. Air. *arr*]. Air : for soprano and 4 instruments / [by] Luciano Berio ; words by Alessandro Striggio. — London : Universal, 1975. — 20p ; fol.
Unpriced
(B75-50573)

KFLE/NYDNQDX — Soprano voice. With wind, strings, keyboard & percussion sextet. Secular cantatas
Hamilton, Iain
Dialogues on lines of Chateaubriand : for high soprano, flute, trumpet, violoncello, percussion, piano and celesta / [by] Iain Hamilton. — London : Central Music Library : Schott, 1974. — 36p ; 4to.
Duration 15 min.
Unpriced
(B75-50574)

KFLE/NYFVNQDX — Soprano voice. With clarinet, keyboard & percussion sextet. Secular cantatas
Birtwistle, Harrison
Nenia. The death of Orpheus : [for soprano solo, crotales, two pianos and three clarinets] / [by] Harrison Birtwistle ; words by Peter Zinovieff. — London : Universal, 1974. — 36p ; obl.4to.
Unpriced
(B75-50575)

KFLE/RXNSDW — Soprano voice. With string quartet. Songs, etc
Dinerstein, Norman
Four settings : for soprano and string quartet / [by] Norman Dinerstein ; poems by Emily Dickinson. — New York ; [London] : Boosey and Hawkes, 1972. — 4to.
Score & 4 parts. — Contents: 1: Dying - 2: The bustle in the house - 3: Apparently with no surprise - 4: I died for beauty.
Unpriced
(B75-50576)

KFLE/RXNSDX — Soprano voice with string quartet. Secular cantatas
Rhodes, Phillip
Autumn setting : soprano and string quartet / [by] Phillip Rhodes ; text by Patricia V. Schneider. — New York ; London : Peters, 1973. — 28p ; 4to.
Duration 11 min.
Unpriced
(B75-51126)

KFLE/SNTPWDX — Soprano voice. With two violins & keyboard. Secular cantatas
Scarlatti, Alessandro
Correa nel seno amato : cantata for soprano, two violins and basso continuo / [by] Alessandro Scarlatti ; edited by Otto Drechsler ; continuo-realization, Hans Ludwig Hirsch. — First edition. — Cassel ; London : Bärenreiter, 1974. — 4to.
Score (40p.) & 4 parts.
£6.00
(B75-50119)

KFLE/SSPMDW — Soprano voice. With double bass. Songs, etc
Seamarks, Colin
Six Mehitabel magpies : for soprano and double bass / by Colin Seamarks ; the poems by Don Marquis. — London : Yorke, 1974. — 9p ; 4to.
Unpriced
(B75-50120)

KFNE/MDX — Mezzo-soprano voice. With orchestra. Secular cantatas
Davies, Peter Maxwell
Stone litany : runes from a House of the Dead, for mezzo-soprano and orchestra / [by] Peter Maxwell Davies. — London : Boosey and Hawkes, 1975. — 64p ; fol.
£7.50
(B75-50577)

KFNE/MRDW — Mezzo-soprano voice. With chamber orchestra. Songs, etc
Hoyland, Vic
Jeux-thème : for mezzo-soprano and chamber orchestra / [by] Vic Hoyland ; text of Debussy setting by Verlaine. — London : Universal, 1975. — 23p ; obl.4to.
Duration 10 min. — The singer quotes 'En sourdine' from 'Fêtes galantes' by Debussy.
Unpriced
(B75-51127)

KFNE/NYDNQDX — Mezzo-soprano voice. With woodwind, strings, keyboard & percussion sextet. Secular cantatas
Antoniou, Theodor
Epilogue after Homer's 'The Odyssey' : for mezzosoprano, narrator, oboe, horn, guitar, piano, percussion and doublebass / [by] Theodor Antoniou. — Cassel ; London : Bärenreiter, 1974. — 16p ; 4to.
Duration 10 min.
Unpriced
(B75-50578)

KFNE/TSDW — Mezzo-soprano voice. With guitar. Songs, etc
Tate, Phyllis
Two ballads : for mezzo-soprano and guitar / by Phyllis Tate. — London : Oxford University Press, 1974. — 8p ; 4to.
ISBN 0-19-345827-6 : £0.80
(B75-50121)

KFQDW — Contralto voice. Songs, etc
Cruft, Adrian
Songs of good counsel. Op.73 : for mezzo-soprano and pianoforte / music Adrian Cruft ; words fifteenth century English. — London : Central Music Library : Chappell, 1975. — 40p ; 4to.
Unpriced
(B75-50579)

KFQE/SRPDE — Contralto voice. With cello & piano. Religious cantatas
Buxtehude, Dietrich
Jubilate Domino : Solokantate für Alt, Viola da gamba (Violoncello) und Basso continuo / [von] Karl Matthei ; Psalm 98, 4-6. — Cassel ; London : Bärenreiter, 1974. — 4to.
Score (14p.) & 3 parts.
£1.80
(B75-50122)

KFQE/VSPDW — Contralto voice. With recorder & piano. Songs, etc
Owen, Elfed
Morys y Gwynt : can ddwy-ran ar gyfer ysgolion cynradd gyda chyfeiliant piano a recorder / gan Elfed Owen ; y geiriau gan I.D. Hoosen. — Cardiff : University of Wales Press, 1974. — 9p ; 4to.
Unpriced
(B75-50123)

KFT — HIGH VOICE
KFTDH/KDD — Motets, Anthems, Hymns, etc. Weddings
Pinkham, Daniel
[Wedding cantata. Set me as a seal. *arr*]. Wedding song : high voice and organ / [by] Daniel Pinkham ; arrangement by the composer. — New York ; London : Peters, 1975. — 7p ; 4to.
Unpriced
(B75-51128)

KFTDW — Songs, etc
Barber, Samuel
[Songs. Op.45]. Three songs. Op.45 : for high voice and piano / [by] Samuel Barber. — New York ; London : Schirmer, 1974. — 17p ; 4to.
Unpriced
(B75-50580)

KFTE/VVPDW — With clarinet & piano. Songs, etc
Josephs, Wilfred
Four Japanese lyrics. Opus 47 for high voice, clarinet & piano / [by] Wilfred Josephs. — Sevenoaks : Novello, 1975. — 8p ; 4to.
£0.85
(B75-50581)

KFV — MIDDLE VOICE
KFVDW — Songs, etc
Argento, Dominick
From the diary of Virginia Woolf : for medium voice and piano / [by] Dominick Argento. — New York ; [London] : Boosey and Hawkes, 1975. — 42p ; 4to.
Unpriced
(B75-50582)

Boatwright, Howard
Sinner man : folk hymn setting, for medium voice and piano with audience participation / [by] Howard Boatwright. — New York [London] : Boosey and Hawkes, 1972. — 7p ; 4to.
Unpriced
(B75-50583)

Crosse, Gordon
The new world. Op.26 : set for medium voice and piano / [by] Gordon Crosse ; six poems by Ted Hughes. — London : Oxford University Press, 1975. — 36p ; 4to.
Duration 20 min.
ISBN 0-19-345275-8 : £2.50
(B75-50584)

Dickinson, Peter
Extravaganza : song cycle for medium voice and piano / [by] Peter Dickinson ; words by Gregory Corso. — Sevenoaks : Novello, 1975. — 11p ; 4to.
£1.25
(B75-50585)

Einem, Gottfried von
Leb wohl, Frau welt. Op:43 : Liederzyklus für mittlere Singstimme und Klavier / [von] Gottfried von Einem ; nach Texten von Hermann Hesse. — London : Boosey and Hawkes, 1975. — 18p ; 4to.
£3.00
(B75-50586)

KFVE/TSDW — With guitar. Songs, etc
Winters, Geoffrey
Three Herrick songs. Op.41 : medium voice and guitar / [by] Geoffrey Winters. — London : Thames, 1975. — 7p ; fol.
Unpriced
(B75-50587)

KFX — LOW VOICE
KFXDW — Songs, etc
Barber, Samuel
[Songs. Op.45]. Three songs. Op.45 : for low voice and piano / [by] Samuel Barber. — New York ; London : Schirmer, 1974. — 17p ; 4to.
Unpriced
(B75-50588)

KG — MALE VOICE
KGHDW — Tenor voice. Songs, etc
Croft, William
My heart is ev'ry beauty's prey : tenor solo, harpsichord and cello (ad lib.) / [by] William Croft ; edited by H. Diack Johnstone. — Wendover : Roberton, 1975. — 4to.
Score (7p) & part.
Unpriced
(B75-50589)

KGHE/MDW — Tenor voice with orchestra. Songs, etc
Fortner, Wolfgang
Machaut-Balladen : für Gesang und Orchester / [von] Wolfgang Fortner ; [text von] Guillaume de Marchaut. — Mainz ; London : Schott, 1975. — 69p ; 4to.
Study score.
£7.30
Primary classification JNGHE/MDW

KGHE/RXMPWTDX — Tenor voice. With French horn & string orchestra. Secular cantatas
Cowie, Edward
The moon, sea and stars : nocturnes for tenor horn and strings / by Edward Cowie. — London : Chester : Hansen, 1974. — 38p ; 8vo.
Study score. — Duration 20 min.
Unpriced
(B75-50124)

KGHE/RXNNDX — Tenor voice with string octet. Secular cantatas
Bedford, David
The tentacles of the dark nebula : for tenor & strings / [by] David Bedford ; text by Arthur C. Clark. — London : Universal, 1975. — 36p ; obl.4to.
Duration 14 1/2 min.
Unpriced
(B75-51129)

KGHE/TSDW — Tenor voice. With guitar. Songs, etc
Hold, Trevor
Early one morning : five poems of Edward Thomas, for tenor and guitar / [by] Trevor Hold. — London : Thames Music, 1975. — 12p ; fol.
Unpriced
(B75-50590)

KGHE/UMDX — Tenor voice with wind band. Secular cantatas
Bedford, David
When I heard the learn'd astronomer : for tenor and wind band / [by] David Bedford ; text by Walt Whitman and Camille Flammarion. — London : Universal, 1975. — 41p ; obl.4to.
Unpriced
(B75-51130)

KGNDR — Baritone voice. Psalms
Killmayer, Wilhelm
Salvum me fac : Bariton und Klavier / [von] Wilhelm Killmayer. — Mainz ; London : Schott, 1975. — 24p ; 4to.
Latin text.
Unpriced
(B75-51131)

KGNDW — Baritone voice. Songs, etc
Bennett, Richard Rodney
Tenebrae : a song cycle for baritone and piano / [by] Richard
Rodney Bennett. — London : Universal, 1975. — 24p ; 4to.
Duration 17 min.
Unpriced
(B75-51132)

Boatwright, Howard
The false knight upon the road : folk song setting for baritone
voice and piano / [by] Howard Boatwright. — New York ;
[London] : Oxford University Press, 1971. — 7p ; 4to.
Unpriced
(B75-50591)

Duclos, Pierre
[Le Voyageur. L'Avenir. *arr*]. L'Avenir : pour baryton / [par]
Pierre Duclos ; texte de Roland Receveur. — Paris ; [London] :
Chappell, 1972. — 3p ; 4to.
Unpriced
(B75-50592)

Glasser, Stanley
Four simple songs : baritone and piano / music by Stanley
Glasser ; words by Adolf Wood. — Banbury : Piers Press, 1975.
— 12p ; 4to.
Contents: 1: Stranger, those cattle you praise - 2: Now she lies sleeping - 3:
Night is over - 4: Old men, young men.
£1.25
(B75-51133)

Laderman, Ezra
Songs from Michelangelo : for baritone and piano / set to music
by Ezra Laderman ; translation by Joseph Tusiani. — New York ;
[London] : Oxford University Press, 1975. — 44p ; 4to.
Duration 23 min.
Unpriced
(B75-51134)

KGNE/MPSRDE — Baritone voice with cello & orchestra. Religious
cantatas
Reimann, Aribert
Wolkenloses Christfest : Requiem für Bariton, Violoncello und
Orchester / [von] Aribert Reimann ; nach Gedichten von Otfried
Buthe. — Mainz ; London : Schott, 1975. — 135p ; 4to.
£11.00
(B75-51135)

KGNE/PVDW — Baritone voice with electronic instruments. Songs,
etc
Crumb, George
Songs, drones and refrains of death : a cycle of poems by Federico
Garcia Lorca [for] baritone, electric guitar, electric contrabass,
electric piano, (electric harpsichord), percussion (2 players) / [by]
George Crumb. — New York ; London : Peters, 1971. — 22p ;
fol.
Duration 30 min.
Unpriced
(B75-51136)

KGXE/NXNRDR — Bass voice. With strings & keyboard quintet.
Psalms
Buxtehude, Dietrich
Mein Herz ist bereit. (57. Psalm Davids) : Solokantate für Bass,
drei Violinen, Violoncello und Basso continuo / [von] Dietrich
Buxtehude ; herausgegeben von Karl Matthei. — Cassel ;
London : Bärenreiter, 1974. — 4to.
Score (15p.) & 6 parts.
£2.40
(B75-50125)

LH — DANCES
LH/G/AYD — Folk dances. Collections. England
8 Morris dances of England and Flamborough sword dance / edited
by Nibs Matthews. — London : English Folk Dance and Song
Society, 1975. — 20p ; 8vo.
ISBN 0-85418-108-3 : Unpriced
(B75-51137)

LH/H/G/AYDJG — Folk dances for dancing. Collections. Yorkshire
Dances from the Yorkshire dales / this edition prepared for
publication by S.A. Matthews and Dennis Darke. — London :
English Folk Dance and Song Society, 1975. — 8p ; 8vo.
Unpriced
(B75-50593)

LN — ENSEMBLES
Kagel, Mauricio
Exotica : für aussereuropäische Instrumente, 1971-72 / [von]
Mauricio Kagel. — London : Universal, 1974. — 90p ; obl. 4to.
Unpriced
(B75-50126)

Mendoza, Anne
The monkey's hornpipe, and other pieces : for school music
ensemble / [by] Anne Mendoza. — London : Chappell, 1975. —
11p ; 4to.
Unpriced
(B75-51138)

LN/AF — Exercises
Schnebel, Dieter
Schulmusik : Übungen mit Klangen, für 6 oder mehr Spieler
(Langtoninstrumente und Stimmen ad lib.) / [von] Dieter
Schnebel. — Mainz ; London : Schott, 1975. — obl.8vo.
Preface (8p.) & 26 parts.
£2.50
(B75-51139)

LNG — Suites
Couperin, François
Les Goûts réunis or Nouveaux concerts : for instrumental
ensemble / [by] François Couperin ; ed. David Lasocki, realization
of the basso continuo by Richard Hervig, (fifth, sixth, seventh and
tenth concerts), and Gerhard Krapf, (eighth, ninth, eleventh,
twelfth and fourteenth concerts). — London : Musica rara.
Volume 1 : Concerts 5-8 : for flute or oboe or violin & basso continuo. —
1975. — 4to.
Score (47p.) & 2 parts. — With a separate leaflet containing a foreword. The
scores of the concerts are in separate volumes contained in a folder.
Unpriced
(B75-51140)
Volume 2 : Concerts 9-10, 12, 14 : for flute or oboe or violin and basso
continuo. — 1975. — 4to.
Score (44p.) & 2 parts. — With a separate leaflet containing a foreword. The
scores of the concerts are in separate volumes contained in a folder.
Unpriced
(B75-51141)
Volume 3 : Concerts 10, 12-13 : for three violas da gamba or cellos or
bassoons. — 1975. — 4to.
Score (12p.) & 3 parts. — With a separate leaflet containing a foreword. The
scores of the concerts are in separate volumes contained in a folder.
Unpriced
(B75-51142)

LNK/DW/AY — Arrangements. Songs, etc. Collections
Pleasure and practice music cards : songs / compiled and arranged
for instruments by Leslie Winters. — London : E.J. Arnold.
Set 1. — 1975. — 20 cards ; 8vo.
With notes on percussion technique, harmony and elementary rudiments.
ISBN 0-560-00487-7 : Unpriced
(B75-51143)
Set 2. — 1975. — 20 cards ; 8vo.
With notes on percussion technique, harmony and elementary rudiments.
ISBN 0-560-00488-5 : Unpriced
(B75-51144)
Set 3. — 1975. — 20 cards ; 8vo.
With notes on percussion technique, harmony and elementary rudiments.
ISBN 0-560-00489-3 : Unpriced
(B75-51145)

LNS — Quartets
Arcadelt, Jacques
[Il primo libro di madrigali. *Selections*]. Three madrigals : for 4
voices or instruments / [by] Jacques Arcadelt ; edited by Iain
Fenlon. — Lustleigh : Antico, 1975. — 9p ; 4to.
Unpriced
Primary classification EZDU
(B75-50473)

Maschera, Florentio
[Libro primo de canzoni da sonare. Canzona 'La Girella'].
Canzona 'La Girella' : for four instruments / by Fiorenzo
Maschera ; edited by Howard Mayer Brown. — London : Oxford
University Press, 1975. — 8vo.
Score (11p.) and an arrangement for lute in tablature / by G.A. Terzi.
ISBN 0-19-341206-3 : £0.55
(B75-51146)

LNU — Duets
Schade, Wernerfritz
Zweistimmige Orgelchorale : gemeinsame Lieder der
deutschsprachigen Kirchen / leicht gesetzt Orgel (manualiter) oder
2 Melodieinstrumente von Wernerfritz Schade. — Mainz ;
London : Schott, 1975. — 60p ; obl.4to.
£4.50
Primary classification RJ

MGM — MARCHES
Berlioz, Hector
[La Damnation de Faust. Marche hongroise. *arr*]. Hungarian
march / [by] Hector Berlioz ; arranged for reduced orchestra by
Ian Cobb. — Sevenoaks : Novello, 1975. — 22p ; 4to.
Duration 5 min.
£1.50
(B75-51147)

MH — DANCES
Ligeti, György
Ballade und Tanz = Ballad and dance : after Roumanian folk songs, for school orchestra / [by] György Ligeti. — Mainz ; London : Schott, 1974. — 20p ; 4to.
£2.90
(B75-50127)

Pavey, Sidney
Clog dance : for orchestra / [by] Sidney Pavey. — London : Bosworth, 1974. — 10p ; 4to.
Unpriced
(B75-50594)

MHQ — Mazurkas
Delibes, Leo
[Coppelia. Prelude and mazurka. *arr*]. Prelude and mazurka / [by] Leo Delibes ; arranged for reduced orchestra by Ian Cobb. — Sevenoaks : Novello, 1975. — 28p ; 4to.
Duration 6 min.
£1.50
(B75-51148)

MJ — MISCELLANEOUS WORKS
Mahler, Gustav
[Symphony no.1 in D major. 3rd movement. *arr*]. 'Bruder Martin' / [by] Gustav Mahler ; arranged for school and amateur orchestra by K.W. Rokos and John Simpson. — London : Bosworth, 1975. — 31p ; 4to.
Duration 11 min.
Unpriced
(B75-50595)

Pavey, Sidney
Windmills : for orchestra / [by] Sidney Pavey. — London : Bosworth, 1975. — 11p ; 4to.
Unpriced
(B75-50596)

Platts, Kenneth
Music for the Maltings. Opus 22 : [for orchestra] / [by] Kenneth Platts. — London : Ashdown, 1975. — 33p ; 4to.
Duration 9 mins.
Unpriced
(B75-50597)

Sitsky, Larry
Apparitions for orchestra / [by] Larry Sitsky. — London : Boosey and Hawkes, 1975. — 4to.
Score (26p.) & 26 parts. — With several copies of various parts.
£6.00
(B75-50598)

MK — ARRANGEMENTS
Rameau, Jean Philippe
[Harpsichord music. *Selections: arr*]. A Rameau suite : keyboard pieces by Rameau / freely adapted for junior orchestra by Anthony Hedges. — London : Chappell, 1974. — 4to.
Score (23p.) & 23 parts. — With several copies of various parts.
Unpriced
(B75-50128)

MK/AGM — Arrangements. Marches
Strauss, Johann, b.1805
[Radetzky march. Op.228. *arr*]. Radetzky march. Op.228 / [by] Johann Strauss ; arr. for school and amateur orchestra by Frank Naylor. — London : Bosworth, 1975. — 12p ; 4to.
Unpriced
(B75-50599)

Strauss, Johann, b.1825
[Persischer Marsch. Op.289. *arr*]. Persian march. Op.289 / [by] Johann Strauss ; arranged for school and amateur orchestra by Frank Naylor. — London : Bosworth, 1975. — 10p ; 4to.
Unpriced
(B75-50600)

MK/AHVH — Arrangements. Polkas
Strauss, Johann, b.1825
[Annen-Polka. Op.117. *arr*]. Annen-Polka. Op.117 : polka française / [by] Johann Strauss ; arr. for school and amateur orchestra by Grank Naylor. — London : Bosworth, 1975. — 10p ; 4to.
Duration 4 min.
Unpriced
(B75-50129)

MM — WORKS FOR SYMPHONY ORCHESTRA
MM/HM — Ballet
Tchaikovsky, Peter
The sleeping beauty / [by] Peter Ilich Tchaikovsky ; foreword by Roger Fiske. — London : Eulenberg, 1975. — xv,1083p ; 8vo.
Unpriced
(B75-50601)

MME — Symphonies
Allanbrook, Douglas
[Symphony no.3. 'Four orchestral landscapes']. Four orchestral landscapes (Symphony no.3) / [by] Douglas Allanbrook. — New York ; [London] : Boosey and Hawkes, 1972. — 100p ; 4to.
Contents: 1: Fall - 2: Winter - 3: Spring - 4: Summer.
Unpriced
(B75-50602)

Binkerd, Gordon
Symphony no.3 / [by] Gordon Binkerd. — New York ; [London] : Boosey and Hawkes, 1972. — 83p ; 4to.
Unpriced
(B75-50603)

Glazunov, Aleksandr Konstantinovich
[Symphony, no.8, op.83, in E flat major]. Eighth symphony, E flat major. Opus 83 / [by] Alexander Glasunow. — Frankfurt : Belaieff ; [London] : [Peters], 1974. — 179p ; 8vo.
Miniature score.
Unpriced
(B75-50130)

Gutche, Gene
[Symphony no.6. Op.45]. Symphony VI. Opus 45 / [by] Gene Gutche. — New York : Highgate Press ; [London] : [Galliard], 1972. — 75p ; 4to.
Unpriced
(B75-51149)

Haydn, Joseph
[Symphony, no.99, in E flat major]. Symphony in E flat major, (London Symphony no.7) / [by] Joseph Haydn ; edited by Horst Walter. — Cassel ; London : Bärenreiter, 1973. — vii,58p ; 8vo.
Miniature score.
£1.80
(B75-50131)

Haydn, Joseph
[Symphony, no.100, in G major, 'Military']. Symphony in G major, 'Military' (London Symphony no.9) / [by] Joseph Haydn ; edited by Horst Walter. — Cassel ; London : Bärenreiter, 1973. — vi,80p ; 8vo.
Miniature score.
£2.40
(B75-50132)

Haydn, Joseph
[Symphony, no.101, in D major, 'The clock']. Symphony in D major, 'The clock' (London Symphony no.8) / [by] Joseph Haydn ; edited by Horst Walter. — Cassel ; London : Bärenreiter, 1973. — vi,86p ; 8vo.
Miniature score.
£2.40
(B75-50133)

Hoddinott, Alun
Symphony no.5. Opus 81 / [by] Alun Hoddinott. — London : Oxford University Press, 1975. — 167p ; 8vo.
Duration 25 min.
ISBN 0-19-364590-4 : £6.75
(B75-50604)

Killmayer, Wilhelm
Symphony no.3, 'Menschen-Los' / [von] Wilhelm Killmayer. — Mainz ; London : Schott, 1975. — 48p ; 4to.
Study score.
£4.50
(B75-51150)

Lees, Benjamin
Symphony no.3 / [by] Benjamin Lees. — London : Boosey and Hawkes, 1975. — 79p ; 8vo.
Miniature score.
Unpriced
(B75-50605)

Mechem, Kirke
Symphony no.1. Op.16 / [by] Kirke Mechem. — New York ; [London] : Boosey and Hawkes, 1974. — 110p ; 4to.
Unpriced
(B75-50134)

MMEM — Sinfoniettas
Rimsky-Korsakoff, Nikolai
Sinfonietta on Russian themes. Op.31 / [by] Nikolai Rimsky-Korsakow. — Frankfurt : Belaieff ; [London] : [Hinrichsen], 1974. — 124p ; 8vo.
Miniature score.
Unpriced
(B75-50135)

MMF — Concertos
Adler, Samuel
Concerto for orchestra / [by] Samuel Adler. — New York ;
[London] : Boosey and Hawkes, 1975. — 68p ; fol.
Duration 20 min.
Unpriced
(B75-50606)

Petrassi, Goffedro
[Concerto no.1 for orchestra]. Primo concerto per orchestra / [di]
Goffedro Petrassi. — London : Eulenberg, 1975. — 95p ; 4to.
Study score.
Unpriced
(B75-51151)

MMG — Suites
Cohn, James
The little circus : orchestral suite / [by] James Cohn. — New
York ; London : Boosey and Hawkes, 1975. — 40p ; fol.
Unpriced
(B75-51152)

Glazunov, Aleksandr Konstantinovich
Suite caracteristique = Characteristic suite. Opus 9 : for
orchestra / [by] Alexander Glasunow. — Frankfurt : Belaieff ;
[London] : [Peters], 1974. — 196p ; 8vo.
Miniature score.
Unpriced
(B75-50136)

Tomlinson, Ernest
English pageant : a suite for orchestra / [by] Ernest Tomlinson.
— London : Central Music Library ; Croydon : Belwin-Mills,
1974. — 117p ; 4to.
Duration 16 min. — Contents: 1: March: Men-at-arms. —
2: The jester. —
3: My lady's pavane. — 4: The fiddler.
Unpriced
(B75-50607)

MMH — Dances
Glinka, Mikhail Ivanovich
[A life for the Tsar. *Selections*]. Drei Tanze aus der Oper 'Ein
Leben für den Zaren' / [von] Michael Glinka. — Frankfurt :
Belaieff ; [London] : [Peters], 1974. — 59p ; 8vo.
Miniature score - The first dance has an optional SATB chorus.
Unpriced
(B75-50137)

MMJ — Miscellaneous works
Antoniou, Theodore
Cheironomies : conductor's improvisation / [by] Theodore
Antoniou. — Cassel ; London : Bärenreiter, 1974. — 29p ;
obl.4to.
Study score.
£3.20
(B75-50138)

Antoniou, Theodore
Events 2 : for large orchestra, 1969 / [by] Theodore Antoniou. —
Cassel ; London : Bärenreiter, 1973. — 36p ; 4to.
Duration 14 min. — Study score.
£4.00
(B75-50139)

Antoniou, Theodore
Events 3 : for orchestra with tape and slides, 1969 / [by]
Theodore Antoniou. — Cassel ; London : Bärenreiter, 1973. —
20p ; 4to.
Duration 12 min. — Study score.
£2.40
(B75-50140)

Arnold, Malcolm
Hongkong anniversary overture. Op.99 / [by] Malcolm Arnold. —
London : Central Music Library : Faber, 1974. — 33p ; 4to.
Duration 4 min.
Unpriced
(B75-50608)

Baird, Tadeusz
Elegeia : für Orchester / [von] Tadeusz Baird. — Frankfurt :
Litolff ; London : Peters, 1975. — 25p ; 8vo.
Study score.
Unpriced
(B75-51153)

Baird, Tadeusz
Psychodrama : für Orchester / [von] Tadeusz Baird. —
Frankfurt : Litolff ; London : Peters, 1973. — 21p ; fol.
Duration 8 1/2 min.
Unpriced
(B75-50141)

Balakirev, Mily
Tamara : symphonic poem / [by] Mily Alexeyevich Balakirev ;
foreword by David Lloyd Jones. — London : Eulenburg, 1975. —
177p ; 8vo.
Miniature score.
£2.50
(B75-50609)

Berkowtiz, Sol
Diversion : for orchestra / [by] Sol Berkowitz. — Boston ;
[London] : Frank Music, 1972. — 4to.
Score & 36 parts. — With several copies of various parts.
Unpriced
(B75-50610)

Birtwistle, Harrison
The triumph of time : [for orchestra] / [by] Harrison Birtwistle.
— London : Universal, 1974. — 53p ; fol.
Duration 28 min.
Unpriced
(B75-50142)

Burgon, Geoffrey
Cantus alleluia : [orchestra] / [by] Geoffrey Burgon. — London :
Chester, 1975. — 35p ; 4to.
Duration 15 min.
Unpriced
(B75-50611)

Connolly, Justin
Antiphonies : for orchestra / [by] Justin Connolly. — London :
Oxford University Press, 1975. — 81p ; 8vo.
ISBN 0-19-362390-0 : £5.50
(B75-50612)

Copland, Aaron
Three Latin-American sketches : [for orchestra] / [by] Aaron
Copland. — London : Boosey and Hawkes, 1975. — 61p ; 4to.
No. 3 was previously published in a version for two pianos. — Contents: 1
Estrebillo - 2: Paisaji mexicano - 3: Danza de Jalisco.
£7.50
(B75-50613)

Einem, Gottfried von
Bruckner Dialog : für Orchester. Op 39 / [von] Gottfried von
Einem. — London : Boosey and Hawkes, 1974. — 92p ; 8vo.
Miniature score.
£3.00
(B75-50143)

Gilbert, Anthony
Regions. Op.6 : for orchestra / [by] Anthony Gilbert. — London :
Central Music Library : Schott, 1974. — 49p ; 4to.
Unpriced
(B75-50614)

Glazunov, Aleksandr Konstantinovich
[Solemn overture. Op.73]. Festouverture = Solemn overture. Opus
73 : [for orchestra] / [by] Alexander Glasunow. — Frankfurt :
Belaieff ; [London] : [Peters], 1974. — 74p ; 8vo.
Miniature score.
Unpriced
(B75-50144)

Gould, Morton
Soundings : for orchestra / by Morton Gould. — New York ;
[London] : Chappell, 1974. — 71p ; 8vo.
Duration 16 min. — Contents: 1: Threnodies - 2: Paëns.
Unpriced
(B75-50145)

Humble, Keith
Arcade V : for orchestra / [by] Keith Humble. — [Sydney] ;
[London] : Universal, 1975. — 21p ; fol.
Unpriced
(B75-50615)

Kelterborn, Rudolf
Changements : pour grand orchestre / [par] Rudolf Kelterborn. —
Cassel ; London : Bärenreiter, 1973. — 43p ; 4to.
Unpriced
(B75-50616)

Liferman, Georges
Nymphes et driades : [pour orchestre] / [par] Georges Liferman et
Paul Bonneau. — Paris ; [London] : Chappell, 1972. — 11p ; fol.
Unpriced
(B75-51154)

McCabe, John
The Chagall windows : for orchestra / [by] John McCabe. —
Sevenoaks : Novello, 1975. — 112p ; 4to.
Duration 30 min.
Unpriced
(B75-50617)

Meale, Richard
Soon it will die : for orchestra / [by] Richard Meale. — Sydney ;
[London] : Universal, 1975. — 23p ; fol.
Duration 8 min.
Unpriced

(B75-51155)

Mendelssohn, Felix
['The Hebrides'. Op.26]. Overture, 'The Hebrides'. Op.26 / [by]
Felix Mendelssohn-Bartholdy ; foreword by Roger Fiske. —
London : Eulenburg, 1974. — xii,50p ; 8vo.
Miniature score.
Unpriced

(B75-51156)

Rimsky-Korsakoff, Nikolai
Russian Easter overture. Op.36 : for orchestra / [by] Nikolai
Rimsky-Korsakov. — Frankfurt : Belaieff ; [London] : [Peters],
1972. — 97p ; 8vo.
Miniature score.
Unpriced

(B75-50146)

Skriabin, Aleksandr
Le Poeme de l'extase = The poem of ecstasy. Op.54 / [by]
Alexander Scriabin. — Frankfurt : Belaieff ; [London] :
[Hinrichsen], 1975. — 101p ; 8vo.
Miniature score.
Unpriced

(B75-51157)

Surinach, Carlos
Las Trompetas de la serafines : overture for orchestra / by Carlos
Surinach. — New York ; London : Associated Music, 1975. —
75p ; 8vo.
£3.90

(B75-51158)

Tchaikovsky, Peter
[The storm. Op.76]. L'Orage : Ouverture für Orchester nach dem
Drama von A.N. Ostrowsky / [von] Peter Tschaikowsky. —
Frankfurt : Belaieff ; [London] : [Hinrichsen], 1971. — 78p ; 8vo.
Miniature score.
£8.00

(B75-50147)

Tcherepnin, Nikolai
[Destiny. Op.59]. Le Destin = Destiny. Opus 59 : three
symphonic fragments on a ballad by Edgar Allan Poe / [by]
Nikolai Tcherepnin. — Frankfurt : Belaieff ; [London] : [Peters],
1974. — 102p ; 8vo.
Miniature score.
Unpriced

(B75-50148)

Ward, Robert
Invocation and toccata : orchestra / [by] Robert Ward. — New
York : Highgate Press ; London : Galliard, 1975. — 44p ; 4to.
Duration 9 min.
Unpriced

(B75-50618)

Washburn, Robert
Excursion : for orchestra / [by] Robert Washburn. — New York ;
[London] : Oxford University Press, 1972. — 28p ; 4to.
Unpriced

(B75-51159)

Washburn, Robert
[Symphony no.1. Allegro con spirito]. Festive overture : for
orchestra / [by] Robert Washburn. — New York ; [London] :
Oxford University Press, 1972. — 38p ; 4to.
Unpriced

(B75-51160)

MMK — Arrangements
Musorgsky, Modest
[Pictures at an exhibition. *arr*]. Pictures at an exhibition / [by]
Modest Mussorgsky ; symphonic transcription by Leopold
Stokowski. — New York : Henmar Press ; London : Peters, 1971.
— 100p ; 4to.
Unpriced

(B75-50619)

MP — WORKS FOR SOLO INSTRUMENT (S) & ORCHESTRA
MPPV — Electronic instrument(s) & orchestra
Lanza, Alcides
Eidesis III (1971-II) : for one or two orchestras and electronic
sounds / [by] Alcides Lanza. — New York ; London : Boosey
and Hawkes, 1975. — 15p ; fol.
Unpriced

(B75-51161)

MPQF — Piano & orchestra. Concertos
Mozart, Wolfgang Amadeus
[Concerto for piano, no.17, in G major. K.453]. Concerto in G
major for pianoforte and orchestra, KV453 / [by] Wolfgang
Amadeus Mozart ; edited by Eva and Paul Badura-Skoda. —
Cassel ; London : Bärenreiter, 1975. — xiv,70p ; 8vo.
Miniature score.
Unpriced

(B75-50620)

Panufnik, Andrzej
Concerto for piano and orchestra / by Andrzej Panufnik. —
London : Boosey and Hawkes, 1974. — 84p ; fol.
£7.00

(B75-50149)

Schurmann, Gerhard
[Concerto for piano]. Piano concerto / [by] Gerhard Schurmann.
— Sevenoaks : Novello, 1975. — 121p ; 8vo.
Duration 29 min.
£4.75

(B75-50621)

Skriabin, Aleksandr
[Concerto for piano, in F sharp minor. Op.20]. Concerto, F sharp
minor, for piano and orchestra. Opus 20 / [by] Alexander
Scriabin. — Frankfurt ; Belaieff ; [London] : [Eulenburg], 1975.
— 1,67p ; 8vo.
Miniature score.
Unpriced

(B75-51162)

MPQRF — Harpsichord & orchestra. Concertos
Chilcot, Thomas
[Concerto for harpsichord, op.2, no.5, in F major]. Concerto in F
major : for harpsichord, two oboes, bassoon and strings / [by]
Thomas Chilcot ; edited by Robin Langley. — London : Oxford
University Press, 1975. — 4to.
Score (24p) & 6 parts. — Duration 11 mins.
ISBN 0-19-362296-3 : Unpriced

(B75-50622)

MPRXNSF — String quartet & orchestra. Concertos
Musgrave, Thea
Memento vitae : a concerto in homage to Beethoven, for solo
string quartet & orchestra / [by] Thea Musgrave. — London :
Chester, 1975. — 105p ; 4to.
Duration 18 min.
Unpriced

(B75-51163)

MPSF — Violin & orchestra. Concertos
Antoniou, Theodore
[Concerto for violin. Opus 28]. Violinkonzert (1965). Opus 28 /
[by] Theodore Antoniou. — Cassel ; London : Bärenreiter, 1973.
— 117p ; 4to.
Duration 20 min. — Study score.
£8.00

(B75-50150)

Delius, Frederick
[Concerto for violin]. Violin concerto / [by] Frederick Delius ;
corrected by R.J. Threfall. — London : Stainer and Bell, 1975. —
45p ; 8vo.
ISBN 0-85249-355-x : Unpriced

(B75-51164)

Szokolay, Sándor
[Concerto for violin]. Konzert für Violine und Orchester / [von]
Sándor Szokolay. — Frankfurt : Litolff ; London : Peters, 1973.
— 105p ; 8vo.
Miniature score.
Unpriced

(B75-50151)

MPSP — Violin, piano & orchestra
Antoniou, Theodore
Events 1 : for violin, piano and orchestra, 1968 / [by] Theodore
Antoniou. — Cassel ; London : Bärenreiter, 1974. — 56p ; 4to.
Duration 18 min. — Study score.
£2.00

(B75-50152)

MPSPLSRF — Violin, cello & orchestra. Concertos
Donizetti, Gaetano
[Concerto for violin & cello in D minor]. Concerto in re minore :
per violino, violoncello e orchestra / [di] Gaetano Donizetti ;
edizione a cara di Antonio Pocaterra. — Padua : Zanibon ;
[London] : [Peters], 1974. — 24p ; fol.
Unpriced

(B75-50153)

MPSQF — Viola & orchestra. Concertos
Bennett, Richard Rodney
  Concerto for viola & chamber orchestra / [by] Richard Rodney
  Bennett. — Sevenoaks : Novello, 1975. — 75p ; 8vo.
  Study score.
  £2.00
                                                              (B75-51165)

Musgrave, Thea
  Concerto for viola / [by] Thea Musgrave. — Sevenoaks : Novello,
  1975. — 105p ; 8vo.
  Unpriced
                                                              (B75-50623)

MPTSF — Guitar & orchestra. Concertos
Dodgson, Stephen
  [Concerto for guitar & chamber orchestra, no.1]. Concerto no.1,
  for guitar and chamber orchestra / [by] Stephen Dodgson. —
  London : Central Music Library : Chappell, 1974. — 79p ; 4to.
  Unpriced
                                                              (B75-50624)

MPVRPLVTF — Flute, oboe & orchestra. Concertos
Ligeti, György
  [Concerto for flute, oboe & orchestra (1972)]. Double concerto for
  flute, oboe and orchestra (1972) / by György Ligeti. — Mainz ;
  London : Schott, 1974. — 72p ; 4to.
  Study score.
  Unpriced
                                                              (B75-50154)

MPVTF — Oboe & orchestra. Concertos
Meyer, Krysztof
  Concerto da camera : per oboe, percussione ed archi / [di]
  Krysztof Meyer. — Frankfurt : Litolff ; London : Peters, 1974. —
  43p ; fol.
  Duration 15 min.
  Unpriced
                                                              (B75-50625)

MR — WORKS FOR CHAMBER ORCHESTRA
MR/T — Variations
Schifrin, Lalo
  Variants on a madrigal by Gesualdo : for large chamber
  ensemble / [by] Lalo Schifrin. — New York ; London :
  Associated Music, 1974. — 50p ; 8vo.
  Duration 18 min.
  £3.25
                                                              (B75-50626)

MRE — Symphonies
Bach, Johann Christian
  [Symphony, Op.6, no.3, in E flat major]. Sinfonia in E flat major.
  Op6/III / [by] Johann Christian Bach ; edited by Hanspeter
  Gmür. — Cassel : Nagel ; [London] : [Bärenreiter], 1973. — 16p ;
  4to.
  £2.40
                                                              (B75-50155)

Torelli, Giuseppe
  [Sinfonia à 4 in C major. G.33]. Sinfonia à 4 in C major. G.33 :
  for 4 trumpets, 4 oboes, 2 bassoons, strings (concertino and rip.)
  and basso continuo / [by] Giuseppe Torelli ; edited by Edward H.
  Tarr. — London : Musica rara, 1974. — 4to.
  Score (54p.) & 19 parts.
  Unpriced
                                                              (B75-51166)

Torelli, Giuseppe
  Sinfonia avanti l'opera. G.14 : for trumpet, strings and continuo /
  [by] Giuseppe Torelli ; edited by E.H. Tarr. — London : Musica
  rara, 1975. — 4to.
  Score (7p.) & 9 parts.
  £4.50
                                                              (B75-51167)

Torelli, Giuseppe
  [Sinfonia in D major. G.3]. Sinfonia in D. G.3 : for trumpet,
  strings and continuo / [by] Giuseppe Torelli ; edited by Edward
  H. Tarr. — London : Musica rara, 1974. — 4to.
  Score (24p.) & 9 parts.
  Unpriced
                                                              (B75-51168)

Torelli, Giuseppe
  [Sinfonia in D major. G.4]. Sinfonia in D. G.4 : for trumpet,
  strings and continuo / [by] Giuseppe Torelli ; edited by Edward
  H. Tarr. — London : Musica rara, 1974. — 4to.
  Score (8p.) & 9 parts.
  Unpriced
                                                              (B75-51169)

Torelli, Giuseppe
  [Sinfonia in D major. G.5]. Sinfonia in D. G.5 : for trumpet,
  strings and continuo / [by] Giuseppe Torelli ; edited by Edward
  H. Tarr, reduction by Robert Paul Block. — London : Musica
  rara, 1974. — 4to.
  Score (8p.) & 9 parts.
  £4.50
                                                              (B75-51170)

MRF — Concertos
Marcello, Alessandro
  [Concerto grosso in F major]. Concerto in fa magg : per archi con
  due oboi (o flauti) e fagotto ad libitum oppure 2 violini e
  violoncello ad libitum e cembalo / [by] A. Marcello ; edizione a
  cura di Giorgia Croci. — Padua : Zanibon ; [London] : [Peters],
  1974. — 10p ; fol.
  Unpriced
                                                              (B75-50156)

MRFL — Concertinos
Antoniou, Theodore
  [Concertino for nine wind instruments, piano & percussion.
  Op.21]. Concertino. Op.21 : for piano, nine wind instruments and
  percussion / [by] Theodore Antoniou. — Cassell ; London :
  Bärenreiter, 1973. — 49p ; 4to.
  Duration 13 min. — Study score.
  £7.00
                                                              (B75-50157)

MRG — Suites
Bach, Johann Sebastian
  [Suite for orchestra, no.1, in C major. S.1066]. Ouverture
  (Orchestral suite), C major / [by] Johann Sebastian Bach ; edited
  by Hans Gruss. — Cassel ; London : Bärenreiter, 1974. — 126p ;
  8vo.
  Miniature score.
  Unpriced
                                                              (B75-50627)

Bach, Johann Sebastian
  [Suite for orchestra, no.2, in B minor. S.1067]. Ouverture =
  (Orchestral suite). B minor / [by] Johann Sebastian Bach ; edited
  by Hans Gruss. — London : Cassel : Bärenreiter, 1974. — 24p ;
  8vo.
  Miniature score.
  Unpriced
                                                              (B75-50628)

Bach, Johann Sebastian
  [Suite for orchestra, no.3, in D major. S.1068]. Ouverture =
  (Orchestral suite), D major / [by] Johann Sebastian Bach ; edited
  by Hans Gruss. — Cassel ; London : Bärenreiter, 1974. — 36p ;
  8vo.
  Miniature score.
  Unpriced
                                                              (B75-50629)

Bach, Johann Sebastian
  [Suite for orchestra, no.4, in D major. S.1069]. Ouverture =
  (Orchestral sutte), D major / [by] Johann Sebastian Bach ; edited
  by Hans Gruss. — Cassel ; London : Bärenreiter, 1974. — 40p ;
  8vo.
  Miniature score.
  Unpriced
                                                              (B75-50630)

MRH — Dances
Courpalay, Maurice de
  Danses de l'echiquier : style baroque, [orchestra] / [par] Maurice
  de Courpalay. — Paris ; [London] : Chappell, 1972. — 36p ; fol.
  Unpriced
                                                              (B75-50631)

MRJ — Miscellaneous works
Bennett, Richard Rodney
  Commedia 3 : for ten instruments / [by] Richard Rodney Bennett.
  — Sevenoaks : Novello, 1975. — 66p ; 8vo.
  Duration 16 1/2 min.
  £2.00
                                                              (B75-50158)

Chapple, Brian
  Green and pleasant : for chamber orchestra / [by] Brian Chapple.
  — London : Chester, 1974. — 44p ; 4to.
  Duration 12 min.
  Unpriced
                                                              (B75-50632)

Handel, George Frideric
  [Atalanta. Overture]. Overture for trumpet, oboes, strings and
  basso continuo / by G.F. Handel ; edited by R.P. Block. —
  London : Musica rara, 1975. — 4to.
  Score (16p.) & 9 parts.
  Unpriced
                                                              (B75-51171)

Handel, George Frideric
[Faramondo. Overture]. Ouverture für Streicher, 2 Oboi (Fl.),
Fagotti ad lib, und Cembalo / [von] Georg Friedrich Händel ;
herausgegeben von Fritz Kneusslin. — Basle : Kneusslin ;
[London] : [Hinrichsen], 1974. — 7p ; 4to.
Unpriced

(B75-50159)

Heider, Werner
Pyramide für Igor Strawinsky : für Kammerensemble / [von]
Werner Heider. — Frankfurt : Litolff ; London : Peters, 1974. —
12p ; 8vo.
Study score.
Unpriced

(B75-50160)

Kelemen, Milko
Olifant : für einen Solisten (Posaune, Trombita Bali-Flöten Zurla,
Buchel, Alphorn) und zwei Kammerensembles / [von] Milko
Kelemen. — Frankfurt : Litolff : Peters ; London : Hinrichsen,
1974. — 69p ; 8vo.
Duration 15 min. — Miniature score.
Unpriced

(B75-50161)

Rands, Bernard
As all get out (after an idea by Bruno Maderna) : [for
instrumental ensemble] / [by] Bernard Rands. — London :
Universal, 1975. — 1ff ; 4to.
Unpriced

(B75-50633)

NU — WIND, STRINGS & KEYBOARD
NUNQE — Sextets. Sonatas
Schmelzer, Johann Heinrich
Sonata à 5 for two violins, trumpet, bassoon, viola da gamba and
basso continuo / [by] Johann Heinrich Schmelzer ; edited by Peter
Harland. — London : Musica rara, 1975. — 4to.
Score (16p.) & 5 parts.
Unpriced

(B75-51172)

NUNR — Quintets
Linike, Johann Georg
[Mortorium à 5]. Sonata (Mortorium) à 5 (1737) : for trumpet,
oboe, flute, violin and basso continuo / [by] J.G. Linike ; edited
by Robert Minter, assisted by Michael Turnbull. — London :
Musica rara, 1974. — 4to.
Score (22p.) & 5 parts.
Unpriced

(B75-51173)

NUNSE — Quartets. Sonatas
Finger, Godfrey
Sonata for trumpet, violin, oboe and basso continuo in C major /
[by] Godfrey Finger ; edited by Robert Minter, basso continuo
realised by Barry Cooper and Michael Turnbull. — London :
Musica rara, 1974. — 4to.
Score (18p.) & 4 parts.
Unpriced

(B75-51174)

NURNR — Flute, strings & keyboard. Quintets
Kreutzer, Konradin
Quintet for flute, clarinet, viola, cello and piano in A major / [by]
Konradin Kreutzer ; edited by R.P. Block. — London : Musica
rara, 1974. — 4to.
Score (85p.) & 4 parts.
Unpriced

(B75-51175)

NURNT — Flute, strings & keyboard. Trios
Bennett, Richard Rodney
Commedia II : flute, cello and piano / [by] Richard Rodney
Bennett. — Sevenoaks : Novello, 1975. — 4to.
Score (16p.) & 2 parts.
£3.50

(B75-50634)

NURNTE — Flute, strings & keyboard. Sonatas
Dussek, Jan Ladislav
[Sonata for flute, cello & piano, op.65, in F major]. Grand sonata
in F major. Opus 65 : for flute (or violin) and piano / [by] Johann
Ladislaus Dussek ; ed. David Lasocki. — London : Musica rara,
1975. — 4to.
Score (45p.) & 2 parts.
£3.80

(B75-51176)

NUTNT — Oboe, strings & keyboard. Trios
Telemann, Georg Philipp
[Sonatina for oboe, violin & basso continuo in E minor]. Sonatine
in E minor : for oboe, violin and basso continuo / [by] Georg
Philipp Telemann ; edited by Klaus Hofmann. — First ed. —
Cassel ; London : Bärenreiter, 1974. — 4to.
Score (10p.) & 3 parts.
Unpriced

(B75-50635)

NUTNTE — Oboe, string & keyboard trio. Sonatas
Quantz, Johann Joachim
[Sonata for oboe, cello & basso continuo in G major]. Trio sonata
in G major : for oboe (or flute, violin, descant or tenor recorder),
violoncello or bassoon, and harpsichord (or piano), with a second
violoncello or basson ad lib. / [by] Johann Joachim Quantz ;
edited by Walter Bergmann. — London : Schott, 1975. — 4to.
Score (15p.) & 3 parts.
£2.00

(B75-50636)

NUVNS — Clarinet, strings & keyboard. Quartets
Wilson, Thomas
Complementi : clarinet doubling bass clarinet, violin, cello, piano /
[by] Thomas Wilson. — London : Central Music Library :
Chappell, 1975. — 29p ; 4to.
Unpriced

(B75-50637)

NUXSNRE — Trumpet, strings & keyboard quintet. Sonatas
Torelli, Giuseppe
[Sonata for trumpet, two violins, viola & basso continuo in D
major. G.6]. Sonata in D.G.6 : for trumpet, strings and continuo /
[by] Giuseppe Torelli ; edited by Edward H. Tarr, reduction by
Robert Paul Block. — London : Musica rara, 1975. — 4to.
Score (8p.) & 9 parts.
£4.50

(B75-51177)

NUXSNSK/LE — Trumpet, string & keyboard quartet.
Arrangements. Symphonies
Bononcini, Giovanni Battista
[Sinfonia no.10 for two trumpets & strings in D major. *arr*].
Sinfonia decima à 7 for 2 trumpets and strings / [by] Giovanni
Bononcini ; edited by Edward H. Tarr, reduction by Robert Paul
Block. — London : Musica rara, 1974. — 4to.
Score (14p.) & 4 parts.
Unpriced

(B75-51178)

NUXTNSK/LF — Horns, string & keyboard quartet. Arrangements.
Concertos
Vivaldi, Antonio
[Concerto for two horns & string orchestra in F major. P.320. *arr*]
. Concerto, F major, for two horns solo, strings, bassoon ad lib.
and basso continuo / [by] Antonio Vivaldi ; arranged for two
horns, violoncello and piano by Felix Schroeder. —
Wilhelmshaven : Heinrichshofen ; London : Hinrichsen, 1974. —
4to.
Score (23p) & 3 parts.
Unpriced

(B75-50638)

NUXUNSE — Trombone, strings & keyboard trio. Sonatas
Bertali, Antonio
[Sonata à 3 for two violins, trombone & basso continuo, no.3, in
A minor]. Sonata à 3, no.3, in A minor for 2 violins, trombone
and basso continuo / [by] Antonio Bertali ; ed. by Robert Wigness
and R.P. Block. — London : Musica rara, 1975. — 4to.
Score (8p.) & 4 parts.
£4.50

(B75-51179)

NV — WIND & STRINGS
NVNM — Nonets
Dalby, Martin
Cancionero para una mariposa : for flute, 2 bassoons, 2 trumpets
in C, 2 trombones, 2 cellos / [by] Martin Dalby. — Sevenoaks :
Novello, 1975. — 23p ; 4to.
Unpriced

(B75-50639)

NVNMF — Nonets. Concertos
Musgrave, Thea
Space play : a concerto for nine instruments / [by] Thea
Musgrave. — Sevenoaks : Novello, 1975. — 58p ; 4to.
Duration 20 min.
Unpriced

(B75-51180)

NVNMHVHM — Nonets. Polonaises
Egk, Werner
Polonaise und Adagio : für 9 instrumente, Oboe, Klarinette in B,
Horn in F, Fagott, Violine I und II, Viola, Violoncello, und
Kontrabass / [von] Werner Egk. — Mainz ; London : Schott,
1975. — 4to.
Study score (24p.) & 9 parts.
£7.50

(B75-51181)

NVNN — Octets
Françaix, Jean
[Octet for wind instruments]. Octuor pour clarinette en si bémol,
cor en Fa, basson, 2 violons, alto, violoncelle et contrebasse /
[par] Jean Françaix. — Mainz ; London : Schott, 1974. — 61p ;
4to.
£5.80
                                                                        (B75-50162)

NVNTK/AHR — Trios. Arrangements. Minuets
Haydn, Michael
[Six menuets for keyboard, nos. 1, 2, 3, 5. Perger 70]. Four
minuets / [by] Michael Haydn ; arranged for two clarinets in B
flat and bassoon (or cello) by Wadham Sutton. — Sevenoaks :
Novello, 1975. — 6p ; 8vo.
£0.30
Primary classification VNTK/AHR
                                                                        (B75-50313)

NVPK/AHW — Woodwind & strings. Arrangements. Waltzes
Strauss, Johann, b.1825
[Waltzes. *Selections: arr*]. Waltz themes from Strauss / arr. for
descant and treble recorders, melodica and guitar by Dick Sadleir.
— London : British and Continental, 1975. — 14p ; 8vo.
Unpriced
                                                                        (B75-51182)

NVPNN — Woodwind & strings. Octets
Josephs, Wilfred
[Octet for string & wind instruments]. Octet. Opus 43 : for strings
& winds, B flat clarinet, F horn, bassoon, violin I, violin II, viola,
violoncello, contrabass / [by] Wilfred Josephs. — New York ;
[London] : Chappell, 1972. — 4to.
Score & 8 parts.
Unpriced
                                                                        (B75-51183)

NVPNR — Woodwind & strings. Quintets
Cambini, Giovanni Giuseppe
[Quintets for wind & strings. Op.8, 9]. Sei quintetti. Op.8 & op.9 :
per flauto, oboe, violino, viola e basso / [di] Giuseppe Cambini ;
edizione a cura di Enrico Pardini ; introduzione storica di Alberto
Cavalli. — Padua ; Zanibon ; [London] : [Hinrichsen], 1974. —
102p ; 8vo.
Unpriced
                                                                        (B75-50163)

Prokofiev, Sergei
[Quintet for oboe, clarinet, violin, viola & double bass. Op.39].
Quintet. Opus 39 : for oboe, clarinet, violin, viola and double
bass / [by] Sergei Prokofieff ; edited by Albert Spalding. —
London : Boosey and Hawkes, 1975. — 52p ; 8vo.
£1.25
                                                                        (B75-50640)

Schwantner, Joseph
Consortium (I) : flute, B flat clarinet, violin, viola, violoncello /
[by] Joseph Schwantner. — New York ; London : Peters, 1973. —
27p ; 4to.
Duration 9 min.
Unpriced
                                                                        (B75-50641)

NVPNRG — Woodwind & strings quintet. Suites
Marshall, Nicholas
Suite for guitar, flute, clarinet, violin and cello / [by] Nicholas
Marshall. — London : Schott, 1975. — 4to.
Score (20p.) & 5 parts.
£1.00
                                                                        (B75-50642)

NVRNS — Flute & strings. Quartets
Cimarosa, Domenico
[Quartet for flute, violin, viola & cello, no.1, in D major]. Quartet
no.1 in D : for flute, violin, viola and cello / [by] Domenico
Cimarosa ; ed. Karl Lenski. — London : Musica rara, 1975. —
4pt ; 4to.
£2.00
                                                                        (B75-51184)

Cimarosa, Domenico
[Quartet for flute, violin, viola & cello, no.2, in F major]. Quarter
no.2 in F : for flute, violin, viola and cello / [by] Domenico
Cimarosa ; ed. Karl Lenski. — London : Musica rara, 1975. —
4pt ; 4to.
£2.00
                                                                        (B75-51185)

Cowell, Henry
[Quartet romantic for 2 flutes, violin & viola]. Quartet romantic :
2 flutes, violin, viola, and, Quartet euphometric : 2 violins, viola,
violoncello / [by] Henry Cowell. — New York ; London : Peters,
1974. — 31p ; 4to.
Unpriced
Also classified at RXNS
                                                                        (B75-50643)

NVRNT — Flute & strings. Trios
Françaix, Jean
[Trio for flute, harp & cello]. Trio pour flûte, harpe et
violoncelle / [par] Jean Françaix. — Mainz ; London : Schott,
1975. — 4to.
Score (51p.) & 2 parts.
£10.00
                                                                        (B75-51186)

Walker, Eldon
Terzetto : flute, viola and guitar / [by] Eldon Walker. —
London : Thames, 1974. — 6p ; fol.
Unpriced
                                                                        (B75-50644)

NVVNR — Clarinet & strings. Quintets
Krommer, Franz
[Quintet for clarinet & strings, op.95, in B flat major]. Quintet in
B flat. Opus 95 : for clarinet and strings / [by] Franz Krommer ;
edited by Georgina Dobrée, assisted by Howard Davis. —
London : Musica rara, 1975. — 6pt ; 4to.
Unpriced
                                                                        (B75-51187)

Reicha, Anton
[Quintet for clarinet & strings. Op.107, in F major]. Quintetto in
fa maggiore. Op.107 : per clarinetto, due violini, viola e
violoncello / [di] Antonin Rejcha ; edizione a cura di Ivan Merka.
— Padua : Zanibon ; [London] : [Hinrichsen], 1973. — 95p ; 8vo.
Unpriced
                                                                        (B75-50164)

NVVNS — Clarinet & strings. Quartets
Krommer, Franz
[Quartet for clarinet, violin, viola & cello, op.82, in D major].
Quartet in D. Opus 82 : for clarinet, violin, viola and cello / [by]
Franz Krommer ; edited by Georgina Dobrée. — London :
Musica rara, 1974. — 4pt ; 4to.
£3.00
                                                                        (B75-51188)

Krommer, Franz
[Quartet for clarinet, violin, viola & cello, op.83, in B flat major].
Quartet in B flat. Opus 83 : for clarinet, violin, viola and cello /
[by] Franz Krommer ; edited by Georgina Dobrée. — London :
Musica rara, 1974. — 4pt ; 4to.
£3.00
                                                                        (B75-51189)

NVVQNR — Clarinet in A & strings. Quartets
Simpson, Robert
Quintet for clarinet in A and string quartet (1968) / by Robert
Simpson. — South Croydon : Lengnick, 1974. — 8vo.
Score (170p.) & 5 parts.
Unpriced
                                                                        (B75-50165)

NWNS — Quartets
Berwald, Franz
[Quartet for wind & piano in E flat major]. Quartet in E flat
major for piano and wind instruments / by Franz Berwald ; edited
by Ingmar Bengtsson and Bonnie Hammar. — London :
Bärenreiter, 1974. — 4to.
Score (48p.) & 3 parts.
£4.80
                                                                        (B75-50166)

NWNTE — Trios. Sonatas
Finger, Godfrey
Sonata for trumpet, oboe and basso continuo in C major / [by]
Godfrey Finger ; edited by Robert Minter, continuo realised by
Barry Cooper and Michael Turnbull. — London : Musica rara,
1974. — 4to.
Score (10p.) & 3 parts.
Unpriced
                                                                        (B75-51190)

NWPNTE — Woodwind & keyboard trio. Sonatas
Platti, Giovanni
[Sonata for flute, oboe & basso continuo in G major]. Trio sonata
in G, for flute, oboe and basso continuo / [by] Giovanni Platti ;
edited by H. Voxman, continuo realisation by R. Hervig. —
London : Musica rara, 1975. — 4to.
Score (14p.) & part.
                                                                        (B75-51191)

Quantz, Johann Joachim
[Sonata for flute, oboe & basso continuo in C minor]. Trio sonata
in C minor for flute, oboe and basso continuo / [by] Johann J.
Qauntz ; edited by David Lasocki ; realisation of basso continuo
by R.P. Block. — London : Musica rara, 1975. — 4to.
Score (16p.) & 3 parts.
Unpriced
                                                                        (B75-51192)

Telemann, Georg Philipp
[Sonata for flute, oboe & continuo in E minor]. Sonata in E minor : for flute, oboe (violin) and basso continuo / [by] Georg Philipp Telemann ; edited by Klaus Hofmann. — 1st ed. — Cassel ; London : Bärenreiter, 1974. — 4to.
Score (14p.) & 3 parts.
£2.40
(B75-50167)

NWPNTK/LF — Woodwind & keyboard trio. Arrangements.
Concertos
Vivaldi, Antonio
[Concerto for oboe, bassoon & string orchestra in G major. P.129. arr]. Concerto in G major for oboe, bassoon, strings and basso continuo. P.129 / [by] Antonio Vivaldi ; ed. David Lasocki; piano reduction by R.P. Block. — London : Musica rara, 1974. — 4to.
Score (16p.) & part.
Unpriced
(B75-51193)

NWXP — BRASS & KEYBOARD
NWXPNR — Quintets
Loeffelholz, Klaus von
Choralbearbeitungen : für Blechbläser und Orgel / [von] Klaus von Loeffelholz. — Cassel ; London : Bärenreiter, 1974. — 16p ; 4to.
Unpriced
(B75-50645)

NWXPNRF — Quintets. Concertos
Wenzel, Eberhard
'Sollt ich meinem Gott nicht singen' : Choralkonzert für zwei Trompeten, zwei Posaunen und Orgel / [von] Eberhard Wenzel. — Cassel ; London : Bärenreiter, 1975. — 15p ; 4to.
Unpriced
(B75-50646)

NWXPNT — Trios
Hanmer, Ronald
[Flight of fancy. arr]. Flight of fancy : duet for cornet and euphonium with piano / [by] Ronald Hanmer. — London : R. Smith, 1975. — 6p ; 4to.
Unpriced
(B75-50647)

NX — STRINGS & KEYBOARD
NXNRG — Quintets. Suites
Schmierer, Johann Abraham
[Zodiaci musici. Part 1. Nos 1, 2]. Suites for four parts (strings or wind instruments and basso continuo) / [by] Johann Abraham Schmikerer ; edited by Waldemar Woehl. — Cassel ; London : Bärenreiter, 1974. — 4to.
Score (37p.) & 5 parts. — Contents: Suite 1 in F major - Suite 2 in D minor.
£4.80
(B75-50168)

NXNS — Quartets
Haydn, Joseph
[Divertimento for two violins, cello & keyboard in C major. Hob. XIV, 8]. Divertimento, C-dur : für Cembalo (Klavier), 2 Violinen und Violocello. Hoboken XIV, 8 / von Joseph Haydn. — Zum ersten Mal herausgegeben von Gyorgy Balla. — Frankfurt : Litolff ; London : Peters, 1973. — 15p ; 4to.
Unpriced
(B75-50169)

NXNT — Trios
Blacher, Boris
[Trio for violin, cello & piano]. Trio : für Klavier, Violine und Violoncello / [von] Boris Blacher. — Frankfurt : Belaieff ; [London] : [Peters], 1973. — 4to.
Score (27p.) & 2 parts.
Unpriced
(B75-50170)

Bochmann, Christopher
De profundis : meditation for violin, violoncello and piano / [by] Christopher Bochmann. — London : Oxford University Press, 1975. — 4to.
Score (14p.) & part.
ISBN 0-19-355560-3 : £2.50
(B75-50648)

Camilleri, Charles
[Trio for violin, cello & piano]. Piano trio / [by] Charles Camilleri. — Sevenoaks : Fairfield Music, 1975. — 4to.
Score (60p.) & 2 parts. — Duration 23 min.
£3.50
(B75-50171)

NXNTE — Trios. Sonatas
Purcell, Henry
[Sonatas of three parts (1683), for strings & basso continuo, nos 1-6, Z.790-5]. Sonatas for three parts, nos.1-6 / [by] Henry Purcell ; edited with a foreword by Roger Fiske. — London : Eulenburg, 1975. — xxi,40p ; 8vo.
Miniature score.
Unpriced
(B75-51194)

NYD — WIND, STRINGS, KEYBOARD & PERCUSSION
Lanza, Alcides
Acúfenos II (1971-IV) : for chamber ensemble, electronic sounds and electronic extensions / [by] Alcides Lanza. — New York ; London : Boosey and Hawkes, 1975. — 10p ; obl.fol.
Unpriced
(B75-51195)

NYDPNQ — Woodwind, strings, keyboard & percussion. Sextets
Harvey, Jonathan
Quantumplation : flute, clarinet in B flat, violin, cello, piano, tam tam / [by] Jonathan Harvey. — London : Central Music Library ; Sevenoaks : Novello, 1974. — 28p ; 4to.
Unpriced
(B75-50649)

Johnson, Robert Sherlaw
Triptych : for flute, clarinet, violin, cello, piano and percussion / [by] Robert Sherlaw Johnson. — London : Oxford University Press, 1975. — 22p ; 8vo.
Duration 12 min.
ISBN 0-19-357331-8 : £2.50
(B75-50650)

Rands, Bernard
Déjà : [for flute, clarinet, viola, cello, piano and percussion] / [by] Bernard Rands. — London : Universal, 1974. — 10p ; obl.4to.
Unpriced
(B75-50651)

NYDPNS — Woodwind, strings keyboard & percussion. Quartets
Jenni, Donald
Cucumber music : 'Metamorphosis' for 4 players, 9 instruments / by D. Jenni. — New York ; London : Associated Music, 1974. — 14ff ; 4to.
Unpriced
(B75-50652)

NYDSK/DW/AYDM — Recorders, strings, keyboard & percussion. Arrangements. Songs, etc. Collections. Ireland
Six Irish tunes / arranged for descant and treble or tenor recorders with piano, guitar, tuned and untuned percussion by Edith M. Lane. — Croydon : Lengnick, 1975. — 10p ; 4to.
Unpriced
(B75-50653)

NYDXU — Trombones, strings, keyboard & percussion
Matsushita, Shin-Ichi
Gestalt 17 : für Harfe, Klavier, Schlagzeug und drei Posaunen / [von] Shin-Ichi Matsushita. — London : Universal, 1974. — 14p ; 4to.
Unpriced
(B75-50172)

NYE — WIND, STRINGS & PERCUSSION
Gilbert, Anthony
Brighton piece. Op.9 : for percussion and instrumental ensemble / [by] Anthony Gilbert. — London : Schott, 1975. — 43p ; obl. 4to.
Unpriced
(B75-50654)

NYF — WIND, KEYBOARD & PERCUSSION
Fišer, Luboš
Report : for wind instruments, piano and percussion / [by] Luboš Fišer. — New York ; London : Peters, 1971. — 39p ; 4to.
Duration 8 min.
Unpriced
(B75-50173)

NYFPNP — Woodwind, keyboard & percussion. Quintets
Bergsma, William
Changes for seven : for woodwind quintet, percussion and piano / [by] William Bergsma. — New York ; Galaxy Music ; [London] : [Galliard], 1975. — 4to.
Score (20p.) & 6 parts.
Unpriced
(B75-51196)

NYFRHVS — Flute, keyboard & percussion. Tarantellas
Bamert, Matthias
Introduction and tarantella : trio for flute, percussion and piano / [by] Matthias Bamert. — New York ; London : Schirmer, 1975. — 21p ; obl.4to.
£1.55
(B75-51197)

NYFXSNNE — Trumpet, keyboard & percussion octet. Sonatas
Biber, Heinrich Ignaz Franz
[Sonata à 7 for six trumpets, timpani & organ]. Sonata à 7 (1688)
for 6 trumpets, timpani and organ / [by] Heinrich Ignaz Franz
Biber ; edited by R.L. Minter, organ part realised by Robert
Block. — London : Musica rara, 1974. — 4to.
Score (10p.) & 8 parts.
Unpriced

(B75-51198)

NYG — STRINGS, KEYBOARD & PERCUSSION
NYGFL — Concertinos
Antoniou, Theodore
[Concertino for piano, strings & percussion. Op.16b]. Concertino.
Op.16b : for piano, strings and percussion / [by] Theodore
Antoniou. — London : Cassel ; London : Bärenreiter, 1973. —
24p ; 4to.
Duration 11 min. — Study score.
£2.40

(B75-50174)

NYL — KEYBOARD & PERCUSSION
Smalley, Roger
Monody : for piano with live electronic modulation (1 player) /
[by] Roger Smalley. — London : Faber Music, 1975. — 10ff ;
obl.fol.
In four sections of the work, the pianist also plays percussion instruments
(triangles and drums).
£3.00
Primary classification QPVJ

(B75-50722)

PWP — KEYBOARD SOLOS
PWPE — Sonatas
Jacob, Gordon
Sonatina for piano or harpsichord / [by] Gordon Jacob. —
London : Chappell, 1975. — 9p ; 4to.
Unpriced

(B75-51199)

PWPJ — Miscellaneous works
Goebels, Franzpeter
Bird-boogie : for harpsichord (piano) / [by] Franzpeter Goebels.
— Cassel ; London : Bärenreiter, 1974. — 12p ; 4to.
Based upon William Byrd's 'Battell'.
£2.00

(B75-50175)

Huscroft, John
Jeykll [sic] and Hyde : solo for harpsichord or piano / [by] John
Huscroft. — Chelmsford (27 Donald Way, Chelmsford) : John
Huscroft, 1975. — 2p ; 4to.
Unpriced

(B75-50655)

Q — PIANO
Q/AC — Tutors
Kirkby-Mason, Barbara
It's time for music : a quick progress course for the piano class /
[by] Barbara Kirkby-Mason. — London : Faber Music, 1974. —
45p ; obl.8vo.
With a diagram of the piano keyboard inserted.
£0.75

(B75-50656)

Q/AF — Exercises
Pasfield, William Reginald
New look scales for piano / by W.R. Pasfield. — London :
Ashdown, 1975. — 16p ; 4to.
Unpriced

(B75-50657)

Q/AL — Examinations
Associated Board of the Royal Schools of Music
Pianoforte examinations, 1976. — London : Associated Board of
the Royal Schools of Music.
Grade 1. Lists A and B (primary). — 1975. — 12p ; 4to. —
£0.50

(B75-51200)
Grade 2. Lists A and B (elementary). — 1975. — 9p ; 4to. —
£0.50

(B75-51201)
Grade 3. Lists A and B (transitional). — 1975. — 14p ; 4to. —
£0.50

(B75-51202)
Grade 4. Lists A and B (lower). — 1975. — 15p ; 4to. —
£0.50

(B75-51203)
Grade 5. List A (higher). — 1975. — 11p ; 4to. —
£0.50

(B75-51204)
Grade 5. List B (higher). — 1975. — 10p ; 4to. —
£0.v0

(B75-51205)
Grade 6. List A (intermediate). — 1975. — 17p ; 4to. —
£0.50

(B75-51206)
Grade 6. List B (intermediate). — 1975. — 18p ; 4to. —
£0.v0

(B75-51207)

Associated Board of the Royal Schools of Music
Pianoforte examinations, 1976. — London : Associated Board of
the Royal School of Music.
Grade 7. List A (advanced). — 1975. — 15p ; 4to. —
£0.50

(B75-51208)

Associated Board of the Royal Schools of Music
Pianoforte examinations, 1976. — London : Associated Board of
the Royal Schools of Music.
Grade 7. List B (advanced). — 1975. — 17p ; 4to. —
£0.50

(B75-51209)
Grade 7. List B (advanced). — 1975. — 15p ; 4to. —
£0.50

(B75-51210)

Q/EG — Sight reading
Brown, Christine
Play at sight : a graded sight reading course / [by] Christine
Brown. — London : EMI.
Part 6. — 1975. — [1],24p ; 4to. —
Unpriced

(B75-51211)

Keilmann, Wilhelm
Ich spiele vom Blatt : Schule des Prima-Vista-Spiels : für Klavier
und andere Tasteninstrumente / [von] Wilhelm Keilman. —
Frankfurt : Litolff ; London : Peters.
Band 2. — 1975. — 64p ; 4to. —
Unpriced

(B75-50658)

Lockhart, Helen
Guided sight-reading / [by] Helen Lockhart. — Manchester :
Forsyth.
Book 3. — 1974. — [1],16p ; 4to. —
Unpriced

(B75-51212)

London College of Music
Examinations in pianoforte playing and singing, sight reading
tests, sight singing tests, as set throughout 1972, grades 1-8 and
diplomas. — London : Ashdown, 1973. — 15p ; 4to.
£0.35

(B75-50176)

QN — Ensembles
Brown, Earle
Twentyfive pages : for 1 to 25 pianos / [by] Earle Brown. —
Toronto ; [London] : Universal, 1975. — 22ff ; 4to.
In a folder bearing 'Directions for performance' in English and German.
Unpriced
Also classified at QPJ

(B75-51213)

Luening, Otto
The bells of Bellagio : 2 or 3 players at 1,2 or 3 pianos / [by]
Otto Luening. — New York ; [London] : Peters, 1973. — 11p ;
4to.
Unpriced

(B75-50177)

QNU — TWO PIANOS, 4 HANDS
Camilleri, Charles
Taqsim : for two pianos / [by] Charles Camilleri. — Sevenoaks :
Fairfield, 1975. — 32p ; 4to.
Duration 16 min.
£1.50

(B75-50659)

QNUK — Arrangements
Mozart, Wolfgang Amadeus
[Fantasy for mechanical organ in F minor. K.608. *arr*]. Fantasy
for mechanical organ. K.608 / [by] Wolfgang Amadeus Mozart ;
arranged for piano, four hands or two pianos, by Paul
Badura-Skoda. — New York ; London : Schirmer, 1974. — 19p ;
obl.4to.
Unpriced
Primary classification QNVK

(B75-50662)

QNUK/LF — Arrangements. Concertos
Panufnik, Andrzej
[Concerto for piano. *arr*]. Concerto for piano and orchestra
(recomposed 1972) / by Andrzej Panufnik ; reduction for two
pianos arranged by the composer. — London : Boosey and
Hawkes, 1974. — 42p ; 4to.
Duration 20 min.
£3.00

(B75-50178)

QNV — ONE PIANO, 4 HANDS
Del Tredici, David
Scherzo : for piano, four hands / [by] David del Tredici. — New
York ; [London] : Boosey and Hawkes, 1975. — 15p ; 4to.
Unpriced
(B75-50660)

Lambert, Cecily
Set of five piano duets / by Cecily Lambert. — London : Forsyth,
1974. — 27p ; 4to.
Unpriced
(B75-51214)

Le Fleming, Antony
Pop moods for young duettists : piano / [by] Antony le Fleming.
— London : Chappell, 1975. — 16p ; 4to.
Unpriced
(B75-51215)

Stravinsky, Soulima
Music alphabet : piano, four hands / [by] Soulima Stravinsky. —
New York ; London : Peters.
Vol.1. — 1973. — 41p ; 4to. —
Unpriced
(B75-50179)
Vol.2. — 1973. — 41p ; 4to. —
Unpriced
(B75-50180)

QNVG — Suites
Dello Joio, Norman
Stage parodies : piano suite for young players, for one piano, four
hands / [by] Norman dello Joio. — New York ; London :
Associated Music, 1975. — 19p ; 4to.
£1.30
(B75-51216)

Lambert, Cecily
Set of five : piano duets / [by] Cecily Lambert. — London :
Forsyth, 1974. — 27p ; 4to.
Unpriced
(B75-50181)

Tate, Phyllis
Lyric suite : for piano duet / [by] Phyllis Tate. — London :
Oxford University Press, 1975. — iv,59p ; 4to.
ISBN 0-19-373807-4 : £2.50
(B75-50661)

QNVH — Dances
Helyer, Marjorie
Two dance duets : for piano / [by] Marjorie Helyer. —
Sevenoaks : Novello, 1975. — 19p ; 4to.
£0.55
(B75-51217)

McMillan, Fiona
Three dances for piano duet / [by] Fiona McMillan. —
Manchester : Forsyth, 1975. — 17p ; 4to.
Contents: 1: Polka - 2: Mazurka - 3: Waltz.
Unpriced
(B75-51218)

QNVK — Arrangements
Mozart, Wolfgang Amadeus
[Fantasy for mechanical organ in F minor. K.608. arr]. Fantasy
for mechanical organ. K.608 / [by] Wolfgang Amadeus Mozart ;
arranged for piano, four hands or two pianos, by Paul
Badura-Skoda. — New York ; London : Schirmer, 1974. — 19p ;
obl.4to.
Unpriced
Also classified at QNUK
(B75-50662)

QNVK/AHM/AY — Arrangements. Gavottes. Collections
Two 18th century gavottes / [by] Samuel Wesley, william Boyce ;
arranged as easy piano duets by William Appleby. — York :
Banks, 1974. — 9p ; 4to.
Unpriced
(B75-50663)

QNVK/DP/LF/AY — Arrangements. Carols. Christmas. Collections
A Christmas pageant : carols from around the world and classical
Christmas excerpts / arranged for piano, piano duet and piano
and treble instrument by Donald Waxman. — New York :
Galaxy ; [London] : [Galliard], 1975. — 48p ; 4to.
Unpriced
Primary classification QPK/DP/LF/AY

QNVK/DW/G/AYC — Arrangements. Folk songs. Collections. Great Britain
Four folk duets / arranged for piano duet by John Longmire. —
Manchester ; London : Forsyth, 1975. — 11p ; 4to.
Unpriced
(B75-51219)

QNVK/DW/G/AYDL — Arrangements. Folk songs. Collections. Scotland
Three Scottish folk tunes / arranged for piano duet by Peter F.
Johnston. — London : Oxford University Press, 1975. — 7p ; 4to.
ISBN 0-19-372985-7 : Unpriced
(B75-51220)

QP — PIANO SOLOS
QP/AY — Collections
World's favourite more classic to contemporary piano music : early
grade piano music in its original form / selected and compiled by
Lawrence Grant. — Carlstadt : Ashley ; [London] : [Phoenix],
1975. — 160p ; 4to.
Unpriced
(B75-51221)

QP/AYG — Collections. Hungary
Ungarisches Klavierbuchlein = Hungarian piano booklet. —
Frankfurt : Litolff ; London : Peters, 1974. — 47p ; 4to.
Unpriced
(B75-50182)

QP/AZ — Collected works of individual composers
Liszt, Franz
[Piano music]. Piano works / [by] Franz Liszt. — Cassel ;
London : Bärenreiter.
Vol.7 : Années de pélerinage II / edited by Imré Sulyok and Imre Mezö ;
fingering revised by Kornel Zempléni. — 1974. — xii,123p ; 4to.
Unpriced
(B75-50664)

QP/GR — Activities
Slack, Roy
Moods and movement : [piano] / by Roy Slack. — London :
Keith Prowse Music, 1975. — 21p ; 4to.
Unpriced
(B75-51222)

QP/JM — Incidental music
Clayton, Kenny
The secret garden : an album for young pianists based on his
music for the recording of Francis Hodgson Burnett's novel / by
Kenny Clayton. — London : United Music, 1975. — 20p ; 4to.
Unpriced
(B75-51223)

QP/RM — Counterpoint
Last, Joan
Two of a kind : 8 short inventions introducing contrapuntal
style / [by] Joan Last. — Manchester ; London : Forsyth, 1975.
— 8p ; 4to.
Unpriced
(B75-50665)

Last, Joan
Two of a kind : 8 short inventions, for piano, introducing
contrapuntal style / by Joan Last. — Manchester ; London :
Forsyth, 1975. — 8p ; 4to.
Unpriced
(B75-51224)

QP/T — Variations
Stoker, Richard
Zodiac variations : twelve pieces of moderate difficulty for piano /
by Richard Stoker. — London : Ashdown, 1975. — 8p ; 4to.
Unpriced
(B75-50183)

QP/Y — Fugues
Reicha, Anton
36 fugues for the piano. Op.36 / [by] Antonin Rejcha ; edited by
Vaclav Jan Sykora. — Cassell ; London : Bärenreiter.
Vol.1 : Nos. 1-13. — 1973. — 51p ; 4to.
£3.20
(B75-50184)

Reicha, Anton
36 fugues for the piano. Op.36 / by Antonin Rejcha ; edited by
Vaclav Jan Sykora. — Cassel ; London : Bärenreiter.
Vol.2 : Nos. 14-24. — 1973. — 58p ; 4to.
£3.20
(B75-50185)
Vol.3 : Nos. 25-36. — 1973. — 54p ; 4to.
£3.20
(B75-50186)

QPE — Sonatas
Bochmann, Christopher
[Sonata for piano]. Sonata : piano / [by] Christopher Bochmann.
— London : Oxford University Press, 1974. — 17p ; 4to.
Duration 15 min.
ISBN 0-19-372287-9 : £2.00
(B75-50666)

Mozart, Wolfgang Amadeus
[Sonata for piano, no.16, in B flat major. K.570]. Sonata in B flat. K.570 / [by] Mozart ; edited by Stanley Sadie, fingering and notes on performance by Denis Matthews. — London : Associated Board of the Royal Schools of Music, 1975. — 17p ; 4to.
Unpriced

(B75-51225)

Stravinsky, Igor
[Sonata for piano in F sharp minor]. Sonata in F sharp minor (1903-4) for piano / [by] Igor Stravinsky ; edited by Eric Walter White. — London : Faber Music, 1974. — 42p ; 4to.
Unpriced

(B75-50667)

Tippett, *Sir* Michael
Sonata no.3 for piano / [by] Michael Tippett. — London : Schott, 1975. — 42p ; 4to.
Unpriced

(B75-51226)

Wuorinen, Charles
Sonata for piano / [by] Charles Wuorinen. — New York ; London : Peters, 1973. — 41p ; 4to.
Duration 20 min.
Unpriced

(B75-50187)

QPE/AY — Sonatas. Collections
Five eighteenth century piano sonatas / edited with introductory notes by Stoddard Lincoln. — London : Oxford University Press, 1975. — 52p ; 4to.
Works by Schroeter, Küffner, Kozeluch, Latrobe and Kirkman.
ISBN 0-19-373206-8 : Unpriced

(B75-51227)

QPE/AZ — Sonatas. Collected works of individual composers
Hummel, Johann Nepomak
[Sonatas for piano. *Collections*]. Complete piano sonatas / [by] J.N. Hummel ; with an introduction by Harold Truscott. — London : Musica rara.
Vol.1. — 1975. — ix,89p ; 4to. — £6.00

(B75-51228)

Vol.2. — 1975. — ix,91p ; 4to. — £6.00

(B75-51229)

QPG — Suites
Agay, Denes
Petit Trianon suite : ten easy pieces on 18th century style dance melodies, for piano / by Denes Agay. — New York ; London : Schirmer, 1974. — 15p ; 4to.
Unpriced

(B75-50668)

Butterworth, Neil
Ewell Court suite : for piano solo / [by] Neil Butterworth. — York : Banks, 1974. — 4p ; 4to.
Unpriced

(B75-50669)

Debussy, Claude
Pour le piano : piano solo / [by] Claude Debussy ; edited by H. Swarsenski. — London : Peters, 1975. — 31p ; 4to.
Unpriced

(B75-51230)

Whittaker, Anthony F
Warwick suite : for pianoforte solo / [by] Anthony F. Whittaker. — Leamington Spa (22 Waller St., Leamington Spa, Warwickshire) : Anthony Music, 1975. — 16p ; 4to.
£0.60

(B75-50670)

QPGM — Marches
Alt, Hansi
March for the piano / [by] Hansi Alt. — New York ; [London] : Oxford University Press, 1971. — 4p ; 4to.
Unpriced

(B75-50671)

Blot, André
Cornouailles march : piano / [par] André Blot et Paul Piot. — Paris ; [London] : Chappell, 1972. — 2p ; 4to.
Unpriced

(B75-50672)

Field, John
Marche triomphale : for piano / [by] John Field ; edited by David Branson. — Hastings : Helicon, 1975. — 3p ; 4to.
Unpriced

(B75-50673)

QPH — Dances
Debussy, Claude
Danse : piano solo / [by] Claude Debussy ; edited by H. Swarsenski. — London : Peters, 1975. — 15p ; 4to.
Unpriced

(B75-50674)

Judd, Margaret
Spring dances : for pianoforte / by Margaret Judd. — London : Bosworth, 1975. — 5p ; 4to.
Unpriced

(B75-50675)

QPHQ — Mazurkas
Chopin, Frederic
[Mazurka for piano, op.68, no.4, in F minor]. Mazurka in F minor. Op.68, no.4, (The final composition) / [by] F. Chopin ; a completely new realisation by Ronald Smith. — London : Hansen House, 1975. — 6p ; 4to.
Unpriced

(B75-50676)

Debussy, Claude
Mazurka : piano solo / [by] Claude Debussy ; edited by H. Swarsenski. — London : Peters, 1975. — 8p ; 4to.
Unpriced

(B75-50677)

QPHVHM — Polonaises
Mozart, Franz Xavier
[Quatre Polonaises mélancoliques. Op.22]. Four polonaises : for piano / [by] Franz Xavier Mozart. — 1st ed. [reprinted] ; with an introduction by Stoddard Lincoln. — London : Oxford University Press, 1975. — 7p ; obl. 4to.
Facsimile reprint.
ISBN 0-19-373410-9 : £1.20

(B75-50678)

QPHVK — Riguadons
Hunt, Reginald Heber
Rigadoon : piano solo / [by] Reginald Hunt. — London : Ashdown, 1975. — 4p ; 4to.
Unpriced

(B75-50679)

QPHVR — Tangos
Neill, David
[Armalita. *arr*]. Armalita : tango / [by] David Neill ; [arranged for piano]. — London : Swan, 1975. — 3p ; 4to.
Unpriced

(B75-50680)

QPHW — Waltzes
Debussy, Claude
Valse romantique : piano solo / [by] Claude Debussy ; edited by H. Swarsenski. — London : Peters, 1975. — 8p ; 4to.
Unpriced

(B75-50681)

Gershwin, George
[Waltzes]. George Gershwin's two waltzes in C : piano solo / edited by Ira Gershwin ; adapted by Saul Chaplin. — New York : Warner ; [London] : [Blossom], 1971. — 7p ; 4to.
Unpriced

(B75-50682)

QPHXJ — Ragtime
Joplin, Scott
[Piano music. *Selections : arr*]. Scott Joplin ragtime rags / piano transcriptions compiled, arranged and edited by John W. Schaum. — London : Bosworth.
Book 1. — 1974. — 16p ; 4to.
Unpriced

(B75-50683)

Book 2. — 1974. — 15p ; 4to.
Unpriced

(B75-50684)

QPJ — Miscellaneous works
Bach, Johann Sebastian
[Keyboard music. *Selections: arr*]. Bach music : simple style, for piano / arranged or simplified by Stan Applebaum. — New York ; London : Schroeder and Gunther, 1975. — iv,40p ; 4to.
Time signatures and note values have been altered, tied notes have been eliminated where the tie would not be missed, embellishments have been written out (and occasionally deleted) and in one instance a key has been changed. The aim: simplification for reading and learning - Editor's note.
£1.30

(B75-51231)

Bailey, Freda O
Nocturne : for pianoforte / [by] Freda O. Bailey. — Leeds : Regina, 1975. — 3p ; 4to.
Unpriced

(B75-51232)

Balta, Freddy
Improvisation no.V : piano / [par] Freddy Balta. — Paris ;
[London] : Chappell, 1972. — 2p ; 4to.
Unpriced
(B75-50685)

Berkowitz, Sol
Nine folk song preludes : for piano / [by] Sol Berkowitz. — New
York ; [London] : Frank Music, 1972. — 23p ; 4to.
Unpriced
(B75-50686)

Binkerd, Gordon
Five pieces : for piano / [by] Gordon Binkerd. — New York ;
[London] : Boosey and Hawkes, 1975. — 18p ; 4to.
£2.00
(B75-50687)

Branson, David
Six preludes for piano (in differing time signatures) / [by] David
Branson. — Hastings : David Branson, 1974. — 15p ; 4to.
Unpriced
(B75-51233)

Brown, Earle
Twentyfive pages : for 1 to 25 pianos / [by] Earle Brown. —
Toronto ; [London] : Universal, 1975. — 22ff ; 4to.
In a folder bearing 'Directions for performance' in English and German.
Unpriced
Primary classification QN

Camilleri, Charles
African dreams : [piano] / [by] Charles Camilleri. — Wendover :
Roberton, 1975. — 28p ; fol.
Contents: Hymn to morning - Rain forest fantasy - Experience of conflict -
Festival drumming - Children's lagoon - A dance - Ritual celebration.
£1.50
(B75-51234)

Camilleri, Charles
Four ragamats, 1967-1970 : [piano] / [by] Charles Camilleri. —
Wendover : Roberton, 1975. — 42p ; fol.
£2.00
(B75-51235)

Camilleri, Charles
Pieces for Anya : for piano solo / by Charles Camilleri. —
London : Roberton, 1975. — 7p ; 4to.
£0.50
(B75-51236)

Cooper, Joseph
Joseph Cooper's hidden melodies : six improvisations for piano /
cartoons by ffolkes. — Sevenoaks : Paxton, 1975. — 24p : ill ; 4to.
Unpriced
(B75-51237)

Da-Veena
To a mountain stream : piano / [by] Da-Veena. — Stamford,
Conn. : Pandian Press ; [London] : [Galliard], 1975. — 6p ; 4to.
Unpriced
(B75-51238)

Debussy, Claude
Ballade : piano solo / [by] Claude Debussy ; edited by H.
Swarsenski. — London : Peters, 1975. — 10p ; 4to.
Unpriced
(B75-50688)

Debussy, Claude
Etudes : piano solo / [by] Claude Debussy ; edited by H.
Swarsenski. — London : Peters.
Book 1. — 1975. — 40p ; 4to.
Unpriced
(B75-51239)
Book 2. — 1975. — 42p ; 4to.
Unpriced
(B75-51240)

Debussy, Claude
Hommage à Haydn : [piano] / by Claude Debussy ; edited by H.
Swarsenksi. — London : Peters, 1975. — 6p ; 4to.
Unpriced
(B75-50689)

Debussy, Claude
Images : piano solo / [by] Claude Debussy ; edited by H.
Swarsenski. — London : Peters.
Book I. — 1975. — 27p ; 4to.
Unpriced
(B75-50690)
Book II. — 1975. — 30p ; 4to.
Unpriced
(B75-50691)

Debussy, Claude
[The little nigar]. The little negro = Le petit Negre : piano solo /
[by] Claude Debussy ; edited by H. Swarsenski. — London :
Peters, 1975. — 7p ; 4to.
Unpriced
(B75-50692)

Debussy, Claude
Masques : [piano] / [by] Claude Debussy ; edited by H.
Swarsenski. — London : Peters, 1975. — 15p ; 4to.
Unpriced
(B75-50693)

Debussy, Claude
Nocturne : piano solo / [by] Claude Debussy. — London : Peters,
1975. — 8p ; 4to.
Unpriced
(B75-50694)

Debussy, Claude
Rêverie : [piano] / [by] Claude Debussy ; edited by H. Swarsenski.
— London : Peters, 1975. — 7p ; 4to.
Unpriced
(B75-50695)

Del Tredici, David
Soliloquy : for piano / [by] David del Trecici. — New York ;
[London] : Boosey and Hawkes, 1975. — 10p ; 4to.
£1.50
(B75-50696)

Duke, Henry
One man went to Mo-zart : piano solo / by Henry Duke. —
London : Feldman, 1974. — 4p ; 4to.
Unpriced
(B75-50188)

Duke, Henry
Two-way pieces : twelve progressive miniatures, for piano solo,
with optional descant recorder / by Henry Duke. — London :
British and Continental, 1975. — 12p ; 4to.
Unpriced
(B75-51241)

Fanshawe, David
African Sanctus : piano with voice-part optional / [by] David
Fanshawe. — London : Chappell, 1975. — 4p ; 4to.
Unpriced
(B75-50697)

Fauré, Gabriel
[Piano music. *Selections*]. Selected pieces / [by] Gabriel Fauré ;
complied [sic] and edited for piano solo by Robin de Smet. —
London : Cramer, 1975. — 72p ; 4to.
Unpriced
(B75-50189)

Fly, Leslie
London pictures : piano solos / [by] Leslie Fly. — Manchester ;
London : Forsyth, 1975. — 10p ; 4to.
Unpriced
(B75-51242)

Gedike, Aleksandr Fedorovich
[Sixty pieces for piano. Op.36]. Sechzig Klavierstücke : für
Anfänger / [von] ; A. Goedicke. — Leipzig ; [London] : Peters.
Heft 1. — 1969. — 24p ; 4to.
Unpriced
(B75-50190)

Gedike, Aleksandr Fedorovich
[Sixty pieces for piano. Op.36]. Sechzig Klavierstücke : für
Anfänger / [von] A. Goedicke. — Leipzig ; [London] : Peters.
Heft 2. — 1969. — 24p ; 4to.
Unpriced
(B75-50191)

Gottschalk, Louis Moreau
[Piano music. *Selections*]. Ten compositions for pianoforte / [by]
Louis Moreau Gottschalk ; edited by Amiram Rigai. — New
York ; [London] : Chappell, 1972. — 103p ; 4to.
Unpriced
(B75-50698)

Grechaninov, Aleksandr Tikhonovich
[Kinderbuch. Op.98]. Kinder-Album. Op.98 : für Klavier
zweihändig / [von] A. Gretschaninoff. — Leipzig ; [London] :
Peters, 1970. — 11p ; 4to.
Unpriced
(B75-50192)

Haydn, Joseph
[Piano music. *Selections*]. Haydn / selected, edited and annotated
by Howard Ferguson. — London : Oxford University Press, 1972.
— 62p ; 4to.
ISBN 0-19-372782-x : £1.50
(B75-51243)

Heiss, John C
  Four short pieces : for piano / [by] John C. Heiss. — New York ;
  [London] : Boosey and Hawkes, 1975. — 4p ; 4to.
  Unpriced
                                                              (B75-50699)

Hovhaness, Alan
  Komachi. Opus 240 : piano solo / [by] Alan Hovhaness ; ed. by
  Naru Hovhaness. — New York ; [London] : Peters, 1973. —
  16p ; 4to.
  Duration 11 min.
  Unpriced
                                                              (B75-50193)

Humble, Keith
  Arcade II : for piano solo / [by] Keith Humble. — [Sydney] ;
  [London] : Universal, 1975. — 4ff ; obl.4to.
  Unpriced
                                                              (B75-50700)

Jenni, Donald
  A game of dates : for piano / [by] Donald Jenni. — New York ;
  London : Associated Music, 1974. — 11p ; 4to.
  Unpriced
                                                              (B75-50701)

Judd, Margaret
  The witches : for piano / [by] Margaret Judd. — London :
  Bosworth, 1975. — 3p ; 4to.
  Unpriced
                                                              (B75-50702)

Judd, Margaret
  The witches : for piano / by Margaret Judd. — London :
  Bosworth, 1975. — 3p ; 4to.
  Unpriced
                                                              (B75-50703)

Kabalevsky, Dmitry
  [Piano music. *Selections*]. Kabalevsky for the young pianist /
  compiled and edited by David Goldberger. — New York ;
  London : Schroeder and Gunther, 1974. — 32p ; 4to.
  Unpriced
                                                              (B75-51244)

Kasschau, Howard
  Five beginner's pieces : for piano / [by] Howard Kasschau. —
  New York ; London : Schirmer, 1974. — 11p ; 4to.
  Unpriced
                                                              (B75-51245)

Kasschau, Howard
  Seven recital pieces : for piano / [by] Howard Kasschau. — New
  York ; London : Schirmer, 1975. — 23p ; 4to.
  Unpriced
                                                              (B75-51246)

Kasschau, Howard
  Six easy pieces : for piano / by Howard Kasschau. — New York ;
  London : Schirmer, 1974. — 13p ; 4to.
  Unpriced
                                                              (B75-51247)

King, Janet
  Time to play : for piano / by Janet King. — London : M.S.M.,
  1975. — 17p ; 4to.
  Unpriced
                                                              (B75-51248)

Last, Joan
  The day's play : [piano] / by Joan Last. — Manchester ; London :
  Forsyth, 1974. — 11p ; 4to.
  Unpriced
                                                              (B75-51249)

Last, Joan
  Village pictures : [piano] / by Joan Last. — London : Forsyth,
  1975. — 8p ; 4to.
  Unpriced
                                                              (B75-50704)

Last, Joan
  Village pictures : piano pieces / by Joan Last. — London :
  Forsyth, 1975. — 8p ; 4to.
  Unpriced
                                                              (B75-51250)

Lavagne, Andre
  Etude baroque : grand étude de concert pour piano / [par] Andre
  Lavagne. — Paris ; [London] : Chappell, 1971. — 17p ; 4to.
  Unpriced
                                                              (B75-50194)

Meale, Richard
  Coruscations : piano / [by] Richard Meale. — [Sydney] ;
  [London] : Universal, 1975. — 15p ; obl.4to.
  Unpriced
                                                              (B75-50705)

Parke, Dorothy
  The little senorita : for piano solo / [by] Dorothy Parke. —
  York : Banks, 1974. — 3p ; 4to.
  Unpriced
                                                              (B75-50706)

Payne, Anthony
  Paean : for piano / [by] Anthony Payne. — London : Chester,
  1974. — 15p ; 4to.
  Contents: Toccata - Aria - Paean. — Duration 10 1/2 min.
  Unpriced
                                                              (B75-50707)

Rose, Michael
  Five portraits : for piano / [by] Michael Rose. — London :
  British and Continental, 1975. — 11p ; 4to.
  Unpriced
                                                              (B75-51251)

Roxburgh, Edwin
  Labyrinth : for piano / [by] Edwin Roxburgh. — London : United
  Music, 1975. — 12p ; 4to.
  Unpriced
                                                              (B75-50708)

Saxton, Robert
  Ritornelli and intermezzi : piano / [by] Robert Saxton. —
  London : Chester, 1975. — 16p ; 4to.
  Unpriced
                                                              (B75-51252)

Schubert, Franz
  [Piano music. *Selections*]. Schubert / a selection edited and
  annotated by Stephen Bishop with an introduction by Howard
  Ferguson. — London : Oxford University Press, 1972. — 58p ;
  4to.
  ISBN 0-19-373653-5 : £1.90
                                                              (B75-51253)

Schurmann, Gerard
  Contrasts : for piano / [by] Gerard Schurmann. — Sevenoaks :
  Novello, 1975. — 28p ; 4to.
  Duration 15 min.
  Unpriced
                                                              (B75-50709)

Skriabin, Aleksandr
  [Piano music. *Selections*]. Selected piano works / [by] Alexander
  Skrjabin. — Leipzig ; [London] : Peters.
  Vol.6 : Sonatas nos 6-10 / edited by Gunter Philipp. — 1974. — 120p ; 4to.
  Unpriced
                                                              (B75-50195)

Smith, J. Ferguson
  A trip to the circus : [piano] / [by] J. Ferguson Smith. —
  Manchester : Forsyth, 1975. — 16p ; 4to.
  Unpriced
                                                              (B75-51254)

Songayllo, Raymond
  Ten short piano pieces / [by] Raymond Songayllo. — New York ;
  [London] : Oxford University Press, 1975. — 12p ; 4to.
  Unpriced
                                                              (B75-50710)

Stravinsky, Igor
  [Scherzo for piano (1902)]. Scherzo (1902) : for piano / [by] Igor
  Stravinsky ; edited by Eric Walter White. — 1st ed. — London :
  Faber Music, 1974. — 7p ; 4to.
  Unpriced
                                                              (B75-50711)

Tchaikowsky, André
  Inventions for piano. Opus 2 / [by] André Tchaikowsky. —
  Sevenoaks : Novello, 1975. — 36p ; 4to.
  £1.00
                                                              (B75-50712)

Thiman, Eric Harding
  Chatter box : piano solo / [by] Eric H. Thiman. — London :
  British and Continental, 1975. — 3p ; 4to.
  Unpriced
                                                              (B75-50713)

Tjeknavorian, Loris
  Armenian sketches : piano solo / [by] Loris Tjeknavorian. —
  Sevenoaks : Novello, 1975. — 32p ; 4to.
  £1.00
                                                              (B75-50714)

QPK — Arrangements
Bach, Johann Sebastian
[Selections. *arr*]. Bach. The fugue / edited for keyboard and annotated by Charles Rosen. — London : Oxford University Press, 1975. — 62p ; 4to.
ISBN 0-19-372220-8 : Unpriced
(B75-51255)

Schumann, Robert
[Selections. *arr*]. Schumann / transcribed and simplified for piano by Cyril C. Dalmaine. — London : Warren and Phillips, 1974. — 26p ; 4to.
Unpriced
(B75-50196)

QPK — Arrangments
Binge, Ronald
[The watermill. *arr*]. The watermill / [by] Ronald Binge ; arranged for solo piano by the composer. — London : Inter-Art, 1975. — 4p ; 4to.
£0.30
(B75-50715)

QPK/AAY — Arrangements. Collections
My first collection : containing interesting examples of works by composers through the ages for the developing pianist / selected and edited by Barbara Kirkby-Mason. — London : Bosworth, 1974. — 23p ; 4to.
Unpriced
(B75-50716)

My second collection : containing interesting examples of works by composers through the ages for the developing pianist / selected and edited by Barbara Kirkby-Mason. — London : Bosworth, 1974. — 24p ; 4to.
Unpriced
(B75-50717)

My third collection containing interesting examples of works by composers through the ages for the developing pianist / selected and edited by Barbara Kirkby-Mason. — London : Bosworth, 1975. — 23p ; 4to.
Unpriced
(B75-50718)

Piano music by the great masters : the baroque era, the classic era, the romantic era / selected by Laurence Grant. — Carlstadt : Ashley ; [London] : [Phoenix], 1975. — 144p ; 4to.
Unpriced
(B75-51256)

World's favorite popular classics : for piano / edited and arranged by Lawrence Grant. — Carlstadt : Ashley ; [London] : [Phoenix], 1972. — 160p ; 4to.
Unpriced
(B75-51257)

QPK/AHVR — Arrangements. Tangos
Smith, Bryan
[Tango el Torro. *arr*]. Tango el Torro : [piano] / [by] Bryan Smith. — London : Swan, 1974. — 3p ; 4to.
Unpriced
(B75-51258)

QPK/AYT — Arrangements. Collections. United States
The America book for piano / compiled, edited, transcribed and with original settings of the traditional works, by William Déguire. — New York : Galaxy ; [London] : [Galliard], 1975. — 83p ; 8vo.
Unpriced
(B75-51259)

QPK/CM — Arrangements. Musical plays
Sondheim, Stephen
[A little night music. A little night music. *arr*]. A little night music : [piano] / by Stephen Sondheim. — London : Chappell, 1975. — 3p ; 4to.
(B75-51260)

QPK/DP/LF/AY — Arrangements. Carols. Christmas. Collections
Christmas carols made easy : for piano with guitar chords / arranged by Janet King. — London : M.S.M., 1975. — 20p ; 4to.
Unpriced
(B75-51261)

A Christmas pageant : carols from around the world and classical Christmas excerpts / arranged for piano, piano duet and piano and treble instrument by Donald Waxman. — New York : Galaxy ; [London] : [Galliard], 1975. — 48p ; 4to.
Unpriced
Also classified at QNVK/DP/LF/AY
(B75-51262)

QPK/DW/G/AYDL — Arrangements. Folk songs. Collections. Scotland
Melodies of Robert Burns / arranged for piano by Harry Dorman. — London : Warren and Phillips, 1975. — 25p ; 4to.
Unpriced
(B75-50719)

QPK/DW/G/AYULD — Arrangements. Folk songs. Collections. Jamaica
Eight Jamaican folk-songs / arranged for piano solo by Barbara Kirkby-Mason. — London : Oxford University Press, 1975. — 7p ; 4to.
ISBN 0-19-373273-4 : £0.50
(B75-50720)

QPK/DW/LF — Arrangements. Songs, etc. Christmas
Naylor, Frank
Twelve days of Christmas : traditional song / arranged for piano by Frank Naylor. — London : Bosworth, 1975. — 3p ; 4to.
Unpriced
(B75-51263)

QPK/JR — Arrangements. Films
Rota, Nina
[The godfather, part 2. Theme. *arr*]. Theme from Godfather 2 : piano solo / by Nina Rota. — New York : Famous Music ; [London] : [Chappell], 1974. — 4to.
Unpriced
(B75-50197)

Rota, Nino
[The godfather, part 2. Kay's theme. *arr*]. Kay's theme : piano solo / music by Nino Rota. — New York : Famous Music ; London : Chappell, 1974. — 3p ; 4to.
Unpriced
(B75-50198)

QPK/JS — Arrangements. Television
Patterson, Paul
[Country search. Theme. *arr*]. Country search : [piano] / music by Paul Patterson from the BBC TV series. — London : Weinberger, 1975. — 4p ; 4to.
£0.30
(B75-51264)

South, Harry
[The Sweeney. Theme. *arr*]. 'The Sweeney' : theme from the Thames television series, [for piana] / by Harry South. — London : Sparta Florida Music : Chappell, 1975. — 4p ; 4to.
Unpriced
(B75-50199)

QPK/JS/AY — Arrangements. Television. Collections
Twenty great TV themes / arranged for piano solo, including six songs with piano accompaniment. — London : Essex Music, 1975. — 76p ; 4to.
Unpriced
Also classified at KDW/JS/AY
(B75-50721)

QPVJ — Piano with electronic modulation. Miscellaneous works
Smalley, Roger
Monody : for piano with live electronic modulation (1 player) / [by] Roger Smalley. — London : Faber Music, 1975. — 10ff ; obl.fol.
In four sections of the work, the pianist also plays percussion instruments (triangles and drums).
£3.00
Also classified at NYL
(B75-50722)

QRP — HARPSICHORD SOLOS
QRP/AZ — Collected works of individual composers
Croft, William
[Harpsichord music]. Complete harpsichord works of William Croft / newly transcribed and edited by Howard Ferguson and Christopher Hogwood. — London : Stainer and Bell.
Vol.1. — 1974. — 47p ; 4to.
Unpriced
(B75-50200)

Vol.2. — 1974. — 48p ; 4to.
Unpriced
(B75-50201)

Handel, George Frideric
[Keyboard music]. Keyboard works / [by] Georg Friedrich Händel. — Cassel ; London : Bärenreiter.
Vol.1 : First set of 1720, The eight great suites / edited by Rudolf Steglich. — 1974. — xxi,81p ; 4to.
£3.00
(B75-50202)

QRPG — Suites
Baumann, Herbert
Suite für Cembalo / [von] Herbert Baumann. — Wilhemshaven : Heinrichshofen ; [London] : [Hinrichsen], 1975. — 10p ; 4to.
Unpriced
(B75-50723)

QRPJ — Miscellaneous works
Clarke, Jeremiah
 [Harpsichord music. *Selections*]. Selected works for keyboard /
 [by] Jeremiah Clarke ; edited by Eve Barsham. — London :
 Oxford University Press, 1975. — 21p ; 4to.
 ISBN 0-19-372417-0 : £1.30
(B75-50724)

QSQ — VIRGINALS
QSQ/AY — Collections
 Anne Cromwell's Virginal Book, 1638 / transcribed and edited by
 Howard Ferguson. — London : Oxford University Press, 1974. —
 iv,51p ; 4to.
 ISBN 0-19-372637-8 : £2.50
(B75-50725)

 Elizabeth Rogers hir virginall booke / editing and calligraphy by
 Charles J.F. Cofone. — New York : Dover ; London : Constable,
 1975. — xxiii,125p ; fol.
 ISBN 0-486-23138-0 : £3.00
(B75-51265)

R — ORGAN
R/AF — Exercises
Stoker, Richard
 Contemporary organ technique : 20 progressive studies and
 pieces / by Richard Stoker ; edited and introduced by Winifred
 M. Smith. — London : Ashdown, 1975. — 22p ; obl.4to.
 £1.20
(B75-51266)

R/AY — Collections
 Organ music for manuals / edited by C.H. Trevor. — London :
 Oxford University Press.
 Book 5. — 1975. — 32p ; 4to.
 ISBN 0-19-375852-0 : Unpriced
(B75-51267)
 Book 6. — 1975. — 32p ; 4to.
 ISBN 0-19-375853-9 : Unpriced
(B75-51268)

 Short chorale preludes with and without pedals / edited by C.H.
 Trevor. — London : Oxford University Press.
 Book 1. — 1975. — 24p ; 4to.
 ISBN 0-19-375843-1 : £0.95
(B75-50726)
 Book 2. — 1975. — 25p ; 4to.
 ISBN 0-19-375844-x : £0.95
(B75-50727)

R/AYC — Collections. Great Britain
 A **second** easy album for organ : six pieces / by contemporary
 British composers. — London : Oxford University Press, 1975. —
 19p ; 4to.
 Contents: 1. Pavane / by Paul Drayton - 2. Scherzo / by Alan Ridout - 3.
 Prelude / by W.H. Harris - 4. Interlude / by David Lord - 5. Saraband and
 interlude / by Herbert Sumsion - 6. Toccata in seven / by John Rutter.
 ISBN 0-19-375129-1 : £0.90
(B75-50728)

R/LEZ — Advent
Reda, Siegfried
 [Sechs Intonationen und Cantus-firmus]. Sechs Intonationen und
 Cantus-firmus-Stücke zu Adventsliedern des EKG (1959), [with]
 Anhang Anbetung des Kindes Jesus (1965) : für Orgel / von
 Siegfried Reda ; herausgegeben von Hans Martin Balz. — Cassel ;
 London : Bärenreiter, 1974. — 27p ; obl.fol.
 Unpriced
(B75-50729)

R/T — Variations
Thomas, Paul Lindsley
 Variations on the Welsh hymn tune 'Aberystwyth', Op.3 : for
 organ / [by] Paul Lindsley Thomas. — New York ; [London] :
 Oxford University Press, 1972. — 12p ; 4to.
 Unpriced
(B75-51269)

R/Y — Fugues
Albrechtsberger, Johann Georg
 [Six fugues for organ. Op.7]. Sechs Fugen für Orgel/Cembalo.
 Opus 7 / [von] Johann Georg Albrechtsberger ; herausgegben von
 Imre Sulyok. — Frankfurt : Litolff ; London : Peters, 1974. —
 32p ; 4to.
 Unpriced
(B75-50203)

Merkel, Gustav
 [Sonata for organ, op.30, in D minor. Fugue]. Fugue for organ
 duet / by Gustav Merkel. — London : Oxford University Press,
 1975. — 11p ; obl. 4to.
 ISBN 0-19-375561-0 : £0.75
(B75-50204)

RE — Sonatas
Hall, John
 [Sonatina for organ, no.1. Op.46]. Sonatina no.1. Op.46 : for organ
 manual / [by] John Hall. — London : Chappell, 1975. — 12p ;
 4to.
 Contents: 1: Intrada - 2: Siciliano - 3: Toccata.
 Unpriced
(B75-51270)

RHG — Dance suites
Ridout, Alan
 Dance suite : for organ / by Alan Ridout. — London : Chappell,
 1975. — 21p ; 4to.
 Unpriced
(B75-51271)

RJ — Miscellaneous works
Balada, Leonardo
 Elementalis : for organ / [by] Leonardo Balada. — New York ;
 London : Schirmer, 1975. — 8p ; 4to.
 £0.80
(B75-51272)

Bialas, Günter
 Ewartung : Orgelspiel / [von] Günter Bialas. — Cassel ; London :
 Bärenreiter, 1973. — 16p ; fol.
 Duration 22 min.
 £2.60
(B75-50205)

Chapple, Brian
 Praeludiana : for organ / [by] Brian Chapple. — London :
 Chester, 1974. — 17p ; 4to.
 Duration 12 min.
 Unpriced
(B75-50730)

Forbes, Sebastian
 Capriccio : organ / [by] Sebastian Forbes. — London : Oxford
 University Press, 1975. — 10p ; 4to.
 Duration 4 min.
 ISBN 0-19-375382-0 : £1.30
(B75-50731)

Gerber, Heinrich Nicolaus
 [Inventions. *Selections*]. Four inventions / by H.N. Gerber ; edited
 by Susi Jeans. — Sevenoaks : Novello, 1975. — 14p ; 4to.
 £0.65
(B75-50206)

Hogner, Friedrich
 Fantasia super H.C. : für Orgel / [von] Friedrich Hogner. —
 Frankfurt : Litolff ; London : Peters, 1975. — 19p ; obl.4to.
 Unpriced
(B75-51273)

James, John
 [Voluntaries. *Selections*]. Two trumpet voluntaries / by John
 James ; edited by H. Diack Johnstone. — London : Oxford
 University Press, 1975. — 5p ; 4to.
 ISBN 0-19-375490-8 : £0.50
(B75-50732)

Kaminsky, Heinrich
 Andante für Orgel und Orgelchoral 'Meine Seele ist stille' / von
 Heinrich Kaminsky. — Cassel ; London : Bärenreiter, 1974. —
 8p ; obl. fol.
 £1.20
(B75-50207)

Kelemen, Milko
 Fabliau : für Orgel / [von] Milko Kelemen. — Frankfurt :
 Litolff ; [London] : [Peters], 1974. — 45p ; obl.4to.
 Unpriced
(B75-50208)

Klotz, Hans
 Sechzehn Vorspiele zu evangelischen Kirchenliedern : für die
 Orgel / [von] Hans Klotz. — Cassel ; London : Bärenreiter, 1974.
 — 44p ; obl.fol.
 £3.26
(B75-50209)

Krebs, Johann Ludwig
 [Organ music]. Orgelwerke / von Johann Ludwig Krebs. —
 Frankfurt : Litolff ; London : Peters.
 Bd.2 / herausgegeben von Karl Tittel. — 1974. — 74p ; obl. 4to.
 Unpriced
(B75-50210)

Mathias, William
 Jubilate. Op.67, no.2 : [organ] / [by] William Mathias. —
 London : Oxford University Press, 1975. — 7p ; 4to.
 ISBN 0-19-375553-x : £0.75
(B75-50733)

Pachelbel, Johann
[Organ music. *Selections].* Selected organ works / by Johann
Pachelbel. — Cassel ; London : Bärenreiter.
6 / edited by Wolfgang Stockmeier. — 1974. — 40p ; obl.fol.
£2.40
(B75-50211)

Praetorius, Jacob
Choral bearbeitungen : für Orgel / [von] Jacob Praetorius ;
herausgegeben von Werner Breig. — Cassel ; London :
Bärenreiter, 1974. — viii,42p ; obl.fol.
£3.60
(B75-50212)

Schade, Wernerfritz
Zweistimmige Orgelchorale : gemeinsame Lieder der
deutschsprachigen Kirchen / leicht gesetzt Orgel (manualiter) oder
2 Melodieinstrumente von Wernerfritz Schade. — Mainz ;
London : Schott, 1975. — 60p ; obl.4to.
£4.50
Also classified at LNU
(B75-51274)

Steel, Christopher
Six pieces for organ. Opus 33 / [by] Christopher Steel. —
Sevenoaks : Novello, 1975. — 26p ; 4to.
£0.85
(B75-50213)

Steigleder, Johann Ulrich
[Recercares for organ, nos.1-4]. Four recercars : for organ / [by]
Johann Ulrich Steigleder ; edited by Ernest Emsheimer ; adapted
for practical use by Hermann Keller. — New ed / revised by
Hans-Arnold Metzger. — Cassel ; London : Bärenreiter, 1974. —
23p ; obl.fol.
Unpriced
(B75-50734)

Stout, Alan
Study in densities and durations : organ / [by] Alan Stout. —
New York ; London : Peters, 1974. — 18p ; obl. 4to.
Unpriced
(B75-50214)

Watson, Walter
Reflection : for organ / [by] Walter Watson. — New York ;
[London] : Oxford University Press, 1972. — 5p ; 4to.
Unpriced
(B75-51275)

Wills, Arthur
Homage to John Stanley : voluntary for organ manuals / [by]
Arthur Wills. — London : Chappell, 1975. — 11p ; 4to.
Unpriced
(B75-51276)

RK — Arrangements
Mozart, Wolfgang Amadeus
[Selections. *arr].* Mozart's greatest hits / arranged for all organ by
James Burt. — London : Chappell, 1975. — 57p ; 4to.
Unpriced
(B75-50735)

RK/AAY — Arrangements. Collections
Baroque music for organ / arr. by Frank E. Brown. — London :
Cramer, 1975. — 40p ; 4to.
Unpriced
(B75-51277)

Easy album for the organ / arranged by Patrick Williams. —
London : Bosworth.
4th. — 1974. — 26p ; 4to.
Unpriced
(B75-50215)

RK/AHXJ — Arrangements. Ragtime
Joplin, Scott
[Piano music. Selections. *arr].* Scott Joplin, king of ragtime : easy
organ / arranged by Lawrence Grant. — Carlstadt : Lewis ;
[London] : [Phoenix], 1975. — 32p ; 4to.
Unpriced
(B75-51278)

RK/AHXJ/AY — Arrangements. Ragtime. Collections
Joplin, Scott
[Piano music. *Selections: arr].* Scott Joplin : the king of ragtime
writers / arranged for all organs by Lawrence Grant. —
Carlstadt : Lewis Music ; [London] : [Phoenix], 1974. — 128p ;
4to.
Unpriced
(B75-50216)

RK/DW — Arrangements. Songs, etc
Beethoven, Ludwig van
[Symphony no.9, op.125, in D minor, 'Choral'. Freude schöne
Gotterfunken. *arr].* Hymn to joy / [by] L. van Beethoven ;
arranged for organ by Ian Hare. — London : Oxford University
Press, 1975. — 4p ; 4to.
ISBN 0-19-375294-8 : £0.40
(B75-50736)

Loewe, Frederick
[Musical plays. *Selections: arr].* Showstoppers : the great songs of
Lerner and Loewe / arranged for all organs by Ashley Miller. —
London : Chappell, 1975. — 42p ; 4to.
Unpriced
(B75-50737)

Rodgers, Richard
[Musical plays. *Selections : arr].* 50 super songs / Rodgers and
Hammerstein ; arranged all organ. — London : Williamson Music,
1975. — 128p ; 4to.
Unpriced
(B75-50738)

Sullivan, *Sir* Arthur Seymour
[Operettas. *Selections: arr].* The best of Gilbert and Sullivan : all
organ / arranged by James Burt. — London : Chappell, 1975. —
64p ; 4to.
Unpriced
(B75-50739)

RK/KDN — Arrangements. Funerals
Mozart, Wolfgang Amadeus
[Maurerische Trauermusik, K.477. *arr].* Masonic funeral music /
[by] W.A. Mozart ; arranged for organ by John Morehen. —
London : Oxford University Press, 1975. — 4p ; 4to.
ISBN 0-19-375582-3 : £0.50
(B75-50740)

RNVQ — Organ, six hands
Rose, Jon
Continuum : for two manual organ with three players / [by] Jon
Rose. — London : United Music, 1975. — 8vo.
Comprises a folding card.
Unpriced
(B75-51279)

RPV — ELECTRIC ORGANS
RPVC/AC — Chord organ. Tutors
Bolton, Cecil
An introduction to the 12 button reed and electronic chord
organ / by Cecil Bolton and Jack Moore. — London : Robbins
Music : EMI, 1975. — 32p ; 4to.
Unpriced
(B75-51280)

RPVCK/DM/AY — Chord organ. Arrangements. Hymns. Collections
Sunday songs for chord organs / arranged by Jack Moore and Cecil
Bolton. — London : EMI Music, 1975. — 32p ; 4to.
Unpriced
(B75-50741)

The **world** of sacred music : for all C or G chord organs / arranged
by Michael Allen. — Carlstadt : Bobrich Music ; [London] :
[Phoenix], 1975. — 64p ; 4to.
Unpriced
(B75-50742)

RPVCK/DW/AY — Chord organ. Arrangements. Songs, etc.
Collections
Any time's children's time : for chord organ / compiled and
arranged for chord organ by Cecil Bolton and Jack Moore. —
London : EMI, 1975. — 32p ; 4to.
Unpriced
(B75-51281)

RPVJ — Miscellaneous works
Sommer, Jurgen
Tanz und Unterhaltung : elektronische Orgel / siebzehn
Originalkompositionen von Jurgen Sommer. — Cassel : Nagel ;
London : Bärenreiter, 1974. — 32p ; 4to.
£2.00
(B75-50217)

RPVK/AAY — Arrangements. Collections
Festliche Stunden : elektronische Orgel / arrangements Jurgen
Sommer. — Cassel : Nagel ; London : Bärenreiter, 1974. — 32p ;
4to.
Contents: Pieces by Beethoven, Brahms and others.
£2.00
(B75-50218)

Romantik : elektronische Orgel / arrangements Jurgen Sommer. —
Cassel : Nagel ; [London] : [Bärenreiter], 1974. — 32p ; 4to.
Contents: Pieces by Brahms, Chopin, Dvorak, Grieg, Mendelssohn,
Rubinstein, Schubert, Schumann, Tchaikovsky.
£2.00
(B75-50219)

RPVK/AHM/AY — Arrangements. Ballet. Collections
Ballet : elektronische Orgel / arrangements Jurgen Sommer. —
Cassel : Nagel ; London : Bärenreiter, 1974. — 32p ; 4to.
Contents: Pieces by Delibes, Gluck, Gounod, Lortzing, Schubert, Smetana, Tchaikovsky.
Unpriced

(B75-50222)

RPVK/DW/AY — Arrangements. Songs, etc. Collections
Operette : elektronische Orgel / arrangements Jurgen Sommer. —
Cassel : Nagel ; [London] : [Bärenreiter], 1974. — 32p ; 4to.
Contents: Pieces by Millucher, Strauss, Suppé, Zeller.
£2.00

(B75-50220)

RPVK/DW/LC/AY — Arrangements. Spirituals. Collections
Spirituals : elektronische Orgel / arrangements Rolf Schweizer. —
Cassel : Nagel ; [London] : [Bärenreiter], 1974. — 32p ; 4to.
£2.00

(B75-50221)

RSN — ACCORDION ENSEMBLE
RSNR — Quintets
Kagel, Mauricio
Aus Zungen Stimmen : für Akkordeonquintett / [von] Mauricio
Kagel. — London : Universal, 1975. — 16p ; 4to.
Unpriced

(B75-50743)

RSPM — UNACCOMPANIED ACCORDION SOLOS
RSPMHW — Waltzes
Balta, Freddy
Improvisation no.1 : valse pour accordeon / [par] Freddy Balta.
— Paris ; [London] : Chappell, 1972. — 4p ; 4to.
Unpriced

(B75-50744)

RSPMJ — Miscellaneous works
Balta, Freddy
Mister Czerny : solo d'accordeon d'aprés une étude de la grande
velocité de Carl Czerny / [par] Freddy Balta. — Paris ;
[London] : Chappell, 1972. — 6p ; 4to.
Unpriced

(B75-50745)

Dubois, Pierre Max
Trois biberons : pour accordeon symphonique / [par] Pierre Max
Dubois. — Paris ; [London] : Chappell, 1971. — 8p ; 4to.
Contents: Champagne - Punch - Gros rouge.
Unpriced

(B75-50223)

Law, Leslie G
[A little impromptu]. A little impromptu, and, Dance time / by
Leslie G. Law. — Leicester : Charnwood Music, 1974. — 2p ;
4to.
Unpriced

(B75-51282)

RSPMK — Arrangements
Daquin, Louis Claude
[Nouveau livre de noëls. Noel 10. arr]. Noel X / [par] Louis
Claude Daquin ; transcription pour accordeon de concert par
Freddy Balta. — Paris ; [London] : Chappell, 1972. — 8p ; 4to.
Unpriced

(B75-50746)

RSPMK/AAY — Arrangements. Collections
Focus on classics / arranged for guitar by Ellis Rich. — London :
EMI, 1975. — 48p ; 4to.
Unpriced

(B75-51283)

RSPMK/AHJN — Arrangements. Chaconnes
Bach, Johann Sebastian
[Partita for violin, no.2. S.1064. Chaconne. arr]. Chaconne / [by]
Johann Sebastian Bach ; transcribed for guitar by Victor van
Puijenbroeck. — Antwerp : Uitgave Metropolis ; [London] :
[Hinrichsen], 1974. — 8p ; 4to.
Unpriced

(B75-50224)

RXM — STRING ORCHESTRA
RXM/JM — Incidental music
Purcell, Henry
[Dioclesian. Selections]. Suite für Streicher / [von] Henry Purcell ;
herausgegeben von Olga Geczy ; Generalbassaussetzung von Imre
Sulyok. — Frankfurt : Litolff ; London : Peters, 1974. — 19p ;
4to.
Unpriced

(B75-50225)

RXMG — Suites
Le Fleming, Antony
Suite : for junior orchestra / [by] Antony le Fleming. — London :
Chappell, 1975. — 4to.
Score (20p.) & 16 parts.
Unpriced

(B75-50747)

RXMJ — Miscellaneous works
Boisvalée, François de
Largo religioso : pour orchestre à cordes et clavecin avec orgue ad
lib. / [par] Francois de Boisvallée et Paul Bonneau. — Paris ;
[London] : Chappell, 1971. — 7p ; 4to.
Unpriced

(B75-50748)

Branson, David
The princess, sedate and merry : for string orchestra / [by] David
Branson. — Hastings : Helicon, 1975. — 7p ; fol.
Unpriced

(B75-50749)

Conyngham, Barry
Crisis. Thoughts in a city : for two string orchestras and
percussion / [by] Barry Conyngham. — Sydney ; [London] :
Universal, 1975. — 26p ; 4to.
Duration 7 min.
Unpriced

(B75-51284)

Hofmann, Wolfgang
[Divertimento for strings]. Divertimento / für Streicher ; [von]
Wolfgang Hofmann. — Frankfurt : Litolff ; London : Peters,
1974. — 46p ; 8vo.
Miniature score.
Unpriced

(B75-50226)

Kelemen, Milko
Abecedarium : für Streicher / [von] Milko Kelemen. —
Frankfurt : Litolff ; London : Peters, 1974. — 52p ; 4to.
Unpriced

(B75-50227)

RXMK — Arrangements
Brahms, Johannes
[Volkskinderlieder. Selections: arr]. Seven pieces / by Brahms ;
arranged for school string orchestra and piano (or violin(s) and
piano) by William Appleby and Frederick Fowler. — London :
Oxford University Press, 1975. — 4to.
Score (12p.) & 6 parts.
ISBN 0-19-361906-7 : £1.00

(B75-50750)

RXMK/AAY — Arrangements. Collections
Binkerd, Gordon
Five transcriptions for string orchestra, (with optional trumpet in
C) / transcribed by Gordon Binkerd. — New York ; [London] :
Boosey and Hawkes, 1974. — 4to.
Contents: 1: Veni redemptor, by John Redford - 2: Lucem tuam, by John
Redford - 3: Toccata per l'elevatione I, by Girolamo Frescobaldi - 4:
Toccata per l'elevationne II, by Giralamo Frescobaldi - 5: Capriccio, by
Giralamo Frescobaldi.
£12.50

(B75-50228)

RXMP — SOLO INSTRUMENT (S) & STRING ORCHESTRA
RXMPQR — Harpsichord & string orchestra
Halffter, Cristóbal
Tiempo para espacios : [for harpsichord and string orchestra] /
[by] Cristóbal Halffter. — London : Universal, 1975. — 22p ; 4to.
Unpriced

(B75-50751)

RXMPQRF — Harpsichord & string orchestra. Concertos
Chilcot, Thomas
[Concerto for harpsichord & string orchestra, op.2, no.2, in A
major]. Concerto in A major : for harpsichord, two violins and
violoncello / [by] Thomas Chilcot ; edited by Robin Langley. —
London : Oxford University Press, 1975. — fol.
Score (17p) & 3 parts. Duration 10 mins.
ISBN 0-19-362290-4 : £2.60

(B75-50752)

RXMPR — Organ & string orchestra
Hofmann, Wolfgang
Adagio : für Orgel and Streicher / [von] Wolfgang Hofmann. —
Frankfurt : Litolff ; London : Peters, 1974. — 15p ; 4to.
Unpriced

(B75-50753)

RXMPSNSK/LFL — Four violins & string orchestra. Arrangements.
Concertinos
Portnoff, Leo
[Concertino for violin & piano. Op.13. *arr*]. Concertino for four violins. Op.13 / [by] L. Portnoff ; accompaniment orchestrated by Frank Naylor. — London : Bosworth, 1975. — 16p ; 4to.
Duration 4 1/4 min.
Unpriced
(B75-50754)

RXMPSQF — Viola & string orchestra. Concertos
Stamitz, Anton
[Concerto for viola & string orchestra, no.4, in D major].
Concerto no.4 in D major : for viola and strings / by Anton Stamitz ; edited with cadences by Walter Lebermann. — Cassel : Nagel ; [London] : [Bärenreiter], 1973. — 27p ; 4to.
£3.60
(B75-50229)

RXMPSR — Cello & string orchestra
Antoniou, Theodore
Jeux. Op.22 : for violoncello and string orchestra / [by] Theodore Antoniou. — Cassel ; London : Bärenreiter, 1973. — 19p ; 4to.
Study score.
£2.80
(B75-50230)

RXMPVRF — Flute & string orchestra. Concertos
Bach, Carl Philipp Emanuel
[Concerto for flute, strings & basso continuo, in B flat major. Wq.167]. Concerto in B flat major. Wq.167 : for flute, strings and basso continuo / [by] Carl Philipp Emanuel Bach ; ed. David Lasocki, realization of basso continuo by Robert Paul Block. — London : Musica rara, 1975. — 4to.
Score (45p.) & 6 parts.
Unpriced
(B75-51285)

RXMPVRPLS — Flute, violin & string orchestra
Haydn, Joseph
[Divertimento for flute, violin, strings & continuo in D major. Hob IV/D2]. Cassation, D-dur, für Flöte, Violine, Streicher und Basso continuo / [von] Joseph Haydn ; instrumentiert von Wolfgang Hofman ; Generalbassaussetzung von Winfried Radeke. — Frankfurt : Litolff ; London : Peters, 1973. — 32p ; 4to.
Unpriced
(B75-50231)

RXMPVT — Oboe & string orchestra
Luening, Otto
Legend : for oboe and strings / [by] Otto Luening. — New York : Highgate Press ; London : Galliard, 1975. — 26p ; 4to.
Unpriced
(B75-50755)

RXMPVTF — Oboe & string orchestra. Concertos
Albinoni, Tommaso
[Concerto à 5 for oboe & string orchestra, op.9, no.11, in B flat major]. Concerto à 5 in B flat. Op.9, no.11 : for oboe, strings and basso continuo / [by] Tommaso Albinoni ; edited and realized by Franz Giegling. — London : Musica rara, 1975. — 4to.
Score (40p.) & 5 parts.
£6.50
(B75-51286)

Holzbauer, Ignas
[Concerto for oboe & string orchestra in D minor]. Konzert, d-moll, für Oboe und Streicher / [von] Ignaz Holzbauer, Kadenzen von Herausgeber. — Zum ersten Mal herausgegeben von Walter Lebermann. — Frankfurt : Litolff ; London : Peters, 1974. — 32p ; 4to.
Unpriced
(B75-50232)

RXMPVTNUF — Two oboes & string orchestra. Concertos
Albinoni, Tommaso
[Concerto à 5 for two oboes, strings & basso continuo, op.9, no.12, in D major]. Concerto à 5 in D. Opus 9, no.12 : for 2 oboes, strings and basso continuo / edited and realised by Franz Giegling. — London : Musica Rara, 1975. — 4to.
Score (24p.) & 7 parts.
£5.00
(B75-51287)

RXMPVTPLVWF — Oboe, bassoon & string orchestra. Concertos
Hirsch, Hans Ludwig
[Concerto for oboe, bassoon & string orchestra]. Konzert : für Oboe, Fagott und Streicher / [von] Hans Ludwig Hirsch. — Frankfurt : Litolff ; London : Peters, 1973. — 112p ; 4to.
Unpriced
(B75-50233)

Vivaldi, Antonio
[Concerto for oboe, bassoon & string orchestra in G major. P.129]. Concerto in G major for oboe, bassoon, strings and basso continuo. P.129 / [by] Antonio Vivaldi ; ed. David Lasocki; realization of basso continuo by Robert Paul Block. — London : Musica rara, 1974. — 4to.
Score (31p.) & 7 parts.
£5.50
(B75-51288)

RXMPVVFL — Clarinet & string orchestra. Concertinos
Genzmer, Harald
[Concertino for clarinet & string orchestra]. Concertino für Klarinette in B und Kammerorchester / [von] Harald Genzmer. — Frankfurt ; London : Peters, 1975. — 42p ; 4to.
Unpriced
(B75-50756)

RXMPWSF — Trumpet & string orchestra. Concertos
Holzer, Gerhard
[Concerto for trumpet & string orchestra]. Concerto für Trompete und Streicher / [von] Gerhard Holzer. — Frankfurt : Litolff ; London : Peters, 1974. — 64p ; 8vo.
Study score.
Unpriced
(B75-51289)

RXMPWSNUE — Two trumpets & string orchestra. Symphonies
Bononcini, Giovanni Battista
[Sinfonia no.10 for two trumpets & strings in D major]. Sinfonia decima à 7 for 2 trumpets and strings / [by] Giovanni Bononcini ; edited by Edward H. Tarr. — London : Musica rara, 1974. — 4to.
Score (20p.) & 10 parts.
Unpriced
(B75-51290)

RXMPWTNUF — Two horns & string orchestra. Concertos
Boisvallée, Francois de
[Concerto for 2 horns & string orchestra, no.4]. 4eme concert pour 2 cors, orchestre à cordes et continuo / [par] Francois de Boisvallée et Paul Bonneau. — Paris ; [London] : Chappell, 1971. — 31p ; 4to.
Unpriced
(B75-50234)

RXNQHG — Sextets. Dance suites
Whitney, Maurice C
Dance suite for strings, with optional piano and string bass / [by] Maurice C. Whitney. — New York : Warner ; [London] : [Blossom], 1971. — 4to.
Condensed score. — Contents: 1: Allemande - 2: Sarabande - 3: Gigue.
Unpriced
(B75-50235)

RXNS — Quartets
Becerra-Schmidt, Gustavo
[Quartet for strings, no.6]. String quartet no.6 / [by] Gustavo Becerra-Schmidt. — New York ; [London] : Oxford University Press, 1972. — 64p ; 4to.
Unpriced
(B75-50757)

Borodin, Aleksandr Porfirevich
[Quartet for strings, no.2, in D major]. Quartet no.2, D major, for 2 violins, viola and violoncello / [by] Alexander Borodin ; with a preface by David Brown. — London : Eulenburg, 1975. — [4], 48p ; 8vo.
Miniature score.
Unpriced
(B75-51291)

Boyd, Anne
[Quartet for strings, no.2]. String quartet no.2 / [by] Anne Boyd. — London : Central Music Library : Faber, 1974. — 37p ; 4to.
Unpriced
(B75-50758)

Britten, Benjamin
[Quartet for strings in D major (1931)]. String quartet in D major (1931) / [by] Benjamin Britten. — London : Faber Music, 1975. — 8vo.
The composer has made a sizeable cut in the third movement. — Miniature score (35p) & 4 parts.
Unpriced
(B75-50759)

Brunner, Adolf
[Quartet for strings]. Streichquartett / von Adolf Brunner. — Cassel ; London : Bärenreiter, 1973. — 4pt ; fol.
£6.00
(B75-50236)

Cowell, Henry
[Quartet romantic for 2 flutes, violin & viola]. Quartet romantic :
2 flutes, violin, viola, and, Quartet euphometric : 2 violins, viola,
violoncello / [by] Henry Cowell. — New York ; London : Peters,
1974. — 31p ; 4to.
Unpriced
Primary classification NVRNS

(B75-50643)

Danzi, Franz
[Quartet for strings, op.6, no.82, in B flat major,
'Figaro-Quartett']. String quartet in B flat major 'Figaro-Quartett'.
Op.6, no.2 / [by] Franz Danzi ; edited by Franz Beyer. —
Cassel ; London : Bärenreiter, 1975. — 4pt ; 4to.
Based upon two themes from 'Il Nozze di Figaro' by Mozart.
Unpriced

(B75-50760)

Křenek, Ernst
Five short pieces for strings / [by] Ernst Křenek. — Cassel ;
London : Bärenreiter, 1974. — 12p ; 4to.
Unpriced

(B75-50761)

Maconchy, Elizabeth
[Quartet for strings, no.10]. String quartet no.10 / by Elizabeth
Maconchy. — London : Chappell, 1975. — 4to.
Score (28p.) & 4 parts.
Unpriced

(B75-50762)

Szkolay, Sándor
[Quartet for strings, no.1]. Streichquartett Nr.1 / von Sándor
Szokolay. — Frankfurt : Litolff ; London : Peters, 1973. — 20p ;
8vo.
Study score.
Unpriced

(B75-50237)

RXNS/Y — Quartets. Fugues
Schacht, Theodor von
Fuga sopra 'l do re mi fa sol la' : für Streichquartett oder
Streichorchester / [von] Theodor von Schacht ; herausgegeben von
Eberhard Klaus. — Regensburg : Bosse ; Cassel ; London :
Bärenreiter, 1974. — 11p ; 4to.
Unpriced

(B75-50763)

RXNSK/DW — Quartets. Arrangements. Songs, etc
Sullivan, *Sir* Arthur Seymour
[Operettas. *Selections: arr*]. Four miniature string quartets, from
the Sullivan operas / arranged by Sydney Twinn. — Sevenoaks :
Paxton, 1974. — 4to.
Score (8p.) & 4 parts.
£1.25

(B75-50238)

RXNT — Trios
Boccherini, Luigi
[Trios for two violins & cello, nos, 1-6. Op.2]. Sei trii per due
violini e violoncello. Op.1a / [di] Luigi Boccherini ; edizione a
cura di G. Guglielmo e A. Pocaterra. — Padua : Zanibon ;
[London] : [Hinrichsen], 1973. — 3pt ; 4to.
Unpriced

(B75-50239)

RXNT/T — Trios. Variations
Riley, Dennis
Variations 2 : trio, violin, viola, violoncello / [by] Dennis Riley.
— New York ; London : Peters, 1973. — 8p ; 4to.
Unpriced

(B75-50240)

SN — VIOLIN ENSEMBLE
SNSQK/LF — Three violins & piano. Arrangements. Concertos
Vivaldi, Antonio
[Concerto for three violins & string orchestra in F major. P.278.
arr]. Concerto F-Dur. P.V.278 : für drei Violinen, Streichorchester
und Basso continuo / Antonio Vivaldi ; herausgegeben vom
Walter Lebermann, Klavierauszug vom Herausgeber. — Mainz ;
London : Schott, 1975. — 4to.
Score (31p.) & 3 parts.
£3.00

(B75-51292)

SNU — Duets
Fletcher, Stanley
Four violin duets / [by] Stanley Fletcher. — New York ;
[London] : Boosey and Hawkes, 1971. — 8p ; 4to.
Two copies.
Unpriced

(B75-50241)

Nelson, Sheila M
Two in one : violin duets in the first finger position / violin duets
by Sheila M. Nelson. — London : Boosey and Hawkes, 1974. —
8p ; 4to.
£1.00

(B75-50242)

SNUK/DW/GJ/AYG — Duets. Arrangements. Children's songs.
Collections. Hungary
Hungarian children's songs / [compiled and arranged] for two and
three violins by Sándor Szokolay. — London : Boosey and
Hawkes, 1975. — 32p ; 4to.
£1.00

(B75-51293)

SP — VIOLIN & PIANO
SP/AY — Collections
Associated Board of the Royal Schools of Music
The well-tuned fiddle : original compositions for violin and
pianoforte by contemporary composers. — London : Associated
Board of the Royal Schools of Music.
Score (39p.) & part.
Book 1. — 1974. — 4to.
£0.70

(B75-50243)

Book 2. — 1974. — 4to.
£0.70

(B75-50244)

Book 3. — 1974. — 4to.
£0.70

(B75-50245)

SP/W — Rondos
Beethoven, Ludwig van
[Rondo for violin & piano in G major. K-H 41]. Rondo for violin
& piano / [by] Ludwig van Beethoven ; edited by Rok Klopčič. —
New York ; London : Schirmer, 1974. — 4to.
Score (13p.) & part.
Unpriced

(B75-50764)

SPE — Sonatas
Festing, Michael Christian
[Sonatas for violin & continuo. Op.4, nos 2,3]. Two sonatas for
violin and basso continuo / by Michael Christian Festing ; edited
by Gwilym Beechey. — London : Oxford University Press, 1975.
— 4to.
Score (16p.) & 4 parts.
ISBN 0-19-356458-0 : £2.00

(B75-50246)

Handel, George Frideric
[Sonata for violin & continuo, Op.1, no.1, in D minor]. Sonata in
D minor for violin and basso continuo / by George Frideric
Handel ; edited by Roy Howat. — London : Oxford University
Press, 1975. — 4to.
Score (15p.) & 2 parts.
ISBN 0-19-356979-5 : £1.50

(B75-50247)

Lees, Benjamin
Sonata for violin and piano, no.2 / by Benjamin Lees. —
London : Boosey and Hawkes, 1974. — 4to.
Score (43p.) & part.
£4.00

(B75-50248)

McLean, Charles
[Sonata for violin & continuo. Op.1, no.2 in G minor]. Sonata in
G minor for violin and basso continuo / by Charles McLean ;
edited by David Johnson. — London : Oxford University Press,
1975. — 4to.
Score (6p.) & 2 parts.
ISBN 0-19-357679-1 : £1.30

(B75-50249)

Sarti, Giuseppe
[Sonata for violin & piano, op.3, no.3, in B flat major]. Sonata in
B flat major : for violin and piano. Op.3, no.3 / [by] Giuseppe
Sarti ; edited by Wolfgang Plath. — Cassel : Nagel ; London :
Bärenreiter, 1975. — 4to.
Score (38p.) & part.
Unpriced

(B75-50765)

SPE/AY — Sonatas. Collections
Eighteenth-century violin sonatas / edited and realised by Lionel
Salter ; with bowing revised and fingering added by Jean Harvey.
— London : Associated Board of the Royal Schools of Music.
Score (38p.) & part.
Book 1. — 1975. — 4to.
Unpriced

(B75-51294)

SPJ — Miscellaneous works
Appleby, William
String along : 22 easy graded pieces for violin and piano / [by]
William Appleby and Frederick Fowler. — London : Oxford
University Press, 1975. — 4to.
Score (30p.) & part.
ISBN 0-19-355204-3 : £1.60
(B75-50766)

Dorward, David
Triad : for violin and piano / [by] David Dorward. — London :
Oxford University Press, 1975. — 4to.
Score (16p.) & part.
ISBN 0-19-356261-8 : Unpriced
(B75-51295)

Gotkovsky, Ida
Caractères : pièces de concert, pour violon et piano / [par] Ida
Gotkovsky. — Paris ; [London] : Chappell, 1971. — fol.
Score & part.
Unpriced
(B75-50767)

Hovhaness, Alan
Saris : violin and piano / [by] Alan Hovhaness. — New York ;
London : Peters, 1974. — 4to.
Score (16p.) & part.
Unpriced
(B75-50250)

Jacob, Gordon
5 pieces for half-size violin and piano / by Gordon Jacob. —
London : Chappell, 1975. — 4to.
Score (7p.) & part.
Unpriced
(B75-51296)

Josephs, Wilfred
Siesta. Op.8 : for violin and piano / [by] Wilfred Josephs. — New
York ; London : Chappell, 1975. — 4to.
Unpriced
(B75-51297)

Kupkovič, Ladislav
[K-Rhapsodie. Souvenir]. Souvenir : für Violine und Klavier /
[von] Ladislav Kupkovič. — London : Universal, 1972. — 4to.
Score (16p.) & part.
Unpriced
(B75-50768)

Nelson, Sheila M
Moving up : a first set of violin pieces in the second position,
violin and piano / by Sheila M. Nelson. — London : Boosey and
Hawkes, 1974. — 4to.
Score (8p.) & part.
£1.45
(B75-50251)

Shifrin, Seymour
Duo : violin and piano / [by] Seymour Shifrin. — New York ;
London : Peters, 1973. — 19p ; 4to.
Duration 12 min.
Unpriced
(B75-50252)

SPK/LF — Arrangements. Concertos
Szokolay, Sandor
[Concerto for violin. arr]. Konzert für Violine und Orchester /
[von] Sandor Szokolay ; Ausgabe für Violine und Klavier. —
Frankfurt : Litolff ; London : Peters, 1973. — 4to.
Score (46p.) & part.
Unpriced
(B75-50253)

SPK/LT — Arrangements. Variations
Vieuxtemps, Henri
[Souvenir d'Amérique, 'Yankee doodle'. arr]. Souvenir
d'Amérique, 'Yankee doodle' : variations burlesques / [by] Henri
Vieuxtemps ; edited, violin and piano, by Mary Canberg. — New
York : Galaxy ; [London] : [Galliard], 1975. — 4to.
Score (12p.) & part.
Unpriced
(B75-51298)

SPK/LW — Arrangements. Rondos
Mozart, Wolfgang Amadeus
[Rondo for violin & orchestra in C major. K.373. arr]. Rondo für
Solo-Violine, Streicher, zwei Oboen und zwei Hörner. K.V.373 /
[von] Wolfgang Amadeus Mozart ; herausgegeben und für Violine
und Piano bearbeitet von Max Rostal. — Mainz ; London :
Schott, 1975. — 4to.
Duration 6 min. — Score (15p.) & part.
£1.75
(B75-51299)

SPLSR — VIOLIN & CELLO
Rhodes, Phillip
Duo : violin and violoncello / [by] Phillip Rhodes. — New York ;
London : Peters, 1973. — 23p ; 4to.
Duration 13 mins.
Unpriced
(B75-50254)

SPM — UNACCOMPANIED VIOLIN
SPME — Sonatas
Luening, Otto
[Sonata for violin, no.1]. Sonata no.1 : violin solo / [by] Otto
Luening. — New York ; London : Peters, 1974. — 12p ; 4to.
Duration 11 min.
Unpriced
(B75-50255)

Luening, Otto
[Sonata for violin, no.2]. Sonata II : violin solo / [by] Otto
Luening. — New York ; London : Peters, 1974. — 8p ; 4to.
Unpriced
(B75-50769)

SPMJ — Miscellaneous works
Luening, Otto
Meditation : violin solo / [by] Otto Luening. — New York ;
London : Peters, 1973. — 2p ; 4to.
Unpriced
(B75-50256)

SQN — VIOLA ENSEMBLE
SQNUEM — Duets. Sonatinas
Jacob, Gordon
Sonatina for two violas / [by] Gordon Jacob. — London : Oxford
University Press, 1975. — 8p ; 4to.
Duration 7 1/2 min.
ISBN 0-19-357357-1 : Unpriced
(B75-50770)

SQP — VIOLA & PIANO
SQP/T — Variations
Cooper, Paul
Variants II : for viola and piano / [by] Paul Cooper. — London :
Chester, 1975. — 4to.
Score (8p.) & part. — Duration 7 min.
Unpriced
(B75-50771)

Joachim, Joseph
Variations for viola and piano. Op.10 / [by] J. Joachim ; with
preface by Harold Truscott. — London : Musica rara, 1975. —
4to.
Score (23p.) & part.
Unpriced
(B75-51300)

SQPJ — Miscellaneous works
Herzogenberg, Heinrich von
[Legenden. Op.62]. Legends for viola and piano / [by] Heinrich
von Herzogenberg ; with a preface by Harold Truscott. —
London : Musica rara, 1975. — 4to.
Score (27p.) & part.
£2.00
(B75-51301)

Joachim, Joseph
[Hebräische Melodien. Op.9]. Hebrew melodies. Impressions of
Byron's poems. Op.9 : for viola and piano / [by] J. Joachim ; with
a preface by Harold Truscott. — London : Musica rara, 1975. —
4to.
Score (17p.) & part.
Unpriced
(B75-51302)

Lantier, Pierre
Diptyque pour alto et piano / [par] Pierre Lantier. — Paris ;
[London] : Chappell, 1971. — 4to.
Score & part.
Unpriced
(B75-50257)

SQPK/LE — Arrangements. Sonatas
Paganini, Nicolò
[Sonata for viola & orchestra. arr]. Sonata per la grand'viola e
orchestra / [von] Nicolo Paganini ; herausgegeben [und revidiert
für Violine und Klavier] von Ulrich Druner. — Mainz ; London :
Schott, 1974. — 4to.
Score (20p.) & part.
Unpriced
(B75-51303)

SQPLSS — VIOLA & DOUBLE BASS
SQPLSS/W — Rondos
Keyper, Franz Anton Leopold Joseph
Rondo solo : for double bass and violoncello or viola / [by] Franz
A.L.J. Keyper ; edited by Rodney Slatford. — London : Yorke,
1974. — 4to.
Score (5p.) & 4 parts.
Unpriced
Primary classification SRPLSS/W

(B75-50264)

SQPM — UNACCOMPANIED VIOLA
SQPMJ — Miscellaneous works
Riley, Dennis
Variations 3 : viola alone / [by] Dennis Riley ; edited by William
Hibbard. — New York ; London : Peters, 1973. — 5p ; 4to.
Duration 5 1/2 min.
Unpriced

(B75-50258)

Stadlmair, Hans
Drei Fantasien : für Viola / [von] Hans Stadlmair. — Frankfurt :
Litolff ; London : Peters, 1974. — 9p ; 4to.
Unpriced

(B75-50772)

Uhl, Alfred
Dreissig Estüden für Viola / [von] Alfred Uhl ; [Fingersatz von]
Karl Stierhof. — Mainz ; London : Schott, 1975. — 36p ; 4to.
£2.25

(B75-51304)

SQQ — VIOLA D'AMORE
SQQPE — Sonatas
Ariosti, Attilio
[Sonatas for viola d'amore & continuo, 'Stockholm']. 'Stockholm
sonatas' : for viola d'amore (viola) and basso continuo / [by]
Attilio Ariosti ; edited by Gunther Weiss ; continuo-realization by
Theodor Klein. — Cassel ; London : Bärenreiter.
Score (19p.) & 2 parts.
1 : Sonatas in F major, A minor, G major. — 1974. — 4to.
£2.80

(B75-50259)

SRN — CELLO ENSEMBLE
SRNRK/Y — Quintets. Arrangements. Fugues
Bach, Johann Sebastian
[Das wohltemperirte Clavier, Tl. 1. S.867. *arr*]. Prelude and
fugue / [by] J.S. Bach ; arranged for five cellos by Anita
Hewitt-Jones. — London : Oxford University Press, 1975. — 8vo.
ISBN 0-19-355238-8 : Score, £0.75 ; Parts, Unpriced

(B75-50773)

SRNU — Duets
Heiden, Bernhard
Inventions for two violoncelli / [by] Bernhard Heiden. — New
York ; London : Associated Music, 1974. — 4to.
Unpriced

(B75-50774)

SRNUE — Duets. Sonatas
Guignon, Jean Pierre
[Sonatas for two cellos. Op.2, nos. 1, 4, 3]. Sonates. Op.2, pour 2
violoncelles basses de violes (Gamben) ou bassons (fagotti) / [von]
Jean-Pierre Guignon ; herausgegeben von Dieter Staekelin. — 1st
ed. — Basle : Kneusslin ; [London] : [Hinrichsen], 1974. — 2pt ;
4to.
Unpriced
Also classified at VWNUE

(B75-50260)

SRNUK/DW/GJ/AYG — Duets. Arrangements. Children's songs.
Collections. Hungary
Hungarian children's songs : for two violoncellos / by Mihály
Hajdu ; bowing and fingering by László Mezö. — London :
Boosey and Hawkes ; Budapest : Editio Musica, 1974. — 23p ;
4to.
£0.75

(B75-50261)

SRP — CELLO & PIANO
SRPG — Suites
Luening, Otto
[Suite for cello & piano]. Suite for cello (or viola) and piano / by
Otto Luening. — New York : Highgate Press ; [London] :
[Galliard], 1972. — 4to.
Score (19p.) & part.
Unpriced

(B75-51305)

SRPJ — Miscellaneous works
Tortelier, Paul
Pishnetto : recital étude no.5, for cello and piano / [by] Paul
Tortelier. — London : Chester, 1975. — 4to.
Score (5p.) & part.
Unpriced

(B75-51306)

Wuorinen, Charles
Adapting to the times : violoncello and piano / [by] Charles
Wuorinen. — New York ; London : Peters, 1973. — 46p ; 4to.
Duration 6 min.
Unpriced

(B75-50262)

SRPK — Arrangements
Bach, Johann Sebastian
[Concertos for keyboard, nos.2, 5. S.1053, 1056. *Selections : arr*].
Siciliano/Largo / [von] Johann Sebastian Bach ;
Konzert-Transkription für Violoncello und Klavier von Joachim
Stutschewsky. — Mainz ; London : Schott, 1975. — 4to.
Score (8p.) & part.
Unpriced

(B75-51307)

SRPK/DW/GJ/AYG — Arrangements. Children's songs. Collections.
Hungary
Hungarian children's songs : for violoncello and piano / [by]
Mihály Hajdu. — London : Boosey and Hawkes ; Budapest :
Editio Musica, 1974. — 4to.
Score & part.
£0.75

(B75-50263)

SRPLSS — CELLO & DOUBLE BASS
SRPLSS/W — Rondos
Keyper, Franz Anton Leopold Joseph
Rondo solo : for double bass and violoncello or viola / [by] Franz
A.L.J. Keyper ; edited by Rodney Slatford. — London : Yorke,
1974. — 4to.
Score (5p.) & 4 parts.
Unpriced
Also classified at SQPLSS/W

(B75-50264)

SRPM — UNACCOMPANIED CELLO
SRPME — Sonatas
Josephs, Wilfred
Sonata for cello solo. Opus 73 / [by] Wilfred Josephs. —
Sevenoaks : Novello, 1975. — 12p ; 4to.
Duration 6 min.
£1.00

(B75-50265)

SRPMJ — Miscellaneous works
Blake, David
Scenes : for cello / [by] David Blake. — Sevenoaks : Novello,
1975. — 12p ; 4to.
£1.00

(B75-50266)

Connolly, Justin
Tesserae C : violoncello solo / [by] Justin Connolly. —
Sevenoaks : Novello, 1975. — 9p ; 4to.
£1.00

(B75-50775)

SS — DOUBLE BASS
SS/AF — Exercises
Associated Board of the Royal Schools of Music
Official book of scales and arpeggios for double bass, (Grades III,
IV, V, VI, and VIII) / fingering by Eugene Cruft ; text by Adrian
Cruft. — London : Associated Board of the Royal Schools of
Music, 1974. — 20p ; 4to.
£0.45

(B75-50267)

SSN — DOUBLE BASS ENSEMBLE
SSNS — Quartets
Lauber, Joseph
Quartet for double basses / [by] Joseph Lauber ; edited by Rodney
Slatford. — London : Yorke, 1975. — 4to.
Score (18p) & 4 parts.
Unpriced

(B75-50776)

SSP — DOUBLE BASS & PIANO
SSP/AZ — Collected works of individual composers
Bottesini, Giovanni
[Works, double bass & piano]. Yorke complete Bottesini : for
double bass and piano / edited by Rodney Slatford. — London :
Yorke.
Score (vi,34p.) & part.
Vol.1. — 1974. — 4to.
Unpriced

(B75-50268)

Volume 2. — 1975. — 4to.
Score (iv,52p.) & part.
Unpriced

(B75-51308)

SSPHM — Gavottes
Walter, David
The elephant's gavotte : for double bass and piano / [by] David
Walter. — London : Yorke, 1975. — 4to.
Score (4p) & part.
Unpriced

(B75-50777)

SSPK/LF — Arrangements. Concertos
Jacob, Gordon
[Concerto for double bass & string orchestra. *arr*]. A little
concerto for double bass and string orchestra / by Gordon Jacob.
— London : Yorke, 1974. — 4to.
Score (20p.) & part. — Duration 12 1/2 min.
Unpriced

(B75-50269)

Ridout, Alan
[Concerto for double bass & string orchestra. *arr*]. Concerto for
double bass and strings / [by] Alan Ridout ; piano reduction. —
London : Yorke, 1975. — 4to.
Score (28p) & part.
Unpriced

(B75-50778)

SSPK/W — Arrangements. Rondos
Dragonetti, Domenico
[Adagio and rondo for double bass & string quartet in C major.
arr]. Adagio and rondo in C major / [by] Domenico Dragonetti ;
edited and reduced for double bass and piano by Adrian Mann. —
London : Yorke, 1975. — 4to.
Score (26p) & part. — From British Library Add. MS.17726f 46r-56v.
Unpriced

(B75-50779)

Keyper, Franz
[Romance and rondo for double bass & orchestra. *arr*]. Romance
and rondo : for double bass and orchestra / [by] Franz Keyper ;
edited by Rodney Slatford ; piano reduction by Clifford Lee. —
London : Yorke, 1974. — 4to.
Score (14p) & part.
Unpriced

(B75-50780)

SSPM — UNACCOMPANIED DOUBLE BASS
SSPMG — Suites
Leach, John
Suite for unaccompanied double bass / by John Leach. —
London : Yorke, 1974. — 5p ; 4to.
Unpriced

(B75-50270)

SSPMJ — Miscellaneous works
Felice, John
From Quasimodo Sunday : for unaccompanied double bass / [by]
John Felice. — London : Yorke, 1975. — 3p ; 4to.
Duration 6 min.
Unpriced

(B75-50781)

Koblitz, David
Nomos : for unaccompanied double bass / [by] David Koblitz. —
London : Yorke, 1974. — 3p ; 4to.
Unpriced

(B75-50782)

STN — VIOL CONSORT
STNR — Quintets
Parsley, Osbert
In nomine : for two treble, two tenor and bass viols / [by] Osbert
Parsley ; edited by John Morehen. — London : Oxford University
Press, 1975. — 8vo.
The only one of Parsley's three five-part In nomines to survive complete. —
Score (6p.) & 3 parts.
ISBN 0-19-341211-x : Score £0.20, Parts unpriced

(B75-50783)

Parsley, Osbert
Parsley's clock a 5 : for two treble, two tenor, and bass viols /
[by] Osbert Parsley ; edited by John Morehen. —- London :
Oxford University Press, 1975. — 4p ; 8vo.
Score (4p) & 3 parts.
ISBN 0-19-341213-6 : Score, £0.20 ; Parts, Unpriced

(B75-50784)

Parsley, Osbert
Spes nostra : for two treble, two tenor and bass viols / [by] Osbert
Parsley ; edited by John Morehen. — London : Oxford University
Press, 1975. — 8vo.
Score (8p.) & 3 parts.
ISBN 0-19-341212-8 : £0.30

(B75-50785)

STNS/AY — Quartets. Collections
Five pieces for four viols / edited by Michael Morrow and Ian
Woodfield ; arranged by Hans Gerle. — London : Oxford
University Press, 1975. — 4to.
ISBN 0-19-343241-2 : Unpriced

(B75-50786)

STNSG — Quartets. Suites
Locke, Matthew
Consort of four parts / [by] Matthew Locke ; transcribed and
edited by Michael Tilmouth. — London : Stainer and Bell, 1972.
— 4pt ; 4to.
Unpriced

(B75-51309)

TMK — Plucked string instruments band. Arrangements
Betti, Henri
[Miniature. *arr*]. Miniature / [par] Henri Betti et Paul Bonneau ;
transcription et arrangement pour 'orchestra a plectre' par Sylvain
Dagosto. — Paris ; [London] : Chappell, 1971. — 9p ; 4to.
Unpriced

(B75-50787)

Bonneau, Paul
Manège / [par] Paul Bonneau ; transcription et arrangement pour
'orchestre a plectre' par Sylvain Dagosto. — Paris ; [London] :
Chappell, 1971. — 8p ; 4to.
Unpriced

(B75-50788)

Dubois, Pierre Max
[Poupée de porcelaine. *arr*]. Poupée de porcelaine : musique de
Pierre Max Dubois et Paul Bonneau / transcription et
arrangement pour 'orchestre a plectre' par Sylvain Dagosto. —
Paris ; [London] : Chappell, 1971. — 4p ; fol.
Unpriced

(B75-50789)

Duclos, Pierre
Paysage ibérique / [par] Pierre Duclos ; transcription et
arrangement pour 'orchestre à plectre' [par] Sylvain Dagosto. —
Paris ; [London] : Chappell, 1971. — 9p ; 4to.
Unpriced

(B75-50271)

Duclos, Pierre
Paysage suedois / [par] Pierre Duclos ; transcription et
arrangement pour 'orchestre à plectre' [par] Sylvain Dagosto. —
Paris ; [London] : Chappell, 1971. — 12p ; 4to.
Unpriced

(B75-50272)

**TMK/AHVG — Plucked string instruments band. Arrangements.
Pavanes**
Boisvallée, Francois de
[Les Fêtes de Terpsichore. *Selections: arr*]. Air en forme de
pavane / [par] Francois de Boisvallée et Paul Bonneau ;
transcription et arrangement pour 'orchestre a plectre' par Sylvain
Dagosto. — Paris ; [London] : Chappell, 1971. — 4p ; 4to.
Unpriced

(B75-50273)

TMK/DW — Arrangements. Songs, etc
Lopez, Anja
[Maria. *arr*]. Maria / [par] Anja Lopez ; transcription et
arrangement pour 'orchestre à plectre' par Sylvain Dagosto. —
Paris ; [London] : Chappell, 1972. — 5p ; fol.
Anja Lopez contributed to Francis Lopez's operetta, 'Viva Napoli'.
Unpriced

(B75-51310)

Lopez, Francis
[Viva Napoli. La Mandoline a du bon. *arr*]. La Mandoline a du
bon / [par] Francis Lopez ; transcription et arrangement pour
'orchestre à plectre' par Sylvain Dagosto. — Paris ; [London] :
Chappell, 1971. — 5p ; fol.
Unpriced

(B75-51311)

Lopez, Francis
[Viva Napoli. Ma sérénade. *arr*]. Ma sérénade / [par] Francis
Lopez ; transcription et arrangement pour 'orchestre à plectre' par
Sylvain Dagosto. — Paris ; [London] : Chappell, 1971. — 5p ; fol.
Unpriced

(B75-51312)

Lopez, Francis
[Viva Napoli. Viva Napoli. *arr*]. Viva Napoli / [par] Francis
Lopez ; transcription et arrangement pour 'orchestre à plectre' par
Sylvain Dagosto. — Paris ; [London] : Chappell, 1971. — 6p ; fol.
Unpriced

(B75-51313)

TQP — HARP & PIANO
TQPJ — Miscellaneous works
  Grundman, Clare
    [Nocturne for harp & wind ensemble. *arr*]. Nocturne : for harp
    and wind ensemble, edition for harp and piano. — New York ;
    London : Boosey and Hawkes, 1975. — 4to.
    Score (12p.) & part.
    Unpriced
                                         (B75-51314)

TQPM — UNACCOMPANIED HARP
TQPMG — Suites
  Mayr, Johann Simon
    [Suite for harp]. Suite für Harfe / von Simon Mayr. — Zum
    ersten Mal herausgegeben von Heinrich Bauer. — Frankfurt :
    Litolff ; London : Peters, 1974. — 16p ; 4to.
    Unpriced
                                         (B75-50790)

TQPMH — Dances
  Challan, Annie
    Danse des glissandi : harpe / [par] Annie Challan. — Paris ;
    [London] : Chappell, 1971. — 4p ; 4to.
    Unpriced
                                         (B75-50791)

TQPMJ — Miscellaneous works
  Challan, Annie
    Cascades : harpe / [par] Annie Challan. — Paris ; [London] :
    Chappell, 1972. — 8p ; fol.
    Unpriced
                                         (B75-50792)

TQPMK/AT — Arrangements. Variations
  Handel, George Frideric
    [Suites de pièces. 1st collection. No.5. Aria con variazioni. *arr*].
    Aria con variazioni 'The harmonious blacksmith' / [by] G.F.
    Handel ; arranged for solo guitar by Hector Quine. — London :
    Oxford University Press, 1975. — 5p ; 4to.
    Variation 4 is omitted and the remainder of the music transcribed to D
    major.
    ISBN 0-19-356993-0 : £0.65
                                         (B75-50794)

TQPMK/DW/AYDK — Arrangements. Songs, etc. Collections.
  Wales
    Telyn y werin : [harp] / arranged by Meinir Heulyn. — Y Fenni :
    Adlais.
    Cyfrol 1. — 1975. — 18p ; 4to.
    Unpriced
                                         (B75-50793)

TS — GUITAR
TS/AF — Exercises
  Dodgson, Stephen
    Progressive reading for guitarists / [by] Stephen Dodgson and
    Hector Quine. — Chesham : Ricordi, 1975. — 39p ; 4to.
    £3.00
                                         (B75-50795)

  Duarte, John William
    14 graded studies in apayando / [by] John W. Duarte. —
    Chesham : Ricordi, 1975. — 4p ; 4to.
    £0.84
                                         (B75-50796)

  Owen, Tom
    Lead guitar / by Tom Owen. — London : Chappell, 1975. —
    32p ; 4to.
    Unpriced
                                         (B75-51315)

TS/P — Pitch
  Clelland, Tom
    The book of open tunings : for guitar / [by] Tom Clelland. —
    London : Robbins Music, 1975. — 32p ; 4to.
    Unpriced
                                         (B75-51317)

TS/RC — Chords
  Roberts, Don
    Chordal solo technique for guitar / [by] Don Roberts. —
    London : EMI Music, 1975. — 80p ; 4to.
    Unpriced
                                         (B75-50797)

TSN — GUITAR ENSEMBLE
TSNK/AHXJ/AY — Arrangements. Ragtime. Collections
  Ragtime for guitar ensemble / arranged by Mary Criswick. —
    London : Chappell, 1975. — 35p ; 4to.
    A selection of works by Scott Joplin, with one work, 'Pam-Am Rag', by
    Tom Turpin.
    Unpriced
                                         (B75-51318)

TSNSK/AH — Quartets. Arrangements. Dances
  Dowland, John
    [Lachrimae, nos 8, 1, 12. *arr*]. Three dances / [by] John
    Dowland ; arranged for guitar quartet by Gilbert Biberian. —
    Sevenoaks : Novello, 1975. — 15p ; 4to.
    £0.75
                                         (B75-51319)

TSNTK — Trios. Arrangements
  Binge, Ronald
    [Elizabethan serenade. *arr*]. Elizabethan serenade / [by] Ronald
    Binge ; arranged for guitar trio by Mary Criswick. — London :
    Ascherberg, Hopwood and Crewe, 1975. — 4p ; 4to.
    Unpriced
                                         (B75-51320)

TSNTK/AAY — Trios. Arrangements. Collections
  Guitar trios : music from four centuries / arranged for three guitars
    by Mary Criswick. — London : Chester, 1975. — 22p ; 4to.
    Unpriced
                                         (B75-50798)

  Spielheft Klassik : für drei Gitarren / bearbeitet von Ekkehard
    Reiser. — Mainz ; London : Schott, 1975. — 17p ; 4to.
    Unpriced
                                         (B75-50799)

TSNUK/AAY — Duets. Arrangements. Collections
  Guitar duets : music from four centuries / arranged for two guitars
    by Mary Criswick. — London : Chester, 1975. — 12p ; 4to.
    Unpriced
                                         (B75-50800)

  A **musical** voyage with two guitars : 64 duets from 34 countries /
    [compiled] by Vladimir Bobri and Carl Miller. — New York ;
    London : Collier Macmillan, 1974. — 192p ; 4to.
    ISBN 0-02-060150-6 : £3.50
                                         (B75-51321)

  Spielheft Klassik : für zwei Gitarren / bearbeitet von Ekkehard
    Reiser. — Mainz ; London : Schott, 1975. — 19p ; 4to.
    Unpriced
                                         (B75-50801)

TSPLX — GUITAR & PERCUSSION
  Humble, Keith
    Arcade IV : for guitar and percussion / [by] Keith Humble. —
    [Sydney] ; [London] : Universal, 1975. — 9p ; obl.4to.
    Unpriced
                                         (B75-50802)

TSPM — UNACCOMPANIED GUITAR
TSPM/T — Variations
  Dale, Mervyn
    Variations on a theme : for guitar / [by] Mervyn Dale. —
    London : Ashdown, 1975. — 5p ; 4to.
    £0.40
                                         (B75-50803)

TSPME — Sonatas
  Wills, Arthur
    Sonata for guitar / [by] Arthur Wills. — London : Oxford
    University Press, 1975. — 10p ; 4to.
    ISBN 0-19-359531-1 : Unpriced
                                         (B75-50804)

TSPMG — Suites
  Marshall, Nicholas
    Partita : for guitar / [by] Nicholas Marshall. — London :
    Thames, 1975. — 9p ; 4to.
    Unpriced
                                         (B75-50805)

  Miletić, Miroslav
    Kroatische Suite nach Volksweisen aus Medjimurje : für Gitarre /
    [von] Miroslav Miletić. — Mainz ; London : Schott, 1975. — 5p ;
    4to.
    £0.90
                                         (B75-51322)

  Selby, Philip
    Suite for solo guitar / [by] Philip Selby. — Leamington Spa :
    Anthony Music, 1975. — 10p ; 4to.
    Contents: 1: Prelude - 2: Scherzino - 3: Nocturne - 4: Arabesque.
    £0.60
                                         (B75-51323)

TSPMH — Dances
Mangore, Agustin Barrios
Danza paraguaya : per chitarra / [di] Agustin Barrios Mangore ; revisione e diteggiatura di Alirio Diaz. — Padua : Zanibon ; [London] : [Hinrichsen], 1973. — 4p ; 4to.
Unpriced

(B75-50274)

Torres, Pedro Manuel
El Gallo : danza venezuelana per chitarra / [di] Pedro Manuel Torres ; armonizzazione e revisione di Alirio Diaz. — Padua : Zanibon ; [London] : [Hinrichsen], 1974. — 2p ; 4to.
Unpriced

(B75-50275)

TSPMHW — Waltzes
Belasco, Lionel
Juliana : valzer venezuelano per chitarra / [di] Lionel Belasco ; armonizzazione e revisione di Alirio Diaz. — Padua : Zanibon ; [London] : [Hinrichsen], 1974. — 2p ; 4to.
Unpriced

(B75-50276)

Calzadilla, Roman
Aires de Mochima : valzer venezuelano, per chitarra / [di] Roman Calzadilla ; armonizzazione e elaborazione di Alirio Diaz. — Padua : Zanibon ; [London] : [Hinrichsen], 1974. — 2p ; 4to.
Unpriced

(B75-50277)

Fernandez, Heraclio
El Diablo suelto : valzer popolare venezuelano per chitarra / [di] Heraclio Fernandez ; armonizzazione e revisione di Alirio Diaz. — Padua : Zanibon ; [London] : [Hinrichsen], 1972. — 3p ; 4to.
Unpriced

(B75-50278)

Flor del campo : valzer venezuelano per chitarra / armonizzazione e elaborazione di Alirio Diaz. — Padua : Zanibon ; [London] : [Hinrichsen], 1974. — 2p ; 4to.
Unpriced

(B75-50279)

Mangore, Agustin Barrios
Oración : valzer popolare venezuelano, per chitarra / [di] Agustin Barrios Mangore ; revisione e diteggiatura di Alirio Diaz. — Padua : Zanibon ; [London] : [Hinrichsen], 1972. — 3p ; 4to.
Unpriced

(B75-50280)

TSPMJ — Miscellaneous works
Aponte, Pedro Arcila
Las Belles noches de Maiquetia : canzone venezuelana per chitarra / [di] Pedro Arcila Aponte ; armonizzazione e elaborazione di Alirio Diaz. — Padua : Zanibon ; [London] : [Hinrichsen], 1974. — 2p ; 4to.
Unpriced

(B75-50281)

Cole, Keith R
A guitarist's album for the young / [by] Keith R. Cole. — Chesham : Ricordi, 1975. — 20p ; 4to.
£1.50

(B75-50806)

Dale, Mervyn
Rhapsodie : for guitar / [by] Mervyn Dale. — London : Ashdown, 1975. — 5p ; 4to.
£0.40

(B75-50807)

Daw, Stephen
Ten Scottish impressions : for guitar / [by] Stephen Daw. — London : Stainer and Bell, 1975. — 14p ; 4to.
Unpriced

(B75-50808)

Duarte, John William
Six easy pictures. Opus 5 : guitar solo / by John W. Duarte. — Sevenoaks : Novello, 1975. — 6p ; 4to.
Unpriced

(B75-50809)

Freedman, Hermann L
Satori : solo guitar / [by] Hermann L. Freedman. — London : Thames, 1974. — 6p ; fol.
Unpriced

(B75-50810)

Margoni, Alain
Quatre personnages de Calderon : pour guitare / [par] Alain Margoni. — Paris ; [London] : Chappell, 1971. — 8p ; 4to.
Contents: 1: Le Savant Tiresias - 2: Nuno le bouffon - 3: Dorotea - 4: L'Imperieux Don Alvaro.
Unpriced

(B75-51324)

Pizzini, Carlo Alberto
Capriccio napoletano : per chitarra / [di] C.A. Pizzini ; diteggiatura di B. Battisti D'Amario. — Padua : Zanibon ; [London] : [Hinrichsen], 1973. — 7p ; 4to.
Duration 3 1/4 min.
Unpriced

(B75-50282)

Pizzini, Carlo Alberto
Improvviso da concerto : per chitarra / [di] C.A. Pizzini ; diteggiatura di B. Battisti D'Amario. — Padua : Zanibon ; [London] : [Hinrichsen], 1973. — 7p ; 4to.
Duration 4 1/2 min.
Unpriced

(B75-50283)

Rawsthorne, Alan
Elegy for guitar / [by] Alan Rawsthorne ; edited and completed by Julian Bream. — London : Oxford University Press, 1975. — 7p ; 4to.
Duration 8 1/2 min.
ISBN 0-19-358510-3 : Unpriced

(B75-51325)

Wanek, Friedrich
Zehn Essays : für Gitarre solo / [von] Friedrich Wanek ; einrichtung und Fingersatz von Gunter Schwartz. — Mainz ; London : Schott, 1975. — 16p ; 4to.
£1.75

(B75-51326)

TSPMK — Arrangements
Dowland, John
[Lute music. *Selections : arr*]. Two pieces / [by] John Dowland ; transcribed for solo guitar by Alberta Gerould. — London : Oxford University Press, 1975. — 5p ; 4to.
Taken from the Jane Pickeringe Lute Book (Egerton 2046). — Contents: 1. Piper's pavinge - 2. Lamentation.
ISBN 0-19-356279-0 : £0.50

(B75-50811)

Flores negras : pasillo ecuatoriano, per chitarra / armonizzazione e elaborazione di Alirio Diaz. — Padua : Zanibon ; [London] : [Hinrichsen], 1974. — 4p ; 4to.
Unpriced

(B75-50284)

Moderne Rhythmen : für Jazz-Gitarre / bearbeitet von Hans Dieter Vermeer. — Mainz ; London : Schott, 1975. — 18p ; 8vo.
£1.75

(B75-51327)

Weiss, Sylvius Leopold
[Lute music. *Selections: arr*]. Fantasia, fuga, tombeau, capriccio : per chitarra dalla intavolutura per liuto / [di] Sylvius Leopold Weiss ; transcrizione e diteggiatura di Giorgio Oltremari. — Padua : Zanibon ; [London] : [Hinrichsen], 1972. — 16p ; 4to.
Unpriced

(B75-50285)

TSPMK/AAY — Arrangements. Collections
A **first** book of guitar solos / [compiled] by John Gavall. — London : Oxford University Press, 1975. — 16p ; 4to.
ISBN 0-19-356727-x : Unpriced

(B75-50812)

The **second** book of solos for the classical guitar / arranged by Alan Hall. — London : Scratchwood Music, 1975. — 12p ; 4to.
Unpriced

(B75-50813)

Three pieces from the Jane Pickering Lute Book (Egerton 2046) / transcribed for solo guitar by Alberta Gerould. — London : Oxford University Press, 1975. — 4p ; 4to.
Contents: 1. The maids in constrite / anon - 2. A galyerd / [by] Philip Rosseter - 3. Carman's whistle / [by] Robert Johnson.
ISBN 0-19-356770-9 : £0.50

(B75-50814)

World's favorite selected masterpieces for classic guitar / compiled and edited by Frantz Casseus. — New York : Ashley ; [London] : [Phoenix].
Vol.2. — 1974. — 126p ; 4to.
Unpriced

(B75-50286)

TSPMK/AE — Arrangements. Sonatas
Kohaut, Karl
[Sonata for lute in D major. *arr*]. Sonata in D / [by] Karl Kohaut ; transcribed from the lute tablature, edited for guitar and fingered by Gerard Reyne. — London : Oxford University Press, 1975. — 6p ; 4to.
ISBN 0-19-357428-4 : Unpriced

(B75-50815)

Weiss, Sylvius Leopold
[Sonata for lute in B minor, London no.16]. Sonate (London nr 16) / [by] Silvio Leopold Weiss ; translated from the lute tablature and transcribed for guitar by Victor van Puijenbroeck. — Antwerp : Uitgave Metropolis ; [London] : [Hinrichsen], 1973. — 8p ; 4to.
Unpriced
(B75-50287)

TSPMK/AG — Arrangements. Suites
Bach, Johann Sebastian
[Partita for lute in C minor. S.997. *arr*]. Partita / [by] Johann Sebastian Bach ; transcribed after the suite BWV 997 for harpsichord and a lute tablature of the post-Bach period by Victor Puijenbroeck. — Antwerp : Uitgave Metropolis ; [London] : [Hinrichsen], 1973. — 6p ; 4to.
£1.00
(B75-50288)

Weiss, Sylvius Leopold
[Suite for lute, no.18, in A major]. Suite in la maggiore : per chitarra dalla intavolatura per lineo / [di] Sylvius Leopold Weiss ; diteggiatura di Giorgio Oltremari. — Padua : Zanibon ; [London] : Hinrichsen, 1973. — 23p ; 4to.
Unpriced
(B75-50289)

TSPMK/AHJK — Arrangements. Boleros
Surinach, Carlos
[Suite espagnole. Bolero de los picaros. *arr*]. Bolero de los picaros / [by] Carlos Surinach ; edited for guitar solo by Michael Lorimer. — New York ; London : Associated Music, 1972. — 7p ; 4to.
Unpriced
(B75-50816)

TSPMK/AHU — Arrangements. Passepieds
Delibes, Leo
[Le Roi s'amuse. Passepied. *arr*]. Passepied / [by] Leo Delibes ; arranged for solo guitar by J.W. Bickel and L.R. Pearson. — London : Oxford University Press, 1975. — 4p ; 4to.
ISBN 0-19-356159-x : Unpriced
(B75-50817)

TSPMK/DP/LF/AY — Arrangements. Carols. Christmas. Collections
Christmas songs for guitar / arranged by Bert Brewis. — London : Chappell, 1971. — 20p ; 4to.
Unpriced
(B75-51328)

TSPMK/DW — Arrangements. Songs, etc
Lennon, John
[Songs. *Selections : arr*]. The Beatles for classical guitar / songs by John Lennon and Paul McCartney ; 20 solos arranged by Joe Washington. — London : Wise, Music Sales, 1975. — 86p ; 4to.
Unpriced
(B75-50818)

Rodgers, Richard
[Musical plays. *Selections : arr*]. Rodgers and Hammerstein guitar book / arrangements by Leon Block. — London : Williamson Music, 1975. — 4to.
Unpriced
(B75-50819)

TSPMK/DW/HHW/AY — Arrangements. Blues. Collections
Picking Blues : leichte Blues - Sätze nach alten und neuen Melodien, für Gitarre / bearbeitet von Dieter Kreidler. — Mainz ; London : Schott, 1975. — 12p ; 8vo.
Unpriced
(B75-51329)

TSPMK/DW/LC — Arrangements. Spirituals
Negro Spirituals für Gitarre solo / bearbeitet von Hans Dieter Vermeer. — Mainz ; London : Schott, 1975. — 16p ; 8vo.
£1.75
(B75-51330)

TSPMK/LF — Arrangements. Concertos
Kelkel, Manfred
[Zagreber concerto for guitar. Op.19. *arr*]. Zagreber Konzert : für Gitarre und Orchester. Op.19 / [von] Manfred Kelkel ; Klavierauszug. — Mainz ; London : Schott, 1974. — 4to.
Score (55p.) & part. — Duration 32 min.
Unpriced
(B75-50290)

TTPM — UNACCOMPANIED BANJO
TTV/RC — Tenor banjo. Chords
Owen, Tom
Tenor banjo chord coloring book : chords and how to use them / by Tom Owen. — New York ; [London] : Chappell, 1975. — 95p ; 4to.
Unpriced
(B75-51331)

TW — LUTE
TW/AZ — Collected works of individual composers
Johnson, Robert
[Lute music]. Complete works for solo lute / by Robert Johnson ; edited and transcribed by Albert Sundermann. — London : Oxford University Press, 1972. — 4to.
Original lute tablature (19p.) & keyboard transcription.
ISBN 0-19-357390-3 : £2.75
(B75-50291)

TWPM — UNACCOMPANIED LUTE
TWPMJ — Miscellaneous works
Bacheler, Daniel
[Lute music. *Selections*]. Selected works for lute / by Daniel Bacheler ; edited and translated by Martin Long. — London : Oxford Universuty Press, 1972. — 4to.
Original lute tablature (27p.) & keyboard transcription.
ISBN 0-19-355305-8 : £4.50
(B75-50292)

UM — WIND BAND
UM/HHW — Blues
Cacavas, John
Heavy band blues : for concert band / [by] John Cacavas. — New York ; [London] : Chappell, 1972. — 4to.
Condensed score & 65 parts - With several copies of various parts.
Unpriced
(B75-50820)

UM/LF — Christmas
Balent, Andrew
The spirit of Christmas : for wind band and optional chorus / by Andrew Balent. — New York : Warner ; [London] : [Blossom], 1975. — 4to.
Score & 49 parts.
Unpriced
(B75-51332)

Cacavas, John
Concertette for Christmas : for concert band / by John Cacavas. — New York ; [London] : Chappell, 1971. — 4to.
Conductor & 49 parts - With several copies of various parts.
Unpriced
(B75-50293)

UM/T — Variations
Lombardo, Mario
Variations in a mod mood : for concert band / by Mario Lombardo. — New York ; [London] : Chappell, 1974. — 4to.
Condensed score (16p.) & 68 parts. — With several copies of various parts.
Unpriced
(B75-50294)

UMH — Dances
Camargo Guarnieri, Mozart
Dansa brasileira : for concert band / by Camargo Guarnieri ; arranged by Charles Brandebury. — New York ; London : Associated Music, 1974. — 20p ; 4to.
Unpriced
(B75-50821)

UMJ — Miscellaneous works
Cacavas, John
Overture, The court of Henry VIII : for concert band / [by] John Cacavas. — New York ; [London] : Chappell, 1972. — 4to.
Score & 47 parts.
Unpriced
(B75-50822)

Chance, John Barnes
Blue lake : overture for concert band / [by] John Barnes Chance. — New York ; [London] : Boosey and Hawkes, 1971. — 4to.
Condensed score and 74 parts. — With several copies of various parts.
Unpriced
(B75-50295)

Grundman, Clare
A colonial legend : for wind band / [by] Clare Grundman. — New York ; [London] : Boosey and Hawkes, 1975. — 4to.
Score (28p.) & 74 parts. — With several copies of various parts.
Unpriced
(B75-51333)

Loudová, Ivana
Hymnos : wind orchestra and percussion / [by] Ivana Loudová. — New York ; London : Peters, 1975. — 24p ; fol.
Unpriced
(B75-51334)

Sutermeister, Heinrich
Modeste Mignon : d'après une valse d'Honoré de Balzac, [i.e. par Daniel Auber], pour dix instruments à vent / [par] Heinrich Sutermeister. — Mainz ; London : Schott, 1974. — 40p ; 4to.
Duration 9 1/2 min.
Unpriced
(B75-51335)

Tull, Fisher
Reflections on Paris : symphonic band / [by] Fisher Tull. — New York ; [London] : Boosey and Hawkes, 1975. — 4to.
Score (76p.) & 71 parts. — With several copies of various parts.
£20.50

(B75-51336)

Washburn, Robert
Saturn V : [wind band] / [by] Robert Washburn. — New York ; [London] : Boosey and Hawkes, 1975. — 4to.
Score (28p.) & 71 parts. — Duration 3 min.
£12.00

(B75-51337)

Wastall, Peter
Babylon's falling : a jazz spiritual for junior band and optional voices in two parts / arranged by Peter Wastall and Derek Hyde ; traditional words adapted by Peter Wastall. — London : Boosey and Hawkes, 1975. — 4to & 8vo.
Score (8p.) & 12 parts.
£2.05

(B75-51338)

Wastall, Peter
Didn't my Lord deliver Daniel? : a jazz spiritual for junior wind band and optional voices in two parts / arranged by Peter Wastall. — London : Boosey and Hawkes, 1975. — 4to & 8vo.
Score (7p.) & 12 parts.
£2.05

(B75-51339)

Wastall, Peter
Joshua fought the battle of Jericho : a jazz spiritual for junior wind band and optional voices in two parts / arranged by Peter Wastall and Derek Hyde ; traditional words adapted by Peter Wastall. — London : Boosey and Hawkes, 1975. — 4to & 8vo.
Score (8p.) & 12 parts.
£2.05

(B75-51340)

UMK — Arrangements
Copland, Aaron
[Preamble for a solemn occasion. *arr*]. Preamble for a solemn occasion / [by] Aaron Copland ; arranged for symphonic band by the composer. — New York ; [London] : Boosey and Hawkes, 1974. — 4to.
Score (16p.) & 65 parts. — With several copies of various parts.
£9.00

(B75-50296)

Ives, Charles
[Variations on 'Jerusalem the golden'. *arr*]. Variations on 'Jerusalem the golden' / [by] Charles Ives ; edited and arranged for concert band and a brass band of old fashioned instruments, or modern brass sextet, or quintet ; by Keith Brion. — New York ; London : Associated Music, 1974. — 12p ; 4to.
£1.30

(B75-51341)

UMK/AAY — Arrangements. Collections
Noble numbers : based on organ music of the 17th and 18th centuries, by Frescobaldi, Pachelbel, Zachau, Vetter, and Walther, for wind ensemble / transcribed by Gordon Binkerd. — New York ; [London] : Boosey and Hawkes, 1974. — 51p ; 4to.
Unpriced

(B75-50297)

Wind band book : seven pieces, for woodwind and brass instruments with optional percussion / arranged by John Kember. — London : Oxford University Press, 1974. — 37p ; 4to.
ISBN 0-19-369800-5 : £2.75

(B75-50298)

UMK/AG — Arrangements. Suites
Walton, *Sir* **William**
[Duets for children. *arr*]. Miniatures for wind band / [by] William Walton ; arranged by Bram Wiggins. — London : Oxford University Press.
Set 1, nos 1-5. — 1974. — 1,32p ; 4to.
ISBN 0-19-368267-2 : £2.50

(B75-50299)

Set 2, nos 6-10. — 1974. — 1,41p ; 4to.
ISBN 0-19-368507-8 : £3.00

(B75-50300)

UMK/DM/AY — Arrangements. Hymns. Collections
50 hymns for band / arranged by Colin Evans ; instrumental descants by Herbert Sumsion. — London : Oxford University Press.
Score (27p) & 16 parts.
Book I : General and Christmas. — 1975. — 4to.
ISBN 0-19-363060-5 : Unpriced

(B75-50823)

UMK/DW — Arrangements. Songs, etc
Bjorn, Frank
[The alley cat song. *arr*]. The alley cat song / [by] Frank Bjorn ; arranged by Eddie Rogers. — London : Chappell, 1975. — 4to.
Score (15p.), Piano conductor & 16 parts.
Unpriced

(B75-50824)

Gershwin, George
[Porgy and Bess. Summertime. *arr*]. Summertime music / by George Gershwin ; arranged by Eddie Rogers. — London : Chappell, 1975. — 4to.
Score (8p.), Piano conductor & 16 parts.
Unpriced

(B75-50825)

UMK/JR — Arrangements. Films
Karas, Anton
[The third man. Harry Lime theme. *arr*]. The third man / by Anton Karas ; arranged by Eddie Rogers. — London : Chappell, 1975. — 4to.
Score (8p.), Piano conductor & 16 parts.
Unpriced

(B75-50826)

Legrand, Michel
[The three musketeers. *Selections: arr*]. Themes from 'The three musketeers' / by Michel Legrand ; arranged for concert band by Bill Holcombe. — New York ; [London] : Chappell, 1974. — 4to.
Condensed score (12p.) & 56 parts. — With several copies of various parts.
Unpriced

(B75-50301)

UMM — MILITARY BAND
UMME — Symphonies
Hovhaness, Alan
Symphony no.23, 'Ani'. City of a thousand and one cathedrals : for large band with antiphonal second brass choir ad lib. / [by] Alan Hovhaness. — New York ; London : Peters, 1972. — 88p ; 4to.
Unpriced

(B75-50827)

UMMGM — Marches
Bennett, Robert Russell
The fabulous country : concert march / [by] Robert Russell Bennett. — New York : Warner ; [London] : [Blossom], 1975. — 4to.
Score (15p.) & 70 parts. — With several copies of various parts.
Unpriced

(B75-50828)

Ellis, Ray
Olympic fanfares : for marching band / [by] Ray Ellis. — New York ; [London] : Unichappell, 1972. — 8vo & obl.8vo.
Conductor & 100 parts.
Unpriced

(B75-50829)

Elms, Albert
On parade : quick march / [by] Albert Elms. — London : Boosey and Hawkes, 1975. — 8vo & obl. 8vo.
Conductor & 48 parts.
Unpriced

(B75-50830)

Neville, Paul
Shrewsbury fair : quick march, for military band / [by] Paul Neville. — London : Boosey and Hawkes, 1975. — 36pt ; obl.8vo.
With several copies of various parts.
£1.00

(B75-51342)

UMMGM/KH — Marches. Regimental music
Davies, Roy Edward Charles
Skywatch (The Royal Observer Corps march past) : for military band / [by] R.E.C. Davies. — London : Boosey and Hawkes, 1975. — 29pt ; obl.8vo.
£1.50

(B75-51343)

UMMHVJ — Reels
Davis, Allan
Razorback reel / arranged for military band by Allan Davis. — New York ; [London] : Oxford University Press, 1975. — 4to.
Score (15p.) & 61 parts. — Duration 5 min.
Unpriced

(B75-50302)

UMMJ — Miscellaneous works
Edmunds, John F
Got it in my soul / composed and arranged for military band by John F. Edmunds. — New York ; [London] : Robbins, 1971. — 8vo.
Score & 104 parts.
Unpriced

(B75-50303)

Edmunds, John F
Wade in the water : traditional / adapted and arranged by John
F. Edmunds. — New York ; [London] : Robbins, 1971. — obl.
8vo.
Score & 109 parts - With several copies of various parts.
Unpriced
(B75-50304)

Elms, Albert
The battle of Trafalgar : for military band / by Albert Elms. —
London : Boosey and Hawkes, 1974. — obl 8vo.
Conductor (22p.) & 37 parts.
Unpriced
(B75-50305)

Gayfer, James McDonald
Canadian landscape : tone poem concert band / [by] James M.
Gayfer. — London : Boosey and Hawkes, 1975. — 4to.
Score (20p.) & 54 parts. — Duration 6 min.
Full band set £4.50, Symphonic band set £6.00, Score £1.50
(B75-50831)

Hanmer, Ronald
[The wild wild west. Conductor]. The wild wild west : an
American medley for military band / by Ronald Hanmer. —
London : Studio Music, 1974. — 8p ; 8vo.
Unpriced
(B75-50306)

Lombardo, Mario
Volcanic rock : for concert band / [by] Mario Lombardo. — New
York ; [London] : Chappell, 1973. — 4to.
Score & 66 parts. — With several copies of various parts.
Unpriced
(B75-51344)

Rawsthorne, Alan
[Street corner overture. *arr*]. Street corner overture / [by] Alan
Rawsthorne ; transcribed for band by Robert O'Brien. — New
York ; [London] : Oxford University Press, 1972. — 40p ; 4to.
Unpriced
(B75-51345)

Walters, Harold L
Country and westerns : [military band] / [by] Harold L. Walters.
— Miami : Rubank ; [Sevenoaks] : Novello], 1975. — 4to.
Conductor (12p.) & 45 parts.
Unpriced
(B75-50832)

Washburn, Robert
Ceremonial music : military band / [by] Robert Washburn. —
New York ; [London] : Oxford University Press, 1972. — 40p ;
4to.
Unpriced
(B75-51346)

Yoder, Paul
Bands around the world / [by] Paul Yoder and Harold L.
Walters. — Miami : Rubank ; [Sevenoaks] : Novello], 1972. —
4to.
Conductor & 46 parts. — With several copies of various parts.
Unpriced
(B75-51347)

UMMK — Arrangements
Holst, Gustav
[The planets. Mars. *arr*]. Mars / [by] Gustav Holst ; arranged for
military band by Norman Richardson. — London : Boosey and
Hawkes, 1975. — 8vo.
Conductor (15p.) & 45 parts.
Unpriced
(B75-50833)

Vaughan Williams, Ralph
[Norfolk rhapsody. *arr*]. Norfolk rhapsody / [by] Ralph Vaughan
Williams ; arranged for military band by Robert O'Brien. — New
York ; [London] : Oxford University Press, 1972. — 42p ; 4to.
Unpriced
(B75-51348)

Vivaldi, Antonio
[L'Estro armonico. Op.3, no.11. Largo, Allegro. *arr*]. Sicilienne
and finale / [by] Antonio Vivaldi ; arranged for concert band by
Louis Jean Brunelli. — New York ; [London] : Chappell, 1972. —
4to.
Full score, Condensed score & 67 parts.
Unpriced
(B75-51349)

UMMK/AGM — Arrangements. Marches
Allen, Rod
[The wonder march. *arr*]. The wonder march / by Rod Allen ;
arranged for military and brass band by Allan Street. — London :
Boosey and Hawkes, 1975. — 37pt ; obl.8vo.
Military band set, £1.00, Brass band set £0.85
Also classified at WMK/AGM
(B75-50834)

Forsblad, Leland
[Bunker hill. *arr*]. Bunker hill : march / [by] Leland Forsblad ;
arranged by Wayne Livingstone. — New York : Warner ;
[London] : [Blossom], 1972. — 4to.
Condensed score & 46 parts.
Unpriced
(B75-50307)

Ives, Charles
[March, Omega Lambda Chi. *arr*]. March, Omega Lambda Chi :
for band / [by] Charles Ives ; edited and arranged by Keith Brion.
— New York ; London : Associated Music, 1974. — iv,11p ; 4to.
Wind ensembles desiring a 19th century sonority may perform the original
instrumentation by consulting the instrumentation table.
Unpriced
(B75-50835)

UMMK/DW — Arrangements. Songs, etc
Bygraves, Max
[Swingalongamax. *arr*]. Swingalongamax. (Back in my childhood
days) / [by] Max Bygraves ; arranged for military band by Allan
Street. — London : Boosey and Hawkes, 1975. — 34pt ; obl.8vo.
With several copies of various parts.
£1.00
(B75-51350)

UMMK/JR — Arrangements. Films
Rota, Nino
[The godfather, part II. Theme. *arr*]. Theme from Godfather II /
music by Nino Rota ; arranged for military band by John
Edmondson. — New York : Famous Music ; [London] :
[Chappell], 1975. — 4to.
Conductor (7p.) & 48 parts. — With several copies of various parts.
Unpriced
(B75-50836)

UMMP — SOLO INSTRUMENT (S) & MILITARY BAND
UMMPWVF — Tuba & military band. Concertos
Ross, Walter
[Concerto for tuba & military band]. Tuba concerto : tuba solo
and symphonic band / [by] Walter Ross. — New York ;
[London] : Boosey and Hawkes, 1975. — 4to.
Score & 65 parts. — Duration 11 1/2 min.
£20.00
(B75-50837)

UMP — SOLO INSTRUMENT (S) & WIND BAND
UMPTQ — Harp & wind band
Grundman, Clare
Nocturne : for harp and wind ensemble / [by] Clare Grundman.
— New York ; [London] : Boosey and Hawkes, 1975. — 4to.
Score (17p.) & 38 parts. — With several copies of various parts.
£7.50
(B75-51351)

UMPWS — Trumpet & wind band
Françaix, Jean
Le Gay Paris : pour trompette, solo flute, 2 hautbois, 2 clarinettes,
basson, contrebasson et 2 cors / [par] Jean Françaix. — Mainz ;
London : Schott, 1975. — 10pt ; 4to.
Contents: Marche - Valse - Galop.
Unpriced
(B75-51352)

UMPWSE — Trumpet & wind band. Symphonies
Molter, Johann Melchior
[Sinfonia concertante for trumpet & wind band in D major. MWV
VIII, 1]. Sinfonia concertante. MWV VIII, 1 : for solo trumpet,
(clarino), 2 oboes, 2 horns and bassoon / [by] J.M. Molter ; edited
by Robert Minter. — London : Musica rara, 1974. — 4to.
Score (20p.) & 6 parts.
Unpriced
(B75-51353)

Molter, Johann Melchior
[Sinfonia concertante for trumpet & wind band in D major. MWV
VIII, 2]. Sinfonia concertante. MWV VIII, 2 : for solo trumpet
(clarino), 2 oboes, 2 horns and bassoon / [by] J.M. Molter ; edited
by Robert Minter. — London : Musica rara, 1974. — 4to.
Score (20p.) & 6 parts.
Unpriced
(B75-51354)

UN — WIND ENSEMBLE
UNNK — Octets. Arrangements
Whitlock, Percy
[Five short pieces for organ. Folk tune. *arr*]. Folk tune / [by]
Percy Whitlock ; arranged for 2 flutes, 1 oboe, 3 clarinets, 1
bassoon, 1 horn ; by Geoffrey Emerson. — Ampleforth : Emerson,
1974. — 4to.
Score (4p.) & 8 parts.
Unpriced
(B75-50308)

UNQ — Sextets
Pleyel, Ignaz
[Sextet for wind instruments in E flat major]. Sextet in E flat major : for 2 clarinets, 2 bassoons and 2 horns / [by] Ignaz Pleyel ; edited by H. Voxman. — London : Musica rara, 1975. — 4to.
Score (23p.) & 5 parts.
£6.50

(B75-51355)

UNQG — Sextets. Suites
Read, Gardner
Nine by six : suite for wind instruments, flute (picc.), oboe (eng. horn), clarinet (bs. cl.), trumpet, horn, bassoon / [by] Gardner Read. — New York ; London : Peters, 1973. — 4to.
Score (38p.) & 6 parts.
Unpriced

(B75-50309)

UNR — Quintets
Egk, Werner
5 Stücke für Bläserquintett / [von] Werner Egk. — Mainz ; London : Schott, 1974. — 4to.
Score (43p.) & 5 parts. — Contents: I: Monolog - II: Choral - III: Mobile - IV: Dialog - V: Finale.
£11.00

(B75-51356)

Meale, Richard
Quintet for winds / [by] Richard Meale. — [Sydney] ; [London] : Universal, 1975. — 29p ; 8vo.
Unpriced

(B75-50838)

Meyer, Jean
Bavardages : cinq pièces brèves en canon pour quintette a vent (flute, hautbois, clarinette, B bémol, cor F, basson) / [par] Jean Meyer. — Paris ; [London] : Chappell, 1971. — 4to.
Score & 5 parts.
Unpriced

(B75-51357)

Milner, Anthony
Quintet for wind instruments / [by] Anthony Milner. — London : Central Music Library ; Sevenoaks : Novello, 1974. — 38p ; 4to.
Unpriced

(B75-50839)

UNR/T — Quintets. Variations
Jacob, Gordon
Swansea town : folk song, theme and variations, for wind quintet / [by] Gordon Jacob. — Ampleforth : Emerson, 1975. — 4to.
Score (13p.) & 5 parts.
Unpriced

(B75-50840)

Jacob, Gordon
Swansea town : wind quintet / [by] Gordon Jacob. — Ampleforth : Emerson, 1975. — 4to.
Score (13p.) & 5 parts.
Unpriced

(B75-51358)

UNRFL — Quintets. Concertinos
Washburn, Robert
Concertino for wind and brass quintets / [by] Robert Washburn. — New York ; [London] : Oxford University Press, 1971. — 4to.
Score & 10 parts.
Unpriced
Also classified at WNRFL

(B75-51359)

VN — WOODWIND ENSEMBLE
VNPK — Septets. Arrangements
Schubert, Franz
[Sonata for piano, no.5, op.147, in B major. Scherzo. *arr*]. Scherzo and trio / [by] Schubert ; arr. for 2 flutes, oboe, 3 clarinets and bassoon by Geoffrey Emerson. — Ampleforth : Emerson, 1975. — 4to.
Score (8p.) & 7 parts.
Unpriced

(B75-51360)

VNQ — Sextets
Lyons, Graham
Pastoral : for two flutes and four clarinets / [by] Graham Lyons. — London : British and Continental Music, 1975. — 4p ; 4to.
Unpriced

(B75-50841)

VNS — Quartets
Hanmer, Ronald
Cuckoo quartet : 2 flutes and 2 clarinets / [by] Ronald Hanmer. — Ampleforth : Emerson, 1975. — 4to.
Score (5p.) & 4 parts.
Unpriced

(B75-51361)

Sitsky, Larry
[Quartet for woodwind instruments]. Woodwind quartet : for flute, oboe, clarinet and bassoon / [by] Larry Sitsky. — London : Boosey and Hawkes, 1974. — 4to.
Score (14p.) & 4 parts.
£5.00

(B75-50310)

VNSF — Quartets. Concertos
Ridout, Alan
Concertante for woodwind quartet / [by] Alan Ridout. — London : Central Music Library : Chappell, 1974. — 21p ; 4to.
Unpriced

(B75-50842)

VNSG — Quartets. Suites
Warren, Edward
3 pieces for 4 : a suite of 3 movements for woodwind quartet, flute, oboe, clarinet in B flat, bassoon / [by] Edward Warren. — Surbiton : Camera Music, 1975. — 4to.
Score (7p.) & 4 parts.
Unpriced

(B75-51362)

VNT — Trios
Musgrave, Thea
Impromptu no.2 : for flute, oboe and clarinet / [by] Thea Musgrave. — London : Chester, 1975. — 3pt ; 4to.
Unpriced

(B75-50843)

Pleyel, Ignaz
[Trio for two clarinets & bassoon in E flat major]. Trio für zwei Klarinetten und Fagott, Es-dur / [von] Ignaz Pleyel ; herausgegeben von Horst Henke und Dieter Klocker. — Frankfurt : Litolff ; London : Peters, 1974. — 3pt ; 4to.
Unpriced

(B75-50311)

Pleyel, Ignaz
[Trio for two clarinets & bassoon, op.20, no.2, in E flat major]. Trio in E flat. Op.20, no.2, for 2 clarinets and bassoon / [by] Ignaz Joseph Pleyel ; edited by H. Voxman. — London : Musica rara, 1975. — 4to.
Score (19p.) & 3 parts.
Unpriced

(B75-51363)

Wenth, Johann
[Divertimento for two oboes & cor anglais in B flat major]. Divertimento, B-dur : für 2 Oboi und Corno inglese B-dur / [von] Johann Wenth ; herausgegeben von Antonin Myslik. — 1st ed. — Basle : Kneusslin ; [London] : [Hinrichsen], 1974. — 3pt ; 4to.
Unpriced

(B75-50312)

VNTK/AHR — Trios. Arrangements. Minuets
Haydn, Michael
[Six menuets for keyboard, nos. 1, 2, 3, 5. Perger 70]. Four minuets / [by] Michael Haydn ; arranged for two clarinets in B flat and bassoon (or cello) by Wadham Sutton. — Sevenoaks : Novello, 1975. — 6p ; 8vo.
£0.30
Also classified at NVNTK/AHR

(B75-50313)

VNTK/AYD — Trios. Arrangements. Collections. England
Old English music : for oboe, clarinet and bassoon (or two clarinets and bassoon) / arranged from the organ works of John Stanley and Samuel Wesley by Pamela Verrall. — London : Oxford University Press, 1975. — 4to.
Score (16p.) & part.
ISBN 0-19-359203-7 : Unpriced

(B75-51364)

VPM — UNACCOMPANIED WOODWIND INSTRUMENT
VQPK/AHXJ — Arrangements. Ragtime
Joplin, Scott
[The entertainer. *arr*]. The entertainer / [by] Scott Joplin ; arr. for C or D flat piccolo with piano accompaniment by Harold L. Walters. — Miami : Rubank ; [London] : [Novello], 1975. — 4to.
Score (3p.) & 2 parts. — Parts for piccolo in C and piccolo in D flat.
Unpriced

(B75-51365)

VRN — FLUTE ENSEMBLE
VRNS — Quartets
Lancen, Serge
Quatre flûtes en balade : pour quatre flûtes / [par] Serge Lancen. — Paris ; [London] : Chappell, 1971. — 4to.
Score & 4 parts.
Unpriced

(B75-50314)

Thomas, Bernard
Two chansons for flutes / edited by Bernard Thomas ; pub. Pierre Attaingnant (1533). — London : Oxford University Press, 1975. — 7p ; 8vo.
Contents: 1 Si bon amour, by Jacotin - 2 Parle qui veult, by Claudin de Sermisy.
ISBN 0-19-341220-9 : £0.12
Primary classification EZDU

(B75-50062)

VRNT — Trios
Novak, Jan
Panisci fistula : tre preludi per tre flauti / [di] Jan Novak. — Padua : Zanibon ; [London] : [Hinrichsen], 1973. — 7p ; fol.
Duration 4 1/2 min.
Unpriced

(B75-50315)

VRNTK/AHXJ — Trios. Arrangements. Ragtime
Joplin, Scott
[The entertainer. *arr*]. The entertainer / [by] Scott Joplin ; arr. for flute trio and piano by Harold L. Walters. — Miami : Rubank ; [London] : [Novello], 1975. — 4to.
Score (3p.) & 3 parts.
Unpriced

(B75-51366)

VRNTQK — Two flutes & piano. Arrangements
Sullivan, Sir Arthur Seymour
[Twilight. *arr*]. Twilight / [by] Sir Arthur Sullivan ; arranged and edited [for] 2 flutes and piano by William Bennett and Trevor Wye. — Ampleforth : Emerson, 1975. — 4to.
Score (8p.) & part.
Unpriced

(B75-51367)

VRNTQK/LE — Two flutes & piano. Arrangements. Symphonies
Devienne, François
[Symphonie concertante for two flutes, op.76, in G major. *arr*]. Symphonie concertante in G. Op.76 : for 2 flutes and orchestra / [by] François Devienne ; edited by David Lasocki, piano reduction by R.P. Block. — London : Musica rara, 1974. — 4to.
Score (27p.) & 2 parts.
£3.00

(B75-51368)

VRNU — Duets
Arma, Paul
Divertimento no.8 : pour 2 flûtes / [par] Paul Arma. — Paris ; [London] : Chappell, 1972. — 10p ; 4to.
Divertimentos 9-15 are the some work as no.8 arranged respectively for two oboes, two clarinets, two bassoons, two saxophones, two trumpets, two horns and two trombones.
Unpriced

(B75-50844)

Harvey, Paul
Graded study duets : for two flutes or two oboes or flute and oboe with optional bassoon part / [by] Paul Harvey. — London : Boosey and Hawkes, 1974. — 4to.
Score (8p.) & part.
£0.85

(B75-50316)

Muczynski, Robert
Duos for flutes. Op.34 / [by] Robert Muczynski. — New York ; London : Schirmer, 1974. — 13p ; 4to.
Unpriced

(B75-50845)

VRNUE — Duets. Sonatas
Mouret, Jean Joseph
[Sonatas for flute duet, nos.1-6]. 6 Sonaten für zwei Querflöten / [von] Jean-Joseph Mouret ; edited by Renée Viollier. — Wilhelmshaven : Heinrichshofen ; London : Hinrichsen.
Heft 1 : Sonatas 1-3. — 1974. — 2,26p ; 4to.
Unpriced

(B75-50846)

Heft 2 : Sonatas 4-6. — 1974. — 24p ; 4to.
Unpriced

(B75-50847)

VRP — FLUTE & PIANO
VRPE — Sonatas
Bach, Johann Sebastian
[Sonata for flute & harpsichord, no.3, in A major. S. 1032]. Sonata in A major for flute and harpsichord / by Johann Sebastian Bach ; edited by Samuel Baron. — London : Oxford University Press, 1975. — 4to.
Score (27p.) & parts. — The first movement has been completed by the editor.
ISBN 0-19-355249-3 : £2.00

(B75-50317)

McLean, Charles
[Sonatas for flute & continuo. Op.1, nos 9,10]. Two sonatas for flute & basso continuo / by Charles McLean ; edited by David Johnson. — London : Oxford University Press, 1975. — 4to.
Score (13p.) & 4 parts.
ISBN 0-19-357681-3 : £2.00

(B75-50318)

Roseingrave, Thomas
[Sonatas for flute & continuo, nos 4,7]. Two sonatas for flute and basso continuo / [by] Thomas Roseingrave ; edited by Richard Platt. — London : Oxford University Press, 1975. — 4to.
Score (14p.) & 4 parts.
ISBN 0-19-358642-8 : £2.00

(B75-50319)

VRPEM — Sonatinas
Binkerd, Gordon
Sonatina for flute and piano / [by] Gordon Binkerd. — New York ; [London] : Boosey and Hawkes, 1972. — 4to.
Score & part.
Unpriced

(B75-50848)

Roe, Betty
[Sonatine for flute & piano]. Sonatina flute/piano / by Betty Roe. — London : Thames, 1975. — 4to.
Score (12p.) & part.
Unpriced

(B75-51369)

VRPF — Concertos
Czerny, Carl
Duo concertant for flute and piano. Op.129 / [by] Carl Czerny ; edited by Frans Vester. — London : Universal, 1975. — 4to.
Score (51p.) & part.
Unpriced

(B75-51370)

VRPHVQ — Sicilianos
Liferman, Georges
Sicilienne : pour flûte et piano / [par] Georges Liferman. — Paris ; [London] : Chappell, 1975. — 4to.
Score (4p.) & part.
Unpriced

(B75-50320)

VRPJ — Miscellaneous works
Cruft, Adrian
Seven pieces for flute and piano. Op.79 / by Adrian Cruft. — London : Chappell, 1975. — 8vo.
Score & part.
Unpriced

(B75-50849)

Ferneyhough, Brian
Cassandra's dream song : solo flute / [by] Brian Ferneyhough. — London : Peters, 1975. — 3ff ; obl. fol.
Unpriced

(B75-50321)

Jacob, Gordon
On a summer evening : flute and piano / by Gordon Jacob. — Ampleforth : Jane Emerson, 1974. — 4to.
Score (3p.) & part.
Unpriced

(B75-50322)

Jenni, Donald
Musique printanière : for flute and piano / [by] Donald Jenni. — New York ; London : Associated Music, 1975. — 5p ; 4to.
Two copies.
Unpriced

(B75-50850)

Simpson, Lionel
Andantino cantabile. Opus 69 : for flute and piano / [by] Lionel Simpson. — London : British and Continental, 1975. — 4to.
Score (4p.) & part.
Unpriced

(B75-50851)

Weaver, John
Rhapsody : for flute and organ / [by] John Weaver. — New York ; [London] : Boosey and Hawkes, 1975. — 4to.
Score (11p.) & part.
£2.25

(B75-51371)

VRPK/AAY — Arrangements. Collections
The **first** year flautist / arranged by Robin de Smet. — London : Ashdown.
Vol.2. — 1975. — 4to.
£1.20

(B75-50852)

World's favorite pure and simple pieces for flute solos, duets and trios : includes basic charts and playing principles with chords for accompaniment by piano, guitar, etc. / arranged by Alexander Shealy. — Carlstadt : Ashley ; [London] : [Phoenix], 1975. — 12p ; 4to.
Unpriced

(B75-50853)

VRPK/B/FK — Arrangements. Musical clocks
Haydn, Joseph
Twelve pieces for the musical clock (Flötenuhr, 1773) / [by] Joseph Haydn ; rescored and edited for flute and piano by Frans Vester. — London : Universal, 1975. — 4to.
Score (28p.) & part.
Unpriced

(B75-51372)

VRPK/DW — Arrangements. Songs, etc
Copland, Aaron
[Vocalise-etude. *arr*]. Vocalise : for flute and piano / by Aaron Copland ; flute part edited by Doriot Anthony Dwyer. — London : Boosey and Hawkes, 1974. — 4p ; 4to.
£0.75

(B75-50323)

VRPK/DW/GJ/AYG — Arrangements. Children's songs. Collections. Hungary
Hungarian children's songs : for flute and piano / [arranged and compiled by] Emil Petrovics. — London : Boosey and Hawkes, 1975. — 4to.
Score & part.
£1.00

(B75-51373)

VRPK/LF — Arrangements. Concertos
Bach, Carl Philipp Emanuel
[Concerto for flute, strings & basso continuo in B flat major. Wq.167. *arr*]. Concerto in B flat major. Wq.167 : for flute, strings and basso continuo / [by] Carl Philipp Emanuel Bach ; ed. David Lasocki, realization of basso continuo and the piano reduction by Robert Paul Block. — London : Musica rara, 1975. — 4to.
Score (27p.) & part.
Unpriced

(B75-51374)

VRPLTQ — FLUTE & HARP
VRPLTQF — Concertos
Lancen, Serge
Duo concertant pour flûte et harpe ou flûte et piano et orchestre à cordes non oblige : edition pour flûte et harpe / [par] Serge Lancen. — Paris ; [London] : Chappell, 1972. — 4to.
Score & part.
Unpriced

(B75-51375)

VRPLTS — FLUTE & GUITAR
VRPLTSK/DW — Arrangements. Songs, etc
Sullivan, Sir Arthur Seymour
[Operettas. *Selections: arr*]. Ten tunes from Gilbert and Sullivan / arranged for descant recorder and guitar or piano by John W. Duarte. — Sevenoaks : Novello, 1975. — 4to.
Score (28p.) & part.
£1.00

(B75-50324)

VRPM — UNACCOMPANIED FLUTE
VRPMJ — Miscellaneous works
Glasser, Stanley
Jabula : for solo flute / [by] Stanley Glasser ; edited by Judith Pearce. — Banbury : Piers Press, 1974. — 5p ; 4to.
£0.75

(B75-50325)

Humble, Keith
Arcade IIIa : solo flute / [by] Keith Humble. — [Sydney] ; [London] : Universal, 1975. — 4p ; 4to.
Unpriced

(B75-50854)

Jungk, Klaus
Esquisses experimentales : für Flöte / [von] Klaus Jungk. — Frankfurt : Litolff ; London : Peters, 1974. — 8p ; 4to.
Unpriced

(B75-50326)

Kuhlau, Friedrich Daniel Rudolph
Three fantasias. Opus 38 : for flute solo / [by] Friedrich Kuhlau ; edited by Frans Vester. — London : Universal, 1975. — 15p ; 4to.
Unpriced

(B75-50855)

Stamitz, Anton
8 Capricen für Flöte / [von] Anton Stamitz ; herausgegeben von Walter Lebermann. — Frankfurt : Litolff ; London : Peters, 1974. — 12p ; 4to.
Unpriced

(B75-50327)

Szervanszky, Endre
Funf Konzertüden : für Flöte / [von] Endre Szervanszky. — Frankfurt : Litolff ; London : Peters, 1973. — 15p ; 4to.
Unpriced

(B75-50328)

VS — RECORDER
VS/AC — Tutors
The **school** recorder book. — Revised ed. — Leeds : Arnold.
Book 3 : Advanced recorder technique / by Carl Dolmetsch. — 1974. — 52p ; 8vo.
ISBN 0-560-00271-8 : Unpriced

(B75-50329)

Simpson, Kenneth
Music through the recorder : a course in musicianship / [by] Kenneth Simpson. — London : Nelson.
Teacher's book (103p) & pupil's book (80p).
Vol.1. — 1975. — 8vo.
ISBN 0-17-436081-9 : Unpriced

(B75-50856)

VSN — RECORDER ENSEMBLE
VSNP — Septets
Hold, Trevor
Rutterkin : an overture for recorders, (descant, 2 trebles, 2 tenors, 2 basses), after a song by Peter Warlock, (from 1st set of Peterisms) / [by] Trevor Hold. — Bury : Tomus, 1975. — 8vo.
Score & 7 parts.
Unpriced

(B75-51376)

VSNR — Quintets
Kear, Warrick
Impressions : for recorder ensemble, descant, treble/sopranino, treble 2, tenors / [by] Warrick Kear. — Bury : Tomus, 1975. — 8vo.
Score (19p.) & 5 parts.
Unpriced

(B75-51377)

VSNRK/AE — Quintets. Arrangements. Sonatas
Legrenzi, Giovanni
[Sonatas in five parts for various instruments. *Selections: arr*]. Two sonatas in five parts : five recorders / [by] Giovanni Legrenzi ; edited and arranged by Carl Dolmetsch. — London : Universal, 1975. — 4to.
Score (8p.) & 5 parts. — Contents: 1: La Fugazza - 2: La Marinona.
Unpriced

(B75-50857)

VSNRK/AHJMP — Quintets. Arrangements. Can-cans
Offenbach, Jacques
[Orphée aux Enfers. Galop infernal. *arr*]. Offenbach's can-can / arranged for recorder quintet by James Middleton. — Banbury : Piers Press, 1975. — 6p ; 4to.
£1.50(for 3 performing scores)

(B75-51378)

VSNS — Quartets
Aichinger, Gregor
[Fasciculus sacrarum harmoniarum. Ricercars nos.1-3]. Three ricercars / by Gregor Aichinger ; transcribed and edited for recorder quartet by William E. Hettrick. — New York : Galaxy ; London : Galliard, 1975. — 4to.
Score (19p.) & 4 parts.
Unpriced

(B75-50858)

Alemann, Eduardo Armando
Spectra : for four recorders / by Eduardo Armando Alemann. — New York : Galaxy ; London : Galliard, 1975. — 8p ; 4to.
Unpriced

(B75-50859)

Geysen, Frans
Periferisch-Diagonaal-Concentrisch = Periperal-Diagonal-Concentric : for recorder quartet / [by] Frans Geysen. — London : Schott, 1975. — 11p ; 4to.
Unpriced

(B75-50860)

Lotz, Hans Georg
Quartett nach einer Intrade aus dem 16. Jahrhundert : für Blockflöten-Quartett (Sopran, Alt, Tenor, Bass) / [von] Hans-Georg Lotz. — Mainz ; London : Schott, 1975. — 10p ; 4to.
£1.20

(B75-51379)

Touchin, Colin M
A royal pageant. Op.11 : for recorder quartet, (2 descant treble tenor) / [by] Colin M. Touchin. — Bury (Carne House, Parsons Lane, Bury, Lancs.) : Tomus, 1974. — 8vo.
Score (20p.) & 5 parts.
Unpriced

(B75-50861)

VSNSK/JM — Quartets. Arrangements. Incidental music
Purcell, Henry
[The Gordian knot untied. *Selections: arr].* The Gordian knot untied / [by] Henry Purcell ; arranged for recorder quartet by Richard Coles. — Banbury : Piers Press, 1974. — 8p ; 4to.
Unpriced
(B75-50330)

VSNSQK/DW/JR — Three recorders & piano. Arrangements. Songs, etc. Films
Loesser, Frank
[Hans Christian Andersen. *Selections : arr].* Songs from Frank Loesser's Hans Andersen / arranged for descant, treble, tenor recorder and piano by Eric Matthes. — London : Edwin H. Morris, 1975. — 5pt ; 4to.
Score (21p) & 19 parts.
Unpriced
(B75-50862)

VSNTG — Trios. Suites
Smith, Peter Melville
Willowbrook suite : for treble, alto and tenor recorders / [by] Peter Melville Smith. — Croydon : Lengnick, 1974. — 7p ; 4to.
Unpriced
(B75-50863)

VSNTK/AHJN — Trios. Arrangements. Chaconnes
Pachelbel, Johann
[Hexachordum Apollinis. Chaconne in C major. *arr].* Chaconne in C / by Johann Pachelbel ; arranged for recorder trio, treble, tenor, bass, by Charles T. Hale. — Bury : Tomus, 1975. — 8vo.
Score & 3 parts.
Unpriced
(B75-50864)

VSNTK/CB/AY — Trios. Arrangements. Vocal music. Collections
Lassus, Victoria, Palestrina : three-part vocal compositions / arranged for recorders by Aaron Williams. — Chesham : Ricordi, 1975. — 15p ; 4to.
Unpriced
(B75-50865)

VSNU — Duets
Hofmann, Wolfgang
Mobile : fünf Skizzen für Sopran und Altblockflöte / [von] Wolfgang Hofmann. — Frankfurt : Litolff ; London : Peters, 1975. — 18p ; 4to.
Unpriced
(B75-50866)

VSNUK/AAY — Duets. Arrangements. Collections
Kleine Stücke grosser Meister : für Sopran-und Altblockflöte / ausgewählt von Ulrika Emden. — Wilhemshaven : Noetzel ; [London] : [Hinrichsen], 1974. — 31p ; obl.8vo.
Unpriced
(B75-50867)

VSNUK/AH/AY — Duets. Arrangements. Dances. Collections
Kleine Tänze grosser Meister : für Sopran-und Altblockflöte / ausgewählt von Ulrika Emden. — Wilhemshaven : Noetzel ; [London] : [Hinrichsen], 1974. — 32p ; obl.8vo.
Unpriced
(B75-50868)

VSPLTS — RECORDER & GUITAR
Linde, Hans Martin
Musica da camera (1972) : for recorder (treble recorder and bass recorder) and guitar / [by] Hans Martin Linde. — Mainz ; London : Schott, 1974. — 19p ; 4to.
The recorder player uses two recorders.
Unpriced
(B75-50331)

VSR — DESCANT RECORDER
VSR/AC — Tutors
Lambert, Cecily
Forsyth descant recorder tutor / by Cecily Lambert and Ried Knechtel. — Manchester ; London : Forsyth, 1974. — 40p ; 8vo.
Unpriced
(B75-50869)

Lambert, Cecily
Forsyth descant recorder tutor / by Cecily Lambert and Ried Knechtel. — Manchester ; London : Forsyth, 1974. — 40p ; 8vo.
Unpriced
(B75-51380)

VSR/AF — Exercises
Davey, Brian
Recorder playing in colour : for descant recorders / edited by Brian Davey. — London : Chappell.
Book 1 : Junior. — 1975. — 32p ; 4to. —
Unpriced
(B75-50870)

VSRNRK/DW/JR — Quintets. Arrangements. Songs, etc. Films
Loesser, Frank
[Hans Christian Andersen. *Selections : arr].* Songs from Frank Loesser's Hans Andersen / arranged for 5 descant recorders by Eric Matthes. — London : Edwin H. Morris, 1975. — 5pt ; 4to.
Unpriced
(B75-50871)

VSRNRQ — Four descant recorders & piano
Heilbut, Peter
Erstes Zusammenspiel : für vier Sopranblockflöten und Klavier / [von] Peter Heilbut. — Wilhelmshaven : Heinrichshofen ; [London] : [Hinrichsen], 1974. — 4to.
Score (16p.) & 4 parts.
Unpriced
(B75-50872)

VSRNTQ — Two descant recorders & piano
Crimlisk, Anthony
Diversions : for two descant recorders and piano / by Anthony Crimlisk. — London : British and Continental, 1975. — 13p ; 4to.
Unpriced
(B75-51381)

VSRNTQG — Two descant recorders & piano. Suites
Hunt, Reginald
Little suite : for two descant recorders and piano / by Reginald Hunt. — London : Ashdown, 1975. — 15p ; 4to.
Contents: 1: Saraband - 2: Gavotte and musette - 3: Waltz.
£0.50
(B75-50332)

VSRPE — Descant recorder & piano. Sonatas
Bach, Carl Philipp Emanuel
[Sonata for descant recorder & basso continuo in C minor]. Sonata for alto recorder (or flute) and harpsichord (or piano) obbligato with cello (or bassoon) continuo / [by] Carl Philipp Emanuel Bach (?) ; edited and arranged by Daniel Waitzman. — New York ; London : Associated Music, 1974. — 4to.
Score (24p.) & part. — The composer is not known. Formerly attributed to J.S. Bach, it is here attributed to C.P.E. Bach.
Unpriced
(B75-50873)

VSRPH — Descant recorder & piano. Dances
Verrall, Pamela Motley
Six dances for descant duets and piano / [by] Pamela Verrall. — Hamburg ; London : Rahter, 1975. — 4to.
Score (15p.) & part.
Unpriced
(B75-50874)

VSRPHM — Descant recorder & piano. Gavottes
Johnson, Thomas Arnold
Gavotte : for descant recorder, oboe or B flat clarinet and piano / by Thomas A. Johnson. — London : Bosworth, 1975. — 4to.
Score (4p.) & part.
Unpriced
(B75-50875)

VSRPHP — Descant recorder & piano. Jigs
Johnson, Thomas Arnold
Gigue : for descant recorder, oboe or clarinet in B flat or A and piano / by Thomas A. Johnson. — London : Bosworth, 1975. — 4to.
Score (4p.) & part.
Unpriced
(B75-50876)

VSRPK/DW/G/AY — Arrangements. Folk songs. Collections
Duett-ABC : Volksweisen in leichten Sätzen für Sopranblockflöten (Gitarre und Schlagwerk ad lib) / [von] Willi Draths. — Mainz ; London : Schott, 1974. — 28p ; obl.8vo.
£1.37
(B75-50333)

VSRPMJ — Unaccompanied descant recorder. Miscellaneous works
Duke, Henry
Two-way pieces : twelve progressive miniatures, for descant recorder with optional piano accompaniment / [by] Henry Duke. — London : British and Continental, 1975. — 5p ; 4to.
Unpriced
(B75-51382)

VSRPMK/DW/AY — Unaccompanied descant recorder. Arrangements. Songs, etc. Collections
Have a blow (on descant recorder) : a graded tune book for beginners, 50 tunes arranged in order of difficulty / by Don Riddell. — London : British and Continental, 1974. — 23p ; 4to.
Unpriced
(B75-50877)

VSS — TREBLE RECORDER
VSSNRK/DW/JR — Quintets. Arrangements. Songs, etc. Films
Loesser, Frank
[Hans Christian Andersen. *Selections : arr*]. Songs from Frank
Loesser's Hans Andersen / arranged for 5 treble recorders by Eric
Matthes. — London : Edwin H. Morris, 1975. — 5pt ; 4to.
Unpriced
(B75-50878)

VSSNTPWE — Two treble recorders & keyboard. Sonatas
Hotteterre, Jacques
[Sonatas for two recorders & basso continuo. Op.3]. Trio sonatas.
Opus 3 : for 2 treble (alto) recorders and basso continuo / [by]
Jacques Hotteterre le Romain ; edited by David Lasocki, assisted
by Robert Paul Block. — London : Musica rara.
Nos.1-3. — 1975. — 4to.
Score (24p.) & 3 parts.
Unpriced
(B75-51383)
Nos.4-6. — 1975. — 4to.
Score (24p.) & 3 parts.
Unpriced
(B75-51384)

VSSNTQK/AAY — Two treble recorders & piano. Arrangements.
Collections
Two trebles : nine pieces arranged for two treble recorders and
piano / [by] William Appleby and Frederick Fowler. — London :
Oxford University Press, 1975. — 4to.
Score (16p.) & 2 parts.
ISBN 0-19-355202-7 : £1.20
(B75-50879)

VSSNU — Treble recorder duets
Finger, Gottfried
[A collection of Musick in two parts. *Selections*]. Leichte Duette
für Altblockflöten / [von] Gottfried Finger ; herausgegeben von
Jost Harf. — Wilhemshaven : Heinrichshofen ; London :
Hinrichsen, 1975. — 15p ; 4to.
Unpriced
(B75-50880)

Gibbons, Orlando
[Fantasias for treble recorder duet]. Three fantasias : for two
treble (alto) recorders / [by] Orlando Gibbons ; edited by Douglas
Ritchie. — London : Faber Music, 1975. — 12p ; 4to.
Unpriced
(B75-50881)

VSSP/AY — Treble recorder & piano. Collections
Neuzeitliches Spielbuch : für Altblockflöte und Klavier. — Mainz ;
London : Schott, 1975. — 4to.
Score (36p.) & part. — Contents: sechs rhythmische Stücke / by Fritz
Luthi - Miniaturen / by Herbert Nobis - Sonatine / by Heinz Walter-Fünf
Studien / by Hans-Martin Linde.
£3.00
(B75-51385)

VSSPE — Treble recorder & piano. Sonatas
Bergmann, Walter
Sonata for treble recorder and piano / [by] Walter Bergmann. —
London : Schott, 1974. — 4to.
Score (20p.) & part.
£2.00
(B75-50334)

Finger, Gottfried
[Sonata for treble recorder & harpsichord, no.6. in F major].
Sonata in F : for treble recorder and harpsichord, (or flute or oboe
and piano) / [by] Godfry Finger ; edited by Paul Hubbard. —
Banbury : Piers Press, 1975. — fol.
Score (8p.) & part.
Unpriced
(B75-50336)

Mancini, Francesco
[Sonata no.1 for treble recorder & continuo in D minor]. Sonata
in D minor for treble recorder and basso continuo / by Francesco
Mancini ; edited by Marcello Castellani, continuo-realization
Annaberta Conti. — Cassel ; London : Bärenreiter, 1974. — 4to.
Score (14p.) & 2 parts.
£2.00
(B75-50335)

VSSPEM — Treble recorder & piano. Sonatinas
Standford, Patric
[Sonatina for treble recorder & harpsichord. Op.26]. Sonatine for
treble recorder and harpsichord. Op.26 / [by] Patric Standford. —
London : Stainer and Bell, 1975. — 4to.
Score (11p.) & part. — Duration 12 min.
Unpriced
(B75-50882)

VSSPK/AE — Treble recorder & piano. Arrangements. Sonatas
Senaillié, Jean Baptiste
[Premier livre de sonates a violon seul. Sonata for violin, no.5, in
C minor. *arr*]. Sonata 5 : treble recorder and keyboard in G
minor / [by] Jean Baptiste Senaillié ; edited and arranged by Carl
Dolmetsch ; keyboard accompaniment by Arnold Dolmetsch. —
London : Universal, 1974. — 4to.
Score (10p.) & part.
Unpriced
(B75-50337)

VSSPLTS — Treble recorder & guitar
Barrell, Bernard
Three preludes for treble recorder and guitar. Op.31 / [by]
Bernard Barrell. — London : Thames, 1975. — 4p ; 4to.
Unpriced
(B75-51386)

VSSPM/AY — Unaccompanied treble recorder. Collections
The flute master : ausgewählte Stücke für Altblockflöte allein (auch
Querflöte oder Oboe) / herausgegeben von Erich Doflein und
Nikolaus Delius. — Mainz ; London : Schott, 1975. — 16p ; 4to.
£1.75
(B75-51387)

VSSPMJ — Unaccompanied treble recorder. Miscellaneous works
Amram, David
Zohar : alto recorder (or flute) / [by] David Amram. — New
York ; London : Peters, 1973. — 3p ; 4to.
Unpriced
(B75-50338)

Dolci, Amico
Nuovi ricercari : per flauto dolce contralto / [di] Amico Dolci. —
Wilhemshaven : Heinrichshofen ; [London] : [Hinrichsen], 1974.
— 16p ; 4to.
Unpriced
(B75-50883)

[James Thomson's Music Book. *Selections*]. Twenty-one Scots tunes
from James Thomson's music book (1702) / edited by David
Johnson. — London : Forsyth, 1975. — 19p ; obl.8vo.
Unpriced
(B75-50884)

VST — TENOR RECORDER
VSTNTK/DW/JR — Trios. Arrangements. Songs, etc. Films
Loesser, Frank
[Hans Christian Andersen. *Selections : arr*]. Songs from Frank
Loesser's Hans Andersen / arranged for 3 tenor recorders by Eric
Matthes. — London : Edwin H. Morris, 1975. — 3pt ; 4to.
Unpriced
(B75-50885)

VSU — BASS RECORDER
VSU/AF — Tutors
Hunt, Edgar
The bass recorder : a concise method for the bass in F and great
bass in C / by Edgar Hunt. — London : Schott, 1975. — 20p ;
8vo.
ISBN 0-901938-49-1 : £1.00
(B75-51388)

VSUS/AF — Crumhorn. Tutors
Hunt, Edgar
The crumhorn : a concise method for the crumhorn and other
wind-cap instruments / [by] Edgar Hunt. — London : Schott,
1975. — 27p ; 8vo.
ISBN 0-901938-52-1 : £1.20
(B75-51389)

VSX — PIPES
VSX/AC — Tutors
Zamfir, Gheorghe
Traité de naï roumain : methode de flûte de Pan / traduit du
roumain par Lena Constante et Raluca Sterian. — Paris ;
[London] : Chappell, 1975. — 125p ; 4to.
Unpriced
(B75-50886)

VSXPMJ — Unaccompanied pipes. Miscellaneous works
Zamfir, Gheorghe
L'Alouette : pour flûte de Pan / [par] Gheorghe Zamfir. —
Paris ; [London] : Chappell, 1975. — 40p ; 4to.
Unpriced
(B75-50887)

VT — OBOE
VT/AC — Tutors
Rothwell, Evelyn
The oboist's companion / [by] Evelyn Rothwell. — London :
Oxford University Press.
Volume 1. — 1974. — 104p ; 4to.
Fingering chart inserted together with a slip listing errata and additions.
ISBN 0-19-322335-x : £3.25
(B75-51390)

VT/AF — Exercises
East, Raina
Technical exercises for the oboe / [by] Raina East. — London :
Schott, 1975. — 29p ; 4to.
Unpriced
(B75-50339)

Sous, Alfred
Etüden für Oboe / [von] Alfred Sous. — Frankfurt : Litolff ;
London : Peters, 1974. — 55p ; 4to.
Unpriced
(B75-50340)

VTN — OBOE ENSEMBLE
VTNU/AY — Duets. Collections
28 selected duets : for two saxophones (or oboes) / compiled and
edited by Jay Arnold. — Carlstadt : Edward Schuberth ;
[London] : [Phoenix], 1975. — 79p ; 4to.
Contents: Ten duets, by J. Sellner - 18 duets, from Opus 11, by J.H. Luft.
Unpriced
Primary classification VUNU/AY

VTP — OBOE & PIANO
VTPEM — Sonatinas
Dalby, Martin
Sonatina for oboe and piano / [by] Martin Dalby. — Sevenoaks :
Novello, 1975. — 4to.
Score (8p.) & part.
£1.00
(B75-50888)

VTPG — Suites
Ridout, Alan
Suite for oboe and piano / by Alan Ridout. — London : Chappell,
1975. — 4to.
Score (15p.) & part.
Unpriced
(B75-51391)

VTPHN — Hornpipes
Johnson, Thomas Arnold
Horn pipe (Allegro moderato) : for oboe (or clarinet) and piano /
[by] Thomas A. Johnson. — London : British and Continental
Music, 1975. — 4to.
Score (5p.) & 2 parts.
Unpriced
(B75-50889)

VTPHVQ — Sicilianos
Head, Michael
Siciliana : oboe and harpsichord or piano / [by] Michael Head ;
edited by Lady Evelyn Barbirolli. — Ampleforth : Emerson, 1975.
— 4to.
Score (6p.) & part.
Unpriced
(B75-51392)

VTPJ — Miscellaneous works
Barthe, Adrian
Ouvre feu : oboe and piano / [by] Adrian Barthe. — Ampleforth :
Emerson, 1975. — 4to.
Score & part.
Unpriced
(B75-51393)

Fievet, Paul
- D'in vieux manoir : pour hautbois et piano / [par] Paul Fievet.
— Paris ; [London] : Chappell, 1971. — 4to.
Score & part.
Unpriced
(B75-50341)

Hanmer, Ronald
Two contrasts : oboe and piano / by Ronald Hanmer. —
Ampleforth : Emerson, 1974. — 4to.
Unpriced
(B75-50342)

VTPK — Arrangements
Rietz, Julius
[Concert-Stück for oboe and orchestra. Op.33. *arr*]. Concert
piece : for oboe and orchestra. Op.33 / [by] Julius Rietz ; edited
by James Ledward. — London : Musica rara, 1975. — 4to.
Score (19p.) & parts.
Unpriced
(B75-51394)

VTPK/LF — Arrangements. Concertos
Albinoni, Tommaso
[Concerto à 5 for oboe & string orchestra, op.9, no.11, in B flat
major. *arr*]. Concerto à 5 in B flat. Op.9, no.11 : for oboe, strings
and basso continuo / [by] Tommaso Albinoni ; edited and realized
as a reduction by Franz Giegling. — London : Musica rara, 1975.
— 4to.
Score (17p.) & part.
£2.50
(B75-51395)

Holzbauer, Ignaz
[Concerto for oboe & string orchestra in D minor. *arr*]. Konzert,
D-moll für Oboe und Streicher / [von] Ignaz Holbauer ;
herausgegeben von Walter Lebermann, Kadenzen vom
Herausgeber, Ausgabe für Oboe und Klavier von Heinrich
Creuzburg. — 1st ed. — Frankfurt : Litolff ; London : Peters,
1975. — 4to.
Score (28p.) & part.
Unpriced
(B75-51396)

VTPM — UNACCOMPANIED OBOE
VTPMEM — Sonatinas
Goodman, Alfred
[Sonatina for oboe]. Sonatine für Oboe / [von] Alfred Goodman.
— Frankfurt : Litolff ; London : Peters, 1974. — 3p ; 4to.
Unpriced
(B75-50890)

VTPMJ — Miscellaneous works
Genzmer, Harald
[Seven studies for oboe]. Sieben Studien : Capriccios für Oboe /
[von] Harald Genzmer. — Frankfurt : Litolff ; [London] :
[Peters], 1974. — 8p ; 4to.
Unpriced
(B75-50343)

VUN — SAXOPHONE ENSEMBLE
VUNS — Quartets
Barraud, Henry
[Quartet for saxophones]. Quatuor de saxophones / [par] Henry
Barraud. — London : Boosey and Hawkes, 1974. — 4to.
Score (26p.) & 4 parts.
£7.50
(B75-50344)

Cordell, Frank
Patterns : for saxophone quartet / [by] Frank Cordell. —
Sevenoaks : Novello, 1975. — 4to.
Score (10p.) & 4 parts. — Duration 8 min.
£3.75
(B75-51397)

VUNS/T — Quartets. Variations
Horovitz, Joseph
Variations on a theme of Paganini : for brass quartet, or
saxophone quartet, or woodwind quartet / by Joseph Horovitz. —
London : R. Smith, 1975. — 15p ; 4to.
Unpriced
Primary classification WNS/T
(B75-50379)

VUNU/AY — Duets. Collections
28 selected duets : for two saxophones (or oboes) / compiled and
edited by Jay Arnold. — Carlstadt : Edward Schuberth ;
[London] : [Phoenix], 1975. — 79p ; 4to.
Contents: Ten duets, by J. Sellner - 18 duets, from Opus 11, by J.H. Luft.
Unpriced
Also classified at VTNU/AY
(B75-51398)

30 selected duets : for two saxophones (or oboes) / compiled and
edited by Jay Arnold. — Carlstadt : Edward Schuberth ;
[London] : [Phoenix], 1975. — 80p ; 4to.
Contents: Ten duets, by H. Klose - Ten duets, by A. Mayner - Ten duets,
by J. Sellner.
Unpriced
(B75-51399)

VUS — ALTO SAXOPHONE
VUSPK/LE — Arrangements. Symphonies
Dondeyne, Desiré
[Sinfonia concertante for alto saxophone. *arr*]. Symphone
concertante pour saxophone alto E bémol et orchestre / [par]
Desire Dondeyne ; reduction pour saxophone alto E bémol et
piano. — Paris ; [London] : Chappell, 1971. — 4to.
Score & part.
Unpriced
(B75-50345)

VV — CLARINET
VV/AF/AYG — Exercises. Collections. Hungary
Collection of studies for clarinet / edited by Gyorgy Balassa. —
London : Boosey and Hawkes ; Budapest : Editio Musica, 1974.
— 32p ; 4to.
£1.00
(B75-50346)

VVN — CLARINET ENSEMBLE
VVNQF — Sextets. Concertos
Lancen, Serge
Concert à six : 1 petite clarinette E bémol, 2 clarinettes B bémol,
1 clarinette alto E bémol (ou 3 ème clarinette B bémol), 1
clarinette basse B bémol, 1 clarinette contrabasse E bémol (ou 2
ème clarinette, basse B bémol / [par] Serge Lancen. — Paris ;
[London] : Chappell, 1971. — 54p ; fol.
Unpriced
(B75-51400)

VVNS — Quartets
Schumann, Gerhard
Audiogramme : für vier Klarinetten / [von] Gerhard Schumann. — Wilhemshaven : Heinrichshofen ; [London] : [Hinrichsen], 1974. — 15p ; 8vo.
Miniature score.
Unpriced

(B75-50891)

VVNSG — Quartets. Suites
Lyons, Graham
Three piece suite : for four clarinets / [by] Graham Lyons. — London : British and Continental Music, 1975. — 7p ; 4to.
Unpriced

(B75-50892)

VVNSK — Quartets. Arrangements
Haydn, Joseph
[Divertimento for two clarinets & two horns in C major. Hob II/14. *arr*]. Divertimento in C / [by] F.J. Haydn ; arranged for 4 clarinets by Neil Butterworth. — York : Banks, 1974. — 4to.
Score (7p.) & 4 parts.
Unpriced

(B75-50893)

VVNSK/AHXJ — Quartets. Arrangements. Ragtime
Joplin, Scott
[Piano music. *Selections : arr*]. Rags / [by] Scott Joplin ; arranged for four clarinets and bass clarinet (optional) by Peter Spink. — London : Oxford University Press, 1975. — 20p ; 8vo.
Contents: The entertainer - Elite syncopations - The favorite - The easy winners.
ISBN 0-19-357320-2 : £1.75

(B75-50894)

VVNTH — Trios. Dances
Slack, Roy
Three little dances : for three clarinets / by Roy Slack. — London : British and Continental, 1975. — 7p ; 4to.
Unpriced

(B75-51401)

VVNTK/AGM — Trios. Arrangements. Marches
Bach, Carl Philipp Emanuel
[Six little marches for wind septet. Wq.195. *arr*]. Six little marches / [by] C.P.E. Bach ; arranged for three equal clarinets by Wadham Sutton. — Sevenoaks : Novello, 1975. — 6p ; 8vo.
£0.30

(B75-50347)

VVNTK/AHXJ — Trios. Arrangements. Ragtime
Joplin, Scott
[The entertainer. *arr*]. The entertainer / [by] Scott Joplin ; arr. for clarinet trio and piano by Harold L. Walters. — Miami : Rubank ; [London] : [Novello], 1975. — 4to.
Score (3p.) & 3 parts.
Unpriced

(B75-51402)

VVNU — Duets
Bavicchi, John
Five dialogues. Op.7 : for two B flat clarinets / [by] John Bavicchi. — New York ; [London] : Oxford University Press, 1972. — 11p ; 4to.
Unpriced

(B75-50895)

Blank, Allan
Four miniatures : for two B flat clarinets / [by] Allan Blank. — New York ; [London] : Associated Music, 1974. — 6p ; 4to.
Two copies.
£1.30

(B75-51403)

Devienne, Francois
[Duets for two clarinets. Op.74]. Sechs Duos für zwei Klarinetten. Opus 74 / [von] Francois Devienne ; herausgegeben von Béla Kovács. — Frankfurt : Litolff ; London : Peters, 1974. — 23p ; 4to.
Unpriced

(B75-50896)

Hofmann, Wolfgang
Fünf Inventionen : für zwei Klarinetten / [von] Wolfgang Hofmann. — Frankfurt : Litolff ; London : Peters, 1974. — 2pt ; 4to.
Unpriced

(B75-50897)

VVP — CLARINET & PIANO
VVP/T — Variations
Duclos, Pierre
Andantino : variation pour clarinette si bémol et piano / [par] Pierre Duclos. — Paris ; [London] : Chappell, 1972. — 4to.
Score & part.
Unpriced

(B75-50898)

VVPE — Sonatas
Lefevre, Jean Xavier
[Méthode de clarinette. Sonata for clarinet & piano, no.1, in B flat major]. Sonata no.1 : for clarinet in B flat and piano / [by] Jean Xavier Lefevre ; realised and edited by Georgina Dobree. — London : Schott, 1974. — 4to.
Score (7p.) & part.
£0.70

(B75-50348)

VVPEM — Sonatinas
Walker, James
Sonatina for clarinet & piano / [by] James Walker. — New York ; London : Schirmer, 1975. — 4to.
Score (11p.) & part.
Unpriced

(B75-50899)

VVPJ — Miscellaneous works
Harvey, Jonathan
Transformations of 'Love bade me welcome' : for clarinet and piano / [by] Jonathan Harvey. — Sevenoaks : Novello, 1975. — 4to.
Score (10p.) & part. — Duration 10 min.
£3.00

(B75-51404)

Heider, Werner
Kunst-Stoff : für Elektro-Klarinette, präpariertes Klavier und Tonband / [von] Werner Heider. — Frankfurt : Litolff ; London : Peters, 1973. — 17ff ; obl. fol.
Unpriced

(B75-50349)

Patterson, Paul
Conversations : for clarinet B flat and piano / [by] Paul Patterson. — London : Weinberger, 1975. — 4to.
Unpriced

(B75-50900)

Simpson, John
The magic clarinet : for clarinet and piano / [by] John Simpson. — Hamburg ; London : Rahter, 1975. — 4to.
Score (21p.) & part.
Unpriced

(B75-50901)

VVPK — Arrangements
Gade, Niels Vilhelm
[Aquarelles. Op.19, no.4. *arr*]. Humoreske. Op.19, no.4 / [by] Niels W. Gade ; arranged for clarinet (B flat) and piano by Ruggero Valbonesi. — London : British and Continental Music, 1975. — 4to.
Score (4p.) & part.
Unpriced

(B75-50902)

Stamaty, Camille
[Chant et mécanisme. Op.37, 38. *Selections : arr*]. Five Stamaty pieces from Op.37 and 38 / freely arranged for B flat clarinet and piano by Adrian Cruft. — London : New Wind Music, 1975. — 4to.
Score (11p.) & part.
£0.50

(B75-51405)

Valbonesi, Ruggero
[Capriccio. *arr*]. Capriccio / [by] Ruggero Valbonesi ; arranged for clarinet (B flat) and piano. — London : British and Continental, EMI Music, 1975. — 4to.
Score (8p.) & part.
Unpriced

(B75-50903)

VVPK/AAY — Arrangements. Collections
Classical and romantic pieces for clarinet and piano / arranged by Alan Frank and Watson Forbes. — London : Oxford University Press.
Book 1. — 1975. — 4to.
Score (14p.) & part.
ISBN 0-19-356517-x : £1.25

(B75-51406)

Book 2. — 1975. — 4to.
Score (20p.) & part.
ISBN 0-19-356520-x : £1.25

(B75-51407)

VVPK/AEM — Arrangements. Sonatinas
Telemann, Georg Philipp
[Sonatina for violin & harpsichord, no.6, in C major. *arr*]. Sonatina no.3 / [by] G.P. Telemann ; arranged for clarinet and piano and edited by Peter Wastall and Derek Hyde. — London : Boosey and Hawkes, 1975. — 4to.
Score (7p.) & part.
£0.65

(B75-51408)

VVPK/LF — Arrangements. Concertos
Hoffmeister, Franz Anton
[Concerto for clarinet in B major. *arr*]. Concerto in B flat for clarinet and orchestra / [by] Franz Anton Hoffmeister ; edited for clarinet and piano by Alison A. Copland. — London : Schott, 1975. — 4to.
Score (30p.) & part.
£1.50
(B75-51409)

VVPM — UNACCOMPANIED CLARINET
VVPMJ — Miscellaneous works
Cheslock, Louis
Descant : for unaccompanied clarinet / [by] Louis Cheslock. — New York ; [London] : Oxford University Press, 1971. — 4p ; 4to.
Unpriced
(B75-50904)

Harvey, Paul
Three etudes on themes of Gershwin : for unaccompanied clarinet / [by] Paul Harvey. — London : Chappell, 1975. — 11p ; 4to.
Unpriced
(B75-51410)

VVQ — CLARINET (A)
VVRPK/AHXJ — Clarinet (E flat) and piano. Arrangements.
Ragtime
Joplin, Scott
[The entertainer. *arr*]. The entertainer / [by] Scott Joplin ; arr. for E flat clarinet with piano accompaniment by Harold L. Walters. — Miami : Rubank ; [London] : [Novello], 1975. — 4to.
Score (3p.) & part.
Unpriced
(B75-51411)

VWN — BASSOON ENSEMBLE
VWNT/Y — Trios. Fugues
Hartley, Geoffrey
Round the mulberry bush : a fugal trio for three bassoons / by Geoffrey Hartley. — Ampleforth : Emerson, 1974. — 3pt ; 4to.
Unpriced
(B75-51412)

VWNUE — Duets. Sonatas
Guignon, Jean Pierre
[Sonatas for two cellos. Op.2, nos. 1, 4, 3]. Sonates. Op.2, pour 2 violoncelles basses de violes (Gamben) ou bassons (fagotti) / [von] Jean-Pierre Guignon ; herausgegeben von Dieter Staekelin. — 1st ed. — Basle : Kneusslin ; [London] : [Hinrichsen], 1974. — 2pt ; 4to.
Unpriced
Primary classification SRNUE
(B75-50260)

VWP — BASSOON & PIANO
VWPE — Sonatas
Boismortier, Joseph Bodin de
[Sonata for bassoon & basso continuo, op.26, no.2, in A minor]. Sonata no.2 in A minor : for bassoon and basso continuo / [by] Joseph-Bodin Boismortier ; ed. Ronald Tyree. — London : Musica rara, 1975. — 4to.
Score (8p.) & 2 parts.
£2.00
(B75-51413)

Telemann, Georg Philipp
[Sonata for bassoon & basso continuo in F minor]. Sonata in F minor for bassoon and basso continuo / [by] Georg Philipp Telemann ; ed. Ronald Tyree. — London : Musica rara, 1975. — 4to.
Score (10p.) & part.
£2.00
(B75-51414)

VWPJ — Miscellaneous works
Boutry, Roger
Interferences I : pour basson et piano / [par] Roger Boutry. — Paris ; [London] : Chappell, 1971. — fol.
Score & part.
Unpriced
(B75-50905)

VWPK/LF — Arrangements. Concertos
Hummel, Johann Nepomuk
[Concerto for bassoon in F major. *arr*]. Bassoon concerto / by J.N. Hummel ; edited and arranged for bassoon and piano by Norman Richardson. — London : Boosey and Hawkes, 1975. — 4to.
Score (40p) & part.
£2.00
(B75-50906)

Luke, Ray
[Concerto for bassoon. *arr*]. Concerto for bassoon and orchestra / [by] Ray Luke ; reduction for bassoon and piano. — New York ; [London] : Oxford University Press, 1971. — 4to.
Unpriced
(B75-50350)

VWPM — UNACCOMPANIED BASSOON
VWPME — Sonatas
Genzmer, Harald
[Sonata for bassoon]. Sonate für Fagott / [von] Harald Genzmer. — Frankfurt : Litolff ; London : Peters, 1974. — 8p ; 4to.
Unpriced
(B75-50351)

VWPMJ — Miscellaneous works
Goodman, Alfred
[Two studies for bassoon]. Zwei Studien : für Fagott / [von] Alfred Goodman. — Frankfurt : Litolff ; London : Peters, 1974. — 5p ; 4to.
Unpriced
(B75-50352)

Hirsch, Hans Ludwig
Drei Monodien : für Fagott / [von] Hans Ludwig Hirsch. — Frankfurt : Litolff ; London : Peters, 1974. — 5p ; 4to.
Unpriced
(B75-50353)

VY — BAGPIPES
VYT/KH/AYDT — Irish bag-pipes. Regimental music. Collections. Northern Ireland
Great Britain. *Army. Royal Irish Rangers*
The Royal Irish Rangers (27th Inniskilling), 83rd and 87th : standard settings of pipe music. — London : Paterson, 1975. — 16,104p ; obl.8vo.
Unpriced
(B75-51415)

W — BRASS WIND INSTRUMENTS
W/AC — Tutors
Ehmann, Wilhelm
[Bläser-Fibel II]. Schule bläserische Gestaltung : eine Bläserschule, für Fortgeschrittene auch zum Selbst und Gruppenuntervicht / [von] Wilhelm Ehmann. — Cassel ; London : Bärenreiter, 1974. — 173p ; obl 8vo.
Bläser-Fibel I published Cassel, Bärenreiter, 1951.
£3.60
(B75-50354)

WM — BRASS BAND
WM/AF — Exercises
Rivers, Patrick
The Novello band book / [by] Patrick Rivers. — Sevenoaks : Novello, 1975. — vi,69p ; obl. 8vo.
£2.50
(B75-50355)

WM/AY — Collections
Salvation Army Brass Band Journal (Festival series). — London : Salvationist Publishing and Supplies.
Nos 357-360 : The suppliant heart: meditation / by Brian Bowen. The warrior psalm: tone poem / by Ray Steadman-Allen. The swan: euphonium or trombone solo / by C. Saint-Saens; arr. Ray Steadman-Allen. Just like John: festival arrangement / by Norman Bearcroft. — 1974. — 61p ; obl. 8vo. —
Unpriced
(B75-50356)

Nos.361-364 : I saw three ships : Christmas fantasy / by Brian Bowen. Selection from 'Jesus Folk' / by Ray Steadman-Allen ; songs John Larsson Ellers ; prelude by Robert Getz. Life's pageant : cornet solo / by Terry Camsey. — 1974. — 77p ; obl.4to. —
Unpriced
(B75-50908)

Nos. 365-368 : New frontier : selection / [by] William Himes. The high council : festival march / [by] Ray Steadman-Allen. The children's song : festival arrangement / by Robert Schramm. The great physician : song arrangement / by Dudley J. Bright. — 1975. — 53p ; obl.8vo. —
Unpriced
(B75-50907)

Salvation Army Brass Band Journal (General series). — London : Salvationist Publishing and Supplies.
Nos 1657-1660 : Wigan citadel: march / by Charles Dove. A singing heart: selection / by Erik Silfverberg. In tune with thy divinity (Londonderry air) / arr. Robert Redhead. Nearer to thee: selection / by Ken James. — 1974. — 41p ; obl. 4to. —
Unpriced
(B75-50357)

Salvation Army Brass Band Journal (General series). — London : Salvationist Publishing & Supplies.

Nos 1661-1664 : Long Point : march / by Norman Bearcroft. A Child's praises : selection / by Christopher Cole. The source of peace : transcription / by Ray Steadman-Allen. Wonder, wonderful Jesus : song arrangement / by Dean Goffin, with, Ask and it shall be given you : transcription / by Dean Goffin. — 1974. — 31p ; obl.8vo. — Unpriced

(B75-50909)

Nos.1665-1668 : Harvest praise : selection / [by] Ray Steadman-Allen. We want the world to know : song transcription / [by] Philip Catelinet. The pure in heart : meditation / [by] R.E. Dorow. God's love : march / [by] Eiliv Herikstad. — 1975. — 38p ; obl.8vo. — Unpriced

(B75-50910)

Salvation Army Brass Band Journal (Triumph series). — London : Salvationist Publishing and Supplies.

Nos 765-768 : St Gallen: march / by Paul Martin. Movements from 'Album for the young' / by Tchaikovsky; arr. Michael Kenyon. Hallelujah! Christ arose: song arrangement / by Ray Steadman-Allen. O sinner man: euphonium solo / by Robin Redhead. — 1973. — 41p ; obl. 8vo. — Unpriced

(B75-50358)

Nos 777-780 : Keep up the flag : march / by Philip Catelinet. Sailors' songs : selection / by Erik Silfverberg. Joy and gladness : trombone solo / by Ray Steadman-Allen. Congregational tunes / arr. Ray Steadman-Allen. — 1974. — 37p ; obl.8vo. — Unpriced

(B75-50911)

Nos. 781-784 : Fighting onward : march / [by] Eiliv Herikstad. Mountain camp : march / [by] Donald Osgood. Beneath the Cross of Jesus : song arrangement / [by] Ira D. Sankey ; arr. Philip Catelinet. The happy warriors : cornet duet / [by] Erik Silfrerberg. — 1975. — 30p ; obl.8vo. — Unpriced

(B75-50912)

Nos.785-788 : If Jesus keeps me polished : humouresque / by Terry Camsey. This I know : selection / by Ray F. Cresswell. Evening prayer (In the gloaming) : song arrangement / arr. Howard Davies. Harwich : march / by Charles Dove. — 1975. — 35p ; obl.4to. — Unpriced

(B75-51416)

WM/T — Variations
Farnon, Robert
Une Vie de matelot = A sailor's life : theme and variations for brass band / by Robert Farnon. — London : R. Smith, 1975. — 44p ; obl. 4to.
Duration 10 min.
Unpriced

(B75-50913)

Howarth, Elgar
Fireworks for brass band : variations on a theme of W. Hogarth Lear / by Elgar Howarth. — Sevenoaks : Paxton, 1975. — 64p ; obl. 4to.
Unpriced

(B75-50914)

WMG — Suites
Butt, James
A whimsey for brass / [by] James Butt ; score revised by Derek Cable. — London : British and Continental Music, 1975. — 8vo.
Short score (4p.) & 25 parts. — Duration 4 3/4 min. — With several copies of various parts.
Unpriced

(B75-50915)

WMGN — Fanfares
Miranda, Sharon Moe
American fanfare : for brass ensemble and timpani / by Sharon Moe Miranda. — New York ; [London] : Chappell, 1974. — 4to.
Score (11p.) & 12 parts.
Unpriced

(B75-50359)

Walton, *Sir* William
Anniversary fanfare : for trumpet, trombones and percussion / by William Walton. — London : Oxford University Press, 1975. — 8vo.
Score (6p) & 11pt. — Duration 1 min. — The fanfare is now used as an introduction to Orb and Sceptre, but it may be played as a separate item when desired.
ISBN 0-19-368100-5 : Unpriced

(B75-50916)

WMH — Dances
Hughes, Eric
Carambina : Spanish dance, [for brass band] / by Eric Hughes. — London : Studio Music, 1975. — 8vo.
Score (4p.) & 25 parts. — With several copies of various parts.
Unpriced

(B75-50917)

Kenny, Terry
Trombone rockanova : brass band / [by] Terry Kenny. — London : Studio Music, 1975. — 24pt ; 8vo.
Conductor & 23 parts. — With several copies of various parts.
Unpriced

(B75-50918)

WMHJMR — Cha-chas
Siebert, Edrich
Chatanooga cha-cha : [brass band] / by Edrich Siebert. — London : Studio Music, 1974. — 8p ; obl. 8vo.
Unpriced

(B75-50360)

WMHLF — Galops
Siebert, Edrich
Grand Canyon galop : [brass band] by Edrich Siebert. — London : Studio Music, 1974. — 10p ; obl. 4to.
Unpriced

(B75-50361)

Siebert, Edrich
Over the sticks : galop / [by] Edrich Siebert. — London : Studio Music, 1975. — obl.8vo.
Conductor & 24 parts.
Unpriced

(B75-51417)

WMHSW — Paso dobles
Siebert, Edrich
El Paso : paso doble [brass band] / by Edrich Siebert. — London : Studio Music, 1974. — 10p ; obl. 4to.
Unpriced

(B75-50362)

WMHVKS — Sambas
Siebert, Edrich
Salt Lake City samba : [brass band] / by Edrich Siebert. — London : Studio Music, 1974. — 9p ; obl. 4to.
Unpriced

(B75-50363)

WMJ — Miscellaneous works
Ball, Eric
Holiday overture : for brass band / [by] Eric Ball. — London : Boosey and Hawkes, 1975. — obl.8vo.
Score (33p.) & 27 parts. — With several copies of various parts.
£6.00

(B75-51418)

Butterworth, Arthur
Caliban. Op.50 : scherzo malevolo, for brass band / [by] Arthur Butterworth. — London : R. Smith, 1975. — 28p ; obl. 4to.
Unpriced

(B75-50919)

Hanmer, Ronald
Latin-Americana : [brass band] / [by] Ronald Hanmer. — London : Studio Music, 1975. — 8vo.
Conductor (4p.) & 27 parts. — With several copies of various parts. — Duration 3 1/2 min.
Unpriced

(B75-50920)

Heath, Reginald
Gay señorita : [brass band] / by Reginald Heath. — London : R. Smith, 1975. — 8vo.
Conductor & 23 parts. — With several copies of various parts. — Duration 2 3/4 min.
Unpriced

(B75-50921)

Kenny, Terry
Trombone rockanova / [by] Terry Kenny. — London : Studio Music, 1975. — 8vo.
Conductor & 24 parts. — With several copies of various parts.
Unpriced

(B75-50922)

Lear, W Hogarth
Pel mel : for brass band / [by] W. Hogarth Lear. — Sevenoaks : Paxton Music, 1975. — 8vo.
Conductor (8p.) & 24 parts. — With several copies of various parts.
£1.75

(B75-50365)

Lear, W Hogarth
Pop goes the posthorn : for brass band / [by] W. Hogarth Lear.
— Sevenoaks : Paxton, 1975. — 8vo.
Conductor (2p.) & 28 parts. — With several copies of various parts.
£1.50
(B75-50366)

Patterson, Paul
Count down : brass band / [by] Paul Patterson. — London :
Weinberger, 1975. — 30p ; obl.8vo.
Unpriced
(B75-50923)

Siebert, Edrich
Boston bounce : [brass band] / by Edrich Siebert. — London :
Studio Music, 1974. — 10p ; obl. 4to.
Unpriced
(B75-50367)

Siebert, Edrich
Connecticut capers : brass band / by Edrich Siebert. — London :
Studio Music, 1974. — 6p ; obl.8vo.
Unpriced
(B75-50368)

Siebert, Edrich
Palm Beach : barcarolle [for] brass band / by Edrich Siebert. —
London : Studio Music, 1974. — 7p ; obl. 4to.
Unpriced
(B75-50369)

Smith-Masters, Stanley
A Texas lullaby : [brass band] / [by] S. Smith-Masters. —
London : Studio Music, 1975. — obl.8vo.
Conductor & 24 parts. — With several copies of various parts.
Unpriced
(B75-51419)

WMK — Arrangements
Badarzewska, Thécla
[La Prière d'une vierge. *arr]*. A maiden's prayer / [by] T.
Badarzewska ; arranged [for brass band] by Allan Street. —
London : Boosey and Hawkes, 1975. — 4to.
Conductor & 25 parts. — With several copies of various parts.
£1.00
(B75-51420)

Debussy, Claude
[Preludes. Bk 1. La Fille aux cheveux de lin. *arr]*. The girl with
the flaxen hair / [by] Debussy ; arranged for brass band by
Michael Brand. — Watford : R. Smith, 1975. — 8vo.
Conductor & 25 parts.
Unpriced
(B75-51421)

MacCunn, Hamish
[The land of the mountain and the flood. *Selections : arr]*.
Sutherland's law / [music by Hamish MacCunn] ; [edited by] Ray
Elms ; arranged for brass band by Ray Woodfield. — London :
Ambleside Music : EMI, 1975. — 8vo.
Conductor & 23 parts. — With several copies of various parts.
Unpriced
(B75-51422)

Stent, Keith
[Sullivan at sea. *arr]*. Sullivan at sea : a trip for trombones / [by]
Keith Stent ; arranged for brass band by Frank Bryce. —
Sevenoaks : Paxton, 1975. — 8vo.
Conductor (4p.) & 22 parts. — With several copies of various parts. —
Based upon 'When I was a lad' from Sullivan's ' H M S Pinafore'.
£1.75
(B75-50370)

Verdi, Giuseppe
[Les Vêpres siciliennes. Overture. *arr]*. Overture, Sicilian vespers /
[by] Verdi ; arranged for brass band by Edrich Siebert. —
London : Studio Music, 1975. — 35p ; obl.4to.
Unpriced
(B75-51423)

WMK/AGM — Arrangements. Marches
Allen, Rod
[The wonder march. *arr]*. The wonder march / by Rod Allen ;
arranged for military and brass band by Allan Street. — London :
Boosey and Hawkes, 1975. — 37pt ; obl.8vo.
Military band set, £1.00, Brass band set £0.85
Primary classification UMMK/AGM
(B75-50834)

Clarke, Jeremiah
[The Prince of Denmark's march. *arr]*. Trumpet voluntary / by
Jeremiah Clarke ; edited and arranged for brass band by John
Iveson. — London : Chester, 1975. — 4to.
Score (4p.) & 14 parts.
Unpriced
(B75-51424)

Farnon, Robert
[Concorde march. *arr]*. Concorde march / by Robert Farnon ;
arranged for brass band by Allan Street. — London : Chappell,
1975. — 8vo.
Conductor (4p.) & 26 parts. — With several copies of various parts.
Unpriced
(B75-51425)

Hanmer, Ronald
Over hill, over dale : based on an American march / arranged [for
brass band] by Ronald Hanmer. — London : Studio Music, 1975.
— 8vo.
Short score (4p.) & 26 parts. — With several copies of various parts.
Unpriced
(B75-51426)

WMK/AHXJ — Arrangements. Ragtime
Joplin, Scott
[Bethena. *arr]*. Bethena / by Scott Joplin ; arranged for brass band
by Goff Richards. — London : Chappell, 1974. — 8vo.
Conductor (4p.) & 26 parts.
Unpriced
(B75-50372)

Joplin, Scott
[The entertainer. *arr]*. The entertainer ; with, Maple leaf rag / by
Scott Joplin ; arranged for brass band by Frank Bryce. —
Sevenoaks : Paxton, 1974. — 8vo.
Conductor & 25 parts. — With several copies of various parts.
Unpriced
(B75-50373)

Joplin, Scott
[Piano music. *Selections: arr]*. The best of Scott Joplin / arranged
for brass band by Goff Richards. — London : Chappell, 1974. —
8vo.
Conductor (12p.) & 26 parts. — With several copies of various parts.
Unpriced
(B75-50371)

Siebert, Edrich
Rhode Island rag : [brass band] / by Edrich Siebert. — London :
Studio Music, 1974. — 10p ; obl.8vo.
Unpriced
(B75-50364)

WMK/DP/LF/AYC — Arrangements. Carols. Christmas. Collections.
England
Three carols for brass / arranged by Stuart Johnson. — London :
British and Continental Music, 1975. — 8vo.
Short score (4p.) & 27 parts. — With several copies of various parts.
Unpriced
(B75-50924)

WMK/DR — Arrangements. Psalms
Rossi, Salomone
[Hashirim asher li Sh'lomo, no.32. Psalm 92. *arr]*. Psalm 92 / [by]
Solomone Rossi ; transcribed for brass ensemble (12 parts), 3 B
flat trumpets, 5 F horns, 3 trombones, tuba, etc. by Samuel Adler.
— New York ; London : Schirmer, 1974. — 4to.
Score (22p.) & 12 parts.
Unpriced
(B75-50925)

WMK/DW — Arrangements. Songs, etc
Beethoven, Ludwig van
[Symphony no.9, op.125, in D minor, 'Choral'. Freude, schöner
Gotterfunken. *arr]*. Song of joy / by Beethoven ; arranged for
brass band by Edrich Siebert. — London : Studio Music, 1975. —
obl.8vo.
Conductor & 24 parts. — With several copies of various parts.
Unpriced
(B75-51427)

Bygraves, Max
[Swingalongamax. *arr]*. Swingalongamax. (Back in my childhood
days) / arranged for brass band by Allan Street. — London :
Boosey and Hawkes, 1975. — 25pt ; obl.8vo.
£0.85
(B75-51428)

Fleming, Jimmy
[Sylvia. *arr]*. Sylvia / [by] Jimmy Fleming ; arranged for brass
band by Anthony Spurgin. — London : Studio Music, 1975. —
8vo.
Conductor & 25 parts. — With several copies of various parts.
Unpriced
(B75-50926)

Harvey, Roger
Camptown races : traditional / arranged for brass band by Robert
[sic] Harvey. — Watford : R. Smith, 1975. — 8vo.
Conductor (3p.) & 26 parts. — With several copies of various parts.
Unpriced
(B75-51429)

Herbert, Victor
[Songs. *Selections. arr*]. Victor Herbert memories / arranged [for brass band] by Ronald Hanmer. — London : Studio Music, 1975. — 8vo.
Conductor (8p.) & 24 parts. — With several copies of various parts.
Unpriced

(B75-50374)

Monckton, Lionel
[A runaway girl. Soldiers in the park. *arr*]. Oh! listen to the band / [by] Lionel Monckton ; arranged for brass band by Ronald Hanmer. — London : Studio Music, 1975. — 8vo.
Score (3p.) & 26 parts. — Duration 2 1/2 min.
Unpriced

(B75-50927)

Puccini, Giacomo
[Operas. *Selections: arr*]. Famous Puccini arias / arranged for brass band by Ronald Hanmer. — London : Studio Music.
Conductor & 26 parts.
1-2 : One fine day (Un bel di vedremo), from Madame Butterfly ; Love and music (Vissi d'arte), from Tosca. — 1975. — 8vo.
Unpriced

(B75-50928)

3-4 : Love duet (Oh! quanti occhi fissi attenti), from Madame Butterfly ; Your tiny hand is frozen (Che gelida manina), from La Bohème. — 1975. — 8vo.
Unpriced

(B75-50929)

5-6 : Musetta's waltz song (Quando me'n vu'), from La Bohème ; Stars are brightly shining (E lucetan le stelle), from Tosca. — 1975. — 8vo.
Unpriced

(B75-50930)

7-8 : Oh my beloved father (O mio babbino caro), from Gianni Schicchi ; They call me Mimi (Mi chiamano Mimi), from La Bohème. — 1975. — 8vo.
Unpriced

(B75-50931)

Siebert, Edrich
Blow the wind southerly / adapted and arranged for brass band by Edrich Siebert. — London : Studio Music, 1975. — 8vo.
Conductor & 25 parts. — Duration 4 min. — With several copies of various parts.
Unpriced

(B75-51430)

WMK/DW/LC — Arrangements. Spirituals
Smith-Masters, Stanley
Joshua fought the battle of Jericho : traditional / arranged for brass band by S. Smith-Masters. — London : Studio Music, 1975. — 8vo.
Conductor & 23 parts. — With several copies of various parts.
Unpriced

(B75-50932)

WMP — SOLO INSTRUMENT (S) & BRASS BAND
WMPWNQ — Brass sextet & brass band
Golland, John
Relay : for 3 cornets, 3 trombones and brass band / [by] John Golland. — London : British and Continental : EMI, 1975. — 8vo.
Conductor & 26 parts. — With several copies of various parts.
Unpriced

(B75-51431)

WMPWNSF — Brass quartet & brass band. Concertos
Gregson, Edward
Concerto grosso for brass band / by Edward Gregson. — London : R. Smith, 1975. — 30p ; obl.8vo.
Duration 8 min.
Unpriced

(B75-50933)

WMPWRNSK — Four cornets & brass band. Arrangements
Elms, Albert
Trumpets sound! / [by] Albert Elms ; arranged for four cornets and brass band by Ray Woodfield. — London : Ambleside Music : EMI, 1975. — 8vo.
Conductor & 26 parts. — Various parts are in duplicate.
Unpriced

(B75-51432)

WMPWRNT — Three cornets & brass band
Siebert, Edrich
Jokers wild : cornet or trumpet trio (based on a theme by Mozart) [from 'Ein musikalischer Spass'. K.522] / [by] Edrich Siebert. — London : Studio Music, 1975. — 8vo.
Conductor (4p.) & 25 parts. — With several copies of various parts.
Unpriced

(B75-50934)

WMPWRNTK — Three cornets & brass band. Arrangements
Finlayson, Walter Alan
[Bright eyes. *arr*]. Bright eyes / by W.A. Finlayson ; arranged for cornet trio and band by Norman Richardson. — London : Boosey and Hawkes, 1975. — 8vo.
Conductor & 26 parts. — Various parts are in duplicate.
£2.20

(B75-51433)

WMPWRPLWW — Cornet, euphonium & brass band
Hanmer, Ronald
Flight of fancy : duet for cornet and euphonium with brass band / [by] Ronald Hanmer. — London : R. Smith, 1975. — 8vo.
Conductor & 28 parts. — With several copies of various parts.
Unpriced

(B75-50935)

WMPWU — Trombone & brass band
Brand, Michael
Rag 'n' bone : trombone solo and brass band / [by] Michael Brand. — Watford : R. Smith, 1975. — 8vo.
Conductor (4p.) & 25 parts. — With several copies of various parts.
Unpriced

(B75-51434)

Hanmer, Ronald
Praeludium and allegro : trombone solo with band accompaniment / [by] Ronald Hanmer. — Watford : R. Smith, 1975. — 8vo.
Conductor & 25 parts.
Unpriced

(B75-51435)

WMPWUU — Bass trombone & brass band
Shield, William
[The farmer. The ploughboy. *arr*]. The ploughboy : traditional, solo for E flat or B flat bass and brass band / arranged by Edrich Siebert. — South Croydon (455 Brighton Rd, South Croydon) : Paul, 1975. — 8vo.
Conductor & 25 parts. — With several copies of various parts. — Not attributed to Shield in this publication.
Unpriced

(B75-50936)

WN — BRASS ENSEMBLE
WNP/W — Septets. Rondos
Hanmer, Ronald
Prelude and rondo : for brass septet / [by] Ronald Hanmer. — London : R. Smith, 1975. — 8vo.
Score (20p.) & 7 parts. — Duration 5 min.
Unpriced

(B75-50375)

WNR — Quintets
Bennett, Richard Rodney
Commedia IV : brass quintet / [by] Richard Rodney Bennett. — Sevenoaks : Novello, 1975. — 18p ; 8vo.
Duration 12 3/4 min.
£1.30

(B75-50937)

Husa, Karel
Divertimento for brass quintet / [by] Karel Husa. — New York ; [London] : Associated Music, 1975. — 4to.
Score (28p.) & 5 parts. — Duration 15 min.
£6.25

(B75-51436)

Previn, André
Four outings for brass / [by] André Previn. — London : Chester, 1975. — 4to.
Score (18p.) & 5 parts.
Unpriced

(B75-51437)

WNR/Y — Quintets. Fugues
Kaplan, Nathan Ivan
Fugue on fugue : for brass quintet, B flat trumpet I, B flat trumpet II, F horn, trombone, tuba / [by] Nathan Ivan Kaplan. — New York ; London : Chappell, 1972. — 4to.
Score & 5 parts.
Unpriced

(B75-51438)

WNRFL — Quintets. Concertinos
Washburn, Robert
Concertino for wind and brass quintets / [by] Robert Washburn. — New York ; [London] : Oxford University Press, 1971. — 4to.
Score & 10 parts.
Unpriced
Primary classification UNRFL

WNRH — Quintets. Dances
Praetorius, Michael
[Terpsichore. *Selections: arr].* Four dances / by Michael
Praetorius ; arr. for 2 trumpets/cornets (B flat), 1 horn (F), 1
trombone by Bernard Hazelgrove. — Chesham : Ricordi.
Set 1. — 1974. — 9p ; 4to.
Unpriced
(B75-50376)
Set 2. — 1974. — 9p ; 4to.
Unpriced
(B75-50377)

Simpson, Thomas
Opus newer Paduanen, Galliarden, Intraden, Canzonen (1617) :
for 3 cornetti (trumpets in C) and 2 trombones / [by] Thomas
Simpson ; edited by Bernard Thomas. — London : Musica rara.
Volume 1. — 1974. — 4to.
Score (23p.) & 5 parts.
Unpriced
(B75-51439)
Volume 2. — 1974. — 4to.
Score (20p.) & 5 parts.
Unpriced
(B75-51440)

WNRH/AY — Quintets. Dances. Collections
[Newe ausserlesene liebliche Branden, Intraden]. Newe auserlesene
Branden, Intraden, Mascheraden, Baletten, Allmanden, Couranten,
Volten, Auffzuge und frembde Tantze (1617) / compiled by
William Brade, edited by Bernard Thomas. — London : Musica
rara.
Volume 1 : for 2 cornetti (trumpets in C) and 3 trombones. — 1974. — 4to.
Score (20p.) & 5 parts.
£4.00
(B75-51441)
Volume 2 : for 2 cornetti (trumpets in C) and 3 trombones. — 1974. — 4to.
Score (20p.) & 5 parts.
£4.00
(B75-51442)
Volume 3 : for 3 cornetti and 2 trombones. — 1974. — 4to.
Score (18p.) & 5 parts.
£4.00
(B75-51443)

WNRK — Quintets. Arrangements
Debussy, Claude
[The little nigar. *arr].* Le petit negre / [by] Debussy; arranged for
brass quintet by Geoffrey Emerson. — Ampleforth : Emerson,
1975. — 5pt ; 4to.
Unpriced
(B75-51444)

Farnaby, Giles
[Keyboard music. *Selections: arr].* Fancies, toyes and dreames /
[by] Giles Farnaby ; edited and arranged for brass quintet by
Elgar Howarth. — London : Chester, 1975. — 4to.
Score (8p.) & 10 parts.
Unpriced
(B75-51445)

Scheidt, Samuel
[Paduana, galliarda, etc. quaternis et quinis vocibus cum basso
continuo. Selections. *arr].* Battle suite / [by] Samuel Scheidt ;
edited and arranged for brass quintet by Philip Jones. — London :
Chester, 1975. — 4to.
Score (11p.) & 10 parts.
Unpriced
(B75-51446)

WNRR/T — Brass & organ quintet. Variations
Ehmann, Heinrich
Verlieh uns Frieden : Variationen für Blechbläser und Orgel /
[von] Heinrich Ehmann. — Cassel ; London : Bärenreiter, 1973.
— 15p ; 4to.
£2.20
(B75-50378)

WNS — Quartets
Bavicchi, John
Quartet no.1 for brass, Op.22 / [by] John Bavicchi. — New
York ; [London] : Oxford University Press, 1971. — 28p ; 4to.
Unpriced
(B75-50938)

Dale, Gordon
Recital hors-d'oevre. Opus 51 : for 2 trumpets, horn and
trombone / by Gordon Dale. — London : British and
Continental : EMI, 1975. — 4to.
Score (4p.) & 4 parts.
Unpriced
(B75-51447)

Kneale, Peter
Quartet for brass / [by] Peter Kneale. — London : R. Smith,
1975. — 8vo.
Score (4p.) & parts.
Unpriced
(B75-50939)

Simpson, Lionel
Prelude for brass quartet. Op.105 / by Lionel Simpson. —
London : British and Continental : EMI, 1975. — 8vo.
Score (4p.) & 4 parts.
Unpriced
(B75-51448)

WNS/T — Quartets. Variations
Horovitz, Joseph
Variations on a theme of Paganini : for brass quartet, or
saxophone quartet, or woodwind quartet / by Joseph Horovitz. —
London : R. Smith, 1975. — 15p ; 4to.
Unpriced
Also classified at VUNS/T
(B75-50379)

WNS/Y — Quartets. Fuges
Dale, Gordon
Fugue for brass quartet. Op.41, no.3 / by Gordon Dale. —
London : British and Continental : EMI, 1975. — 8vo.
Score (6p.) & 4 parts.
Unpriced
(B75-51449)

WNSG — Quartets. Suites
Barrell, Bernard
Suite for brass (2 trumpets, 2 trombones). Op.21 / by Bernard
Barrell. — Chesham : Ricordi, 1974. — 7p ; 4to.
Unpriced
(B75-50380)

WNSK/AH — Quartets. Arrangements. Dances
Gervaise, Claude
[Danceries. Selections. *arr].* Three dances / [by] Claude Gervaise ;
edited and arranged for brass quartet by Peter Reeve. — London :
Chester, 1975. — 4to.
Score (3p.) & parts.
Unpriced
(B75-51450)

WNSK/DW — Quartets. Arrangements. Songs, etc
Siebert, Edrich
Greensleeves : for brass quartet / arranged by Edrich Siebert. —
London : British and Continental, 1975. — 8vo.
Score (2p.) & 4 parts.
Unpriced
(B75-50940)

Siebert, Edrich
Oh! dem golden slippers : for brass quartet / arranged by Edrich
Siebert. — London : British and Continental, 1975. — 8vo.
Score (3p.) & 4 parts.
Unpriced
(B75-50941)

Siebert, Edrich
Santa Lucia : Neapolitan air, for brass quartet / arranged by
Edrich Siebert. — London : British and Continental, 1975. — 8vo.
Score (2p.) & 4 parts.
Unpriced
(B75-50942)

WNT — Trios
Luening, Otto
Trio trumpet in C, horn in F and trombone / [by] Otto Luening.
— New York ; London : Peters, 1974. — 4p ; 4to.
Unpriced
(B75-50943)

WNTGN — Trios. Fanfares
Kirchner, Leon
Fanfare for brass trio (2 trumpets and horn) / [by] Leon
Kirchner. — New York ; London : Associated Music, 1974. —
4to.
Score (4p.) & 3 parts.
Unpriced
(B75-50944)

WRN — CORNET ENSEMBLE
WRNS — Quartets
Hanmer, Ronald
Foursome fantasy : for four cornets / by Ronald Hanmer. —
London : Studio Music, 1975. — 8vo.
Score (8p.) & 4 parts.
Unpriced
(B75-51451)

WRP — CORNET & PIANO
WRPK — Arrangements
Gregson, Edward
[Prelude and capriccio for cornet & band. *arr*]. Prelude and
capriccio for cornet and band / [by] Edward Gregson ; reduction
for cornet or trumpet in B flat and piano. — London : R. Smith,
1973. — 4to & partly 8vo.
Score (12p.) & piano.
Unpriced

(B75-50945)

WS — TRUMPET
Handel, George Frideric
[Selections]. Complete trumpet repertoire / [by] G.F. Handel ;
edited by Robert Minter. — London : Musica rara.
Volume 1 : The operas. — 1974. — 43p ; 4to.
£4.50

(B75-51452)

Volume 2 : The sacred oratorios. — 1974. — 112p ; 4to.
Unpriced

(B75-51453)

Volume 3 : The church music. — 1974. — 58p ; 4to.
£4.50

(B75-51454)

Volume 4 : Miscellaneous. — 1974. — 52p ; 4to.
£4.50

(B75-51455)

WSN — TRUMPET ENSEMBLE
WSNTQ — Two trumpets & piano
Vallier, Jacques
[Fantasie for two trumpets & piano]. Fantasie : pour 2 trompettes
(ut ou si bémol) et piano / musique de Jacques Vallier. — Paris ;
[London] : Chappell, 1975. — 4to.
Score (7p.) & 2 parts.
Unpriced

(B75-50381)

WSNTRK — Two trumpets & organ. Arrangements
Stanley, John
[Voluntaries for organ. *Selections: arr*]. Six voluntaries for 2
trumpets and organ / [by] John Stanley ; selected and arranged by
Barry Cooper. — London : Musica rara, 1975. — 4to.
Score (24p.) & 4 parts.
Unpriced

(B75-51456)

WSP — TRUMPET & PIANO
WSPEM — Sonatinas
Walker, James
Sonatina for trumpet and piano / [by] James Walker. — New
York ; London : Schirmer, 1974. — 4to.
Score (17p.) & part.
Unpriced

(B75-50946)

WSPJ — Miscellaneous works
Beck, Conrad
Facetten : drei Impromptus, für Trompete in C und Klavier /
[von] Conrad Beck. — Mainz ; London : Schott, 1975. — 4to.
Score (12p.) & 2 parts. — Duration 4 min.
£2.25

(B75-51457)

Marischal, Louis
Introduction et mascarade : pour trompette en ut (C) et piano /
[par] Louis Marischal. — Paris ; [London] : Chappell, 1971. —
fol.
Score & part.
Unpriced

(B75-51458)

WSPK — Arrangements
Françaix, Jean
[Le Gay Paris. *arr*]. Le Gay Paris : pour trompette et instruments
à vent / [von] Jean Françaix ; Klavierauszug von Henning Branel.
— Mainz ; London : Schott, 1975. — 4to.
Score (19p.) & 2 parts.
£2.25

(B75-51459)

Handel, George Frideric
[Atalanta. Overture. *arr*]. Overture for trumpet. oboes, strings and
basso continuo / [by] G.F. Handel ; edited for trumpet and piano
reduction by R.P. Block. — London : Musica rara, 1975. — 4to.
Score (8p.) & part.
Unpriced

(B75-51460)

WSPK/AAY — Arrangements. Collections
A classical and romantic album : for trumpet in B flat and piano /
arranged by Watson Forbes. — London : Oxford University Press.
Score (12p) & part.
2nd. — 1975. — 4to.
ISBN 0-19-356523-4 : £0.90

(B75-50947)

3rd. — 1975. — 4to.
ISBN 0-19-356525-0 : £0.90

(B75-50948)

WSPK/AE — Arrangements. Sonatas
Hook, James
[Sonatas for flute & piano. Op.99, nos.3, 2. *arr*]. Two sonatas /
[by] James Hook ; arranged for trumpet in B flat and piano by
Peter Wastall. — London : Boosey and Hawkes, 1975. — 4to.
Score (24p.) & part.
£1.25

(B75-51461)

WSPK/LE — Arrangements. Symphonies
Torelli, Giuseppe
[Sinfonia avanti l'opera. G.14. *arr*]. Sinfonia avanti l'opera, G.14 :
for trumpet, strings and continuo / [by] Giuseppe Torelli ; edited
by Edward H. Tarr, reduction by Robert Paul Block. — London :
Musica rara, 1975. — 4to.
Score (4p.) & 2 parts.
£1.50

(B75-51462)

Torelli, Giuseppe
[Sinfonia in D major. G.3. *arr*]. Sinfonia in D. G.3 : for trumpet,
strings and continuo / [by] Giuseppe Torelli ; edited by Edward
H. Tarr, reduction by Robert Paul Block. — London : Musica
rara, 1974. — 4to.
Score (8p.) & 2 parts.
£1.50

(B75-51463)

Torelli, Giuseppe
[Sinfonia in D major. G.4. *arr*]. Sinfonia in D. G.4 : for trumpet,
strings and continuo / [by] Giuseppe Torelli ; edited by Edward
H. Tarr, reduction by Robert Paul Block. — London : Musica
rara, 1974. — 4to.
Score (6p.) & part.
£1.50

(B75-51464)

Torelli, Giuseppe
[Sinfonia in D major. G.5. *arr*]. Sinfonia in D. G.5 : for trumpet,
strings and continuo / [by] Giuseppe Torelli ; edited by Edward
H. Tarr, reduction by Robert Paul Block. — London : Musica
rara, 1974. — 4to.
Score (4p.) & 2 parts.
£1.50

(B75-51465)

Torelli, Giuseppe
[Sonata for trumpet, two violins, viola & basso continuo in D
major. G.6. *arr*]. Sonata in D.G.6 : for trumpet, strings and
continuo / [by] Giuseppe Torelli ; edited by Edward H. Tarr,
reduction by Robert Paul Block. — London : Musica rara, 1975.
— 4to.
Score (6p.) & 2 parts.
£1.50

(B75-51466)

WSPK/LF — Arrangements. Concertos
Carradot, André
[Concerto for trumpet. *arr*]. Concerto pour trompette et
orchestre / [par] André Carradot ; trompette et piano. — Paris ;
[London] : Chappell, 1972. — fol.
Score & part.
Unpriced

(B75-50949)

Neruda, Johann Baptist Georg
[Concerto for trumpet & string orchestra in E flat major. *arr*].
Concerto in E flat for trumpet and strings / by J.B.G Neruda ;
ed. and reduced for trumpet and piano by David Hickman. —
London : Musica rara, 1975. — 4to.
Score (19p.) & part. — This concerto was originally for the corno-de-caccia.
Unpriced

(B75-51467)

WSPLR — TRUMPET & PIANO
Stockmeier, Wolfgang
Zwei Stücke : für Trompete und Orgel / [von] Wolfgang
Stockmeier. — Cassel ; London : Bärenreiter, 1973. — 10p ; 4to.
£3.20

(B75-50382)

WSPLX — TRUMPET & PERCUSSION
WSPLXR — Trumpet & timpani
Leonard, Stanley
Fanfare and allegro : for trumpet and solo timpani / [by] Stanley
Leonard. — London : Simrock, 1974. — 4to.
Score (4p.) & 2 parts.
Unpriced

(B75-50383)

WSPM — UNACCOMPANIED TRUMPET
WSPMJ — Miscellaneous works
Adler, Samuel
Canto I : four concert études, for unaccompanied trumpet / [by]
Samuel Adler. — New York ; [London] : Oxford University Press,
1972. — 7p ; 4to.
Unpriced

(B75-50950)

WT — HORN
WT/AF — Exercises
Borris, Siegfried
Musik für Waldhorn. Op.109 : übungs-und Spielbuche für 1
Horn / [von] Siegfried Borris. — Wilhemshaven : Heinrichshofen ;
[London] : [Hinrichsen].
Heft 1/1. — 1974. — 28p ; 4to. —
Unpriced
(B75-50951)

Borris, Siegfried
Musik für Waldhorn. Op.109 : Ubungs-und Spielbuche für 1
Horn / [von] Siegfried Borris. — Wilhemshaven : Heinrichshofen ;
[London] : [Hinrichsen].
Heft 1/2. — 1974. — 24p ; 4to. —
Unpriced
(B75-50952)

WTP — HORN & PIANO
WTP/LF — Christmas
Brightmore, C Victor
Noël : for horn and piano / [by] C.V. Brightmore. — London :
British and Continental, 1975. — 8vo.
Based on a French noël. Score & part.
Unpriced
(B75-50953)

WTP/W — Rondos
Bartos, Jan Zdenek
Adagio elegiaeo und Rondo : für Horn und Klavier / [von] Jan
Zdenek Bartos. — Mainz ; London : Schott, 1974. — 4to.
Score (11p.) & part.
£1.89
(B75-50384)

WTPHVQT — Tambourins
Brightmore, C Victor
Tambourin : for horn and piano / by C.V. Brightmore. —
London : British and Continental, 1975. — 4to.
Score (3p.) & part.
Unpriced
(B75-50954)

WTPJ — Miscellaneous works
Brightmore, C Victor
Cantering on : for horn in F with piano accompaniment / by C.V.
Brightmore. — London : British and Continental Music, 1975. —
4to.
Score (3p.) & part.
Unpriced
(B75-50955)

Moscheles, Ignaz
[Introduction et rondeau écossais. Op.63]. Duo. Op.63 : for horn
and piano / [by] Ignaz Moscheles ; edited by H. Voxman. —
London : Musica rara, 1974. — 4to.
Score (20p.) & part.
£1.50
(B75-51468)

Noble, Harold
Arietta : for horn and piano / [by] Harold Noble. — London :
British and Continental, 1975. — 4to.
Score (4p.) & part.
Unpriced
(B75-50956)

Pitfield, Thomas
A folkish tune : for horn in F and piano / by Thomas Pitfield. —
London : British and Continental Music Agencies, 1975. — 4to.
Score (3p.) & part.
Unpriced
(B75-50957)

WTPK — Arrangements
Marischal, Louis
[Promenade. arr]. Promenade : pour cor et orchestre à cordes /
[par] Louis Marischal ; réduction pour cor (F) et piano. — Paris ;
[London] : Chappell, 1971. — fol.
Score & part.
Unpriced
(B75-51469)

WTPK/LF — Arrangements. Concertos
Gregson, Edward
[Concerto for horn & brass band. arr]. Concerto for horn and
piano / by Edward Gregson. — London : R. Smith, 1972. — 4to.
Score (36p.) & part.
Unpriced
(B75-50385)

WU — TROMBONE
WU/AC — Tutors
Bright, Clive
Play the trombone, treble clef / [by] Clive Bright. — London :
Chappell, 1975. — 39p ; 4to.
Unpriced
(B75-51470)

WUN — TROMBONE ENSEMBLE
WUNSK/DW — Quartets. Arrangements. Songs, etc
Nugent, Maud
[Sweet Rosie O'Grady. arr]. Sweet Rosie O'Grady / [by] Maud
Nugent ; arranged, in barber-shop quartet style, for 4 tenor
trombones or any 4 instruments of uniform pitch by Edrich
Siebert. — South Croydon (455 Brighton Rd, South Croydon) :
Paul, 1975. — obl.8vo.
Score (2p.) & 4 parts.
Unpriced
(B75-50958)

Siebert, Edrich
Home on the range : traditional tune / arranged in barber-shop
quartet style, for four tenor trombones or any 4 instruments of
uniform pitch by Edrich Siebert. — South Croydon (455 Brighton
Rd, South Croydon) : Paul, 1975. — obl.8vo.
Score (2p.) & 4 parts.
Unpriced
(B75-50959)

WUNU — Duets
Genzmer, Harald
Zwolf Duos : für zwei Posaunen / [von] Harald Genzmer. —
Frankfurt : Litolff ; London : Peters, 1975. — 17p ; 4to.
Two scores.
Unpriced
(B75-50960)

WUP — TROMBONE & PIANO
WUPK — Arrangements
Hanmer, Ronald
[Praeludium and allegro for trombone & brass band. arr].
Praeludium and allegro : trombone solo with piano
accompaniment / [by] Ronald Hanmer. — Watford : R. Smith,
1975. — 4to.
Score (8p.) & part.
Unpriced
(B75-51471)

WUPM — UNACCOMPANIED TROMBONE
WUPMJ — Miscellaneous works
Adler, Samuel
Canto II : four concert études, for unaccompanied trombone /
[by] Samuel Adler. — New York ; [London] : Oxford University
Press, 1972. — 7p ; 4to.
Unpriced
(B75-50961)

WVP — TUBA & PIANO
WVP/AY — Collections
Concert and contest collection : for E flat or BB flat bass (tuba or
sousaphone) with piano accompaniment / compiled and edited by
H. Voxman. — Miami ; [London] : Rubank, 1972. — 4to.
Score & part.
Unpriced
(B75-51472)

WVPK/LF — Arrangements. Concertos
Ross, Walter
[Concerto for tuba. arr]. Tuba concerto / [by] Walter Ross ; tuba
solo and piano reduction by Walter Ross. — New York ;
[London] : Boosey and Hawkes, 1975. — 4to.
Duration 11 1/2 min.
Unpriced
(B75-50962)

WVPM — UNACCOMPANIED TUBA
WVPMJ — Miscellaneous works
Blank, Allan
Three for Barton : for solo brass tuba / [by] Allan Blank. — New
York ; London : Associated Music, 1975. — 9p ; 4to.
£1.05
(B75-51473)

Kagel, Mauricio
Mirum : für Tuba, 1965 / [von] Mauricio Kagel. — London :
Universal, 1974. — 6p ; 4to.
Unpriced
(B75-50386)

WVPMK/AH — Arrangements. Dances
Bach, Johann Sebastian
[Suites for cello. S.1007-12. Selections: arr]. Dance movements /
[by] Johann Sebastian Bach ; transcribed for tuba (or euphonium)
by Abe Torchinsky. — New York ; London : Schirmer, 1975. —
17p ; 4to.
Unpriced
(B75-50963)

WWP — EUPHONIUM & PIANO
WWPG — Suites
White, Donald H
Lyric suite : for euphonium and piano with treble clef and bass clef parts / by Donald H. White. — New York ; London : Schirmer, 1972. — 4to.
Score (20p.) & bass clef part. — The treble clef part is missing from the work catalogued.
Unpriced

(B75-51474)

XM — PERCUSSION BAND
Russell, Armand
Facets : in four movements, for percussion solo, two timbales, tom-toms (or bongos), snare drum, two suspended cymbals, triangle, five temple blocks / [by] Armand Russell. — New York ; London : Schirmer, 1975. — 7p ; 4to.
£1.30

(B75-51475)

XN — PERCUSSION ENSEMBLE
Dennis, Brian
Crosswords : for any number of players with non-pitched percussion instruments / [by] Brian Dennis. — London : Universal, 1975. — s.sh ; obl. 8vo.
Unpriced

(B75-50964)

XNNHJNC — Octets. Congas
Fink, Siegfried
Conga Brazil : Brazilian impression for percussion ensemble (8 players) / [by] Siegfried Fink. — London : Simrock, 1975. — 4to.
Score (16p.) & 4 parts.
£3.60

(B75-51476)

XNQK — Sextets. Arrangements
Bach, Johann Sebastian
[Notenbuch der Anna Magdalena Bach, 1725. *Selections: arr*].
Bachiana for percussion : [four pieces] / [by Johann Sebastian Bach] ; arranged for 6 players by Stanley Leonard. — Hamburg ; London : Simrock, 1974. — 4to.
Unpriced

(B75-50965)

XNS — Quartets
Frank, Marcel Gustave
Six reflections : for percussion quartet / by Marcel G. Frank. — New York ; [London] : Boosey and Hawkes, 1975. — 18p ; 4to.
Four copies.
Unpriced

(B75-50966)

Humble, Keith
Trois poèmes à crier et à danser / [by] Keith Humble ; text Pierre Albert-Birot. — [Sydney] ; [London] : Universal.
Members of the ensemble are also instructed to shout, hiss or laugh at appropriate moments.
Chant 1. — 1975. — 1ff ; 8vo.
Unpriced

(B75-50967)

Chant 2. — 1975. — 1ff ; 8vo.
Unpriced

(B75-50968)

Chant 3. — 1975. — 1ff ; 8vo.
Unpriced

(B75-50969)

Hummel, Bertold
Frescoes 70 : for percussion quartet / [by] Bertold Hummel. — Hamburg ; London : Simrock, 1975. — 4to.
Score (32p) & 4 parts.
£5.95

(B75-51477)

XNT — Trios
Regner, Hermann
Sechs leichte Schlagzeugtrios / [von] Hermann Regner. — Mainz ; London : Schott, 1975. — 16p ; 4to.
£2.00

(B75-51478)

Schingerlin, Rudolf
Fünf Studien für Schlagzeugtrio / [von] Rudolf Schingerlin. — Mainz ; London : Schott, 1975. — 23p ; 4to.
£2.00

(B75-51479)

Stadler, Werner
Fünf Schlagzeugtrois / [von] Werner Stadler. — Mainz ; London : Schott, 1975. — 20p ; 4to.
£2.00

(B75-51480)

XPQ — MELODIC PERCUSSION
XPQNU — Melodic percussion. Duets
Hiller, Wilfried
Katalog für Schlagzeug II = Catalogue for percussion II : 2 players / [by] Wilfried Hiller. — Mainz ; London : Schott, 1975. — 20p ; 4to.
Unpriced

(B75-51481)

XQ — DRUM
XQ/AC — Tutors
De Caro, Louis
21 steps for the beginning drummer / [by] Louis de Caro. — New York : Warner ; [London] : [Blossom], 1971. — 24p ; 4to.
Unpriced

(B75-50970)

Manne, Shelly
Let's play drums / as taught by Shelly Manne. — New York ; [London] : Chappell, 1974. — 67p ; 4to.
Unpriced

(B75-50387)

XQN — DRUM ENSEMBLE
XQNP — Septets
Jenni, Donald
Tympanorum musices : for four timpani and three bongos / [by] Donald Jenni. — New York ; London : Associated Music, 1974. — 3p ; 4to.
Unpriced

(B75-50971)

XQPMJ — Miscellaneous works
Dawson, Alan
Blues and syncopation in 3/4 and 4/4 for the drumset / [by] Alan Dawson. — Hamburg ; London : Simrock, 1975. — 22p ; 4to.
£1.75

(B75-51482)

XS — BELLS
XSQMK/AAY — Arrangements. Collections
A **recital** for handbells : ten classical pieces / arranged by Norris L. Stephens. — New York ; London : Schirmer, 1974. — 10p ; 4to.
Verso of page 5 is blank.
Unpriced

(B75-50972)

COMPOSER AND TITLE INDEX

- Inwending voller figur - ' : for chorus, loudspeakers, tape and large orchestra (1970/71). (Huber, Klaus). *Ars Viva : Schott. £6.00* EMDE (B75-50035)
3 pieces for 4 : a suite of 3 movements for woodwind quartet, flute, oboe, clarinet in B flat, bassoon. (Warren, Edward). *Camera Music. Unpriced* VNSG (B75-51362)
5 pieces for half-size violin and piano. (Jacob, Gordon). *Chappell. Unpriced* SPJ (B75-51296)
8 Morris dances of England and Flamborough sword dance. *English Folk Dance and Song Society. Unpriced* LH/G/AYD (B75-51137) ISBN 0-85418-108-3
14 graded studies in apayando. (Duarte, John William). *Ricordi. £0.84* TS/AF (B75-50796)
14 songs on American poetry : voice and piano. (Rorem, Ned). *Peters. Unpriced* KDW (B75-50558)
21 steps for the beginning drummer. (De Caro, Louis). *Warner : Blossom. Unpriced* XQ/AC (B75-50970)
28 selected duets : for two saxophones (or oboes). *Edward Schuberth : Phoenix. Unpriced* VUNU/AY (B75-51398)

30 selected duets : for two saxophones (or oboes). *Edward Schuberth : Phoenix. Unpriced* VUNU/AY (B75-51399)

50 hymns for band
Book I: General and Christmas. *Oxford University Press. Unpriced* UMK/DM/AY (B75-50823) ISBN 0-19-363060-5
50 super songs. (Rodgers, Richard). *Williamson Music. Unpriced* RK/DW (B75-50738)
Abecedarium : für Streicher. (Kelemen, Milko). *Litolff : Peters. Unpriced* RXMJ (B75-50227)
Abraham, Gerald. A hundred years of music. 4th ed. *Duckworth. £6.95* A(YB/XHN141) (B75-12695) ISBN 0-7156-0703-0
Abrahams, Roger David. Deep the water, shallow the shore : three essays on shantying in the West Indies. *University of Texas Press for the American Folklore Society. £3.80* ADW/GMC(YUH) (B75-00739) ISBN 0-292-71502-1
Absalom. (Rorem, Ned). *Boosey and Hawkes. Unpriced* KDW (B75-51108)
Acúfenos II (1971-IV) : for chamber ensemble, electronic sounds and electronic extensions. (Lanza, Alcides). *Boosey and Hawkes. Unpriced* NYD (B75-51195)
Ad flumina Babyloniae : for mixed voices (unaccompanied minimum 3333). (Dalby, Martin). *Novello. £0.25* EZDJ (B75-51039)
Ad te levavi : for full chorus of mixed voices a cappella. (Jenni, Donald). *Associated Music. Unpriced* EZDH/LEZ (B75-50464)
Adagio elegiaeo und Rondo : für Horn und Klavier. (Bartos, Jan Zdenek). *Schott. £1.89* WTP/W (B75-50384)
Adami, Giuseppe. Letters of Giacomo Puccini : mainly connected with the composition and production of his operas. (Puccini, Giacomo). New ed. *Harrap. £4.00* BPU(N) (B75-05793) ISBN 0-245-52422-3
Adapting to the times : violoncello and piano. (Wuorinen, Charles). *Peters. Unpriced* SRPJ (B75-50262)
Adelmann, Marianne. Musical Europe : an illustrated guide to musical life in 18 European countries. *Paddington Press. £3.50* A(YB/WE) (B75-01174) ISBN 0-8467-0031-x
Adler, Israel. Yuval : studies of the Jewish Music Research Centre
Vol.3. *Magnes Press : Distributed by Oxford University Press. £10.25* A(YBU/D) (B75-08735) ISBN 0-19-647920-7
Adler, Samuel.
Canto I : four concert études, for unaccompanied trumpet. *Oxford University Press. Unpriced* WSPMJ (B75-50950)

Canto II : four concert études, for unaccompanied trombone. *Oxford University Press. Unpriced* WUPMJ (B75-50961)
Concerto for orchestra. *Boosey and Hawkes. Unpriced* MMF (B75-50606)
Hashirim asher li Sh'lomo, no.32. Psalm 92. *arr.* Psalm 92. (Rossi, Salomone). *Schirmer. Unpriced* WMK/DR (B75-50925)
Adrian, Karlo. Numerical listing of Edison Bell 'Winner'. *19 Glendale Rd, Bournemouth BH6 4JA : 'Talking Machine Review'. £2.00* A/FD(T/WT) (B75-19333) ISBN 0-902338-17-x
Adriensen, Emanuel. Ecco ch'io lass'il core : SSATTB (unacc. or with lutes). (Striggio, Alessandro). *Oxford University Press. Unpriced* ETWNUDU (B75-50457) ISBN 0-19-341221-7
Advent to Easter : short musical plays for junior and middle schools. (O'Gorman, Denis). *Grail Publications. £1.00* BOFGACN/L (B75-18364) ISBN 0-901829-25-0
Adventures of Paddington Bear. Paddington Bear. *arr.* Paddington Bear : song. (Chappell, Herbert). *Music Sales. £0.25* KDW (B75-50106)
African dreams : piano. (Camilleri, Charles). *Roberton. £1.50* QPJ (B75-51234)
African music : a people's art. (Bebey, Francis). *Harrap. £4.50* BZK (B75-20391) ISBN 0-245-52735-4
African Sanctus : a story of travel and music. (Fanshawe, David). *Collins : Harvill Press. £4.50* A(N) (B75-12857) ISBN 0-00-262002-2
African Sanctus : piano with voice-part optional. (Fanshawe, David). *Chappell. Unpriced* QPJ (B75-50697)
Agay, Denes. Petit Trianon suite : ten easy pieces on 18th century style dance melodies, for piano. *Schirmer. Unpriced* QPG (B75-50668)
Ager, Laurence. Mary and Joseph : a Christmas calypso unison. *Ashdown. £0.08* JDP/LF (B75-51080)
Agricola, Martin. Her ich verkund euch neue Mar. Weihnachtsgesang : for four-part mixed choir. *Bärenreiter. £0.60* EZDP/LF (B75-50060)
Aichinger, Gregor. Fasciculus sacrarum harmoniarum. Ricercars nos.1-3. Three ricercars. *Galaxy : Galliard. Unpriced* VSNS (B75-50858)
Air en forme de pavane. (Boisvallée, Francois de). *Chappell. Unpriced* TMK/AHVG (B75-50273)
Air : for soprano and 4 instruments. (Berio, Luciano). *Universal. Unpriced* KFLE/NXNSDW (B75-50573)
Air : for soprano and orchestra. (Berio, Luciano). *Universal. Unpriced* KFLE/MDW (B75-50572)
Aires de Mochima : valzer venezuelano, per chitarra. (Calzadilla, Roman). *Zanibon : Hinrichsen. Unpriced* TSPMHW (B75-50277)
Akond of Swat : for voice and percussion. (Gerhard, Roberto). *Oxford University Press. Unpriced* KE/XDW (B75-50568) ISBN 0-19-345361-4
Alban Berg : the man and his work. (Carner, Mosco). *Duckworth. £12.00* BBKR (B75-28636) ISBN 0-7156-0769-3
Albert-Birot, Pierre.
Trois poèmes à crier et à danser
Chant 1. (Humble, Keith). *Universal. Unpriced* XNS (B75-50967)
Chant 2. (Humble, Keith). *Universal. Unpriced* XNS (B75-50968)
Chant 3. (Humble, Keith). *Universal. Unpriced* XNS (B75-50969)
Alberti, Luciano. Music through the ages. *Cassell. £7.50* A(X) (B75-02995) ISBN 0-304-29420-9
Albinoni, Tommaso.
Concerto à 5 for oboe & string orchestra, op.9, no.11, in B flat major. Concerto à 5 in B flat. Op.9, no.11 : for oboe, strings and basso continuo. *Musica rara. £6.50* RXMPVTF (B75-51286)
Concerto à 5 for oboe & string orchestra, op.9, no.11, in B flat major. *arr.* Concerto à 5 in B flat. Op.9, no.11 : for oboe, strings and basso continuo. *Musica rara. £2.50* VTPK/LF (B75-51395)
Concerto à 5 for two oboes, strings & basso continuo, op.9, no.12, in D major. Concerto à 5 in D. Opus 9, no.12 : for 2 oboes, strings and basso continuo. *Musica Rara. £5.00* RXMPVTNUF (B75-51287)
Albrechtsberger, Johann Georg. Six fugues for organ. Op.7. Sechs Fugen für Orgel/Cembalo. Opus 7. *Litolff : Peters. Unpriced* R/Y (B75-50203)
Alemann, Eduardo Armando. Spectra : for four recorders. *Galaxy : Galliard. Unpriced* VSNS (B75-50859)
Allanbrook, Douglas. Symphony no.3. 'Four orchestral landscapes'. Four orchestral landscapes (Symphony no.3). *Boosey and Hawkes. Unpriced* MME (B75-50602)
Allen, Kenneth. Mary and Joseph : a Christmas calypso unison. (Ager, Laurence). *Ashdown. £0.08* JDP/LF (B75-51080)
Allen, Michael. The world of sacred music : for all C or G chord organs. *Bobrich Music : Phoenix. Unpriced* RPVCK/DM/AY (B75-50742)
Allen, Rod. The wonder march. *arr.* The wonder march. *Boosey and Hawkes. Military band set, £1.00, Brass band set £0.85* UMMK/AGM (B75-50834)
Alley cat song. (Bjorn, Frank). *Chappell. Unpriced* UMK/DW (B75-50824)
Alley cat song. *arr.* The alley cat song. (Bjorn, Frank). *Chappell. Unpriced* UMK/DW (B75-50824)
Allitt, John. Donizetti and the tradition of romantic love : (a collection of essays on a theme). *56 Harbut Rd, SW11 2RB : Donizetti Society. £5.00* BDRAC (B75-08295) ISBN 0-9503333-1-x
Alma redemptoris : antiphon of the Blessed Virgin, for five voices, S.S.A.T.B. (Philips, Peter). *Chester. Unpriced* EZDGKJ (B75-51033)
Alouette : pour flûte de Pan. (Zamfir, Gheorghe). *Chappell. Unpriced* VSXPMJ (B75-50887)
Alt, Hansi. March for the piano. *Oxford University Press. Unpriced* QPGM (B75-50671)
Alvin, Juliette. Music therapy. *Hutchinson. £4.25* A(ZD) (B75-08620) ISBN 0-09-120320-1
Amario, B Battisti d'. Capriccio napoletano : per chitarra. (Pizzini, Carlo Alberto). *Zanibon : Hinrichsen. Unpriced* TSPMJ (B75-50282)
Amario, B Battisti d'. *See* D'Amario, B Batt.sti d'.
Ameln, Konrad.
Biblische Motetten für das Kirchenjahr. Band 2: Darstellung des Herrn bis Trinitas. *Selections.* Spruchmotten
3: Motetten. *Bärenreiter. £1.40* EZDJ/AYE (B75-50056)

Traditionen und Reforman in der Kirchenmusik : Festschrift für Konrad Ameln zum 75. Geburstag am 6, Juli 1974. *32 Great Titchfield St., W.1 : Bärenreiter-Verlag. £13.80* AD/LD(YE/X)
America book for piano. *Galaxy : Galliard. Unpriced* QPK/AYT (B75-51259)
American Arts Documentation Centre. *See* University of Exeter. *American Arts Documentation Centre.*
American fanfare : for brass ensemble and timpani. (Miranda, Sharon Moe). *Chappell. Unpriced* WMGN (B75-50359)
American Folklore Society. Memoir series. Abrahams, Roger David. Deep the water, shallow the shore : three essays on shantying in the West Indies. *University of Texas Press for the American Folklore Society. £3.80* ADW/GMC(YUH) (B75-00739) ISBN 0-292-71502-1
American music handbook. (Pavlakis, Christopher). *Free Press : Collier Macmillan. £10.00* A(YT) (B75-11221) ISBN 0-02-925180-x
American popular song : the great innovators, 1900-1950. (Wilder, Alec). *Oxford University Press. £3.25* ADW/GB(YT/XM51) (B75-18368) ISBN 0-19-284009-6
Amram, David. Zohar : alto recorder (or flute). *Peters. Unpriced* VSSPMJ (B75-50338)
And when I am entombed : for voices, guitar & piano. (Huscroft, John). *27 Donald Way, Chelmsford : John Huscroft. Unpriced* KE/TSPDW (B75-50567)
And will you leave me so? : SATB unaccompanied. (Baksa, Robert F). *Boosey and Hawkes. Unpriced* EZDW (B75-50474)
And wilt thou leave me thus? : SATB. (Brydson, John Collis). *Cramer. £0.12* EZDW (B75-50475)
Andante für Orgel und Orgelchoral 'Meine Seele ist stille'. (Kaminsky, Heinrich). *Bärenreiter. £1.20* RJ (B75-50207)
Andantino cantabile. Opus 69 : for flute and piano. (Simpson, Lionel). *British and Continental. Unpriced* VRPJ (B75-50851)
Andantino : variation pour clarinette si bémol et piano. (Duclos, Pierre). *Chappell. Unpriced* VVP/T (B75-50898)
Andrew Crawfurd's collection of ballads and songs
Vol.1. *27 George Sq., Edinburgh EH8 9LD : The Scottish Text Society. Unpriced* ADW/G(YDL) (B75-29319) ISBN 0-9500245-4-6
Andrewes, John. A hymn of St Columba (Regis regum rectissimi) : SATB and organ. (Britten, Benjamin). *Boosey and Hawkes. £0.20* DH (B75-50418)
Andrews, Frank. 'His Master's Voice' recordings, plum label 'C' series (12 inch). (Gramophone Company). *Old School House, Tarrant Hinton, Blandford, Dorset : Oakwood Press. £4.50* A/FD(T/WT) (B75-08384) ISBN 0-85361-166-1
Angel Gabriel : for S.S.A. (Toplis, Gloria). *Ricordi. Unpriced* FEZDP/LF (B75-51063)
Anglican folk mass. An Anglican folk mass : unison. (Shaw, Martin). *Roberton. £0.30* JDGS (B75-51077)
Anne Cromwell's Virginal Book, 1638. *Oxford University Press. £2.50* QSQ/AY (B75-50725) ISBN 0-19-372637-8
Annen-Polka. Op.117. *arr.* Annen-Polka. Op.117 : polka française. (Strauss, Johann, *b.1825*). *Bosworth. Unpriced* MK/AHVH (B75-50129)
Anniversary fanfare : for trumpet, trombones and percussion. (Walton, *Sir* William). *Oxford University Press. Unpriced* WMGN (B75-50916) ISBN 0-19-368100-5
Annotations of Auschwitz : soprano, flute (bass flute), trumpet, horn, violin, cello, piano. (Lumsdaine, David). *Universal. Unpriced* KFLE/NUNQDX (B75-51124)
Anthem of faith 'Lord increase our faith' : for four-part chorus of mixed voices with piano or organ accompaniment. (Mueller, Carl Frank). *Associated Music. Unpriced* DK (B75-50426)
Antiphonies : for orchestra. (Connolly, Justin). *Oxford University Press. £5.50* MMJ (B75-50612) ISBN 0-19-362390-0
Antoniou, Theodor. Epilogue after Homer's 'The Odyssey' : for mezzosoprano, narrator, oboe, horn, guitar, piano, percussion and doublebass. *Bärenreiter. Unpriced* KFNE/NYDNQDX (B75-50578)
Antoniou, Theodore.
Cheironomies : conductor's improvisation. *Bärenreiter. £3.20* MMJ (B75-50138)
Concertino for nine wind instruments, piano & percussion. Op.21. Concertino. Op.21 : for piano, nine wind instruments and percussion. *Bärenreiter. £7.00* MRFL (B75-50157)
Concertino for piano, strings & percussion. Op.16b. Concertino. Op.16b : for piano, strings and percussion. *Cassel : Bärenreiter. £2.40* NYGFL (B75-50174)
Concerto for violin. Opus 28. Violinkonzert (1965). Opus 28. *Bärenreiter. £8.00* MPSF (B75-50150)
Events 1 : for violin, piano and orchestra, 1968. *Bärenreiter. £2.00* MPSP (B75-50152)
Events 2 : for large orchestra, 1969. *Bärenreiter. £4.00* MMJ (B75-50139)
Events 3 : for orchestra with tape and slides, 1969. *Bärenreiter. £2.40* MMJ (B75-50140)
Jeux. Op.22 : for violoncello and string orchestra. *Bärenreiter. £2.80* RXMPSR (B75-50230)
Klima tis apussias = Stimmung der Abwesenheit = Sense of absence : for voice and chamber orchestra. *Bärenreiter. £2.40* KE/MRDW (B75-50116)
Klima tis apussias. *Vocal score.* Klima tis apussias = Stimmung der Abwesenheit = Sense of absence : for voice and piano. *Bärenreiter. £2.40* KDW (B75-50104)
Any time's children's time : for chord organ. *EMI. Unpriced* RPVCK/DW/AY (B75-51281)
Anywhere I wander : for mixed chorus (SATB) and piano with optional rhythm guitar, bass guitar and drums. (Loesser, Frank). *Frank Music. Unpriced* DW (B75-51019)
Aponte, Pedro Arcila. Las Belles noches de Maiquetia :

canzone venezuelana per chitarra. *Zanibon : Hinrichsen. Unpriced* TSPMJ (B75-50281)
Apotheosis of this earth : for orchestra and chorus. (Husa, Karel). *Associated Music. Unpriced* EMDX (B75-50450)

Apparitions for orchestra. (Sitsky, Larry). *Boosey and Hawkes. £6.00* MJ (B75-50598)
Appelbaum, Stanley. Show songs from 'The black crook' to 'The red mill' : original sheet music for 60 songs from 50 shows, 1866-1906. *Dover : Constable. £4.20* KDW/GB/AYT(XKF41) (B75-51117)
Applebaum, Stan. Keyboard music. *Selections: arr.* Bach music : simple style, for piano. (Bach, Johann Sebastian). *Schroeder and Gunther. £1.30* QPJ (B75-51231)
Appleby, William.
String along : 22 easy graded pieces for violin and piano. *Oxford University Press. £1.60* SPJ (B75-50766) ISBN 0-19-355204-3
Two 18th century gavottes. *Banks. Unpriced* QNVK/AHM/AY (B75-50663)
Two trebles : nine pieces arranged for two treble recorders and piano. *Oxford University Press. £1.20* VSSNTQK/AAY (B75-50879) ISBN 0-19-355202-7
Volkskinderlieder. *Selections: arr.* Seven pieces. (Brahms, Johannes). *Oxford University Press. £1.00* RXMK (B75-50750) ISBN 0-19-361906-7
Appleton, Jon Howard. The development and practice of electronic music. *Prentice-Hall. £8.80* APV (B75-15702) ISBN 0-13-207605-5
April and May : two songs. (Kennedy, John Brodbin). *Boosey and Hawkes. Unpriced* KDW (B75-51106)
Apusskidu : songs for children, with piano accompaniments, with chords for guitar and with parts for descant recorders, glockenspiel, chime bars and percussion. *Black. Unpriced* JFE/NYJDW/AY (B75-50539) ISBN 0-7136-1553-2
Aquarelles. Op.19, no.4. *arr.* Humoreske. Op.19, no.4. (Gade, Niels Vilhelm). *British and Continental Music. Unpriced* VVPK (B75-50902)
Arcade II : for piano solo. (Humble, Keith). *Universal. Unpriced* QPJ (B75-50700)
Arcade IIIa : solo flute. (Humble, Keith). *Universal. Unpriced* VRPMJ (B75-50854)
Arcade IV : for guitar and percussion. (Humble, Keith). *Universal. Unpriced* TSPLX (B75-50802)
Arcade V : for orchestra. (Humble, Keith). *Universal. Unpriced* MMJ (B75-50615)
Arcadelt, Jacques. Il primo libro di madrigali. *Selections.* Three madrigals : for 4 voices or instruments. *Antico. Unpriced* EZDU (B75-50473)
Arch, Gwyn.
The discontented man : musical play for voices, piano and percussion. *British and Continental Music : EMI Music. Unpriced* CQN (B75-50011)
Four negro spirituals : SSA and piano. *Boosey and Hawkes. £1.00* FDW/LC (B75-50073)
My friend Androcles : musical play for voices, piano and percussion. *British and Continental Music : EMI Music. Unpriced* CQN (B75-50012)
Argento, Dominick.
From the diary of Virginia Woolf : for medium voice and piano. *Boosey and Hawkes. Unpriced* KFVDW (B75-50582)
The masque of angels. Gloria. *arr.* Gloria : unaccompanied mixed chorus. *Boosey and Hawkes. £0.40* EZDH (B75-51034)
Ariadne auf Naxos : opera in one act with a prelude. (Hofmannsthal, Hugo von). *Boosey and Hawkes. £1.50* BSUAC (B75-08737) ISBN 0-85162-026-4
Arietta : for horn and piano. (Noble, Harold). *British and Continental. Unpriced* WTPJ (B75-50956)
Ariosti, Attilio. Sonatas for viola d'amore & continuo, 'Stockholm'. 'Stockholm sonatas' : for viola d'amore (viola) and basso continuo
1: Sonatas in F major, A minor, G major. *Bärenreiter. £2.80* SQQPE (B75-50259)
Arma, Paul. Divertimento no.8 : pour 2 flûtes. *Chappell. Unpriced* VRNU (B75-50844)
Armada pop quiz book. (Kinn, Maurice). *Armada Books. £0.35* A(DE) (B75-05789) ISBN 0-00-690953-1
Armalita. *arr.* Armalita : tango. (Neill, David). *Swan. Unpriced* QPHVR (B75-50680)
Armalita : tango. (Neill, David). *Swan. Unpriced* QPHVR (B75-50680)
Armenian sketches : piano solo. (Tjeknavorian, Loris). *Novello. £1.00* QPJ (B75-50714)
Armstrong, Alan. Maori action songs. *Reed. £3.45* BZWYADW/GR (B75-50981) ISBN 0-589-00777-7
Arne, Michael. Selected songs. (Arne, Thomas Augustine). *Cramer. Unpriced* KDW (B75-50548)
Arne, Thomas Augustine. Selected songs. *Cramer. Unpriced* KDW (B75-50548)
Arnold, Denis.
Giovanni Gabrieli. *Oxford University Press. £1.80* BG (B75-07792) ISBN 0-19-315231-2
Monteverdi. Revised ed. *Dent. £3.95* BMN (B75-27353) ISBN 0-460-03155-4
Arnold, Jay.
28 selected duets : for two saxophones (or oboes). *Edward Schuberth : Phoenix. Unpriced* VUNU/AY (B75-51398)

30 selected duets : for two saxophones (or oboes). *Edward Schuberth : Phoenix. Unpriced* VUNU/AY (B75-51399)

Arnold, Malcolm. Hongkong anniversary overture. Op.99. *Central Music Library : Faber. Unpriced* MMJ (B75-50608)
Art of listening : developing musical perception. (Bamberger, Jeanne Shapiro). 3rd ed. *Harper and Row. £3.85* A/C (B75-21064) ISBN 0-06-040948-7
Art of record buying : a list of recommended microgroove recordings
1975. *E.M.G. £3.20* A/FD(WT) (B75-06145) ISBN 0-900982-06-3
Artman, Ruth.
I can't sing pretty! (But I shore sing loud!) : for unison or SA chorus and piano. *Warner : Blossom. Unpriced* FDW (B75-50488)
Lord, walk with me : for SATB chorus and piano. *Warner : Blossom. Unpriced* DH (B75-50417)
Arts Council of Great Britain. The audience for orchestral concerts : a report on surveys in Birmingham, Bournemouth, Glasgow, Liverpool and Manchester. (Mann, Peter Henry). *Arts Council of Great Britain. £0.50* AM(W) (B75-13446) ISBN 0-7287-0059-x
As all get out (after an idea by Bruno Maderna) : for instrumental ensemble. (Rands, Bernard). *Universal. Unpriced* MRJ (B75-50633)
As fit as a fiddle
Book 2: Six health education songs for younger children. (Reaks, Brian). *British and Continental. Unpriced* JFDW (B75-50098)
Ashfield, Robert. Salvator mundi : SATB. *Banks. Unpriced* DGMS (B75-50412)
Associated Board of the Royal Schools of Music.
Official book of scales and arpeggios for double bass, (Grades III, IV, V, VI, and VIII). *Associated Board of the Royal Schools of Music. £0.45* SS/AF (B75-50267)
Pianoforte examinations, 1976
Grade 1. Lists A and B (primary). *Associated Board of the Royal Schools of Music. £0.50* Q/AL (B75-51200)
Grade 2. Lists A and B (elementary). *Associated Board of the Royal Schools of Music. £0.50* Q/AL (B75-51201)
Grade 3. Lists A and B (transitional). *Associated Board of the Royal Schools of Music. £0.50* Q/AL (B75-51202)
Grade 4. Lists A and B (lower). *Associated Board of the Royal Schools of Music. £0.50* Q/AL (B75-51203)
Grade 5. List A (higher). *Associated Board of the Royal Schools of Music. £0.50* Q/AL (B75-51204)
Grade 5. List B (higher). *Associated Board of the Royal Schools of Music. £0.v0* Q/AL (B75-51205)
Grade 6. List A (intermediate). *Associated Board of the Royal Schools of Music. £0.50* Q/AL (B75-51206)
Grade 6. List B (intermediate). *Associated Board of the Royal Schools of Music. £0.v0* Q/AL (B75-51207)
Grade 7. List A (advanced). *Associated Board of the Royal School of Music. £0.50* Q/AL (B75-51208)
Grade 7. List B (advanced). *Associated Board of the Royal Schools of Music. £0.50* Q/AL (B75-51209)
Grade 7. List B (advanced). *Associated Board of the Royal Schools of Music. £0.50* Q/AL (B75-51210)
The well-tuned fiddle : original compositions for violin and pianoforte by contemporary composers
Book 1. *Associated Board of the Royal Schools of Music. £0.70* SP/AY (B75-50243)
Book 2. *Associated Board of the Royal Schools of Music. £0.70* SP/AY (B75-50244)
Book 3. *Associated Board of the Royal Schools of Music. £0.70* SP/AY (B75-50245)
Aston, Peter. Seasonal sentences from Series 3. *Royal School of Church Music. Unpriced* DGSKAD (B75-50415)
At the mighty organ. (Wyatt, Geoffrey). *Oxford Illustrated Press. £3.75* ARPV/JR(X) (B75-12698) ISBN 0-902280-22-8
Atalanta. Overture. Overture for trumpet, oboes, strings and basso continuo. (Handel, George Frideric). *Musica rara. Unpriced* MRJ (B75-51171)
Atalanta. Overture. *arr.* Overture for trumpet. oboes, strings and basso continuo. (Handel, George Frideric). *Musica rara. Unpriced* WSPK (B75-51460)
Atkinson, Condit. Four things a man must learn to do : for mixed chorus and piano with optional bass and guitar. *Galaxy : Galliard. Unpriced* DW (B75-50436)
Attaingnant, Pierre. Two chansons for flutes. (Thomas, Bernard). *Oxford University Press. £0.12* EZDU (B75-50062) ISBN 0-19-341220-9
Audience for orchestral concerts : a report on surveys in Birmingham, Bournemouth, Glasgow, Liverpool and Manchester. (Mann, Peter Henry). *Arts Council of Great Britain. £0.50* AM(W) (B75-13446) ISBN 0-7287-0059-x
Audiogramme : für vier Klarinetten. (Schumann, Gerhard). *Heinrichshofen : Hinrichsen. Unpriced* VVNS (B75-50891)
Aus Zungen Stimmen : für Akkordeonquintett. (Kagel, Mauricio). *Universal. Unpriced* RSNR (B75-50743)
Autumn setting : soprano and string quartet. (Rhodes, Phillip). *Peters. Unpriced* KFLE/RXNSDX (B75-51126)

Ave maris stella : for unaccompanied mixed voices. (Williams, Grace). *Oxford University Press. £0.50* EZDH (B75-50462) ISBN 0-19-338755-7
Avenir : pour baryton. (Duclos, Pierre). *Chappell. Unpriced* KGNDW (B75-50592)
Avshalomov, Jacob. I saw a stranger yester'en : for mixed chorus and violin or piano. *Galaxy : Galliard. Unpriced* ESDW (B75-50454)
Ayre, Leslie. The Gilbert and Sullivan companion. *Pan Books. £1.50* BSWACF(C) (B75-01796) ISBN 0-330-24138-9
Ayres, songs and dialogues. (Johnson, Robert, *b.1582*). 2nd revised ed. *Stainer and Bell. Unpriced* KE/TWDW/AZ (B75-51123)
Babe is born : SSA unacc. (Lane, Philip). *Banks. Unpriced* FEZDP/LF (B75-51061)
Babylon's falling : a jazz spiritual for junior band and optional voices in two parts. (Wastall, Peter). *Boosey and Hawkes. £2.05* UMJ (B75-51338)
Bach, Carl Philipp Emanuel.
Concerto for flute, strings & basso continuo, in B flat major. Wq.167. Concerto in B flat major. Wq.167 : for flute, strings and basso continuo. *Musica rara. Unpriced* RXMPVRF (B75-51285)
Concerto for flute, strings & basso continuo in B flat major. Wq.167. *arr.* Concerto in B flat major. Wq.167 : for flute, strings and basso continuo. *Musica rara. Unpriced* VRPK/LF (B75-51374)
Six little marches for wind septet. Wq.195. *arr.* Six little marches. *Novello. £0.30* VVNTK/AGM (B75-50347)
Sonata for descant recorder & basso continuo in C minor. Sonata for alto recorder (or flute) and harpsichord (or piano) obbligato with cello (or bassoon) continuo. *Associated Music. Unpriced* VSRPE (B75-50873)
Bach, Johann Christian. Symphony, Op.6, no.3, in E flat major. Sinfonia in E flat major. Op6/III. *Nagel Bärenreiter. £2.40* MRE (B75-50155)
Bach, Johann Sebastian.
Bric-a-Bach (constructed from five different compositions by J.S. Bach) : for full chorus of mixed voices with optional guitar, bass and drums accompaniment. (Jergenson, Dale). *Schirmer. Unpriced* EZDX (B75-50484)
Concertos for keyboard, nos.2, 5. S.1053, 1056. *Selections : arr.* Siciliano/Largo. *Schott. Unpriced* SRPK (B75-51307)
Keyboard music. *Selections: arr.* Bach music : simple style, for piano. *Schroeder and Gunther. £1.30* QPJ (B75-51231)
Notenbuch der Anna Magdalena Bach, 1725. *Selections: arr.* Bachiana for percussion : four pieces. *Simrock. Unpriced* XNQK (B75-50965)
Partita for lute in C minor. S.997. *arr.* Partita. *Uitgave Metropolis : Hinrichsen. £1.00* TSPMK/AG (B75-50288)
Partita for violin, no.2. S.1064. Chaconne. *arr.* Chaconne. *Uitgave Metropolis : Hinrichsen. Unpriced* RSPMK/AHJN (B75-50224)
St Matthew passion S.244. Matthaus-Passion = St Matthew Passion. *Bärenreiter. £4.40* EMDD/LK (B75-50034)
Selections. *arr.* Bach. The fugue. *Oxford University Press. Unpriced* QPK (B75-51255) ISBN 0-19-372220-8
Sonata for flute & harpsichord, no.3, in A major. S. 1032. Sonata in A major for flute and harpsichord. *Oxford University Press. £2.00* VRPE (B75-50317) ISBN 0-19-355249-3
Suite for orchestra, no.1, in C major. S.1066. Ouverture (Orchestral suite), C major. *Bärenreiter. Unpriced* MRG (B75-50627)
Suite for orchestra, no.2, in B minor. S.1067. Ouverture = (Orchestral suite). B minor. *Cassel : Bärenreiter. Unpriced* MRG (B75-50628)
Suite for orchestra, no.3, in D major. S.1068. Ouverture = (Orchestral suite), D major. *Bärenreiter. Unpriced* MRG (B75-50629)
Suite for orchestra, no.4, in D major. S.1069. Ouverture = (Orchestral sutte), D major. *Bärenreiter. Unpriced* MRG (B75-50630)
Suites for cello. S.1007-12. *Selections: arr.* Dance movements. *Schirmer. Unpriced* WVPMK/AH (B75-50963)
Das wohltemperirte Clavier, Tl. 1. S.867. *arr.* Prelude and fugue. *Oxford University Press. Score, £0.75 ; Parts, Unpriced* SRNRK/Y (B75-50773) ISBN 0-19-355238-8
Bach music : simple style, for piano. (Bach, Johann Sebastian). *Schroeder and Gunther. £1.30* QPJ (B75-51231)
Bach. The fugue. (Bach, Johann Sebastian). *Oxford University Press. Unpriced* QPK (B75-51255) ISBN 0-19-372220-8
Bacheler, Daniel. Selected works for lute. *Oxford Universuty Press. £4.50* TWPMJ (B75-50292) ISBN 0-19-355305-8
Bachiana for percussion : four pieces. (Bach, Johann Sebastian). *Simrock. Unpriced* XNQK (B75-50965)
Bacon, Ernst. Of a feather : five songs for high and low voices and piano. *Novello. Unpriced* FDW (B75-50489)
Bądarzewska, Thécla. La Prière d'une vierge. *arr.* A maiden's prayer. *Boosey and Hawkes. £1.00* WMK (B75-51420)
Badura-Skoda, Eva. Concerto for piano, no.17, in G major. K.453. Concerto in G major for pianoforte and orchestra, KV453. (Mozart, Wolfgang Amadeus). *Bärenreiter. Unpriced* MPQF (B75-50620)
Badura-Skoda, Paul.
Concerto for piano, no.17, in G major. K.453. Concerto in G major for pianoforte and orchestra, KV453. (Mozart, Wolfgang Amadeus). *Bärenreiter. Unpriced* MPQF (B75-50620)
Fantasy for mechanical organ in F minor. K.608. *arr.* Fantasy for mechanical organ. K.608. (Mozart, Wolfgang Amadeus). *Schirmer. Unpriced* QNVK (B75-50662)
Bagpipe : the history of a musical instrument. (Collinson, Francis). *Routledge and Kegan Paul. £7.50* AVY/B(X) (B75-04509) ISBN 0-7100-7913-3
Bailey, Freda O. Nocturne : for pianoforte. *Regina. Unpriced* QPJ (B75-51232)
Baily, John. Krishna Govinda's rudiments of tabla playing. *Llan-fynydd, Carmarthen, Dyfed SA32 7TT : Unicorn Bookshop. £2.50* BZFLAXQ/AC (B75-04510) ISBN 0-85659-018-5
Baird, Tadeusz.
Elegeia : für Orchester. *Litolff : Peters. Unpriced* MMJ (B75-51153)
Psychodrama : für Orchester. *Litolff : Peters. Unpriced* MMJ (B75-50141)

Baker, Richard, *b.1925.* The magic of music. *Hamilton.* *£3.95* A(X) (B75-11220) ISBN 0-241-89194-9
Baksa, Robert F. And will you leave me so? : SATB unaccompanied. *Boosey and Hawkes. Unpriced* EZDW (B75-50474)
Balada, Leonardo. Elementalis : for organ. *Schirmer. £0.80* RJ (B75-51272)
Balakirev, Mily. Tamara : symphonic poem. *Eulenburg.* *£2.50* MMJ (B75-50609)
Balent, Andrew. The spirit of Christmas : for wind band and optional chorus. *Warner : Blossom. Unpriced* UM/LF (B75-51332)
Ball, Eric. Holiday overture : for brass band. *Boosey and Hawkes. £6.00* WMJ (B75-51418)
Balla, Gyorgy. Divertimento for two violins, cello & keyboard in C major. Hob. XIV, 8. Divertimento, C-dur : für Cembalo (Klavier), 2 Violinen und Violocello. Hoboken XIV, 8. (Haydn, Joseph). Zum ersten Mal herausgegeben von Gyorgy Balla. *Litolff : Peters. Unpriced* NXNS (B75-50169)
Ballad 2 : music/theatre piece for voice and piano. (Rands, Bernard). *Universal. Unpriced* CB/J (B75-50986)
Ballade : piano solo. (Debussy, Claude). *Peters. Unpriced* QPJ (B75-50688)
Ballade und Tanz = Ballad and dance : after Roumanian folk songs, for school orchestra. (Ligeti, György). *Schott.* *£2.90* MH (B75-50127)
Ballet : elektronische Orgel. *Nagel : Bärenreiter. Unpriced* RPVK/AHM/AY (B75-50222)
Balloonmusic 1 : for any number of players from 2 to 1000 each with 2 balloons, a pin and their voices. (Bedford, David). *Universal. Unpriced* JFE/YBPN (B75-50543)
Balta, Freddy.
Improvisation no.1 : valse pour accordeon. *Chappell. Unpriced* RSPMHW (B75-50744)
Improvisation no.V : piano. *Chappell. Unpriced* QPJ (B75-50685)
Mister Czerny : solo d'accordeon d'aprés une étude de la grande velocité de Carl Czerny. *Chappell. Unpriced* RSPMJ (B75-50745)
Nouveau livre de noëls. Noel 10. *arr.* Noel X. (Daquin, Louis Claude). *Chappell. Unpriced* RSPMK (B75-50746)

Balulalow : carol for SAATB with divisions unaccompanied. (Inness, Peter). *Novello. £0.10* EZDP/LF (B75-50061)
Balz, Hans Martin. Sechs Intonationen und Cantus-firmus. Sechs Intonationen und Cantus-firmus-Stücke zu Adventsliedern des EKG (1959), with Anhang Anbetung des Kindes Jesus (1965) : für Orgel. (Reda, Siegfried). *Bärenreiter. Unpriced* R/LEZ (B75-50729)
Bamberger, Jeanne Shapiro. The art of listening : developing musical perception. 3rd ed. *Harper and Row. £3.85* A/C (B75-21064) ISBN 0-06-040948-7
Bamert, Matthias. Introduction and tarantella : trio for flute, percussion and piano. *Schirmer. £1.55* NYFRHVS (B75-51197)
Band rats. (Mays, Spike). *P. Davies. £4.50* AUMM (B75-24238) ISBN 0-432-09230-7
Bands around the world. (Yoder, Paul). *Rubank : Novello. Unpriced* UMMJ (B75-51347)
Barber, Samuel.
Songs. Op.45. Three songs. Op.45 : for high voice and piano. *Schirmer. Unpriced* KFTDW (B75-50580)
Songs. Op.45. Three songs. Op.45 : for low voice and piano. *Schirmer. Unpriced* KFXDW (B75-50588)
Barbirolli, *Lady* Evelyn. Siciliana : oboe and harpsichord or piano. (Head, Michael). *Emerson. Unpriced* VTPHVQ (B75-51392)
Barmherzige Samariter : für gemischten Chor und Sprecher. (Hufschmidt, Wolfgang). *Bärenreiter. £1.00* EZDH (B75-50050)
Barnard, Elizabeth. Hurry, little pony : Spanish traditional song. (Bonsor, Brian). *Oxford University Press. Unpriced* JFE/NYFSDW (B75-51097) ISBN 0-19-344836-x
Barnes, Norman J. The Spirit of the Lord : SATB. *Banks. Unpriced* DK (B75-50424)
Baron, Samuel. Sonata for flute & harpsichord, no.3, in A major. S. 1032. Sonata in A major for flute and harpsichord. (Bach, Johann Sebastian). *Oxford University Press. £2.00* VRPE (B75-50317) ISBN 0-19-355249-3
Baroque music for organ. *Cramer. Unpriced* RK/AAY (B75-51277)
Barraud, Henry. Quartet for saxophones. Quatuor de saxophones. *Boosey and Hawkes. £7.50* VUNS (B75-50344)
Barrell, Bernard.
Suite for brass (2 trumpets, 2 trombones). Op.21. *Ricordi. Unpriced* WNSG (B75-50380)
Three preludes for treble recorder and guitar. Op.31. *Thames. Unpriced* VSSPLTS (B75-51386)
Barsham, Eve. Selected works for keyboard. (Clarke, Jeremiah). *Oxford University Press. £1.30* QRPJ (B75-50724) ISBN 0-19-372417-0
Barth, Herbert. Wagner : a documentary study. *Thames and Hudson. £12.00* BWC(N) (B75-30568) ISBN 0-500-01137-0
Barthe, Adrian. Ouvre feu : oboe and piano. *Emerson. Unpriced* VTPJ (B75-51393)
Bartholdy, Felix Mendelssohn. *See* Mendelssohn, Felix.
Bartlet, M E C. Ecco ch'io lass'il core : SSATTB (unacc. or with lutes). (Striggio, Alessandro). *Oxford University Press. Unpriced* ETWNUDU (B75-50457) ISBN 0-19-341221-7
Bartók orchestral music. (McCabe, John). *British Broadcasting Corporation. £0.55* BBGAM (B75-02998) ISBN 0-563-12674-4
Bartos, Jan Zdenek. Adagio elegiaeo und Rondo : für Horn und Klavier. *Schott. £1.89* WTP/W (B75-50384)
Bates, Tom. The Lord's Prayer : SATB with alternative version for unison voices. *Banks. Unpriced* EZDTF (B75-50471)
Batt, Mike. The giant Wombles music book : containing words and music of 32 compositions. *Chappell. Unpriced* KDW/JS (B75-50561)
Battle of Trafalgar : for military band. (Elms, Albert). *Boosey and Hawkes. Unpriced* UMMJ (B75-50305)
Battle suite. (Scheidt, Samuel). *Chester. Unpriced* WNRK (B75-51446)
Bauer, Heinrich. Suite for harp. Suite für Harfe. (Mayr, Johann Simon). Zum ersten Mal herausgegeben von Heinrich Bauer. *Litolff : Peters. Unpriced* TQPMG (B75-50790)
Baughen, M A. Der Weg der Barmherzigkeit. There's a road (which leads from Jerusalem) : hymn. (Schneider, Martin Gotthard). *Bosworth. Unpriced* JDM (B75-50524)
Baumann, Herbert. Suite für Cembalo. *Heinrichshofen Hinrichsen. Unpriced* QRPG (B75-50723)
Bavardages : cinq pièces brèves en canon pour quintette a vent (flute, hautbois, clarinette, B bémol, cor F, basson). (Meyer, Jean). *Chappell. Unpriced* UNR (B75-51357)
Bavicchi, John.
Five dialogues. Op.7 : for two B flat clarinets. *Oxford University Press. Unpriced* VVNU (B75-50895)
Quartet no.1 for brass, Op.22. *Oxford University Press. Unpriced* WNS (B75-50938)
Bawdy songs of the early music hall. *David and Charles.* *£3.95* AKDW/K/G/KDX(XHK11) (B75-31191) ISBN 0-7153-7013-8
Bay City Rollers. (Paton, Tam). *Everest. £0.45* AKDW/GB/E(P) (B75-29316) ISBN 0-903925-60-5
Bayer, Bathja. Yuval : studies of the Jewish Music Research Centre
Vol.3. *Magnes Press : Distributed by Oxford University Press. £10.25* A(YBU/D) (B75-08735) ISBN 0-19-647920-7
Bazhov, Pavel Petrovich. The fire maid. *Vocal score.* The fire maid : an opera for schools. (Long, Robert). *Oxford University Press. £2.50* CN (B75-50402) ISBN 0-19-337374-2
BBC. *See* British Broadcasting Corporation.
Beach of Falesa : opera in three acts. (Hoddinott, Alun). *Oxford University Press. £8.50* CC (B75-50394)
Beach of Falesa. *Vocal score.* The beach of Falesa : opera in three acts. (Hoddinott, Alun). *Oxford University Press. £8.50* CC (B75-50394)
Beatles : an illustrated record. (Carr, Roy). *New English Library. £1.95* AKDW/GB/E(P) (B75-13736) ISBN 0-450-02626-4
Beatles for classical guitar. (Lennon, John). *Wise, Music Sales. Unpriced* TSPMK/DW (B75-50818)
Beatles : the fabulous story of John, Paul, George and Ringo. *Octopus Books. £1.99* AKDW/GB/E(P) (B75-21666) ISBN 0-7064-0446-7
Beatus vir, Psalm 112 : SATB. (Carissimi, Giacomo). *Oxford University Press. Unpriced* DR (B75-50433) ISBN 0-19-350351-4
Beaumont, Adrian. Long long ago : for four-part female chorus, unaccompanied. *Roberton. £0.08* FEZDP/LF (B75-51059)
Beaumont, Joseph. To words by Joseph Beaumont : three songs for soprano and alto voices (SSA) and piano. (Tate, Phyllis). *Oxford University Press. £0.90* FDW (B75-50496) ISBN 0-19-338382-9
Beavan, Peter. Klempererisms : a few of Dr Klemperer's lighter moments. *15 Dungarvan Ave., S.W.15 : Cock Robin Press. Free* A/EC(P) (B75-09268) ISBN 0-9500594-2-0
Bebey, Francis. African music : a people's art. *Harrap. £4.50* BZK (B75-20391) ISBN 0-245-52735-4
Becerra-Schmidt, Gustavo. Quartet for strings, no.6. String quartet no.6. *Oxford University Press. Unpriced* RXNS (B75-50757)
Beck, Conrad. Facetten : drei Impromptus, für Trompete in C und Klavier. *Schott. £2.25* WSPJ (B75-51457)
Bedford, David.
Balloonmusic 1 : for any number of players from 2 to 1000 each with 2 balloons, a pin and their voices. *Universal. Unpriced* JFE/YBPN (B75-50543)
The tentacles of the dark nebula : for tenor & strings. *Universal. Unpriced* KGHE/RXNNDX (B75-51129)
Twelve hours of sunset. *Choral score.* Twelve hours of sunset. *Universal. Unpriced* DADX (B75-50406)
When I heard the learn'd astronomer : for tenor and wind band. *Universal. Unpriced* KGHE/UMDX (B75-51130)
Beecham, *Sir* Thomas, *bart.* Frederick Delius. Revised ed. *Severn House. £5.25* BDL(N) (B75-27351) ISBN 0-7278-0073-6
Beechey, Gwilym.
An Easter introit : SATB. *Banks. Unpriced* EZDM (B75-50466)
If music be the food of love (3rd setting). Z.379C. (Purcell, Henry). *Oxford University Press. £0.50* KDW (B75-50557) ISBN 0-19-345707-5
Sonatas for violin & continuo. Op.4, nos 2,3. Two sonatas for violin and basso continuo. (Festing, Michael Christian). *Oxford University Press. £2.00* SPE (B75-50246) ISBN 0-19-356458-0
Beeny Bud : 12 Jamaican folk-songs for children. *Oxford University Press. Unpriced* FEZDW/G/AYULD (B75-51066) ISBN 0-19-330543-7
Beeson, Jack.
Everyman's handyman : nine rounds and canons for men's voices. *Boosey and Hawkes. Unpriced* GEZDW/XC (B75-50519)
The model housekeeper : nine rounds and canons for women's voices. *Boosey and Hawkes. Unpriced* FEZDW/XC (B75-50505)
Beethoven, Ludwig van.
Rondo for violin & piano in G major. K-H 41. Rondo for violin & piano. *Schirmer. Unpriced* SP/W (B75-50764)
Symphony no.9, op.125, in D minor, 'Choral'. Freude schöne Gotterfunken. *arr.* Hymn to joy. *Oxford University Press. £0.40* RK/DW (B75-50736) ISBN 0-19-375294-8
Symphony no.9, op.125, in D minor, 'Choral'. Freude, schöner Gotterfunken. *arr.* Song of joy. *Studio Music. Unpriced* WMK/DW (B75-51427)
Beethoven : a documentary study. Abridged ed. *Thames and Hudson. £3.00* BBJ (B75-03644) ISBN 0-500-18146-2
Beethoven string quartets
1. (Lam, Basil). *British Broadcasting Corporation. £0.70* BBJARXNS (B75-30569) ISBN 0-563-10166-0
2. (Lam, Basil). *British Broadcasting Corporation. £0.70* BBJARXNS (B75-30570) ISBN 0-563-12675-2
Beethoven's sketches : an analysis of his style based on a study of his sketch-books. (Mies, Paul). *Dover Publications etc. : Constable. £1.40* BBJ/D (B75-25553) ISBN 0-486-23042-2
Behold your King : a devotion for choir and congregation devised by Erik Routley. *Royal School of Church Music. Unpriced* DP/LF/AY (B75-51015) ISBN 0-85402-059-4
Belasco, Lionel. Juliana : valzer venezuelano per chitarra. *Zanibon : Hinrichsen. Unpriced* TSPMHW (B75-50276)
Belcher, Supply. Harmony of Maine. *Selections.* Deep North Spirituals, 1794 : mixed or male voices in three and four parts. *Peters. Unpriced* EZDM (B75-50058)
Bell, Arnold Craig. Handel before England. *Darley, Harrogate, N. Yorkshire : Grian-Aig Press. £4.10* BHC(N/XEZE28) (B75-31189) ISBN 0-9500714-5-5
Bell, Sybil. Six Christmas carols : six easy carols from five countries, for easy wind and percussion. *Ricordi. Unpriced* JFE/NYHDP/LF/AYB (B75-51098)
Bell, Sydney. Peggy, my love : Uist boat song, traditional Scottish melody. (Nelson, Havelock). *Elkin. £0.15* GEZDW (B75-51075)
Bell, William. A young man's song : TTBB unacc. (Clements, John). *Oxford University Press. £0.10* GEZDW (B75-50514) ISBN 0-19-341020-6
Bell carol : based on the tune 'Puer nobis', for junior choir, mixed choir, and organ, with optional bells. (Wichmann, Russell G). *Oxford University Press. Unpriced* DP/LF (B75-51013)
Belles noches de Maiquetia : canzone venezuelana per chitarra. (Aponte, Pedro Arcila). *Zanibon : Hinrichsen. Unpriced* TSPMJ (B75-50281)
Belloc, Hilaire. Ha'nacker Mill : song. (Plumstead, Mary). *Roberton. Unpriced* KDW (B75-50556)
Bells : a carol for S.S.A. and piano. (Walters, Edmund). *Boosey and Hawkes. £0.15* FDP/LF (B75-51054)
Bells of Bellagio : 2 or 3 players at 1,2 or 3 pianos. (Luening, Otto). *Peters. Unpriced* QN (B75-50177)
Benger, Richard.
October songs : SSA unacc. *Banks. Unpriced* FEZDW (B75-50500)
Winter fragments : SSA unacc. *Banks Music. Unpriced* FEZDW (B75-50501)
Bengtsson, Ingmar. Quartet for wind & piano in E flat major. Quartet in E flat major for piano and wind instruments. (Berwald, Franz). *Bärenreiter. £4.80* NWNS (B75-50166)
Bennett, John Reginald. Smetana on 3000 records. *Oakwood Press. £8.75* BSIM/FD (B75-14334) ISBN 0-85361-158-0
Bennett, Josephine. African music : a people's art. (Bebey, Francis). *Harrap. £4.50* BZK (B75-20391) ISBN 0-245-52735-4
Bennett, Richard Rodney.
The Bermudas : for chorus and orchestra. *Universal. Unpriced* EMDX (B75-51026)
Boulez on music today. (Boulez, Pierre). *Faber. £0.80* A (B75-06414) ISBN 0-571-10587-4
Commedia 3 : for ten instruments. *Novello. £2.00* MRJ (B75-50158)
Commedia II : flute, cello and piano. *Novello. £3.50* NURNT (B75-50634)
Commedia IV : brass quintet. *Novello. £1.30* WNR (B75-50937)
Concerto for viola & chamber orchestra. *Novello. £2.00* MPSQF (B75-51165)
Spells. *Vocal score.* Spells : soprano solo, mixed chorus & orchestra. *Novello. £1.00* DX (B75-50448)
Tenebrae : a song cycle for baritone and piano. *Universal. Unpriced* KGNDW (B75-51132)
Bennett, Robert Russell. The fabulous country : concert march. *Warner : Blossom. Unpriced* UMMGM (B75-50828)
Bennett, William. Twilight. *arr.* Twilight. (Sullivan, *Sir* Arthur Seymour). *Emerson. Unpriced* VRNTQK (B75-51367)
Benoy, Arthur William. Two rounds for voices. *Oxford University Press. Unpriced* EZDW/XC (B75-51050) ISBN 0-19-343509-8
Bentley, Arnold. Music in education : a point of view. *NFER. £2.95* A(V) (B75-26085) ISBN 0-85633-066-3
Bergmann, Walter.
Sonata for oboe, cello & basso continuo in G major. Trio sonata in G major : for oboe (or flute, violin, descant or tenor recorder), violoncello or bassoon, and harpsichord (or piano), with a second violoncello or basson ad lib. (Quantz, Johann Joachim). *Schott. £2.00* NUTNTE (B75-50636)
Sonata for treble recorder and piano. *Schott. £2.00* VSSPE (B75-50334)
Bergsma, William. Changes for seven : for woodwind quintet, percussion and piano. *Galliard. Unpriced* NYFPNP (B75-51196)

Berio, Luciano.
Opera. Air. Air : for soprano and orchestra. *Universal. Unpriced* KFLE/MDW (B75-50572)
Opera. Air. *arr.* Air : for soprano and 4 instruments. *Universal. Unpriced* KFLE/NXNSDW (B75-50573)
Opus number zoo : children's play for wind quintet (1951, rev. 1970). *Universal. Unpriced* CQN (B75-50994)
Berke, Dietrich. Unaccompanied part-songs for men's voices. (Schubert, Franz). *Bärenreiter. £1.70* GEZDW (B75-50084)
Berkowitz, Sol. Nine folk song preludes : for piano. *Frank Music. Unpriced* QPJ (B75-50686)
Berkowtiz, Sol. Diversion : for orchestra. *Frank Music. Unpriced* MMJ (B75-50610)
Berlin, Irving. Songs. *Selections : arr.* The golden years of Irving Berlin : songs. *Chappell. Unpriced* KDW (B75-51102)
Berlioz, Hector.
La Damnation de Faust. Marche hongroise. *arr.* Hungarian march. *Novello. £1.50* MGM (B75-51147)
Les Troyens. *Eulenburg. Unpriced* CQC (B75-50010)
Les Troyens. Gloire, gloire à Didon. *Vocal score.* Hail all hail to the queen : SATB. *Oxford University Press. £0.08* DW (B75-50028) ISBN 0-19-343046-0
Bermudas : for chorus and orchestra. (Bennett, Richard Rodney). *Universal. Unpriced* EMDX (B75-51026)
Bernstein, Leonard.
An album of songs. *Schirmer. Unpriced* KDW (B75-50549)
Candide. *Selections: arr.* Candide : vocal selections. *Schirmer. Unpriced* KDW (B75-50550)
The joy of music. *White Lion Publishers. £3.25* A/C (B75-04502) ISBN 0-85617-717-2
Bertali, Antonio. Sonata à 3 for two violins, trombone & basso continuo, no.3, in A minor. Sonata à 3, no.3, in A minor for 2 violins, trombone and basso continuo. *Musica rara. £4.50* NUXUNSE (B75-51179)
Bertati, Giovanni. Don Giovanni. Don Giovanni o sai Il Convitato di pietra : dramma giocoso in un atto di Giovanni Bertati. (Gazzaniga, Guiseppe). *Bärenreiter. Unpriced* CQC (B75-50404)
Berthold, G.
Duetto buffo di due gatti = Comic duet for two cats. *28 Knolls Way, Clifton, Beds. : Lindsay Music. £0.15* JNFEDW (B75-50546) ISBN 0-85957-005-3
Duetto buffo di due gatti = Comic duet for two cats. (Berthold, G). *28 Knolls Way, Clifton, Beds. : Lindsay Music. £0.15* JNFEDW (B75-50546) ISBN 0-85957-005-3
Berwald, Franz. Quartet for wind & piano in E flat major. Quartet in E flat major for piano and wind instruments. *Bärenreiter. £4.80* NWNS (B75-50166)
Best of Gilbert and Sullivan : all organ. (Sullivan, *Sir* Arthur Seymour). *Chappell. Unpriced* RK/DW (B75-50739)
Best of Gilbert and Sullivan : SATB. (Sullivan, *Sir* Arthur Seymour). *Chappell. Unpriced* DW (B75-50445)
Best of Jerome Kern. (Kern, Jerome). *Chappell. Unpriced* KDW (B75-50554)
Bethena. (Joplin, Scott). *Chappell. Unpriced* WMK/AHXJ (B75-50372)
Bethena. *arr.* Bethena. (Joplin, Scott). *Chappell. Unpriced* WMK/AHXJ (B75-50372)
Betti, Henri. Miniature. *arr.* Miniature. *Chappell. Unpriced* TMK (B75-50787)
Beyer, Franz. Quartet for strings, op.6, no.82, in B flat major, 'Figaro-Quartett'. String quartet in B flat major 'Figaro-Quartett'. Op.6, no.2. (Danzi, Franz). *Bärenreiter. Unpriced* RXNS (B75-50760)
Bialas, Günter. Ewartung : Orgelspiel. *Bärenreiter. £2.60* RJ (B75-50205)
Biber, Heinrich Ignaz Franz. Sonata à 7 for six trumpets, timpani & organ. Sonata à 7 (1688) for 6 trumpets, timpani and organ. *Musica rara. Unpriced* NYFXSNNE (B75-51198)
Biberian, Gilbert. Lachrimae, nos 8, 1, 12. *arr.* Three dances. (Dowland, John). *Novello. £0.75* TSNSK/AH (B75-51319)
Biblische Motetten für das Kirchenjahr. Band 2: Darstellung des Herrn bis Trinitas. *Selections.* Spruchmotten 3: Motetten. *Bärenreiter. £1.40* EZDJ/AYE (B75-50056)
Bickel, J W. Le Roi s'amuse. Passepied. *arr.* Passepied. (Delibes, Leo). *Oxford University Press. Unpriced* TSPMK/AHU (B75-50817) ISBN 0-19-356159-x
Billie's blues : a survey of Billie Holiday's career, 1933-1959. (Chilton, John). *Quartet Books. £3.95* **AKDW/HHW/E(P)** (B75-19732) ISBN 0-7043-2091-6
Bing : the authorised biography. (Thompson, Charles). *W.H. Allen. £3.95* AKDW/GB/E(P) (B75-25558) ISBN 0-491-01715-4
Binge, Ronald.
Elizabethan serenade. *arr.* Elizabethan serenade. *Ascherberg, Hopwood and Crewe. Unpriced* TSNTK (B75-51320)
The watermill. *arr.* The watermill. *Inter-Art. £0.30* QPK (B75-50715)
Binkerd, Gordon.
Five pieces : for piano. *Boosey and Hawkes. £2.00* QPJ (B75-50687)
Five transcriptions for string orchestra, (with optional trumpet in C). *Boosey and Hawkes. £12.50* RXMK/AAY (B75-50228)
Noble numbers : based on organ music of the 17th and 18th centuries, by Frescobaldi, Pachelbel, Zachau, Vetter, and Walther, for wind ensemble. *Boosey and Hawkes. Unpriced* UMK/AAY (B75-50297)
O sweet Jesu : SATB. *Boosey and Hawkes. Unpriced* EZDH (B75-50048)
Psalm 23 : mixed voices, tenor solo and organ. *Boosey and Hawkes. Unpriced* DR (B75-50432)
Sonatina for flute and piano. *Boosey and Hawkes. Unpriced* VRPEM (B75-50848)
Song of praise and prayer : children's hymn. *Boosey and Hawkes. Unpriced* KFDM (B75-50569)
Song of praise and prayer : children's hymn, unison, with organ or piano accompaniment. *Boosey and Hawkes. Unpriced* JFDM (B75-50530)
Symphony no.3. *Boosey and Hawkes. Unpriced* MME (B75-50603)
There is a garden in her face : TTB, unaccompanied. *Boosey and Hawkes. Unpriced* GEZDW (B75-50513)
Tomorrow the fox will come to town : mixed chorus, SATB. *Boosey and Hawkes. Unpriced* EZDW (B75-50064)
Binns, Patricia Ann. Music and language with young children. (Chacksfield, Kathleen Merle). *Blackwell. £4.50* A/GR(VG) (B75-22597) ISBN 0-631-15330-6
Bird-boogie : for harpsichord (piano). (Goebels, Franzpeter). *Bärenreiter. £2.00* PWPJ (B75-50175)
Birot, Pierre Albert-. *See* Albert-Birot, Pierre.
Birthday carol : SATB. (Willcocks, David). *Oxford University Press. £0.08* DP/LF (B75-50026) ISBN 0-19-343050-9
Birtwistle, Harrison.
Nenia. The death of Orpheus : for soprano solo, crotales, two pianos and three clarinets. *Universal. Unpriced* KFLE/NYFVNQDX (B75-50575)
The triumph of time : for orchestra. *Universal. Unpriced* MMJ (B75-50142)
Bishop, Stephen. Piano music. *Selections.* Schubert. (Schubert, Franz). *Oxford University Press. £1.90* QPJ (B75-51253) ISBN 0-19-373653-5
Bizony, Celia. The family of Bach : a brief history. *Artemis Press. £0.90* BBCB(N) (B75-13733) ISBN 0-85141-281-5
Bjorn, Frank. The alley cat song. *arr.* The alley cat song. *Chappell. Unpriced* UMK/DW (B75-50824)
Blacher, Boris. Trio for violin, cello & piano. Trio : für Klavier, Violine und Violoncello. *Belaieff : Peters. Unpriced* NXNT (B75-50170)
Black, Leo. Style and idea : selected writings of Arnold Schoenberg. (Schoenberg, Arnold). *Faber. £17.50* A(D) (B75-11219) ISBN 0-571-09722-7
Black music. *Hamlyn. £1.95* AKDW/GB/E(YTLD/M) (B75-03641) ISBN 0-600-31343-3
Blades, James. Percussion instruments and their history. New and revised ed. *Faber. £15.00* **AX/B(X)** (B75-13738) ISBN 0-571-04832-3
Blake, David. Scenes : for cello. *Novello. £1.00* SRPMJ (B75-50266)
Blank, Allan.
Four miniatures : for two B flat clarinets. *Associated Music. £1.30* VVNU (B75-51403)
Three for Barton : for solo brass tuba. *Associated Music. £1.05* WVPMJ (B75-51473)
Bläser-Fibel II. Schule bläserische Gestaltung : eine Bläserschule, für Fortgeschrittene auch zum Selbst und Gruppenuntervicht. (Ehmann, Wilhelm). *Bärenreiter. £3.60* W/AC (B75-50354)
Blessed be that maid Mary : Christmas carol, SATB and organ. (Mario of the Cross, *Sister*). *Oxford University Press. Unpriced* FDP/LF (B75-51052)
Bliss, *Sir* Arthur.
Shield of faith : cantata for soprano and baritone soli, SATB and organ. *Novello. £1.00* DE (B75-50407)
Sing mortals! : a sonnet for the festival of St Cecilia, for SATB and organ. *Novello. Unpriced* DH (B75-50021)
Block, Leon. Musical plays. *Selections : arr.* Rodgers and Hammerstein guitar book. (Rodgers, Richard). *Williamson Music. Unpriced* TSPMK/DW (B75-50819)
Block, Robert Paul.
Atalanta. Overture. Overture for trumpet, oboes, strings and basso continuo. (Handel, George Frideric). *Musica rara. Unpriced* MRJ (B75-51171)
Atalanta. Overture. *arr.* Overture for trumpet. oboes, strings and basso continuo. (Handel, George Frideric). *Musica rara. Unpriced* WSPK (B75-51460)
Concerto for flute, strings & basso continuo, in B flat major. Wq.167. Concerto in B flat major. Wq.167 : for flute, strings and basso continuo. (Bach, Carl Philipp Emanuel). *Musica rara. Unpriced* RXMPVRF (B75-51285)
Concerto for flute, strings & basso continuo in B flat major. Wq.167. *arr.* Concerto in B flat major. Wq.167 : for flute, strings and basso continuo. (Bach, Carl Philipp Emanuel). *Musica rara. Unpriced* VRPK/LF (B75-51374)
Concerto for oboe, bassoon & string orchestra in G major. P.129. Concerto in G major for oboe, bassoon, strings and basso continuo. P.129. (Vivaldi, Antonio). *Musica rara. £5.50* RXMPVTPLVWF (B75-51288)
Concerto for oboe, bassoon & string orchestra in G major. P.129. *arr.* Concerto in G major for oboe, bassoon, strings and basso continuo. P.129. (Vivaldi, Antonio). *Musica rara. Unpriced* NWPNTK/LF (B75-51193)
Quintet for flute, clarinet, viola, cello and piano in A major. (Kreutzer, Konradin). *Musica rara. Unpriced* NURNR (B75-51175)
Sinfonia avanti l'opera. G.14. *arr.* Sinfonia avanti l'opera, G.14 : for trumpet, strings and continuo. (Torelli, Giuseppe). *Musica rara. £1.50* WSPK/LE (B75-51462)
Sinfonia in D major. G.3. *arr.* Sinfonia in D. G.3 : for trumpet, strings and continuo. (Torelli, Giuseppe). *Musica rara. £1.50* WSPK/LE (B75-51463)
Sinfonia in D major. G.4. *arr.* Sinfonia in D. G.4 : for trumpet, strings and continuo. (Torelli, Giuseppe). *Musica rara. £1.50* WSPK/LE (B75-51464)
Sinfonia in D major. G.5. *arr.* Sinfonia in D. G.5 : for trumpet, strings and continuo. (Torelli, Giuseppe). *Musica rara. £1.50* WSPK/LE (B75-51465)
Sinfonia no.10 for two trumpets & strings in D major. *arr.* Sinfonia decima à 7 for 2 trumpets and strings. (Bononcini, Giovanni Battista). *Musica rara. Unpriced* NUXSNSK/LE (B75-51178)
Sonata à 3 for two violins, trombone & basso continuo, no.3, in A minor. Sonata à 3, no.3, in A minor for 2 violins, trombone and basso continuo. (Bertali, Antonio). *Musica rara. £4.50* NUXUNSE (B75-51179)
Sonata à 7 for six trumpets, timpani & organ. Sonata à 7 (1688) for 6 trumpets, timpani and organ. (Biber, Heinrich Ignaz Franz). *Musica rara. Unpriced* NYFXSNNE (B75-51198)
Sonata for flute, oboe & basso continuo in C minor. Trio sonata in C minor for flute, oboe and basso continuo. (Quantz, Johann Joachim). *Musica rara. Unpriced* NWPNTE (B75-51192)
Sonata for trumpet, two violins, viola & basso continuo in D major. G.6. *arr.* Sonata in D.G.6 : for trumpet, strings and continuo. (Torelli, Giuseppe). *Musica rara. £1.50* WSPK/LE (B75-51466)
Sonatas for two recorders & basso continuo. Op.3. Trio sonatas. Opus 3 : for 2 treble (alto) recorders and basso continuo
Nos.1-3. (Hotteterre, Jacques). *Musica rara. Unpriced* VSSNTPWE (B75-51383)
Sonatas for two recorders & basso continuo. Op.3. Trio sonatas. Opus 3 : for 2 treble (alto) recorders and basso continuo
Nos.4-6. (Hotteterre, Jacques). *Musica rara. Unpriced* VSSNTPWE (B75-51384)
Symphonie concertante for two flutes, op.76, in G major. *arr.* Symphonie concertante in G. Op.76 : for 2 flutes and orchestra. (Devienne, François). *Musica rara. £3.00* VRNTQK/LE (B75-51368)
Blom, Eric. Mozart. Revised ed. *Dent. £3.15* BMS (B75-04504) ISBN 0-460-03157-0
Blom, Michael. Hip-hip Horatio : an 'oratorio' for narrator (tenor), chorus (high and low voices) and piano. (Hurd, Michael). *Novello. £0.90* FDX (B75-50498)
Blossom's a possum : for mixed chorus, SATB. (Cassey, Charles R). *Chappell. Unpriced* DW (B75-50437)
Blot, André. Cornouailles march : piano. *Chappell. Unpriced* QPGM (B75-50672)
Blow the wind southerly. (Siebert, Edrich). *Studio Music. Unpriced* WMK/DW (B75-51430)
Blue lake : overture for concert band. (Chance, John Barnes). *Boosey and Hawkes. Unpriced* UMJ (B75-50295)
Blues and syncopation in 3/4 and 4/4 for the drumset. (Dawson, Alan). *Simrock. £1.75* XQPMJ (B75-51482)
Blues records, January, 1943 to December, 1966. (Leadbitter, Mike). *Music Sales Ltd, 78 Newman St., W.1 : Oakwood Publications. Unpriced* AKDW/HHW/FD(WT/XPC18) (B75-50977) ISBN 0-86001-089-9
Blüh nur mein Sommerkorn : songs aus der klingenden Saat. *Bärenreiter. £3.20* FEZDW/G/AY (B75-50078)
Blume, Friedrich. Renaissance and Baroque music : a comprehensive survey. *Faber. £1.25* A(XCQ351) (B75-08734) ISBN 0-571-10719-2
Blyton, Carey. Konrad of the mountains : a pageant for voice and instruments. *Belwin-Mills. Unpriced* JFE/NYEDX (B75-50538)
Bo-peep : based on the traditional air and a fugue by Pachelbel. (Gardner, Ward). *Banks. Unpriced* EZDW (B75-51046)
Boatwright, Howard.
The false knight upon the road : folk song setting for baritone voice and piano. *Oxford University Press. Unpriced* KGNDW (B75-50591)
Sinner man : folk hymn setting, for medium voice and piano with audience participation. *Boosey and Hawkes. Unpriced* KFVDW (B75-50583)
Bobri, Vladimir. A musical voyage with two guitars : 64 duets from 34 countries. *Collier Macmillan. £3.50* TSNUK/AAY (B75-51321) ISBN 0-02-060150-6
Boccherini, Luigi. Trios for two violins & cello, nos, 1-6. Op.2. Sei trii per due violini e violoncello. Op.1a. *Zanibon : Hinrichsen. Unpriced* RXNT (B75-50239)
Bochmann, Christopher.
De profundis : meditation for violin, violoncello and piano. *Oxford University Press. £2.50* NXNT (B75-50648) ISBN 0-19-355560-3
Sonata for piano. Sonata : piano. *Oxford University Press. £2.00* QPE (B75-50666) ISBN 0-19-372287-9
Boismortier, Joseph Bodin de. Sonata for bassoon & basso continuo, op.26, no.2, in A minor. Sonata no.2 in A minor : for bassoon and basso continuo. *Musica rara. £2.00* VWPE (B75-51413)
Boisvalée, François de. Largo religioso : pour orchestra à cordes et clavecin avec orgue ad lib. *Chappell. Unpriced* RXMJ (B75-50748)
Boisvallée, Francois de.
Concerto for 2 horns & string orchestra, no.4. 4eme concert pour 2 cors, orchestre à cordes et continuo. *Chappell. Unpriced* RXMPWTNUF (B75-50234)
Les Fêtes de Terpsichore. *Selections: arr.* Air en forme de pavane. *Chappell. Unpriced* TMK/AHVG (B75-50273)
Bolero de los picaros. (Surinach, Carlos). *Associated Music. Unpriced* TSPMK/AHJK (B75-50816)
Bolton, Cecil.
An introduction to the 12 button reed and electronic chord organ. *Robbins Music : EMI. Unpriced* RPVC/AC (B75-51280)
Sunday songs for chord organs. *EMI Music. Unpriced* RPVCK/DM/AY (B75-50741)
Bonneau, Paul.
Concerto for 2 horns & string orchestra, no.4. 4eme

concert pour 2 cors, orchestre à cordes et continuo. (Boisvallée, Francois de). *Chappell. Unpriced* RXMPWTNUF (B75-50234)
Les Fêtes de Terpsichore. *Selections: arr.* Air en forme de pavane. (Boisvallée, François de). *Chappell. Unpriced* TMK/AHVG (B75-50273)
Largo religioso : pour orchestra à cordes et clavecin avec orgue ad lib. (Boisvalée, François de). *Chappell. Unpriced* RXMJ (B75-50748)
Manège. *Chappell. Unpriced* TMK (B75-50788)
Miniature. *arr.* Miniature. (Betti, Henri). *Chappell. Unpriced* TMK (B75-50787)
Viva Napoli. *Vocal score.* Viva Napoli : operette à grand spectacle en 2 actes et 12 tableaux. (Lopez, Francis). *Chappell. Unpriced* CF (B75-50990)
Bononcini, Giovanni Battista.
Sinfonia no.10 for two trumpets & strings in D major. Sinfonia decima à 7 for 2 trumpets and strings. *Musica rara. Unpriced* RXMPWSNUE (B75-51290)
Sinfonia no.10 for two trumpets & strings in D major. *arr.* Sinfonia decima à 7 for 2 trumpets and strings. *Musica rara. Unpriced* NUXSNSK/LE (B75-51178)
Bonsor, Brian. Hurry, little pony : Spanish traditional song. *Oxford University Press. Unpriced* JFE/NYFSDW (B75-51097) ISBN 0-19-344836-x
Book of Christmas music. *Schott. Unpriced* CB/LF/AY (B75-50987) ISBN 0-901938-56-4
Book of golden discs. (Murrells, Joseph). *Barrie and Jenkins. £9.95* A/GB/FD(X) (B75-14337) ISBN 0-214-20032-9
Book of open tunings : for guitar. (Clelland, Tom). *Robbins Music. Unpriced* TS/P (B75-51317)
Boreham histories. Smith, William Joseph Thomas. The organ & organists. *Boreham Vicarage, Chelmsford, Essex CM3 3EG : The author. £0.25* AR/B(YDDB) (B75-21667) ISBN 0-9504312-0-6
Borgese, Elisabeth Mann. Harmony. (Schenker, Heinrich). *M.I.T. Press. £2.00* A/R (B75-02996) ISBN 0-262-69044-6
Boris Godunov : opera in four acts with a prologue. (Mussorgsky, Modest). *Oxford University Press. Unpriced* CQC (B75-50993) ISBN 0-19-337699-7
Born in Bethlehem : a carol for treble voices with optional S.A. or S.A.T.B. chorus. (Walters, Edmund). *Boosey and Hawkes. £0.10* FDP/LF (B75-51055)
Borodin, Aleksandr Porfirevich. Quartet for strings, no.2, in D major. Quartet no.2, D major, for 2 violins, viola and violoncello. *Eulenburg. Unpriced* RXNS (B75-51291)
Borris, Siegfried.
Musik für Waldhorn. Op.109 : übungs-und Spielbuche für 1 Horn
Heft 1/1. *Heinrichshofen : Hinrichsen. Unpriced* WT/AF (B75-50951)
Musik für Waldhorn. Op.109 : Übungs-und Spielbuche für 1 Horn
Heft 1/2. *Heinrichshofen : Hinrichsen. Unpriced* WT/AF (B75-50952)
Boston bounce : brass band. (Siebert, Edrich). *Studio Music. Unpriced* WMJ (B75-50367)
Botrel, Theodore. Trois chansons tristes, from the late 19th century collection of old French songs by Theodore Botrel. *Oxford University Press. £0.90* KE/TSDW/G/AYH (B75-50566) ISBN 0-19-345828-4
Bottesini, Giovanni.
Works, double bass & piano. Yorke complete Bottesini : for double bass and piano
Vol.1. *Yorke. Unpriced* SSP/AZ (B75-50268)
Volume 2. *Yorke. Unpriced* SSP/AZ (B75-51308)
Boulez, Pierre. Boulez on music today. *Faber. £0.80* A (B75-06414) ISBN 0-571-10587-4
Boulez on music today. (Boulez, Pierre). *Faber. £0.80* A (B75-06414) ISBN 0-571-10587-4
Boutry, Roger. Interferences I : pour basson et piano. *Chappell. Unpriced* VWPJ (B75-50905)
Bow down thine ear : short anthem for baritone or bass solo, SATB and organ, suitable for Lent or general use. (McClelland-Young, Thomas). *Novello. £0.15* DK (B75-50425)
Bowers, Roger. The organs and organists of Wells Cathedral. *22 Vicars' Close, Wells, Somerset BA5 2UJ : The Friends of Wells Cathedral. £0.20* AR/B(YDFGWB) (B75-00741) ISBN 0-902321-12-9
Boyd, Anne. Quartet for strings, no.2. String quartet no.2. *Central Music Library : Faber. Unpriced* RXNS (B75-50758)
Boys in a pie : two-part song with piano. (Kelly, Bryan). *Roberton. £0.12* FDW (B75-50490)
Brade, William.
Newe ausserlesene liebliche Branden, Intraden. Newe auserlesene Branden, Intraden, Mascheraden, Baletten, Allmanden, Couranten, Volten, Auffzuge und frembde Tantze (1617)
Volume 1 : for 2 cornetti (trumpets in C) and 3 trombones. *Musica rara. £4.00* WNRH/AY (B75-51441)

Newe ausserlesene liebliche Branden, Intraden. Newe auserlesene Branden, Intraden, Mascheraden, Baletten, Allmanden, Couranten, Volten, Auffzuge und frembde Tantze (1617)
Volume 2 : for 2 cornetti (trumpets in C) and 3 trombones. *Musica rara. £4.00* WNRH/AY (B75-51442)

Newe ausserlesene liebliche Branden, Intraden. Newe auserlesene Branden, Intraden, Mascheraden, Baletten, Allmanden, Couranten, Volten Auffzuge und frembde Tantze (1617)
Volume 3 : for 3 cornetti and 2 trombones. *Musica rara. £4.00* WNRH/AY (B75-51443)
Bradshaw, Susan. Boulez on music today. (Boulez, Pierre). *Faber. £0.80* A (B75-06414) ISBN 0-571-10587-4
Brady, Nicholas. Ode on St Cecilia's day, 1692. Z.328. *Vocal score.* Ode on St Cecilia's day, 1692 : Hail! bright Cecilia : for soprano, two altos, tenor and two basses soli, SSAATB and instruments. (Purcell, Henry). *Novello. £1.20* DX (B75-51025)
Brahms, Caryl. Gilbert and Sullivan : lost chords and discords. *Weidenfeld and Nicolson. £5.25* BSW(N) (B75-26088) ISBN 0-297-76936-7
Brahms, Johannes. Volkskinderlieder. *Selections: arr.* Seven pieces. *Oxford University Press. £1.00* RXMK (B75-50750) ISBN 0-19-361906-7
Brahms. (Latham, Peter, *b.1894*). Revised ed.. *Dent. £2.95* BBT (B75-27352) ISBN 0-460-03158-9
Bran-Ricci, Josiane. Eighteenth century musical instruments, France and Britain = Les Instruments de musique au XVIIIe Siecle, France et Grande-Bretagne : catalogue of an exhibition. (Thibault, G). *Victoria and Albert Museum. £2.50* AL/B(YH/XF101) (B75-03646) ISBN 0-901486-71-x
Brand, Jim. Advent to Easter : short musical plays for junior and middle schools. (O'Gorman, Denis). *Grail Publications. £1.00* BOFGACN/L (B75-18364) ISBN 0-901829-25-0
Brand, Michael.
Preludes. Bk 1. La Fille aux cheveux de lin. *arr.* The girl with the flaxen hair. (Debussy, Claude). *R. Smith. Unpriced* WMK (B75-51421)
Rag 'n' bone : trombone solo and brass band. *R. Smith. Unpriced* WMPWU (B75-51434)
Brandebury, Charles. Dansa brasileira : for concert band. (Camargo Guarnieri, Mozart). *Associated Music. Unpriced* UMH (B75-50821)
Branel, Henning. Le Gay Paris. *arr.* Le Gay Paris : pour trompette et instruments à vent. (Françaix, Jean). *Schott. £2.25* WSPK (B75-51459)
Branson, David.
Marche triomphale : for piano. (Field, John). *Helicon. Unpriced* QPGM (B75-50673)
The princess, sedate and merry : for string orchestra. *Helicon. Unpriced* RXMJ (B75-50749)
Six preludes for piano (in differing time signatures). *David Branson. Unpriced* QPJ (B75-51233)
Bravado and travellers all : nine folk songs for voices and guitar. *Oxford University Press. £0.35* JE/TSDW/G/AY (B75-50096) ISBN 0-19-330630-1
Bream, Julian. Elegy for guitar. (Rawsthorne, Alan). *Oxford University Press. Unpriced* TSPMJ (B75-51325) ISBN 0-19-358510-3
Brecht, Bertolt. Von der Freundlichkeit der Welt = The world's welcome (1930/1973) : choral settings on texts by Bert Brecht for mixed chorus, three pianos and percussion instruments. (Orff, Carl). *Schott. Unpriced* ENYLDW (B75-51027)
Breckoff, Werner. Liedermagazin : für die Sekundarstufen. *Cassel : Bärenreiter. Unpriced* JDW/AY (B75-50528)
Breig, Werner. Choral bearbeitungen : für Orgel. (Praetorius, Jacob). *Bärenreiter. £3.60* RJ (B75-50212)
Brennan, John Frederick. The classical organ in Britain, 1955-1974. (Rowntree, John Pickering). *130 Southfield Rd, Oxford OX4 1PA : Positif Press. £2.95* AR/B(YC/XPQ20) (B75-13170) ISBN 0-9503892-1-8
Brett, Bernard. What instrument shall I play? (Ingman, Nicholas). *Ward Lock. £2.95* AL/B (B75-29314) ISBN 0-7063-1988-5
Brett, Philip.
Dum transisset Sabbatum : S.A.T. Bar. B. unacc. (Taverner, John). *Oxford University Press. Unpriced* EZDGKH/LL (B75-51031) ISBN 0-19-350350-6
Musica Britannica : a national collection of music
Vol.22: Consort songs. 2nd revised ed. *Stainer and Bell. Unpriced* C/AYD (B75-50006)
Brewis, Bert. Christmas songs for guitar. *Chappell. Unpriced* TSPMK/DP/LF/AY (B75-51328)
Bric-a-Bach (constructed from five different compositions by J.S. Bach) : for full chorus of mixed voices with optional guitar, bass and drums accompaniment. (Jergenson, Dale). *Schirmer. Unpriced* EZDX (B75-50484)
Bridge, Frank. Four songs. *Galliard : Stainer and Bell. Unpriced* KDW (B75-50105) ISBN 0-85249-319-3
Brief history of the organs of Wells Cathedral. *See* Colchester, Linzee Sparrow.
Brieg, Werner. Jesu dulcissime : motet for six voices. (Schütz, Heinrich). First edition. *Bärenreiter. £1.40* EZDJ (B75-50054)
Bright, Clive. Play the trombone, treble clef. *Chappell. Unpriced* WU/AC (B75-51470)
Bright eyes. *arr.* Bright eyes. (Finlayson, Walter Alan). *Boosey and Hawkes. £2.20* WMPWRNTK (B75-51433)
Brightmore, C Victor.
Cantering on : for horn in F with piano accompaniment. *British and Continental Music. Unpriced* WTPJ (B75-50955)
Noël : for horn and piano. *British and Continental. Unpriced* WTP/LF (B75-50953)
Tambourin : for horn and piano. *British and Continental. Unpriced* WTPHVQT (B75-50954)
Brighton piece. Op.9 : for percussion and instrumental ensemble. (Gilbert, Anthony). *Schott. Unpriced* NYE (B75-50654)
Brindle, Reginald Smith. The new music : the avant-garde since 1945. *Oxford University Press. £3.95* A(XPE30) (B75-27956) ISBN 0-19-315424-2
Brion, Keith.
March, Omega Lambda Chi. *arr.* March, Omega Lambda Chi : for band. (Ives, Charles). *Associated Music. Unpriced* UMMK/AGM (B75-50835)
Variations on 'Jerusalem the golden'. *arr.* Variations on 'Jerusalem the golden'. (Ives, Charles). *Associated Music. £1.30* UMK (B75-51341)
Bristol University. *See* University of Bristol.
British Broadcasting Corporation. Music guides.
Cox, David, *b.1916.* Debussy orchestral music. *British Broadcasting Corporation. £0.55* BDJAM (B75-50004) ISBN 0-563-12678-7
Lam, Basil. Beethoven string quartets
1. *British Broadcasting Corporation. £0.70* BBJARXNS (B75-30569) ISBN 0-563-10166-0
Lam, Basil. Beethoven string quartets
2. *British Broadcasting Corporation. £0.70* BBJARXNS (B75-30570) ISBN 0-563-12675-2
McCabe, John. Bartók orchestral music. *British Broadcasting Corporation. £0.55* BBGAM (B75-02998) ISBN 0-563-12674-4
Warrack, John. Tchaikovsky symphonies and concertos. 2nd ed. *British Broadcasting Corporation. £0.45* BTDAMME (B75-00740) ISBN 0-563-12773-2
British music yearbook. *For earlier issues of this yearbook see* The music yearbook.
British music yearbook : a survey and directory with statistics and reference articles
1975. *Bowker. £7.50* A(YC/BC) (B75-16403) ISBN 0-85935-024-x
Britten, Benjamin.
Death in Venice. *Vocal score.* Death in Venice. Op.88 : an opera in two acts. *Faber Music. Unpriced* CC (B75-50988)
A hymn of St Columba (Regis regum rectissimi) : SATB and organ. *Boosey and Hawkes. £0.20* DH (B75-50418)
Quartet for strings in D major (1931). String quartet in D major (1931). *Faber Music. Unpriced* RXNS (B75-50759)
Brofsky, Howard. The art of listening : developing musical perception. (Bamberger, Jeanne Shapiro). 3rd ed. *Harper and Row. £3.85* A/C (B75-21064) ISBN 0-06-040948-7
Brooks, Nigel. Sing a new song : twenty-three hymns and songs from Southern Television Hymn Contest, 1975. *Weinberger. £0.85* JDM/JS/AY (B75-50525)
Broven, John. Walking to New Orleans : the story of New Orleans rhythm & blues. *38a Sackville Rd, Bexhill-on-Sea, Sussex : Blues Unlimited. £3.75* AKDW/HHR(YTRN/XPF28) (B75-00201) ISBN 0-9500229-3-4
Brown, Christine. Play at sight : a graded sight reading course
Part 6. *EMI. Unpriced* Q/EG (B75-51211)
Brown, Earle. Twentyfive pages : for 1 to 25 pianos. *Universal. Unpriced* QN (B75-51213)
Brown, Frank Edwin. Baroque music for organ. *Cramer. Unpriced* RK/AAY (B75-51277)
Brown, Howard Mayer.
Libro primo de canzoni da sonare. Canzona 'La Girella'. Canzona 'La Girella' : for four instruments. (Maschera, Florentio). *Oxford University Press. £0.55* LNS (B75-51146) ISBN 0-19-341206-3
Musica duorum, Rome, 1521. (Romano, Eustachio). *Chicago University Press. Unpriced* C/AZ (B75-50983) ISBN 0-226-22646-8
Brown, Robert, *b.1943.* Experimenting with electronic music. *Foulsham-Tab. £1.50* APV/B (B75-05798) ISBN 0-7042-0129-1
Brown, Steve. Fashion : a musical comedy. (Mowatt, Anna Cora). *French. £1.10* BPIACM (B75-20393) ISBN 0-573-68065-5
Browning, Robert. Love in a life. (Rorem, Ned). *Boosey and Hawkes. Unpriced* KDW (B75-51110)
Bruckner. (Watson, Derek). *Dent. £2.95* BBUE (B75-21066) ISBN 0-460-03144-9
Bruckner Dialog : für Orchester. Op 39. (Einem, Gottfried von). *Boosey and Hawkes. £3.00* MMJ (B75-50143)
'Bruder Martin'. (Mahler, Gustav). *Bosworth. Unpriced* MJ (B75-50595)
Brun, John Anatole. *See* Brune, John A.
Brune, John A. Resonant rubbish. *2 Regent's Park Rd, NW1 7AY : English Folk Dance and Song Society. Unpriced* AL/BC (B75-08293) ISBN 0-85418-097-4
Brunelli, Louis Jean. L'Estro armonico. Op.3, no.11. Largo, Allegro. *arr.* Sicilienne and finale. (Vivaldi, Antonio). *Chappell. Unpriced* UMMK (B75-51349)
Brunner, Adolf. Quartet for strings. Streichquartett. *Bärenreiter. £6.00* RXNS (B75-50236)
Bryant, Ivor. I was glad when they said unto me : a paraphrase of Psalm 122, for two equal voices. (Coombes, Douglas). *28 Knolls Way, Clifton, Beds. : Lindsay Music. £0.12* FDR (B75-50487)
Bryce, Frank.
The entertainer. *arr.* The entertainer ; with, Maple leaf rag. (Joplin, Scott). *Paxton. Unpriced* WMK/AHXJ (B75-50373)
Sullivan at sea. *arr.* Sullivan at sea : a trip for trombones. (Stent, Keith). *Paxton. £1.75* WMK (B75-50370)
Brydson, John Collis. And wilt thou leave me thus? : SATB. *Cramer. £0.12* EZDW (B75-50475)
Buber, Martin. Davids Danklied : für Bariton, vierstimmigen gemischten Chor, Bläser und Orgel. (Gardonyi, Zoltan). *Bärenreiter. £3.20* EWSNSRDH (B75-50044)
Buck, *Sir* Percy Carter. Psychology for musicians. *Oxford University Press. £1.25* A/CS (B75-18003) ISBN 0-19-311914-5
Bune, Robert. Tell me what month : an American Christmas folk song. *Warner : Blossom. Unpriced* ENVSNRDW/LF (B75-50451)
Bunker hill. *arr.* Bunker hill : march. (Forsblad, Leland). *Warner : Blossom. Unpriced* UMMK/AGM (B75-50307)
Bunker hill : march. (Forsblad, Leland). *Warner : Blossom. Unpriced* UMMK/AGM (B75-50307)

Burgon, Geoffrey. Cantus alleluia : orchestra. *Chester. Unpriced* MMJ (B75-50611)
Burnett, Michael. Songs for Naomi : unison voices, glockenspiel and/or chime bars, xylophone, descant recorder, triangle, tambourine, wood blocks, piano (one stave). *Ricordi. Unpriced* JFE/NYFSRDW (B75-50099)
Burns, Robert. Oh! I am come to the Low Countrie : traditional melody. (Nelson, Havelock). *Elkin. £0.15* EZDW (B75-50481)
Burt, James.
The best of Gilbert and Sullivan : all organ. (Sullivan, *Sir* Arthur Seymour). *Chappell. Unpriced* RK/DW (B75-50739)
Mozart's greatest hits. (Mozart, Wolfgang Amadeus). *Chappell. Unpriced* RK (B75-50735)
Swing low, sweet chariot. *Chappell. Unpriced* KDW/LC (B75-50562)
Burt, Robert. The Beatles : the fabulous story of John, Paul, George and Ringo. *Octopus Books. £1.99* AKDW/GB/E(P) (B75-21666) ISBN 0-7064-0446-7
Burtch, Mervyn. The lantern festival : S.S.A. unacc. *Banks. Unpriced* FEZDW (B75-51064)
Bush, Geoffrey. Invitation to the partsong
No.2: Part songs for SATB : a selection of four-part works. *Stainer and Bell. Unpriced* EZDW/AY (B75-50067) ISBN 0-85249-288-x
Buthe, Otfried. Wolkenloses Christfest : Requiem für Bariton, Violoncello und Orchester. (Reimann, Aribert). *Schott. £11.00* KGNE/MPSRDE (B75-51135)
Butt, James. A whimsey for brass. *British and Continental Music. Unpriced* WMG (B75-50915)
Butterworth, Arthur. Caliban. Op.50 : scherzo malevolo, for brass band. *R. Smith. Unpriced* WMJ (B75-50919)
Butterworth, George.
Eleven songs from 'A Shropshire Lad'. *Galliard. Unpriced* KDW (B75-50552) ISBN 0-85249-333-9
Folk songs from Sussex and other songs. *Galliard. Unpriced* KDW (B75-50551) ISBN 0-85249-332-0
Butterworth, Neil.
Divertimento for two clarinets & two horns in C major. Hob II/14. *arr.* Divertimento in C. (Haydn, Joseph). *Banks. Unpriced* VVNSK (B75-50893)
Ewell Court suite : for piano solo. *Banks. Unpriced* QPG (B75-50669)
A music quiz. *139 Holgate Rd, York : Banks Music Publications. £0.45* A(DE) (B75-27348) ISBN 0-9503337-0-0
Buxtehude, Dietrich.
Jubilate Domino : Solokantate für Alt, Viola da gamba (Violoncello) und Basso continuo. *Bärenreiter. £1.80* KFQE/SRPDE (B75-50122)
Mein Herz ist bereit. (57. Psalm Davids) : Solokantate für Bass, drei Violinen, Violoncello und Basso continuo. *Bärenreiter. £2.40* KGXE/NXNRDR (B75-50125)
By winding roads : fifteen unison songs of the Irish countryside. (Parke, Dorothy). *Roberton. £1.00* JFDW (B75-51094)
Bygraves, Max.
Swingalongamax. *arr.* Swingalongamax. (Back in my childhood days). *Boosey and Hawkes. £1.00* UMMK/DW (B75-51350)
Swingalongamax. *arr.* Swingalongamax. (Back in my childhood days). *Boosey and Hawkes. £0.85* WMK/DW (B75-51428)
Byrd ; &, Victoria. (Sharp, Geoffrey Brinsley). *Novello. £0.20* BBX(N) (B75-03643) ISBN 0-85360-060-0
Cable, Howard.
'Hans Christian Andersen'. Anywhere I wander. *arr.* Anywhere I wander : for mixed chorus (SATB) and piano with optional rhythm guitar, bass guitar and drums. (Loesser, Frank). *Frank Music. Unpriced* DW (B75-51019)
'Hans Christian Andersen'. The inch worm. *arr.* The inch worm : for mixed chorus (SATB) and piano with optional rhythm guitar, bass guitar and drums. (Loesser, Frank). *Frank Music. Unpriced* DW (B75-51020)
'Hans Christian Andersen'. The ugly duckling. *arr.* The ugly duckling : for two-part chorus of treble voices with piano. (Loesser, Frank). *Frank Music. Unpriced* FLDW (B75-51068)
'Hans Christian Andersen'. Wonderful Copenhagen. *arr.* Wonderful Copenhagen : for two-part chorus of treble voices with piano. (Loesser, Frank). *Frank Music. Unpriced* FLDW (B75-51069)
Cacavas, John.
Concertette for Christmas : for concert band. *Chappell. Unpriced* UM/LF (B75-50293)
Heavy band blues : for concert band. *Chappell. Unpriced* UM/HHW (B75-50820)
Overture, The court of Henry VIII : for concert band. *Chappell. Unpriced* UMJ (B75-50822)
Calculation of organ pipe scales from the middle ages to the mid-nineteenth century. (Mahrenholz, Christhard). *130 Southfield Rd, Oxford OX4 1PA : Positif Press. £2.50* AR/BPPG (B75-31193) ISBN 0-9503892-2-6
Caliban. Op.50 : scherzo malevolo, for brass band. (Butterworth, Arthur). *R. Smith. Unpriced* WMJ (B75-50919)
Calisto. *Vocal score.* La Calisto : opera in two acts with a prologue. (Cavalli, Francesco). *Faber Music. Unpriced* CC (B75-50989)
Calzadilla, Roman. Aires de Mochima : valzer venezuelano, per chitarra. *Zanibon : Hinrichsen. Unpriced* TSPMHW (B75-50277)
Camargo Guarnieri, Mozart. Dansa brasileira : for concert band. *Associated Music. Unpriced* UMH (B75-50821)
Cambini, Giovanni Giuseppe. Quintets for wind & strings. Op.8, 9. Sei quintetti. Op.8 & op.9 : per flauto, oboe, violino, viola e basso. *Hinrichsen. Unpriced* NVPNR (B75-50163)
Cambridge University. *See* University of Cambridge.
Camilleri, Charles.
African dreams : piano. *Roberton. £1.50* QPJ (B75-51234)
Four ragamats, 1967-1970 : piano. *Roberton. £2.00* QPJ (B75-51235)
Missa brevis : for full chorus of mixed voices, unaccompanied. *Roberton. £0.30* EZDG (B75-51030)
Pieces for Anya : for piano solo. *Roberton. £0.50* QPJ (B75-51236)
Taqsim : for two pianos. *Fairfield. £1.50* QNU (B75-50659)
Trio for violin, cello & piano. Piano trio. *Fairfield Music. £3.50* NXNT (B75-50171)
Camp, John. Discovering bells and bellringing. 2nd ed. *Shire Publications. £0.35* AXSR (B75-08739) ISBN 0-85263-290-8
Camp, Leonard van. *See*
Van Camp. *Leonard.*
Van Camp, Leonard.
Campion, Thomas.
Heart's music : TTBB (unacc.). (Noble, Harold). *Banks. Unpriced* GEZDW (B75-50515)
There is a garden in her face : TTB, unaccompanied. (Binkerd, Gordon). *Boosey and Hawkes. Unpriced* GEZDW (B75-50513)
Camptown races : traditional. (Harvey, Roger). *R. Smith. Unpriced* WMK/DW (B75-51429)
Camrose Lord's Prayer : SATB with optional accompaniment. (Rose, Gregory). *Boosey and Hawkes. £0.10* EZDTF (B75-50472)
Canadian landscape : tone poem concert band. (Gayfer, James McDonald). *Boosey and Hawkes. Full band set £4.50, Symphonic band set £6.00, Score £1.50* UMMJ (B75-50831)
Canberg, Mary. Souvenir d'Amérique, 'Yankee doodle'. *arr.* Souvenir d'Amérique, 'Yankee doodle' : variations burlesques. (Vieuxtemps, Henri). *Galaxy : Galliard. Unpriced* SPK/LT (B75-51298)
Cancionero para una mariposa : for flute, 2 bassoons, 2 trumpets in C, 2 trombones, 2 cellos. (Dalby, Martin). *Novello. Unpriced* NVNM (B75-50639)
Candide. *Selections: arr.* Candide : vocal selections. (Bernstein, Leonard). *Schirmer. Unpriced* KDW (B75-50550)
Candide : vocal selections. (Bernstein, Leonard). *Schirmer. Unpriced* KDW (B75-50550)
Candlin, Clara M. The lantern festival : S.S.A. unacc. (Burtch, Mervyn). *Banks. Unpriced* FEZDW (B75-51064)
Caneuon Lili Lon. (Huw Jones, Sheila). *Christopher Davies. £0.90* JFEZDW/JS (B75-51099) ISBN 0-7154-0167-x
Canle, Derek. A whimsey for brass. (Butt, James). *British and Continental Music. Unpriced* WMG (B75-50915)
Cantata on German folksong texts. Op. 20. *Choral score.* Cantata on German folksong texts. Op. 20 : for mezzo-soprano solo, chorus and chamber orchestra. (Spinner, Leopold). *Boosey and Hawkes. £1.50* DADX (B75-50014)
Cantata on German folksong texts. Op. 20 : for mezzo-soprano solo, chorus and chamber orchestra. (Spinner, Leopold). *Boosey and Hawkes. £1.50* DADX (B75-50014)
Cantering on : for horn in F with piano accompaniment. (Brightmore, C Victor). *British and Continental Music. Unpriced* WTPJ (B75-50955)
Cantica sacra, 1618. (Dering, Richard). *Stainer & Bell. Unpriced* DJ (B75-50025)
Canticle of the Lamb : SATB unaccompanied. (Rorem, Ned). *Boosey and Hawkes. Unpriced* EZDH (B75-51036)
Cantiones sacrae. Alma redemptoris. Alma redemptoris : antiphon of the Blessed Virgin, for five voices, S.S.A.T.B. (Philips, Peter). *Chester. Unpriced* EZDGKJ (B75-51033)
Canto I : four concert études, for unaccompanied trumpet. (Adler, Samuel). *Oxford University Press. Unpriced* WSPMJ (B75-50950)
Canto II : four concert études, for unaccompanied trombone. (Adler, Samuel). *Oxford University Press. Unpriced* WUPMJ (B75-50961)
Cantus alleluia : orchestra. (Burgon, Geoffrey). *Chester. Unpriced* MMJ (B75-50611)
Canzona 'La Girella' : for four instruments. (Maschera, Florentio). *Oxford University Press. £0.55* LNS (B75-51146) ISBN 0-19-341206-3
Canzonette. Hor va canzona mia. Hor va canzona mia = How freely flies my song : SATB a cappella. (Hassler, Hans Leo). *Warner : Blossom. Unpriced* EZDU (B75-51045)
Capriccio. (Valbonesi, Ruggero). *British and Continental, EMI Music. Unpriced* VVPK (B75-50903)
Capriccio. *arr.* Capriccio. (Valbonesi, Ruggero). *British and Continental, EMI Music. Unpriced* VVPK (B75-50903)
Capriccio napoletano : per chitarra. (Pizzini, Carlo Alberto). *Zanibon : Hinrichsen. Unpriced* TSPMJ (B75-50282)
Capriccio : organ. (Forbes, Sebastian). *Oxford University Press. £1.30* RJ (B75-50731) ISBN 0-19-375382-0
Capricornus, Samuel. Mein Gott und Herr : concerto for two sopranos and bass, (chorus or soloists), two violins and basso continuo. *Bärenreiter. £2.40* ESNTPWDH (B75-50039)
Caractères : pièces de concert, pour violon et piano. (Gotkovsky, Ida). *Chappell. Unpriced* SPJ (B75-50767)
Carambina : Spanish dance, for brass band. (Hughes, Eric). *Studio Music. Unpriced* WMH (B75-50917)
Cardew, Cornelius. Stockhausen serves imperialism, and other articles : with commentary and notes. *Latimer New Dimensions. £3.00* A(ZC/D) (B75-04503) ISBN 0-901539-29-5
Careers with music ... (Fortescue, Margaret). *Careers Centre, University of East Anglia, University Plain, Norwich NR4 7TJ : University of East Anglia. £0.15(£0.10 to university and polytechnic careers services)* A(MN/YD) (B75-15001)
Carissimi, Giacomo. Beatus vir, Psalm 112 : SATB. *Oxford University Press. Unpriced* DR (B75-50433) ISBN 0-19-350351-4
Carner, Mosco.
Alban Berg : the man and his work. *Duckworth. £12.00* BBKR (B75-28636) ISBN 0-7156-0769-3
Letters of Giacomo Puccini : mainly connected with the composition and production of his operas. (Puccini, Giacomo). New ed. *Harrap. £4.00* BPU(N) (B75-05793) ISBN 0-245-52422-3
Caro, Louis de. *See* De Caro, Louis.
Carols for today : two-part. (Chappell, Herbert). *Chappell. Unpriced* JDP/LF/AY (B75-50089)
Carols of the elements : for unison voices, optional 2 part melodic instruments, percussion, and piano. (Coombes, Douglas). *28 Knolls Way, Clifton, Beds. : Lindsay Music. £0.25* JFDP (B75-50532) ISBN 0-85957-004-5
Carr, Roy. The Beatles : an illustrated record. *New English Library. £1.95* AKDW/GB/E(P) (B75-13736) ISBN 0-450-02626-4
Carradot, André. Concerto for trumpet. *arr.* Concerto pour trompette et orchestre. *Chappell. Unpriced* WSPK/LF (B75-50949)
Carter, Elliott. Three poems of Robert Frost : for voice and piano. *Associated Music. £1.30* KDW (B75-51103)
Carter, Sydney.
Green print for song : a book of carols. *Galliard. Unpriced* JDP/AY (B75-50088) ISBN 0-85249-284-7
Nine carols or ballads. Lord of the dance. *arr.* Lord of the dance. *Galaxy : Galliard. Unpriced* DP (B75-50429)
Nine carols or ballads. Lord of the dance. *arr.* Lord of the dance. *Galaxy : Galliard. Unpriced* FLDP (B75-50506)
Cartledge, T M. National anthems of the world. 4th and revised ed. *Blandford Press. £5.80* JDW/KM/AY (B75-50529) ISBN 0-7137-0679-1
Caruso, Enrico. Caruso and Tetrazzini on the art of singing. *Dover Publications : Constable. £0.84* AB/E (B75-22212) ISBN 0-486-23140-2
Caruso and Tetrazzini on the art of singing. (Caruso, Enrico). *Dover Publications : Constable. £0.84* AB/E (B75-22212) ISBN 0-486-23140-2
Cascades : harpe. (Challan, Annie). *Chappell. Unpriced* TQPMJ (B75-50792)
Caserta, Peggy. Going down with Janis. *Talmy Franklin. £1.95* AKDW/GB/E(P) (B75-29317) ISBN 0-900735-40-6
Cashmore, Donald. Stille Nacht. *arr.* Stille Nacht = Silent night. (Gruber, Franz). *Oxford University Press. Unpriced* EZDP/LF (B75-51042) ISBN 0-19-343053-3
Cassandra's dream song : solo flute. (Ferneyhough, Brian). *Peters. Unpriced* VRPJ (B75-50321)
Casseus, Frantz. World's favorite selected masterpieces for classic guitar
Vol.2. *Ashley : Phoenix. Unpriced* TSPMK/AAY (B75-50286)
Cassey, Charles R. Blossom's a possum : for mixed chorus, SATB. *Chappell. Unpriced* DW (B75-50437)
Cassey, Chuck. Sounds I prefer. *arr.* Sounds I prefer : for mixed chorus (SATB). (Lombardo, Mario). *Chappell. Unpriced* DW (B75-51021)
Castellani, Marcello. Sonata no.1 for treble recorder & continuo in D minor. Sonata in D minor for treble recorder and basso continuo. (Mancini, Francesco). *Bärenreiter. £2.00* VSSPE (B75-50335)
Castrati in opera. (Heriot, Angus). *Calder and Boyars. £5.75* AKGGC/E(M) (B75-26087) ISBN 0-7145-0153-0
Catalyst : the Sun Records story. (Escott, Colin). *Aquarius Books; Station Rd, Kings Langley, Herts. : Distributed by Argus Books. £2.90* A/FD(Q) (B75-21384) ISBN 0-904619-00-1
Cathedral music. Morning and Evening Service in D major. Magnificat and Nunc dimittis : for SATB and organ. (Walmisley, Thomas Attwood). *Oxford University Press. £0.50* DGPP (B75-50414) ISBN 0-19-395316-1
Cavalli, Francesco. La Calisto. *Vocal score.* La Calisto : opera in two acts with a prologue. *Faber Music. Unpriced* CC (B75-50989)
Cello. (Cowling, Elizabeth). *Batsford. £6.50* ASR (B75-13737) ISBN 0-7134-2879-1
Celluloid rock : twenty years of movie rock. (Jenkinson, Philip). *Lorrimer. £1.95* A/GB/JR(XPP21) (B75-06416) ISBN 0-85647-046-5
CEM. *See* Christian Education Movement.
Ceol mor notation : a new and abbreviated system of musical notation for the piobaireachd as played on the Highland bagpipe, with examples. (Thomason, Charles Simson). *EP Publishing etc.. £6.75* AVY/T(QU) (B75-22850) ISBN 0-7158-1114-2
Ceremonial music : military band. (Washburn, Robert). *Oxford University Press. Unpriced* UMMJ (B75-51346)
Ceremony after a fire raid. Op.63 : for mixed voices (SATB Bar B), piano and percussion. (Mathias, William). *Oxford University Press. £1.50* ENYLDX (B75-50452) ISBN 0-19-337434-x
Ceska mse vanocni = Böhmische Hirtenmesse = Czech Christmas Mass. (Ryba, Jakub Jan). *Supraphon Achauer. £5.60* DE/LF (B75-50999)
Chacksfield, Kathleen Merle. Music and language with young children. *Blackwell. £4.50* A/GR(VG) (B75-22597) ISBN 0-631-15330-6
Chadwick, George Whitfield. Judith. God. Jehovah. God, Jehovah : mixed chorus and keyboard. *Galaxy : Galliard.*

Unpriced DH (B75-51003)
Chagall windows : for orchestra. (McCabe, John). *Novello. Unpriced* MMJ (B75-50617)
Challan, Annie.
Cascades : harpe. *Chappell. Unpriced* TQPMJ (B75-50792)
Danse des glissandi : harpe. *Chappell. Unpriced* TQPMH (B75-50791)
Chambure, G de. *See* Thiabult, G.
Chance, John Barnes. Blue lake : overture for concert band. *Boosey and Hawkes. Unpriced* UMJ (B75-50295)
Chandler, John. Bell carol : based on the tune 'Puer nobis', for junior choir, mixed choir, and organ, with optional bells. (Wichmann, Russell G). *Oxford University Press. Unpriced* DP/LF (B75-51013)
Changements : pour grand orchestre. (Kelterborn, Rudolf). *Bärenreiter. Unpriced* MMJ (B75-50616)
Changes for seven : for woodwind quintet, percussion and piano. (Bergsma, William). *Galliard. Unpriced* NYFPNP (B75-51196)
Chant et mécanisme. Op.37, 38. *Selections : arr.* Five Stamaty pieces from Op.37 and 38. (Stamaty, Camille). *New Wind Music. £0.50* VVPK (B75-51405)
Chaplin, Saul. George Gershwin's two waltzes in C : piano solo. (Gershwin, George). *Warner : Blossom. Unpriced* QPHW (B75-50682)
Chappell, Herbert.
The adventures of Paddington Bear. Paddington Bear. *arr.* Paddington Bear : song. *Music Sales. £0.25* KDW (B75-50106)
Carols for today : two-part. *Chappell. Unpriced* JDP/LF/AY (B75-50089)
Chapple, Brian.
Green and pleasant : for chamber orchestra. *Chester. Unpriced* MRJ (B75-50632)
Praeludiana : for organ. *Chester. Unpriced* RJ (B75-50730)
Charles Ives : a portrait. (Wooldridge, David). *Faber. £6.00* BIV(N) (B75-15003) ISBN 0-571-10687-0
Charles Ives and the American band tradition : a centennial tribute. (Elkus, Jonathan). *American Arts Documentation Centre, University of Exeter. £0.60* BIVUMM (B75-05796) ISBN 0-85989-005-8
Charles Ives remembered : an oral history. (Perlis, Vivian). *Yale University Press. £6.25* BIV(N) (B75-05791) ISBN 0-300-01758-8
Charters, Samuel Barclay. The legacy of the blues : a glimpse into the art and the lives of twelve great bluesmen : an informal study. *Calder and Boyars. £3.95* AKDW/HHW/E(M) (B75-50976) ISBN 0-7145-1098-x
Chatanooga cha-cha : brass band. (Siebert, Edrich). *Studio Music. Unpriced* WMHJMR (B75-50360)
Chateaubriand, François René. Dialogues on lines of Chateaubriand : for high soprano, flute, trumpet, violoncello, percussion, piano and celesta. (Hamilton, Iain). *Central Music Library : Schott. Unpriced* KFLE/NYDNQDX (B75-50574)
Chatter box : piano solo. (Thiman, Eric Harding). *British and Continental. Unpriced* QPJ (B75-50713)
Cheironomies : conductor's improvisation. (Antoniou, Theodore). *Bärenreiter. £3.20* MMJ (B75-50138)
Cherepnin, Nikolai. *See* Tcherepnin, Nikolai.
Cheslock, Louis. Descant : for unaccompanied clarinet. *Oxford University Press. Unpriced* VVPMJ (B75-50904)
Chiang K'uei. The lantern festival : S.S.A. unacc. (Burtch, Mervyn). *Banks. Unpriced* FEZDW (B75-51064)
Chicago breakdown. (Rowe, Mike). *2 Greycoat Place, S.W.1 : Eddison Press Ltd. £2.50* AKDW/HHW(YTKC/XNK43) (B75-03645) ISBN 0-85649-015-6
Chilcot, Thomas.
Concerto for harpsichord & string orchestra, op.2, no.2, in A major. Concerto in A major : for harpsichord, two violins and violoncello. *Oxford University Press. £2.60* RXMPQRF (B75-50752) ISBN 0-19-362290-4
Concerto for harpsichord, op.2, no.5, in F major. Concerto in F major : for harpsichord, two oboes, bassoon and strings. *Oxford University Press. Unpriced* MPQRF (B75-50622) ISBN 0-19-362296-3
Child in the manger : carol for SATB. (Hill, Anthony Herschel). *Thames. Unpriced* EZDP/LF (B75-50468)
Chilton, John. Billie's blues : a survey of Billie Holiday's career, 1933-1959. *Quartet Books. £3.95* **AKDW/HHW/E(P) (B75-19732)** ISBN 0-7043-2091-6
Chopin, Frederic. Mazurka for piano, op.68, no.4, in F minor. Mazurka in F minor. Op.68, no.4, (The final composition). *Hansen House. Unpriced* QPHQ (B75-50676)
Choral bearbeitungen : für Orgel. (Praetorius, Jacob). *Bärenreiter. £3.60* RJ (B75-50212)
Choralbearbeitungen : für Blechbläser und Orgel. (Loeffelholz, Klaus von). *Bärenreiter. Unpriced* NWXPNR (B75-50645)
Chordal solo technique for guitar. (Roberts, Don). *EMI Music. Unpriced* TS/RC (B75-50797)
Choristers of light : for mixed voices. (Davis, Katherine Kennicott). *Galaxy : Galliard. Unpriced* EZDM (B75-50059)
Christ in competition. *Edwardian Music. Unpriced* JDM/AY (B75-51078) ISBN 0-551-05530-8
Christian Education Movement. Music as stimulus in secondary assembly and RE ... (Tillman, June). *2 Chester House, Pages La., N10 1PR : Christian Education Movement, Religious Education Service. £0.40* A/FD(VK/WT) (B75-15228) ISBN 0-905022-00-9
Christmas carols made easy : for piano with guitar chords. *M.S.M. Unpriced* QPK/DP/LF/AY (B75-51261)
Christmas is coming. (Dittersdorf, Carl Ditters von). *Robbins. Unpriced* DW/LF (B75-50031)
Christmas magic. *arr.* Christmas magic. (Van Dresar, Mary). *Warner : Blossom. Unpriced* DW/LF (B75-51024)
Christmas music from Colonial America : an anthology of Christmas psalms and anthems from the revolutionary and federal eras : for mixed chorus, organ and optional instruments. *Galaxy : Galliard. Unpriced* EZDH/AYT (B75-50463)
Christmas pageant : carols from around the world and classical Christmas excerpts. *Galaxy : Galliard. Unpriced* QPK/DP/LF/AY (B75-51262)
Christmas presentation album : songs. *Chappell. Unpriced* KDW/LF/AY (B75-51121)
Christmas songs for guitar. *Chappell. Unpriced* TSPMK/DP/LF/AY (B75-51328)
Chronicle of my life. *See* Stravinsky, Igor.
Cimarosa, Domenico.
Quartet for flute, violin, viola & cello, no.1, in D major. Quartet no.1 in D : for flute, violin, viola and cello. *Musica rara. £2.00* NVRNS (B75-51184)
Quartet for flute, violin, viola & cello, no.2, in F major. Quarter no.2 in F : for flute, violin, viola and cello. *Musica rara. £2.00* NVRNS (B75-51185)
City of high renown = Urbs Syon unica : unaccompanied mixed chorus. (Parker, Horatio). *Galaxy : Galliard. Unpriced* EZDH (B75-51035)
Clapham, John. Czech Christmas mass. *Vocal score.* Ceska mse vanocni = Böhmische Hirtenmesse = Czech Christmas Mass. (Ryba, Jakub Jan). *Supraphon Achauer. £5.60* DE/LF (B75-50999)
Clare, John. Song's eternity : part-song for unaccompanied female voices (SSA). (Short, Michael). *Roberton. £0.14* FEZDW (B75-50503)
Clark, Arthur C. The tentacles of the dark nebula : for tenor & strings. (Bedford, David). *Universal. Unpriced* KGHE/RXNNDX (B75-51129)
Clark, Leonard. A midnight carol. Op.21 : two-part. (Platts, Kenneth). *Ashdown. Unpriced* FDW (B75-50495)
Clarke, Harold. Sing hosanna : hymns. *Holmes McDougall. £3.80* JFDM/AY (B75-51091) ISBN 0-7157-0934-8
Clarke, Jeremiah.
Prince of Denmark's march. *arr.* Let the earth resound ('Lobt den Herrn der Welt'). *Bosworth. Unpriced* JDH (B75-50522)
The Prince of Denmark's march. *arr.* Trumpet voluntary. *Chester. Unpriced* WMK/AGM (B75-51424)
Selected works for keyboard. *Oxford University Press. £1.30* QRPJ (B75-50724) ISBN 0-19-372417-0
Classical and romantic album : for trumpet in B flat and piano
2nd. *Oxford University Press. £0.90* WSPK/AAY (B75-50947) ISBN 0-19-356523-4
3rd. *Oxford University Press. £0.90* WSPK/AAY (B75-50948) ISBN 0-19-356525-0
Classical and romantic pieces for clarinet and piano
Book 1. *Oxford University Press. £1.25* VVPK/AAY (B75-51406) ISBN 0-19-356517-x
Book 2. *Oxford University Press. £1.25* VVPK/AAY (B75-51407) ISBN 0-19-356520-x
Classical organ in Britain, 1955-1974. (Rowntree, John Pickering). *130 Southfield Rd, Oxford OX4 1PA : Positif Press. £2.95* AR/B(YC/XPQ20) (B75-13170) ISBN 0-9503892-1-8
Clayton, Kenny. The secret garden : an album for young pianists based on his music for the recording of Francis Hodgson Burnett's novel. *United Music. Unpriced* QP/JM (B75-51223)
Clelland, Tom. The book of open tunings : for guitar. *Robbins Music. Unpriced* TS/P (B75-51317)
Clements, John. A young man's song : TTBB unacc. *Oxford University Press. £0.10* GEZDW (B75-50514) ISBN 0-19-341020-6
Cliff Richard story. (Tremlett, George). *Futura Publications. £0.50* AKDW/GB/E(P) (B75-29318) ISBN 0-86007-232-0
Clifton, Geoffrey. Sing it in the morning : hymns. Teachers' ed. *Nelson. Unpriced* JFDM/AY (B75-50531) ISBN 0-17-428009-2
Clog dance : for orchestra. (Pavey, Sidney). *Bosworth. Unpriced* MH (B75-50594)
Coasters. (Millar, Bill). *44 Hill St., W1X 8LB : Star Books. £0.60* AKDW/GB/E(P) (B75-04508) ISBN 0-352-30020-5
Cobb, Ian.
Coppelia. Prelude and mazurka. *arr.* Prelude and mazurka. (Delibes, Leo). *Novello. £1.50* MHQ (B75-51148)
La Damnation de Faust. Marche hongroise. *arr.* Hungarian march. (Berlioz, Hector). *Novello. £1.50* MGM (B75-51147)
Cockney ding dong. *Kestrel Books : EMI. £3.95* KE/TSDW/AYDB (B75-51122) ISBN 0-7226-5061-2
Coffin, Charles. Bell carol : based on the tune 'Puer nobis', for junior choir, mixed choir, and organ, with optional bells. (Wichmann, Russell G). *Oxford University Press. Unpriced* DP/LF (B75-51013)
Cofone, Charles J F. Elizabeth Rogers hir virginall booke. *Dover : Constable. £3.00* QSQ/AY (B75-51265) ISBN 0-486-23138-0
Cohn, James. The little circus : orchestral suite. *Boosey and Hawkes. Unpriced* MMG (B75-51152)
Colchester, Linzee Sparrow. Brief history of the organs of Wells Cathedral. *Adaptations.* The organs and organists of Wells Cathedral. (Bowers, Roger). *22 Vicars' Close, Wells, Somerset BA5 2UJ : The Friends of Wells Cathedral. £0.20* AR/B(YDFGWB) (B75-00741) ISBN 0-902321-12-9
Cole, Keith R. A guitarist's album for the young. *Ricordi. £1.50* TSPMJ (B75-50806)
Coleman, Henry. National anthems of the world. 4th and revised ed. *Blandford Press. £5.80* JDW/KM/AY (B75-50529) ISBN 0-7137-0679-1
Coles, Richard. The Gordian knot untied. *Selections: arr.* The Gordian knot untied. (Purcell, Henry). *Piers Press. Unpriced* VSNSK/JM (B75-50330)
Collection of Musick in two parts. *Selections.* Leichte Duette für Altblockflöten. (Finger, Gottfried). *Heinrichshofen : Hinrichsen. Unpriced* VSSNU (B75-50880)
Collection of studies for clarinet. *Boosey and Hawkes : Editio Musica. £1.00* VV/AF/AYG (B75-50346)
Collins, Lee. Oh, didn't he ramble : the life story of Lee Collins. *University of Illinois Press. £5.50* AMT(P) (B75-01179) ISBN 0-252-00234-2
Collins, Mary. Oh, didn't he ramble : the life story of Lee Collins. (Collins, Lee). *University of Illinois Press. £5.50* AMT(P) (B75-01179) ISBN 0-252-00234-2
Collinson, Francis. The bagpipe : the history of a musical instrument. *Routledge and Kegan Paul. £7.50* AVY/B(X) (B75-04509) ISBN 0-7100-7913-3
Colonial legend : for wind band. (Grundman, Clare). *Boosey and Hawkes. Unpriced* UMJ (B75-51333)
Columba, *Saint.* A hymn of St Columba (Regis regum rectissimi) : SATB and organ. (Britten, Benjamin). *Boosey and Hawkes. £0.20* DH (B75-50418)
Come along, sweet Liza Jane : SATB and piano. (Davis, Katherine Kennicott). *Warner : Blossom. Unpriced* DW (B75-50438)
Come where my love lies dreaming : for four-part chorus of mixed voices a cappella. (Foster, Stephen Collins). *Schirmer. Unpriced* EZDW (B75-50479)
Commedia 3 : for ten instruments. (Bennett, Richard Rodney). *Novello. £2.00* MRJ (B75-50158)
Commedia II : flute, cello and piano. (Bennett, Richard Rodney). *Novello. £3.50* NURNT (B75-50634)
Commedia IV : brass quintet. (Bennett, Richard Rodney). *Novello. £1.30* WNR (B75-50937)
Complementi : clarinet doubling bass clarinet, violin, cello, piano. (Wilson, Thomas). *Central Music Library : Chappell. Unpriced* NUVNS (B75-50637)
Complete trumpet repertoire
Volume 1: The operas. (Handel, George Frideric). *Musica rara. £4.50* WS (B75-51452)
Volume 2: The sacred oratorios. (Handel, George Frideric). *Musica rara. Unpriced* WS (B75-51453)
Volume 3: The church music. (Handel, George Frideric). *Musica rara. £4.50* WS (B75-51454)
Volume 4: Miscellaneous. (Handel, George Frideric). *Musica rara. £4.50* WS (B75-51455)
Composer in the market place. (Peacock, Alan). *Faber. £5.50* A(JC/K/YC/XM70) (B75-18726) ISBN 0-571-10011-2
Concert and contest collection : for E flat or BB flat bass (tuba or sousaphone) with piano accompaniment. *Rubank. Unpriced* WVP/AY (B75-51472)
Concert piece : for oboe and orchestra. Op.33. (Rietz, Julius). *Musica rara. Unpriced* VTPK (B75-51394)
Concert-Stück for oboe and orchestra. Op.33. *arr.* Concert piece : for oboe and orchestra. Op.33. (Rietz, Julius). *Musica rara. Unpriced* VTPK (B75-51394)
Concertette for Christmas : for concert band. (Cacavas, John). *Chappell. Unpriced* UM/LF (B75-50293)
Concerto for trumpet & string orchestra in E flat major. *arr.* Concerto in E flat for trumpet and strings. (Neruda, Johann Baptist Georg). *Musica rara. Unpriced* WSPK/LF (B75-51467)
Concorde march. *arr.* Concorde march. (Farnon, Robert). *Chappell. Unpriced* WMK/AGM (B75-51425)
Conductor and his score. (Green, Elizabeth Adine Herkimer). *Prentice-Hall. £4.40* A/EC (B75-16405) ISBN 0-13-167312-2
Conga Brazil : Brazilian impression for percussion ensemble (8 players). (Fink, Siegfried). *Simrock. £3.60* XNNHJNC (B75-51476)
Congo jive : for choir, percussion and piano. (Paviour, Paul). *Boosey and Hawkes. £3.60* ENYLNTDW (B75-50037)
Connecticut capers : brass band. (Siebert, Edrich). *Studio Music. Unpriced* WMJ (B75-50368)
Connolly, Justin.
Antiphonies : for orchestra. *Oxford University Press. £5.50* MMJ (B75-50612) ISBN 0-19-362390-0
Tesserae C : violoncello solo. *Novello. £1.00* SRPMJ (B75-50775)
Consort of four parts. (Locke, Matthew). *Stainer and Bell. Unpriced* STNSG (B75-51309)
Consortium (I) : flute, B flat clarinet, violin, viola, violoncello. (Schwantner, Joseph). *Peters. Unpriced* NVPNR (B75-50641)
Constante, Lena. Traité de naï roumain : methode de flûte de Pan. (Zamfir, Gheorghe). *Chappell. Unpriced* VSX/AC (B75-50886)
Contemporary life : eight folk-songs for voices and guitar. *Oxford University Press. £0.35* JE/TSDW/G/AY (B75-50091) ISBN 0-19-330627-1
Contemporary organ technique : 20 progressive studies and pieces. (Stoker, Richard). *Ashdown. £1.20* R/AF (B75-51266)
Conti, Annaberta. Sonata no.1 for treble recorder & continuo in D minor. Sonata in D minor for treble recorder and basso continuo. (Mancini, Francesco). *Bärenreiter. £2.00* VSSPE (B75-50335)
Continuum : for two manual organ with three players. (Rose, Jon). *United Music. Unpriced* RNVQ (B75-51279)
Contrasts : for piano. (Schurmann, Gerard). *Novello. Unpriced* QPJ (B75-50709)
Conversations : for clarinet B flat and piano. (Patterson, Paul). *Weinberger. Unpriced* VVPJ (B75-50900)
Conyngham, Barry. Crisis. Thoughts in a city : for two string orchestras and percussion. *Universal. Unpriced* RXMJ (B75-51284)

Cook, Bruce. Listen to the blues. *Robson Books. £4.35* AKDW/HHW(X) (B75-21070) ISBN 0-903895-47-1
Coombes, Douglas.
Carols of the elements : for unison voices, optional 2 part melodic instruments, percussion, and piano. *28 Knolls Way, Clifton, Beds. : Lindsay Music. £0.25* JFDP (B75-50532) ISBN 0-85957-004-5
Duetto buffo di due gatti = Comic duet for two cats. (Berthold, G). *28 Knolls Way, Clifton, Beds. : Lindsay Music. £0.15* JNFEDW (B75-50546) ISBN 0-85957-005-3
I was glad when they said unto me : a paraphrase of Psalm 122, for two equal voices. *28 Knolls Way, Clifton, Beds. : Lindsay Music. £0.12* FDR (B75-50487)
Seven space songs : music for voices, melodic instruments, percussion and piano. *28 Knolls Way, Clifton, Beds. : Lindsay Music. £0.58* JFE/NYLDW (B75-50541)
Zalzabar : a Christmas cantata for children, music for voices, melodic instrument, percussion & piano. *28 Knolls Way, Clifton, Beds. : Lindsay Music. £0.49* JFE/NYLDE/LF (B75-50540)
Cooper, Barry.
Sonata for trumpet, oboe and basso continuo in C major. (Finger, Godfrey). *Musica rara. Unpriced* NWNTE (B75-51190)
Sonata for trumpet, violin, oboe and basso continuo in C major. (Finger, Godfrey). *Musica rara. Unpriced* NUNSE (B75-51174)
Voluntaries for organ. *Selections: arr.* Six voluntaries for 2 trumpets and organ. (Stanley, John). *Musica rara. Unpriced* WSNTRK (B75-51456)
Cooper, Joseph. Joseph Cooper's hidden melodies : six improvisations for piano. *Paxton. Unpriced* QPJ (B75-51237)
Cooper, Paul. Variants II : for viola and piano. *Chester. Unpriced* SQP/T (B75-50771)
Copland, Aaron.
Preamble for a solemn occasion. *arr.* Preamble for a solemn occasion. *Boosey and Hawkes. £9.00* UMK (B75-50296)
Three Latin-American sketches : for orchestra. *Boosey and Hawkes. £7.50* MMJ (B75-50613)
Vocalise-etude. *arr.* Vocalise : for flute and piano. *Boosey and Hawkes. £0.75* VRPK/DW (B75-50323)
Copland, Alison A. Concerto for clarinet in B major. *arr.* Concerto in B flat for clarinet and orchestra. (Hoffmeister, Franz Anton). *Schott. £1.50* VVPK/LF (B75-51409)
Copley, Ian Alfred.
The holy son of God : carol for SATB. *Thames. Unpriced* EZDP/LF (B75-50467)
Two lullaby carols : for 4-part female voices unaccompanied. *Roberton. £0.10* FEZDP/LF (B75-51060)
Coppelia. Prelude and mazurka. *arr.* Prelude and mazurka. (Delibes, Leo). *Novello. £1.50* MHQ (B75-51148)
Cordell, Frank. Patterns : for saxophone quartet. *Novello. £3.75* VUNS (B75-51397)
Cormier, Robert de. *See* De Cormier, Robert.
Cornish song book = Lyver canow Kernewek
Part 1. *Lodenek Press : Ascherberg Hopwood and Crew. £1.50* CB/AYDFR (B75-50984) ISBN 0-902899-32-5
Part 2: Carols and sacred music. *Lodenek Press : Ascherberg Hopwood and Crew. £1.20* CB/AYDFR (B75-50985) ISBN 0-902899-34-1
Cornouailles march : piano. (Blot, André). *Chappell. Unpriced* QPGM (B75-50672)
Correa nel seno amato : cantata for soprano, two violins and basso continuo. (Scarlatti, Alessandro). First edition. *Bärenreiter. £6.00* KFLE/SNTPWDX (B75-50119)
Corso, Gregory. Extravaganza : song cycle for medium voice and piano. (Dickinson, Peter). *Novello. £1.25* KFVDW (B75-50585)
Coruscations : piano. (Meale, Richard). *Universal. Unpriced* QPJ (B75-50705)
Cotton, Reynell. The Hambledon cricket song of the Rev Reynell Cotton. (Knight, Ronald David). *40A Abbotsbury Rd, Weymouth, Dorset DT4 0AE : R.D. Knight. £0.30* BCMTADW (B75-12697) ISBN 0-903769-00-x
Count down : brass band. (Patterson, Paul). *Weinberger. Unpriced* WMJ (B75-50923)
Country and westerns : military band. (Walters, Harold L). *Rubank : Novello. Unpriced* UMMJ (B75-50832)
Country search. Theme. *arr.* Country search : piano. (Patterson, Paul). *Weinberger. £0.30* QPK/JS (B75-51264)
Couperin, François.
Les Goûts réunis or Nouveaux concerts : for instrumental ensemble
Volume 1: Concerts 5-8 : for flute or oboe or violin & basso continuo. *Musica rara. Unpriced* LNG (B75-51140)
Volume 2: Concerts 9-10, 12, 14 : for flute or oboe or violin and basso continuo. *Musica rara. Unpriced* LNG (B75-51141)
Volume 3: Concerts 10, 12-13 : for three violas da gamba or cellos or bassoons. *Musica rara. Unpriced* LNG (B75-51142)
Courpalay, Maurice de. Danses de l'echiquier : style baroque, orchestra. *Chappell. Unpriced* MRH (B75-50631)
Cowell, Henry. Quartet romantic for 2 flutes, violin & viola. Quartet romantic : 2 flutes, violin, viola, and, Quartet euphometric : 2 violins, viola, violoncello. *Peters. Unpriced* NVRNS (B75-50643)
Cowie, Edward. The moon, sea and stars : nocturnes for tenor horn and strings. *Chester : Hansen. Unpriced* KGHE/RXMPWTDX (B75-50124)
Cowling, Elizabeth. The cello. *Batsford. £6.50* ASR (B75-13737) ISBN 0-7134-2879-1
Cowper, William.
Song of praise and prayer : children's hymn. (Binkerd, Gordon). *Boosey and Hawkes. Unpriced* KFDM (B75-50569)
Song of praise and prayer : children's hymn, unison, with organ or piano accompaniment. (Binkerd, Gordon). *Boosey and Hawkes. Unpriced* JFDM (B75-50530)
Cox, David, *b.1916.* Debussy orchestral music. *British Broadcasting Corporation. £0.55* BDJAM (B75-50004) ISBN 0-563-12678-7
Crawford, John.
The maid's song : for SSAA and piano. *Oxford University Press. Unpriced* FDW (B75-50070)
Psalm 98 : for men's chorus (TBB), accompanied by brass quintet and piano, or by organ and piano alone. *Oxford University Press. Unpriced* GE/NWXPNQDR (B75-50083)
Crawford, Richard. William Billings of Boston : eighteenth-century composer. (McKay, David Phares). *Princeton University Press. £8.40* BBNS (B75-50980) ISBN 0-691-09118-8
Crawfurd, Andrew. Andrew Crawfurd's collection of ballads and songs
Vol.1. *27 George Sq., Edinburgh EH8 9LD : The Scottish Text Society. Unpriced* 784.49411 (B75-29319) ISBN 0-9500245-4-6
Creature conforts : a fantasy for voices and percussion. (Tomlinson, Geoffrey). *Boosey and Hawkes. 2.50* JFE/NYLDX (B75-50542)
Creuzburg, Heinrich. Concerto for oboe & string orchestra in D minor. *arr.* Konzert, D-moll für Oboe und Streicher. (Holzbauer, Ignaz). 1st ed. *Litolff : Peters. Unpriced* VTPK/LF (B75-51396)
Crimlisk, Anthony. Diversions : for two descant recorders and piano. *British and Continental. Unpriced* VSRNTQ (B75-51381)
Crisis. Thoughts in a city : for two string orchestras and percussion. (Conyngham, Barry). *Universal. Unpriced* RXMJ (B75-51284)
Criswick, Mary.
Elizabethan serenade. *arr.* Elizabethan serenade. (Binge, Ronald). *Ascherberg, Hopwood and Crewe. Unpriced* TSNTK (B75-51320)
Guitar duets : music from four centuries. *Chester. Unpriced* TSNUK/AAY (B75-50800)
Guitar trios : music from four centuries. *Chester. Unpriced* TSNTK/AAY (B75-50798)
Ragtime for guitar ensemble. *Chappell. Unpriced* TSNK/AHXJ/AY (B75-51318)
Croci, Giorgio. Concerto grosso in F major. Concerto in fa magg : per archi con due oboi (o flauti) e fagotto ad libitum oppure 2 violini e violoncello ad libitum e cembalo. (Marcello, Alessandro). *Zanibon : Peters. Unpriced* MRF (B75-50156)
Croft, William.
Complete harpsichord works of William Croft
Vol.1. *Stainer and Bell. Unpriced* QRP/AZ (B75-50200)
Vol.2. *Stainer and Bell. Unpriced* QRP/AZ (B75-50201)
My heart is ev'ry beauty's prey : tenor solo, harpsichord and cello (ad lib.). *Roberton. Unpriced* KGHDW (B75-50589)
Cromwell, Anne. Anne Cromwell's Virginal Book, 1638. *Oxford University Press. £2.50* QSQ/AY (B75-50725) ISBN 0-19-372637-8
Crosse, Gordon. The new world. Op.26 : set for medium voice and piano. *Oxford University Press. £2.50* KFVDW (B75-50584) ISBN 0-19-345275-8
Crossing the bar : anthem for solo quartet or mixed choir and organ. (Ives, Charles). *Associated Music. Unpriced* DH (B75-50419)
Crossland, Anthony. The organs and organists of Wells Cathedral. (Bowers, Roger). *22 Vicars' Close, Wells, Somerset BA5 2UJ : The Friends of Wells Cathedral. £0.20* AR/B(YDFGWB) (B75-00741) ISBN 0-902321-12-9
Crosswords : for any number of players with non-pitched percussion instruments. (Dennis, Brian). *Universal. Unpriced* XN (B75-50964)
Crowhurst, Norman Herbert. Electronic musical instruments. *Foulsham-Tab. £1.80* APV/B (B75-50978) ISBN 0-7042-0144-5
Crowley, Terence Eldon. Discovering mechanical music. *Shire Publications. £0.35* A/FH (B75-08740) ISBN 0-85263-257-6
Crowther, Sidney Hirst. Huddersfield Glee & Madrigal Society, 1875-1975. (Huddersfield Glee and Madrigal Society). *Princess Alexandra Walk, Huddersfield HD1 2SU : Kirklees Libraries and Museums Service. £0.50* AD/E(YDJGH/QB) (B75-07343) ISBN 0-9502568-1-1
Cruft, Adrian.
Chant et mécanisme. Op.37, 38. *Selections : arr.* Five Stamaty pieces from Op.37 and 38. (Stamaty, Camille). *New Wind Music. £0.50* VVPK (B75-51405)
Official book of scales and arpeggios for double bass, (Grades III, IV, V, VI, and VIII). (Associated Board of the Royal Schools of Music). *Associated Board of the Royal Schools of Music. £0.45* SS/AF (B75-50267)
Seven pieces for flute and piano. Op.79. *Chappell. Unpriced* VRPJ (B75-50849)
Songs of good counsel. Op.73 : for mezzo-soprano and pianoforte. *Central Music Library : Chappell. Unpriced* KFQDW (B75-50579)
Cruft, Eugene. Official book of scales and arpeggios for double bass, (Grades III, IV, V, VI, and VIII). (Associated Board of the Royal Schools of Music). *Associated Board of the Royal Schools of Music. £0.45* SS/AF (B75-50267)
Crumb, George. Songs, drones and refrains of death : a cycle of poems by Federico Garcia Lorca for baritone, electric guitar, electric contrabass, electric piano, (electric harpsichord), percussion (2 players). *Peters. Unpriced* KGNE/PVDW (B75-51136)
Cry out with joy : unison. (Walker, Christopher). *Oxford University Press. Unpriced* JDR (B75-51083) ISBN 0-19-351121-5
Crystal spring : English folk songs
Book 1. *Oxford University Press. Unpriced* JE/TSDW/G/AYD (B75-51088) ISBN 0-19-330516-x
Book 2. *Oxford University Press. Unpriced* JE/TSDW/G/AYD (B75-51089) ISBN 0-19-330517-8
Cuckoo carol : a traditional Czech carol. (Walters, Edmund). *Boosey and Hawkes. £0.10* JFLDP/LF (B75-51100)
Cuckoo quartet : 2 flutes and 2 clarinets. (Hanmer, Ronald). *Emerson. Unpriced* VNS (B75-51361)
Cucumber music : 'Metamorphosis' for 4 players, 9 instruments. (Jenni, Donald). *Associated Music. Unpriced* NYDPNS (B75-50652)
Cumming, Richard. Lonesome valley : spiritual, SATB. *Boosey and Hawkes. Unpriced* DW/LC (B75-50446)
Cummings, E E. A wind has blown the rain away : SATB and piano. (King, Jeffrey). *Boosey and Hawkes. Unpriced* DW (B75-51018)
Curtis, Mira Stella. The folk directory
1975. *The Society. £2.00(£1.00 to members)* A/G(BC) (B75-19082) ISBN 0-85418-107-5
Cutts, Peter. New church praise. *Saint Andrew Press. Unpriced* DM/LSG/AY (B75-50428) ISBN 0-7152-0311-8
Czech Christmas mass. *Vocal score.* Ceska mse vanocni = Böhmische Hirtenmesse = Czech Christmas Mass. (Ryba, Jakub Jan). *Supraphon : Achauer. £5.60* DE/LF (B75-50999)
Czerny, Carl. Duo concertant for flute and piano. Op.129. *Universal. Unpriced* VRPF (B75-51370)
Da Palestrina, Giovanni Pierluigi. *See* Palestrina, Giovanni Pierluigi da.
Da Ponte, Lorenzo. *See* Ponte, Lorenzo da.
Da-Veena. To a mountain stream : piano. *Pandian Press Galliard. Unpriced* QPJ (B75-51238)
Dagosto, Sylvain.
Les Fêtes de Terpsichore. *Selections: arr.* Air en forme de pavane. (Boisvallée, Francois de). *Chappell. Unpriced* TMK/AHVG (B75-50273)
Manège. (Bonneau, Paul). *Chappell. Unpriced* TMK (B75-50788)
Maria. *arr.* Maria. (Lopez, Anja). *Chappell. Unpriced* TMK/DW (B75-51310)
Miniature. *arr.* Miniature. (Betti, Henri). *Chappell. Unpriced* TMK (B75-50787)
Paysage ibérique. (Duclos, Pierre). *Chappell. Unpriced* TMK (B75-50271)
Paysage suedois. (Duclos, Pierre). *Chappell. Unpriced* TMK (B75-50272)
Poupée de porcelaine. *arr.* Poupée de porcelaine : musique de Pierre Max Dubois et Paul Bonneau. (Dubois, Pierre Max). *Chappell. Unpriced* TMK (B75-50789)
Viva Napoli. La Mandoline a du bon. *arr.* La Mandoline a du bon. (Lopez, Francis). *Chappell. Unpriced* TMK/DW (B75-51311)
Viva Napoli. Ma sérénade. *arr.* Ma sérénade. (Lopez, Francis). *Chappell. Unpriced* TMK/DW (B75-51312)
Viva Napoli. Viva Napoli. *arr.* Viva Napoli. (Lopez, Francis). *Chappell. Unpriced* TMK/DW (B75-51313)
Dalby, Martin.
Ad flumina Babyloniae : for mixed voices (unaccompanied minimum 3333). *Novello. £0.25* EZDJ (B75-51039)
Cancionero para una mariposa : for flute, 2 bassoons, 2 trumpets in C, 2 trombones, 2 cellos. *Novello. Unpriced* VNM (B75-50639)
Sonatina for oboe and piano. *Novello. £1.00* VTPEM (B75-50888)
Dale, Gordon.
Fugue for brass quartet. Op.41, no.3. *British and Continental : EMI. Unpriced* WNS/Y (B75-51449)
Recital hors-d'oevre. Opus 51 : for 2 trumpets, horn and trombone. *British and Continental : EMI. Unpriced* WNS (B75-51447)
Dale, Mervyn.
Rhapsodie : for guitar. *Ashdown. £0.40* TSPMJ (B75-50807)
Thou wert my purer mind : unaccompanied part song for SATB. *Ashdown. £0.15* EZDW (B75-50476)
Three more songs for two-part choir. *Ashdown. £0.15* FDW (B75-50071)
Variations on a theme : for guitar. *Ashdown. £0.40* TSPM/T (B75-50803)
Dalmaine, Cyril C. Schumann. (Schumann, Robert). *Warren and Phillips. Unpriced* QPK (B75-50196)
Daly, Wally K. Follow the star. *Selections: arr.* Follow the star : song album from a new musical for Christmas. (Parker, Jim). *Chappell. Unpriced* KDW/LF (B75-51120)
D'Amario, B Battisti. *See* Amario, B Battisti d'.
D'Amario, B. Battisti d'. Improvviso da concerto : per chitarra. (Pizzini, Carlo Alberto). *Zanibon : Hinrichsen. Unpriced* TSPMJ (B75-50283)
Damnation de Faust. Marche hongroise. *arr.* Hungarian march. (Berlioz, Hector). *Novello. £1.50* MGM (B75-51147)
Danceries. Selections. *arr.* Three dances. (Gervaise, Claude). *Chester. Unpriced* WNSK/AH (B75-51450)
Dandy Shandy : 12 Jamaican folk-songs for children. *Oxford University Press. £0.40* FEZDW/G/AYULD (B75-50504) ISBN 0-19-330545-3

Daniel, Oliver. Harmony of Maine. *Selections.* Deep North Spirituals, 1794 : mixed or male voices in three and four parts. (Belcher, Supply). *Peters. Unpriced* EZDM (B75-50058)
Daniels, Arthur. Music. *Holt, Rinehart and Winston. £7.00* A (B75-29313) ISBN 0-03-012681-9
Dansa brasileira : for concert band. (Camargo Guarnieri, Mozart). *Associated Music. Unpriced* UMH (B75-50821)

Danse des glissandi : harpe. (Challan, Annie). *Chappell. Unpriced* TQPMH (B75-50791)
Danses de l'echiquier : style baroque, orchestra. (Courpalay, Maurice de). *Chappell. Unpriced* MRH (B75-50631)
Danza paraguaya : per chitarra. (Mangore, Agustin Barrios). *Zanibon : Hinrichsen. Unpriced* TSPMH (B75-50274)
Danzi, Franz. Quartet for strings, op.6, no.82, in B flat major, 'Figaro-Quartett'. String quartet in B flat major 'Figaro-Quartett'. Op.6, no.2. *Bärenreiter. Unpriced* RXNS (B75-50760)
Daquin, Louis Claude. Nouveau livre de noëls. Noel 10. *arr.* Noel X. *Chappell. Unpriced* RSPMK (B75-50746)
Darke, Dennis. Dances from the Yorkshire dales. *English Folk Dance and Song Society. Unpriced* LH/H/G/AYDJG (B75-50593)
Das ist ein kestlich Ding, dem Herren danken : Motette für vier gleiche Stimmen und zweistimmige Kinderchor. (Poos, Heinrich). *Bärenreiter. £0.20* FEZDJ (B75-50076)

Davey, Brian. Recorder playing in colour : for descant recorders
Book 1: Junior. *Chappell. Unpriced* VSR/AF (B75-50870)

David, Russ. Christ in competition. *Edwardian Music. Unpriced* JDM/AY (B75-51078) ISBN 0-551-05530-8
David and Goliath : a masque, for soloists, SATB chorus and instrumental ensemble, and optional narrator. (Detweiler, Alan). *Novello. £2.50* CPF (B75-50403)
David and Goliath. *Vocal score.* David and Goliath : a masque, for soloists, SATB chorus and instrumental ensemble, and optional narrator. (Detweiler, Alan). *Novello. £2.50* CPF (B75-50403)
Davids Danklied : für Bariton, vierstimmigen gemischten Chor, Bläser und Orgel. (Gardonyi, Zoltan). *Bärenreiter. £3.20* EWSNSRDH (B75-50044)
Davies, Hugh. New/rediscovered musical instruments
Vol.1. *15 Bayonne Rd, W.6 : Mirliton Publications. £0.75* AY/B (B75-04507) ISBN 0-904414-03-5
Davies, Laurence Hector. Lovely Scouse song : unison modern comedy folk song, with chorus, words and music. *Ashdown. £0.07* JFDW (B75-50534)
Davies, Peter Maxwell. Stone litany : runes from a House of the Dead, for mezzo-soprano and orchestra. *Boosey and Hawkes. £7.50* KFNE/MDX (B75-50577)
Davies, Roy Edward Charles. Skywatch (The Royal Observer Corps march past) : for military band. *Boosey and Hawkes. £1.50* UMMGM/KH (B75-51343)
Davis, Allan. Razorback reel. *Oxford University Press. Unpriced* UMMHVJ (B75-50302)
Davis, Howard. Quintet for clarinet & strings, op.95, in B flat major. Quintet in B flat. Opus 95 : for clarinet and strings. (Krommer, Franz). *Musica rara. Unpriced* NVVNR (B75-51187)
Davis, Katherine Kennacott. A wonderful thing : Easter carol, unison, piano (flute hand bells optional). *Warner : Blossom. Unpriced* JDP/LL (B75-50090)
Davis, Katherine Kennicot. Come along, sweet Liza Jane : SATB and piano. *Warner : Blossom. Unpriced* DW (B75-50438)
Davis, Katherine Kennicott.
Choristers of light : for mixed voices. *Galaxy : Galliard. Unpriced* EZDM (B75-50059)
Early American anthem book : anthem tunes and verses from the colonial period in new settings. *Galaxy Galliard. Unpriced* DH/AYT (B75-50422)
Daw, Stephen. Ten Scottish impressions : for guitar. *Stainer and Bell. Unpriced* TSPMJ (B75-50808)
Dawney, Michael. The iron man : English occupational songs. *Galliard : Stainer and Bell. Unpriced* JE/TSDW/GM/AYD (B75-50097) ISBN 0-85249-294-4
Dawson, Alan. Blues and syncopation in 3/4 and 4/4 for the drumset. *Simrock. £1.75* XQPMJ (B75-51482)
Dawson, Ann. Advent to Easter : short musical plays for junior and middle schools. (O'Gorman, Denis). *Grail Publications. £1.00* BOFGACN/L (B75-18364) ISBN 0-901829-25-0
Dawson, Mary.
Here on a bed of straw : carol for unison voices, SAB or SATB. (Parfrey, Raymond). *Thames. Unpriced* JFDP/LF (B75-50533)
October songs : SSA unacc. (Benger, Richard). *Banks. Unpriced* FEZDW (B75-50500)
Day's play : piano. (Last, Joan). *Forsyth. Unpriced* QPJ (B75-51249)
De Boismortier, Joseph Bodin. *See* Boismortier, Joseph Bodin de.
De Boisvallée, Francois. *See* Baoisvallée, Francois de.
De Boisvallée, Francois. *See* Boisvallée, Francois de.
De Caro, Louis. 21 steps for the beginning drummer. *Warner : Blossom. Unpriced* XQ/AC (B75-50970)
De Chambure, G . *See* Thibault, G.
De Cormier, Robert. The whistling gypsy : Irish folk song, for four-part chorus of mixed voices with baritone solo, piano and guitar accompaniment. *Roberton. £0.16* ETSPDW (B75-50456)
De Courpalay, Maurice. *See* Courpalay, Maurice de.
De L. Welch, Marie. Of a feather : five songs for high and low voices and piano. (Bacon, Ernst). *Novello. Unpriced* FDW (B75-50489)
De la Mare, Walter.
The listeners. *Vocal score.* The listeners : a dramatic cantata for soprano solo, male speaker and small soprano chorus, with chamber orchestra. (Young, Douglas). *Faber Music. Unpriced* FLDX (B75-51073)
The road of evening : song with piano accompaniment. (Noble, Harold). *Lengnick. £0.35* KDW (B75-50555)
De Machaut, Guillaume. *See* Machaut, Guillaume de.
De Monte Regali Gallus, Eustachius. *See* Monte Regali Gallus, Eustachius de.
De Morlaix, Bernard. *See* Morlaix, Bernard de.
De profundis : meditation for violin, violoncello and piano. (Bochmann, Christopher). *Oxford University Press. £2.50* NXNT (B75-50648) ISBN 0-19-355560-3
De Smet, Robin. The first year flautist
Vol.2. *Ashdown. £1.20* VRPK/AAY (B75-50852)
De Smet, Robin. *See* Smet, Robin de.
Deacon, Helen. Rabbits : unison song. *Roberton. £0.10* JFDW (B75-51092)
Deale, Edgar Martin. The lark in the clear air : Irish air. *Banks. Unpriced* DW (B75-50439)
Dearmer, Percy. The cuckoo carol : a traditional Czech carol. (Walters, Edmund). *Boosey and Hawkes. £0.10* JFLDP/LF (B75-51100)
Deas, Stewart. In defence of Hanslick. Revised ed. *Gregg. £3.00* A/CC(P) (B75-02991) ISBN 0-576-28242-1
Death, be not proud : for four-part chorus of mixed voices with chimes and piano accompaniment. (Jenni, Donald). *Associated Music. Unpriced* EXTPRPDW (B75-50458)
Death in Venice. *Vocal score.* Death in Venice. Op.88 : an opera in two acts. (Britten, Benjamin). *Faber Music. Unpriced* CC (B75-50988)
Debussy, Claude.
Ballade : piano solo. *Peters. Unpriced* QPJ (B75-50688)
Danse : piano solo. *Peters. Unpriced* QPH (B75-50674)
Etudes : piano solo
Book 1. *Peters. Unpriced* QPJ (B75-51239)
Book 2. *Peters. Unpriced* QPJ (B75-51240)
Hommage à Haydn : piano. *Peters. Unpriced* QPJ (B75-50689)
Images : piano solo
Book I. *Peters. Unpriced* QPJ (B75-50690)
Book II. *Peters. Unpriced* QPJ (B75-50691)
Jeux-thème : for mezzo-soprano and chamber orchestra. (Hoyland, Vic). *Universal. Unpriced* KFNE/MRDW (B75-51127)
The little nigar. The little negro = Le petit Negre : piano solo. *Peters. Unpriced* QPJ (B75-50692)
The little nigar. *arr.* Le petit negre. *Emerson. Unpriced* WNRK (B75-51444)
Masques : piano. *Peters. Unpriced* QPJ (B75-50693)
Mazurka : piano solo. *Peters. Unpriced* QPHQ (B75-50677)
Nocturne : piano solo. *Peters. Unpriced* QPJ (B75-50694)
Pour le piano : piano solo. *Peters. Unpriced* QPG (B75-51230)
Preludes. Bk 1. La Fille aux cheveux de lin. *arr.* The girl with the flaxen hair. *R. Smith. Unpriced* WMK (B75-51421)
Rêverie : piano. *Peters. Unpriced* QPJ (B75-50695)
Valse romantique : piano solo. *Peters. Unpriced* QPHW (B75-50681)
Debussy orchestral music. (Cox, David, *b.1916*). *British Broadcasting Corporation. £0.55* BDJAM (B75-50004) ISBN 0-563-12678-7
Decca Group records & tapes, main catalogue (alphabetical & numerical
1975 : up to and including September 1974 ..). *Decca Record Co. £5.00 yearly* A/FD(WM) (B75-09383) ISBN 0-901364-07-x
Deep North Spirituals, 1794 : mixed or male voices in three and four parts. (Belcher, Supply). *Peters. Unpriced* EZDM (B75-50058)
Deep the water, shallow the shore : three essays on shantying in the West Indies. (Abrahams, Roger David). *University of Texas Press for the American Folklore Society. £3.80* ADW/GMC(YUH) (B75-00739) ISBN 0-292-71502-1
Déguire, William. The America book for piano. *Galaxy Galliard. Unpriced* QPK/AYT (B75-51259)
Déjà : for flute, clarinet, viola, cello, piano and percussion. (Rands, Bernard). *Universal. Unpriced* NYDPNQ (B75-50651)
Del Tredici, David.
Scherzo : for piano, four hands. *Boosey and Hawkes. Unpriced* QNV (B75-50660)
Soliloquy : for piano. *Boosey and Hawkes. £1.50* QPJ (B75-50696)
Syzygy : for soprano, French horn and chamber orchestra. *Boosey and Hawkes. £9.00* KFLE/MPWTDX (B75-50118)
Delibes, Leo.
Coppelia. Prelude and mazurka. *arr.* Prelude and mazurka. *Novello. £1.50* MHQ (B75-51148)
Le Roi s'amuse. Passepied. *arr.* Passepied. *Oxford University Press. Unpriced* TSPMK/AHU (B75-50817) ISBN 0-19-356159-x
Delius, Frederick. Concerto for violin. Violin concerto. *Stainer and Bell. Unpriced* MPSF (B75-51164) ISBN 0-85249-355-x
Delius, Nikolaus. The flute master : ausgewählte Stücke für Altblockflöte allein (auch Querflöte oder Oboe). *Schott. £1.75* VSSPM/AY (B75-51387)
Delius Trust. Frederick Delius 1862-1934, a catalogue of the Music Archive of the Delius Trust, London. *Delius Trust : Distributed by Boosey and Hawkes. £7.50* BDL(TE) (B75-08382) ISBN 0-85162-023-x
Dello Joio, Norman.
The poet's song : for four-part chorus of mixed voices with piano accompaniment. *Associated Music. £0.25* DW (B75-51017)
Stage parodies : piano suite for young players, for one piano, four hands. *Associated Music. £1.30* QNVG (B75-51216)
Dennis, Brian. Crosswords : for any number of players with non-pitched percussion instruments. *Universal. Unpriced* XN (B75-50964)
Dennison, Peter. Ode on St Cecilia's day, 1692. Z.328. *Vocal score.* Ode on St Cecilia's day, 1692 : Hail! bright Cecilia : for soprano, two altos, tenor and two basses soli, SSAATB and instruments. (Purcell, Henry). *Novello. £1.20* DX (B75-51025)
Dent, E J. Les Troyens. Gloire, gloire à Didon. *Vocal score.* Hail all hail to the queen : SATB. (Berlioz, Hector). *Oxford University Press. £0.08* DW (B75-50028) ISBN 0-19-343046-0
Dent, Edward Joseph. Ferruccio Busoni : a biography. *48 Great Marlborough St., W.1 : Eulenberg Books. £3.75* BBVM(N) (B75-24235) ISBN 0-903873-15-x
Dering, Richard. Cantica sacra, 1618. *Stainer & Bell. Unpriced* DJ (B75-50025)
Descant : for unaccompanied clarinet. (Cheslock, Louis). *Oxford University Press. Unpriced* VVPMJ (B75-50904)
'Desert Island Discs'. (Plomley, Roy). *Kimber. £2.95* A/FD/JT(P/X) (B75-50973) ISBN 0-7183-0024-6
Destin = Destiny. Opus 59 : three symphonic fragments on a ballad by Edgar Allan Poe. (Tcherepnin, Nikolai). *Belaieff : Peters. Unpriced* MMJ (B75-50148)
Destiny. Op.59. Le Destin = Destiny. Opus 59 : three symphonic fragments on a ballad by Edgar Allan Poe. (Tcherepnin, Nikolai). *Belaieff : Peters. Unpriced* MMJ (B75-50148)
Detweiler, Alan. David and Goliath. *Vocal score.* David and Goliath : a masque, for soloists, SATB chorus and instrumental ensemble, and optional narrator. *Novello. £2.50* CPF (B75-50403)
Development and practice of electronic music. *Prentice-Hall. £8.80* APV (B75-15702) ISBN 0-13-207605-5
Devienne, Francois. Duets for two clarinets. Op.74. Sechs Duos für zwei Klarinetten. Opus 74. *Litolff : Peters. Unpriced* VVNU (B75-50896)
Devienne, François. Symphonie concertante for two flutes, op.76, in G major. *arr.* Symphonie concertante in G. Op.76 : for 2 flutes and orchestra. *Musica rara. £3.00* VRNTQK/LE (B75-51368)
Diablo suelto : valzer popolare venezuelano per chitarra. (Fernandez, Heraclio). *Zanibon : Hinrichsen. Unpriced* TSPMHW (B75-50278)
Dialogues on lines of Chateaubriand : for high soprano, flute, trumpet, violoncello, percussion, piano and celesta. (Hamilton, Iain). *Central Music Library : Schott. Unpriced* KFLE/NYDNQDX (B75-50574)
Diaz, Alirio.
Aires de Mochima : valzer venezuelano, per chitarra. (Calzadilla, Roman). *Zanibon : Hinrichsen. Unpriced* TSPMHW (B75-50277)
Las Belles noches de Maiquetia : canzone venezuelana per chitarra. (Aponte, Pedro Arcila). *Zanibon : Hinrichsen. Unpriced* TSPMJ (B75-50281)
Danza paraguaya : per chitarra. (Mangore, Agustin Barrios). *Zanibon : Hinrichsen. Unpriced* TSPMH (B75-50274)
El Diablo suelto : valzer popolare venezuelano per chitarra. (Fernandez, Heraclio). *Zanibon : Hinrichsen. Unpriced* TSPMHW (B75-50278)
Flor del campo : valzer venezuelano per chitarra. *Zanibon : Hinrichsen. Unpriced* TSPMHW (B75-50279)
Flores negras : pasillo ecuatoriano, per chitarra. *Zanibon Hinrichsen. Unpriced* TSPMK (B75-50284)
El Gallo : danza venezuelana per chitarra. (Torres, Pedro Manuel). *Zanibon : Hinrichsen. Unpriced* TSPMH (B75-50275)
Juliana : valzer venezuelano per chitarra. (Belasco, Lionel). *Zanibon : Hinrichsen. Unpriced* TSPMHW (B75-50276)
Oración : valzer popolare venezuelano, per chitarra. (Mangore, Agustin Barrios). *Zanibon : Hinrichsen. Unpriced* TSPMHW (B75-50280)
Dickinson, Emily. Four settings : for soprano and string quartet. (Dinerstein, Norman). *Boosey and Hawkes. Unpriced* KFLE/RXNSDW (B75-50576)
Dickinson, Peter. Extravaganza : song cycle for medium voice and piano. *Novello. £1.25* KFVDW (B75-50585)
Dickson, Andrew Wilson-. *See* Wilson-Dickson, Andrew.
Didn't my Lord deliver Daniel? : a jazz spiritual for junior wind band and optional voices in two parts. (Wastall, Peter). *Boosey and Hawkes. £2.05* UMJ (B75-51339)
Diemer, Emma Lou. The prophecy : SSAA unaccompanied. *Boosey and Hawkes. Unpriced* FEZDK (B75-50077)
D'in vieux manoir : pour hautbois et piano. (Fievet, Paul). *Chappell. Unpriced* VTPJ (B75-50341)
Dinerstein, Norman. Four settings : for soprano and string quartet. *Boosey and Hawkes. Unpriced* KFLE/RXNSDW (B75-50576)
Dinham, Kenneth J.
Jesus, Jesus, rest your head : Southern Appalachian carol. *Banks. Unpriced* EZDP/LF (B75-51041)
Jesus, Jesus, rest your head : Southern Appalachian carol. *Banks. Unpriced* GEZDP/LF (B75-51074)
Dioclesian. *Selections.* Suite für Streicher. (Purcell, Henry). *Litolff : Peters. Unpriced* RXM/JM (B75-50225)
Diptyque pour alto et piano. (Lantier, Pierre). *Chappell. Unpriced* SQPJ (B75-50257)
Directory of tunes and musical themes. (Parsons, Denys). *Spencer Brown. £6.00* A(TD) (B75-13381) ISBN 0-904747-00-x
'Disc' specials. Pop today. *Hamlyn. £1.95* AKDW/GB/E(M) (B75-02994) ISBN 0-600-37080-1
Discontented man : musical play for voices, piano and

percussion. (Arch, Gwyn). *British and Continental Music : EMI Music. Unpriced* CQN (B75-50011)
Discovering bells and bellringing. (Camp, John). 2nd ed. *Shire Publications. £0.35* AXSR (B75-08739) ISBN 0-85263-290-8
Discovering mechanical music. (Crowley, Terence Eldon). *Shire Publications. £0.35* A/FH (B75-08740) ISBN 0-85263-257-6
Dittersdorf, Carl Ditters von. Concerto for harpsichord in A major. Rondeau. *arr.* Christmas is coming. *Robbins. Unpriced* DW/LF (B75-50031)
Diversion : for orchestra. (Berkowtiz, Sol). *Frank Music. Unpriced* MMJ (B75-50610)
Diversions : for two descant recorders and piano. (Crimlisk, Anthony). *British and Continental. Unpriced* VSRNTQ (B75-51381)
Divertimento, C-dur : für Cembalo (Klavier), 2 Violinen und Violocello. Hoboken XIV, 8. (Haydn, Joseph). Zum ersten Mal herausgegeben von Gyorgy Balla. *Litolff : Peters. Unpriced* NXNS (B75-50169)
Dobree, Georgina. Méthode de clarinette. Sonata for clarinet & piano, no.1, in B flat major. Sonata no.1 : for clarinet in B flat and piano. (Lefevre, Jean Xavier). *Schott. £0.70* VVPE (B75-50348)
Dobrée, Georgina.
Quartet for clarinet, violin, viola & cello, op.82, in D major. Quartet in D. Opus 82 : for clarinet, violin, viola and cello. (Krommer, Franz). *Musica rara. £3.00* NVVNS (B75-51188)
Quartet for clarinet, violin, viola & cello, op.83, in B flat major. Quartet in B flat. Opus 83 : for clarinet, violin, viola and cello. (Krommer, Franz). *Musica rara. £3.00* NVVNS (B75-51189)
Quintet for clarinet & strings, op.95, in B flat major. Quintet in B flat. Opus 95 : for clarinet and strings. (Krommer, Franz). *Musica rara. Unpriced* NVVNR (B75-51187)
Dodgson, Stephen.
Concerto for guitar & chamber orchestra, no.1. Concerto no.1, for guitar and chamber orchestra. *Central Music Library : Chappell. Unpriced* MPTSF (B75-50624)
Progressive reading for guitarists. *Ricordi. £3.00* TS/AF (B75-50795)
Doflein, Erich. The flute master : ausgewählte Stücke für Altblockflöte allein (auch Querflöte oder Oboe). *Schott. £1.75* VSSPM/AY (B75-51387)
Dolci, Amico. Nuovi ricercari : per flauto dolce contralto. *Heinrichshofen : Hinrichsen. Unpriced* VSSPMJ (B75-50883)
Dolmetsch, Arnold. Premier livre de sonates a violon seul. Sonata for violin, no.5, in C minor. *arr.* Sonata 5 : treble recorder and keyboard in G minor. (Senaillié, Jean Baptiste). *Universal. Unpriced* VSSPK/AE (B75-50337)
Dolmetsch, Carl.
Premier livre de sonates a violon seul. Sonata for violin, no.5, in C minor. *arr.* Sonata 5 : treble recorder and keyboard in G minor. (Senaillié, Jean Baptiste). *Universal. Unpriced* VSSPK/AE (B75-50337)
The school recorder book
Book 3: Advanced recorder technique. Revised ed. *Arnold. Unpriced* VS/AC (B75-50329) ISBN 0-560-00271-8
Sonatas in five parts for various instruments. *Selections: arr.* Two sonatas in five parts : five recorders. (Legrenzi, Giovanni). *Universal. Unpriced* VSNRK/AE (B75-50857)
Don Giovanni. Don Giovanni o sai Il Convitato di pietra : dramma giocoso in un atto di Giovanni Bertati. (Gazzaniga, Guiseppe). *Bärenreiter. Unpriced* CQC (B75-50404)
Don Giovanni. K 527. *Vocal score.* Don Giovanni. KV 527. (Mozart, Wolfgang Amadeus). *Cassel : Bärenreiter. Unpriced* CC (B75-50396)
Don Giovanni. KV 527. (Mozart, Wolfgang Amadeus). *Cassel : Bärenreiter. Unpriced* CC (B75-50396)
Don Giovanni o sai Il Convitato di pietra : dramma giocoso in un atto di Giovanni Bertati. (Gazzaniga, Guiseppe). *Bärenreiter. Unpriced* CQC (B75-50404)
Dondeyne, Desiré. Sinfonia concertante for alto saxophone. *arr.* Symphone concertante pour saxophone alto E bémol et orchestre. *Chappell. Unpriced* VUSPK/LE (B75-50345)
Donizetti, Gaetano. Concerto for violin & cello in D minor. Concerto in re minore : per violino, violoncello e orchestra. *Zanibon : Peters. Unpriced* MPSPLSRF (B75-50153)
Donizetti and the tradition of romantic love : (a collection of essays on a theme). (Allitt, John). *56 Harbut Rd, SW11 2RB : Donizetti Society. £5.00* BDRAC (B75-08295) ISBN 0-9503333-1-x
Donizetti Society. Donizetti and the tradition of romantic love : (a collection of essays on a theme). (Allitt, John). *56 Harbut Rd, SW11 2RB : Donizetti Society. £5.00* BDRAC (B75-08295) ISBN 0-9503333-1-x
Donkey carol : two-part. (Rutter, John). *Oxford University Press. £0.20* FDP/LF (B75-50486) ISBN 0-19-341511-9
Donkey : the Christmas story portrayed by the animals. (Sansom, Clive A). *Studio Music. Unpriced* FDE/LF (B75-50068)
Donne, John. Death, be not proud : for four-part chorus of mixed voices with chimes and piano accompaniment. (Jenni, Donald). *Associated Music. Unpriced* EXTPRPDW (B75-50458)
Doorman, Ludwig. Opella nova. Tl. 1,2. *Selections.* Sechs Choral konzerte : für zwei gleiche Stimmen und Basso continuo. (Schein, Johann Hermann). *Bärenreiter. £2.00* JNEDH (B75-50102)
Dorman, Harry. Melodies of Robert Burns. *Warren and Phillips. Unpriced* QPK/DW/G/AYDL (B75-50719)
Dorward, David. Triad : for violin and piano. *Oxford University Press. Unpriced* SPJ (B75-51295) ISBN 0-19-356261-8
Dowland, John.
Lachrimae, nos 8, 1, 12. *arr.* Three dances. *Novello. £0.75* TSNSK/AH (B75-51319)
Lute music. *Selections : arr.* Two pieces. *Oxford University Press. £0.50* TSPMK (B75-50811) ISBN 0-19-356279-0
Down by the riverside : American traditional song. (Rutter, John). *Oxford University Press. Unpriced* DW/LC (B75-51023) ISBN 0-19-343049-5
Dragonetti, Domenico. Adagio and rondo for double bass & string quartet in C major. *arr.* Adagio and rondo in C major. *Yorke. Unpriced* SSPK/W (B75-50779)
Dramatic genius of Verdi : studies of selected operas
Vol.1. (Godefroy, Vincent). *Gollancz. £6.00* BVEAC (B75-19731) ISBN 0-575-01979-4
Draths, Willi. Duett-ABC : Volksweisen in leichten Sätzen für Sopranblockflöten (Gitarre und Schlagwerk ad lib). *Schott. £1.37* VSRPK/DW/G/AY (B75-50333)
Drayton, Paul. Templa quam dilecta. *Vocal score.* Templa quam dilecta : cantata for SATB and orchestra. *Novello. £0.95* DE (B75-50997)
Drei Fragmente : für Chor, SATB 1973. (Kelterborn, Rudolf). *Bärenreiter. £3.00* EZDW (B75-50066)
Drei Monodien : für Fagott. (Hirsch, Hans Ludwig). *Litolff : Peters. Unpriced* VWPMJ (B75-50353)
Drei slowakische Volkslieder : für Männerchor. *Bärenreiter. £2.00* GEZDW/G/AYFS (B75-50085)
Drei Tanze aus der Oper 'Ein Leben für den Zaren'. (Glinka, Mikhail Ivanovich). *Belaieff : Peters. Unpriced* MMH (B75-50137)
Dresar, Mary van. *See* Van Dresar, Mary.
Druner, Ulrich. Sonata for viola & orchestra. *arr.* Sonata per la grand'viola e orchestra. (Paganini, Nicolò). *Schott. Unpriced* SQPK/LE (B75-51303)
Dryden, John. King Arthur. *Choral score.* King Arthur. (Purcell, Henry). *Faber Music. Unpriced* DACB/JM (B75-50996)
Duarte, John W. Ten tunes from Gilbert and Sullivan. (Sullivan, *Sir* Arthur Seymour). *Novello. £1.00* VRPLTSK/DW (B75-50324)
Duarte, John William.
14 graded studies in apayando. *Ricordi. £0.84* TS/AF (B75-50796)
Six easy pictures. Opus 5 : guitar solo. *Novello. Unpriced* TSPMJ (B75-50809)
Dublin University, Trinity College. *See* Trinity College, *Dublin.*
Dubois, Pierre Max.
Poupée de porcelaine. *arr.* Poupée de porcelaine : musique de Pierre Max Dubois et Paul Bonneau. *Chappell. Unpriced* TMK (B75-50789)
Trois biberons : pour accordeon symphonique. *Chappell. Unpriced* RSPMJ (B75-50223)
Duckles, Vincent. Music reference and research materials : an annotated bibliography. 3rd ed. *Free Press : Collier Macmillan. £5.50* A(T) (B75-00957) ISBN 0-02-907700-1
Duclos, Pierre.
Andantino : variation pour clarinette si bémol et piano. *Chappell. Unpriced* VVP/T (B75-50898)
Le Voyageur. L'Avenir. *arr.* L'Avenir : pour baryton. *Chappell. Unpriced* KGNDW (B75-50592)
Paysage ibérique. *Chappell. Unpriced* TMK (B75-50271)
Paysage suedois. *Chappell. Unpriced* TMK (B75-50272)
Duett-ABC : Volksweisen in leichten Sätzen für Sopranblockflöten (Gitarre und Schlagwerk ad lib). *Schott. £1.37* VSRPK/DW/G/AY (B75-50333)
Duetto buffo di due gatti = Comic duet for two cats. (Berthold, G). *28 Knolls Way, Clifton, Beds. : Lindsay Music. £0.15* JNFEDW (B75-50546) ISBN 0-85957-005-3
Duke, Henry.
One man went to Mo-zart : piano solo. *Feldman. Unpriced* QPJ (B75-50188)
Two-way pieces : twelve progressive miniatures, for descant recorder with optional piano accompaniment. *British and Continental. Unpriced* VSRPMJ (B75-51382)
Two-way pieces : twelve progressive miniatures, for piano solo, with optional descant recorder. *British and Continental. Unpriced* QPJ (B75-51241)
Dum transisset Sabbatum : S.A.T. Bar. B. unacc. (Taverner, John). *Oxford University Press. Unpriced* EZDGKH/LL (B75-51031) ISBN 0-19-350350-6
Dunn, Geoffrey.
La Calisto. *Vocal score.* La Calisto : opera in two acts with a prologue. (Cavalli, Francesco). *Faber Music. Unpriced* CC (B75-50989)
Operettas. *Selections : arr.* The Johann Strauss song book : containing twelve songs for solo voice and piano. (Strauss, Johann, *b.1825*). *Weinberger. Unpriced* KDW (B75-51113)
Dunstan, Ralph.
The Cornish song book = Lyver canow Kernewek
Part 1. *Lodenek Press : Ascherberg Hopwood and Crew. £1.50* CB/AYDFR (B75-50984) ISBN 0-902899-32-5
Part 2: Carols and sacred music. *Lodenek Press : Ascherberg Hopwood and Crew. £1.20* CB/AYDFR (B75-50985) ISBN 0-902899-34-1
Durr, Alfred. St Matthew passion S.244. Matthaus-Passion = St Matthew Passion. (Bach, Johann Sebastian). *Bärenreiter. £4.40* EMDD/LK (B75-50034)
Durr, Walther. Don Giovanni. K 527. *Vocal score.* Don Giovanni. KV 527. (Mozart, Wolfgang Amadeus). *Cassel : Bärenreiter. Unpriced* CC (B75-50396)
Dürr, Walther. Selve caverne e monti : cantata for soprano and basso continuo. (Scarlatti, Domenico). 1st ed. *Bärenreiter. £1.80* KFLDX (B75-50117)
Dussek, Jan Ladislav. Sonata for flute, cello & piano, op.65, in F major. Grand sonata in F major. Opus 65 : for flute (or violin) and piano. *Musica rara. £3.80* NURNTE (B75-51176)
Dwyer, Doriot Anthony. Vocalise-etude. *arr.* Vocalise : for flute and piano. (Copland, Aaron). *Boosey and Hawkes. £0.75* VRPK/DW (B75-50323)
Dwyer, Terence.
Making electronic music : a course for schools
Book 1. *Oxford University Press. £1.50* APV/D (B75-24850) ISBN 0-19-321071-1
Book 2. *Oxford University Press. £1.50* APV/D (B75-24851) ISBN 0-19-321072-x
Teacher's book. *Oxford University Press. £2.50* APV/D (B75-24852) ISBN 0-19-321070-3
Dyke, Henry van. *See* Van Dyke, Henry.
E Hebrides'. Op.26. Overture, 'The Hebrides'. Op.26. (Mendelssohn, Felix). *Eulenburg. Unpriced* MMJ (B75-51156)
Ealing Strings *(Firm).* The Retford centenary exhibition. *4 Station Parade, Uxbridge Rd, W5 3LD : Ealing Strings. £12.50* ARXT/BC(P/WJ) (B75-22849) ISBN 0-9504357-0-8
Early American anthem book : anthem tunes and verses from the colonial period in new settings. *Galaxy Galliard. Unpriced* DH/AYT (B75-50422)
Early one morning : five poems of Edward Thomas, for tenor and guitar. (Hold, Trevor). *Thames Music. Unpriced* KGHE/TSDW (B75-50590)
Early spring : for four part chorus of mixed voices a cappella. (Jenni, Donald). *Associated Music. £0.20* EZDW (B75-51048)
Earth song : mixed voices with brass accompaniment and timpani, trumpets 1 and 2 in B flat, horns 1 and 2 in F, trombones 1 and 2, tuba, timpani (optional). (Washburn, Robert). *Boosey and Hawkes. Unpriced* EWNPDW (B75-50043)
Earth song. *Vocal score.* Earth song : mixed voices with brass accompaniment and timpani, trumpets 1 and 2 in B flat, horns 1 and 2 in F, trombones 1 and 2, tuba, timpani (optional). (Washburn, Robert). *Boosey and Hawkes. Unpriced* EWNPDW (B75-50043)
East, Raina. Technical exercises for the oboe. *Schott. Unpriced* VT/AF (B75-50339)
East Anglia University. *See* University of East Anglia.
Easter introit : SATB. (Beechey, Gwilym). *Banks. Unpriced* EZDM (B75-50466)
Easy album for the organ
4th. *Bosworth. Unpriced* RK/AAY (B75-50215)
Eaton, Quaintance. Opera production
2 : a handbook. *University of Minnesota Press : Oxford University Press. £7.25* AC (B75-26794) ISBN 0-8166-0689-7
Ecco ch'io lass'il core : SSATTB (unacc. or with lutes). (Striggio, Alessandro). *Oxford University Press. Unpriced* ETWNUDU (B75-50457) ISBN 0-19-341221-7
Eddison blues books. Rowe, Mike. Chicago breakdown. *2 Greycoat Place, S.W.1 : Eddison Press Ltd. £2.50* AKDW/HHW(YTKC/XNK43) (B75-03645) ISBN 0-85649-015-6
Eddystone light. (Miller, Carl). *Chappell. Unpriced* FDW (B75-50491)
Edmondson, John. The godfather, part II. Theme. *arr.* Theme from Godfather II. (Rota, Nino). *Famous Music : Chappell. Unpriced* UMMK/JR (B75-50836)
Edmunds, John F.
Got it in my soul. *Robbins. Unpriced* UMMJ (B75-50303)
Wade in the water : traditional. *Robbins. Unpriced* UMMJ (B75-50304)
Education Development Center. The musical instrument recipe book. *Penguin Education. £0.50* AY/BC (B75-08294) ISBN 0-14-081185-0
Edwardian popular music. (Pearsall, Ronald). *David and Charles. £4.95* ADW/GB(YC/XMA14) (B75-11753) ISBN 0-7153-6814-1
Edwards, John Emlyn.
Carols of the elements : for unison voices, optional 2 part melodic instruments, percussion, and piano. (Coombes, Douglas). *28 Knolls Way, Clifton, Beds. : Lindsay Music. £0.25* JFDP (B75-50532) ISBN 0-85957-004-5
Seven space songs : music for voices, melodic instruments, percussion and piano. (Coombes, Douglas). *28 Knolls Way, Clifton, Beds. : Lindsay Music. £0.58* JFE/NYLDW (B75-50541)
Zalzabar : a Christmas cantata for children, music for voices, melodic instrument, percussion & piano. (Coombes, Douglas). *28 Knolls Way, Clifton, Beds. : Lindsay Music. £0.49* JFE/NYLDE/LF (B75-50540)
Egk, Werner.
5 Stücke für Bläserquintett. *Schott. £11.00* UNR (B75-51356)
Polonaise und Adagio : für 9 instrumente, Oboe, Klarinette in B, Horn in F, Fagott, Violine I und II, Viola, Violoncello, und Kontrabass. *Schott. £7.50* NVNMHVHM (B75-51181)
Ehmann, Heinrich.
Gott, wie dein Name, so ist auch dein Ruhm : Kantate für dreistimmigen Männerchor, drei Trompeten und Basso continuo, (Bläsersatz), Pauken (ad lib.). (Lübeck, Vincent). *Bärenreiter. Unpriced* GE/WNPDE (B75-50511)
Kirchen - und Tafelmusik, no.21. Gelobet seist du, Jesu Christ : Choralkonzert für Tenor (einstimmigen Chor), zwei Trompeten, vier Posaunen und Basso continuo (ad lib). (Hammerschmidt, Andreas). *Bärenreiter. Unpriced* JGHE/WNQDH (B75-50544)
Verlieh uns Frieden : Variationen für Blechbläser und

Orgel. *Bärenreiter. £2.20* WNRR/T (B75-50378)

Ehmann, Wilhelm.

Bläser-Fibel II. Schule bläserische Gestaltung : eine Bläserschule, für Fortgeschrittene auch zum Selbst und Gruppenuntervicht. *Bärenreiter. £3.60* W/AC (B75-50354)

Vier Choral-Motetten = Four chorale motets. Op.102 : for unaccompanied four-part chorus. (Herzogenberg, Heinrich von). *Bärenreiter. £1.20* EZDH (B75-50049)

Ehret, Walter.

Friends, relatives, parents. *arr.* Friends, relatives, parents : a program opener for two-part chorus of treble voices with piano and optional guitar. (Williams, Phyllis). *Frank Music. Unpriced* FLDW (B75-51070)

How do you open a show without a curtain?. *arr.* How do you open a show without a curtain? : a program opener, for two-part chorus of treble voices with piano and optional guitar. (Williams, Phyllis). *Frank Music. Unpriced* FLDW (B75-51071)

That's a very good sign. *arr.* That's a very good sign : for two-part chorus of treble voices and piano. (Williams, Phyllis). *Frank Music. Unpriced* FLDW (B75-51072)

Eichendorff, Joseph von. Sechs geistliche Lieder = Six sacred songs : for four-part chorus of mixed voices. (Wolf, Hugo). *Bärenreiter. £1.60* EZDH (B75-50053)

Eidesis III (1971-II) : for one or two orchestras and electronic sounds. (Lanza, Alcides). *Boosey and Hawkes. Unpriced* MPPV (B75-51161)

Eight Jamaican folk-songs. *Oxford University Press. £0.50* QPK/DW/G/AYULD (B75-50720) ISBN 0-19-373273-4

Eight Morris dances of England and Flamborough sword dance. *See* 8 Morris dances of England and Flamborough sword dance.

Eighteenth century musical instruments, France and Britain = Les Instruments de musique au XVIIIe Siecle, France et Grande-Bretagne : catalogue of an exhibition. (Thibault, G). *Victoria and Albert Museum. £2.50* AL/B(YH/XF101) (B75-03646) ISBN 0-901486-71-x

Eighteenth-century violin sonatas

Book 1. *Associated Board of the Royal Schools of Music. Unpriced* SPE/AY (B75-51294)

Einem, Gottfried von.

Bruckner Dialog : für Orchester. Op 39. *Boosey and Hawkes. £3.00* MMJ (B75-50143)

Leb wohl, Frau welt. Op:43 : Liederzyklus für mittlere Singstimme und Klavier. *Boosey and Hawkes. £3.00* KFVDW (B75-50586)

Ekwueme, Laz. Hombe : Kenya (Luo) folk song, for 4-part mixed choir and contralto solo unaccompanied. *Roberton. Unpriced* EZDW (B75-50477)

El Paso : paso doble brass band. (Siebert, Edrich). *Studio Music. Unpriced* WMHSW (B75-50362)

Electric muse : the story of folk into rock. *Eyre Methuen. £1.70* A/HK(ZF) (B75-21664) ISBN 0-413-31860-5

Electronic music synthesis : concepts, facilities, techniques. (Howe, Hubert S). *Dent. £6.50* APV/B (B75-07344) ISBN 0-460-04251-3

Electronic musical instruments. (Crowhurst, Norman Herbert). *Foulsham-Tab. £1.80* APV/B (B75-50978) ISBN 0-7042-0144-5

Elegeia : für Orchester. (Baird, Tadeusz). *Litolff : Peters. Unpriced* MMJ (B75-51153)

Elegy for guitar. (Rawsthorne, Alan). *Oxford University Press. Unpriced* TSPMJ (B75-51325) ISBN 0-19-358510-3

Elementalis : for organ. (Balada, Leonardo). *Schirmer. £0.80* RJ (B75-51272)

Elephant's gavotte : for double bass and piano. (Walter, David). *Yorke. Unpriced* SSPHM (B75-50777)

Elgar on record : the composer and the gramophone. (Moore, Jerrold Northrop). *Oxford University Press. £5.00* BEP(N/XM21) (B75-06901) ISBN 0-19-315434-x

Elizabeth Rogers hir virginall booke. *Dover : Constable. £3.00* QSQ/AY (B75-51265) ISBN 0-486-23138-0

Elizabethan serenade. *arr.* Elizabethan serenade. (Binge, Ronald). *Ascherberg, Hopwood and Crewe. Unpriced* TSNTK (B75-51320)

Elkus, Jonathan. Charles Ives and the American band tradition : a centennial tribute. *American Arts Documentation Centre, University of Exeter. £0.60* BIVUMM (B75-05796) ISBN 0-85989-005-8

Ellis, Ray. Olympic fanfares : for marching band. *Unichappell. Unpriced* UMMGM (B75-50829)

Elms, Albert.

The battle of Trafalgar : for military band. *Boosey and Hawkes. Unpriced* UMMJ (B75-50305)

The land of the mountain and the flood. *Selections : arr.* Sutherland's law. (MacCunn, Hamish). *Ambleside Music : EMI. Unpriced* WMK (B75-51422)

On parade : quick march. *Boosey and Hawkes. Unpriced* UMMGM (B75-50830)

Trumpets sound! *Ambleside Music : EMI. Unpriced* WMPWRNSK (B75-51432)

Elton John. (Stein, Cathi). *Futura Publications. £0.45* AKDW/GB/E(P) (B75-19733) ISBN 0-86007-201-0

Elytis, Odysseas.

Klima tis apussias = Stimmung der Abwesenheit = Sense of absence : for voice and chamber orchestra. (Antoniou, Theodore). *Bärenreiter. £2.40* KE/MRDW (B75-50116)

Klima tis apussias. *Vocal score.* Klima tis apussias = Stimmung der Abwesenheit = Sense of absence : for voice and piano. (Antoniou, Theodore). *Bärenreiter. £2.40* KDW (B75-50104)

Emden, Ulrika.

Kleine Stücke grosser Meister : für Sopran-und Altblockflöte. *Noetzel : Hinrichsen. Unpriced* VSNUK/AAY (B75-50867)

Kleine Tänze grosser Meister : für Sopran-und Altblockflöte. *Noetzel : Hinrichsen. Unpriced* VSNUK/AH/AY (B75-50868)

Emerson, Geoffrey.

Five short pieces for organ. Folk tune. *arr.* Folk tune. (Whitlock, Percy). *Emerson. Unpriced* UNNK (B75-50308)

Sonata for piano, no.5, op.147, in B major. Scherzo. *arr.* Scherzo and trio. (Schubert, Franz). *Emerson. Unpriced* VNPK (B75-51360)

Emerson, Ralph Waldo. And when I am entombed : for voices, guitar & piano. (Huscroft, John). *27 Donald Way, Chelmsford : John Huscroft. Unpriced* KE/TSPDW (B75-50567)

EMG Handmade Gramophones Limited. The art of record buying : a list of recommended microgroove recordings 1975. *E.M.G. £3.20* A/FD(WT) (B75-06145) ISBN 0-900982-06-3

Emsheimer, Ernest. Recercares for organ, nos.1-4. Four recercars : for organ. (Steigleder, Johann Ulrich). New ed. *Bärenreiter. Unpriced* RJ (B75-50734)

Enchanted valley : traditional Irish air. (Nelson, Havelock). *Roberton. £0.12* FEZDW (B75-50502)

English church music : a collection of essays

1975. *Addington Palace, Croydon CR9 5AD : Royal School of Church Music. £1.00* AD/LD(YD/D) (B75-21074) ISBN 0-85402-060-8

English Folk Dance and Song Society. The folk directory 1975. *The Society. £2.00(£1.00 to members)* A/G(BC) (B75-19082) ISBN 0-85418-107-5

English Folk Dance and Song Society. Folk shop instrumental series. *See* Folk shop instrumental series.

English pageant : a suite for orchestra. (Tomlinson, Ernest). *Central Music Library : Belwin-Mills. Unpriced* MMG (B75-50607)

Entertainer ; with, Maple leaf rag. (Joplin, Scott). *Paxton. Unpriced* WMK/AHXJ (B75-50373)

Entertainer. (Joplin, Scott). *Rubank : Novello. Unpriced* VQPK/AHXJ (B75-51365)

Entertainer. (Joplin, Scott). *Rubank : Novello. Unpriced* VRNTK/AHXJ (B75-51366)

Entertainer. (Joplin, Scott). *Rubank : Novello. Unpriced* VVNTK/AHXJ (B75-51402)

Entertainer. (Joplin, Scott). *Rubank : Novello. Unpriced* VVRPK/AHXJ (B75-51411)

Entertainer. *arr.* The entertainer. (Joplin, Scott). *Rubank Novello. Unpriced* VQPK/AHXJ (B75-51365)

Entertainer. *arr.* The entertainer. (Joplin, Scott). *Rubank Novello. Unpriced* VRNTK/AHXJ (B75-51366)

Entertainer. *arr.* The entertainer. (Joplin, Scott). *Rubank Novello. Unpriced* VVNTK/AHXJ (B75-51402)

Entertainer. *arr.* The entertainer. (Joplin, Scott). *Rubank Novello. Unpriced* VVRPK/AHXJ (B75-51411)

Entertainer. *arr.* The entertainer ; with, Maple leaf rag. (Joplin, Scott). *Paxton. Unpriced* WMK/AHXJ (B75-50373)

Entertainer. *arr.* The entertainer : two-part song. (Joplin, Scott). *Ashdown. £0.12* FDW (B75-51056)

Entertainer : two-part song. (Joplin, Scott). *Ashdown. £0.12* FDW (B75-51056)

Epilogue after Homer's 'The Odyssey' : for mezzosoprano, narrator, oboe, horn, guitar, piano, percussion and doublebass. (Antoniou, Theodor). *Bärenreiter. Unpriced* KFNE/NYDNQDX (B75-50578)

Epitaffio no. 1, 2 & 3. (Nono, Luigi). *Ars Viva : Schott. £11.60* HYE/M (B75-50086)

Erb, James. Shenandoah : American folk song, for full chorus of mixed voices unaccompanied. *Roberton. £0.12* EZDW (B75-50478)

Erickson, Robert. Sound structure in music. *University of California Press. £6.00* A/PU (B75-27354) ISBN 0-520-02376-5

Erik Satie. (Harding, James). *Secker and Warburg. £5.75* BSCT(N) (B75-24234) ISBN 0-436-19106-7

Erstes Zusammenspiel : für vier Sopranblockflöten und Klavier. (Heilbut, Peter). *Heinrichshofen : Hinrichsen. Unpriced* VSRNRQ (B75-50872)

Eschenbach, Wolfram von. Vom Hönensagen : für Frauenstimmen und obligates Harmonium. (Kagel, Mauricio). *Universal. Unpriced* FDE (B75-50485)

Escott, Colin. Catalyst : the Sun Records story. *Aquarius Books; Station Rd, Kings Langley, Herts. : Distributed by Argus Books. £2.90* A/FD(Q) (B75-21384) ISBN 0-904619-00-1

Esquisses experimentales : für Flöte. (Jungk, Klaus). *Litolff : Peters. Unpriced* VRPMJ (B75-50326)

Estro armonico. Op.3, no.11. Largo, Allegro. *arr.* Sicilienne and finale. (Vivaldi, Antonio). *Chappell. Unpriced* UMMK (B75-51349)

Etkin, Ruth. Playing & composing on the recorder. *Sterlin etc. : Distributed by Ward Lock. £1.95* AVS/E (B75-28638) ISBN 0-7061-2080-9

'Etude baroque : grand étude de concert pour piano. (Lavagne, Andre). *Chappell. Unpriced* QPJ (B75-50194)

Etüden für Oboe. (Sous, Alfred). *Litolff : Peters. Unpriced* VT/AF (B75-50340)

'Etudes : piano solo

Book 1. (Debussy, Claude). *Peters. Unpriced* QPJ (B75-51239)

Book 2. (Debussy, Claude). *Peters. Unpriced* QPJ (B75-51240)

Evans, Colin. 50 hymns for band

Book I: General and Christmas. *Oxford University Press. Unpriced* UMK/DM/AY (B75-50823) ISBN 0-19-363060-5

Events 1 : for violin, piano and orchestra, 1968. (Antoniou, Theodore). *Bärenreiter. £2.00* MPSP (B75-50152)

Events 2 : for large orchestra, 1969. (Antoniou, Theodore). *Bärenreiter. £4.00* MMJ (B75-50139)

Events 3 : for orchestra with tape and slides, 1969. (Antoniou, Theodore). *Bärenreiter. £2.40* MMJ (B75-50140)

Everyman's handyman : nine rounds and canons for men's voices. (Beeson, Jack). *Boosey and Hawkes. Unpriced* GEZDW/XC (B75-50519)

Ewartung : Orgelspiel. (Bialas, Günter). *Bärenreiter. £2.60* RJ (B75-50205)

Ewell Court suite : for piano solo. (Butterworth, Neil). *Banks. Unpriced* QPG (B75-50669)

Exaudi Domine vocem meam : vier Psalm-Motetten, für gemischten Chor. (Schwarz-Schilling, Reinhard). *Bärenreiter. £1.20* EZDJ (B75-50055)

Excursion : for orchestra. (Washburn, Robert). *Oxford University Press. Unpriced* MMJ (B75-51159)

Exeter University. *See* University of Exeter.

Exotica : für aussereuropäische Instrumente, 1971-72. (Kagel, Mauricio). *Universal. Unpriced* LN (B75-50126)

Experimenting with electronic music. (Brown, Robert, *b.1943*). *Foulsham-Tab. £1.50* APV/B (B75-05798) ISBN 0-7042-0129-1

Extensions. Education Development Center. The musical instrument recipe book. *Penguin Education. £0.50* AY/BC (B75-08294) ISBN 0-14-081185-0

Extravaganza : song cycle for medium voice and piano. (Dickinson, Peter). *Novello. £1.25* KFVDW (B75-50585)

Exultate Deo : for four-part chorus of mixed voices with piano accompaniment. (Najera, Edmund). *Schirmer. Unpriced* DJ (B75-50423)

Fabliau : für Orgel. (Kelemen, Milko). *Litolff : Peters. Unpriced* RJ (B75-50208)

Fabulous country : concert march. (Bennett, Robert Russell). *Warner : Blossom. Unpriced* UMMGM (B75-50828)

Facets : in four movements, for percussion solo, two timbales, tom-toms (or bongos), snare drum, two suspended cymbals, triangle, five temple blocks. (Russell, Armand). *Schirmer. £1.30* XMG (B75-51475)

Facetten : drei Impromptus, für Trompete in C und Klavier. (Beck, Conrad). *Schott. £2.25* WSPJ (B75-51457)

False knight upon the road : folk song setting for baritone voice and piano. (Boatwright, Howard). *Oxford University Press. Unpriced* KGNDW (B75-50591)

Family of Bach : a brief history. (Bizony, Celia). *Artemis Press. £0.90* BBCB(N) (B75-13733) ISBN 0-85141-281-5

Famous Puccini arias

1-2: One fine day (Un bel di vedremo), from Madame Butterfly ; Love and music (Vissi d'arte), from Tosca. (Puccini, Giacomo). *Studio Music. Unpriced* WMK/DW (B75-50928)

3-4: Love duet (Oh! quanti occhi fissi attenti), from Madame Butterfly ; Your tiny hand is frozen (Che gelida manina), from La Bohème. (Puccini, Giacomo). *Studio Music. Unpriced* WMK/DW (B75-50929)

5-6: Musetta's waltz song (Quando me'n vu'), from La Bohème ; Stars are brightly shining (E lucetan le stelle), from Tosca. (Puccini, Giacomo). *Studio Music. Unpriced* WMK/DW (B75-50930)

7-8: Oh my beloved father (O mio babbino caro), from Gianni Schicchi ; They call me Mimi (Mi chiamano Mimi), from La Bohème. (Puccini, Giacomo). *Studio Music. Unpriced* WMK/DW (B75-50931)

Fancies, toyes and dreames. (Farnaby, Giles). *Chester. Unpriced* WNRK (B75-51445)

Fanfare and allegro : for trumpet and solo timpani. (Leonard, Stanley). *Simrock. Unpriced* WSPLXR (B75-50383)

Fanfare for brass trio (2 trumpets and horn). (Kirchner, Leon). *Associated Music. Unpriced* WNTGN (B75-50944)

Fanshawe, David.

African Sanctus : a story of travel and music. *Collins : Harvill Press. £4.50* A(N) (B75-12857) ISBN 0-00-262002-2

African Sanctus : piano with voice-part optional. *Chappell. Unpriced* QPJ (B75-50697)

Fantasia super H.C. : für Orgel. (Hogner, Friedrich). *Litolff : Peters. Unpriced* RJ (B75-51273)

Fantasie for two trumpets & piano. Fantasie : pour 2 trompettes (ut ou si bémol) et piano. (Vallier, Jacques). *Chappell. Unpriced* WSNTQ (B75-50381)

Fantasie : pour 2 trompettes (ut ou si bémol) et piano. (Vallier, Jacques). *Chappell. Unpriced* WSNTQ (B75-50381)

Fantasy for mechanical organ in F minor. K.608. *arr.* Fantasy for mechanical organ. K.608. (Mozart, Wolfgang Amadeus). *Schirmer. Unpriced* QNVK (B75-50662)

Fantasy for mechanical organ. K.608. (Mozart, Wolfgang Amadeus). *Schirmer. Unpriced* QNVK (B75-50662)

Faramondo. Overture. Ouverture für Streicher, 2 Oboi (Fl.), Fagotti ad lib, und Cembalo. (Handel, George Frideric). *Kneusslin : Hinrichsen. Unpriced* MRJ (B75-50159)

Fares, Louise. 'Music Week' industry yearbook

No.6 : 1975-76. *7 Carnaby St., W1V 1PG : Billboard Publications Ltd. £2.50* A/FD(BC) (B75-12986) ISBN 0-902285-01-7

Farish, Margaret K. String music in print. 2nd ed. *Bowker. £18.00* ARXN(TC) (B75-25110) ISBN 0-8352-0596-7

Farmer. The ploughboy. *arr.* The ploughboy : traditional, solo for E flat or B flat bass and brass band. (Shield, William). *455 Brighton Rd, South Croydon : Paul. Unpriced* WMPWUU (B75-50936)

Farnaby, Giles. Keyboard music. *Selections: arr.* Fancies, toyes and dreames. *Chester. Unpriced* WNRK

(B75-51445)
Farnon, Robert.
Une Vie de matelot = A sailor's life : theme and variations for brass band. *R. Smith. Unpriced* WM/T (B75-50913)
Concorde march. *arr.* Concorde march. *Chappell. Unpriced* WMK/AGM (B75-51425)
Fasciculus sacrarum harmoniarum. Ricercars nos.1-3. Three ricercars. (Aichinger, Gregor). *Galaxy : Galliard. Unpriced* VSNS (B75-50858)
Fashion : a musical comedy. (Mowatt, Anna Cora). *French. £1.10* BPIACM (B75-20393) ISBN 0-573-68065-5
Fauré, Gabriel.
Requiem. Op.48. *Vocal score.* Requiem. Op.48 : for four-part chorus of mixed voices with soprano and baritone soli. *Schirmer. Unpriced* DGKAV (B75-51001)
Requiem. Op.48. *Vocal score.* Requiem. Opus 48 : for soprano and baritone soli, SATB and orchestra. *Novello. £0.75* DGKAV (B75-50018)
Requiem. Opus 48. *Vocal score: arr.* Requiem. Opus 48. *Novello. £1.00* DGKAV (B75-51000)
Selected pieces. *Cramer. Unpriced* QPJ (B75-50189)
Faustini, Giovanni. La Calisto. *Vocal score.* La Calisto : opera in two acts with a prologue. (Cavalli, Francesco). *Faber Music. Unpriced* CC (B75-50989)
Feast song for Saint Cecilia : for SATB with divisions (unaccompanied). (Rose, Bernard). *Novello. £0.20* EZDH (B75-51037)
Feather, Leonard. From Satchmo to Miles. *Quartet Books. £1.50* AMT(M) (B75-10770) ISBN 0-7043-1223-9
Felice, John. From Quasimodo Sunday : for unaccompanied double bass. *Yorke. Unpriced* SSPMJ (B75-50781)
Fellowes, Edmund Horace. Sing joyfully : SSATB and strings (or organ) with verses for bass solo. (Mundy, John). Revised ed. *Oxford University Press. £0.40* ERXNRDK (B75-50453) ISBN 0-19-352184-9
Fenlon, Iain. Il primo libro di madrigali. *Selections.* Three madrigals : for 4 voices or instruments. (Arcadelt, Jacques). *Antico. Unpriced* EZDU (B75-50473)
Ferguson, Barry. Praise the Lord, O my soul : anthem for unison voices or SATB and organ, suitable for Rogation, Harvest or general use. *Novello. £0.10* JDK/LP (B75-50523)
Ferguson, Howard.
Anne Cromwell's Virginal Book, 1638. *Oxford University Press. £2.50* QSQ/AY (B75-50725) ISBN 0-19-372637-8
Complete harpsichord works of William Croft
Vol.1. (Croft, William). *Stainer and Bell. Unpriced* QRP/AZ (B75-50200)
Vol.2. (Croft, William). *Stainer and Bell. Unpriced* QRP/AZ (B75-50201)
Keyboard interpretation from the 14th to the 19th century : an introduction. *Oxford University Press. £2.95* APW/E(XCX601) (B75-21076) ISBN 0-19-318419-2
Piano music. *Selections.* Haydn. (Haydn, Joseph). *Oxford University Press. £1.50* QPJ (B75-51243) ISBN 0-19-372782-x
Ferguson, *Sir* Samuel. The lark in the clear air : Irish air. (Deale, Edgar Martin). *Banks. Unpriced* DW (B75-50439)
Fernandez, Heraclio. El Diablo suelto : valzer popolare venezuelano per chitarra. *Zanibon : Hinrichsen. Unpriced* TSPMHW (B75-50278)
Ferneyhough, Brian. Cassandra's dream song : solo flute. *Peters. Unpriced* VRPJ (B75-50321)
Ferruccio Busoni : a biography. (Dent, Edward Joseph). *48 Great Marlborough St., W.1 : Eulenberg Books. £3.75* BBVM(N) (B75-24235) ISBN 0-903873-15-x
Festing, Michael Christian. Sonatas for violin & continuo. Op.4, nos 2,3. Two sonatas for violin and basso continuo. *Oxford University Press. £2.00* SPE (B75-50246) ISBN 0-19-356458-0
Festival chorus. Slavnostní sbor = Festlicher Chor = Festival chorus : for four male voices, women's and men's chorus and piano. (Janacek, Leos). *Bärenreiter. £1.20* DX (B75-50033)
Festival for autumn : for dramatic presentation or concert performance, for voices, recorder, guitar, piano and percussion. *Novello. £0.50* JFE/NYDSDX (B75-50537)
Festive overture : for orchestra. (Washburn, Robert). *Oxford University Press. Unpriced* MMJ (B75-51160)
Festliche Stunden : elektronische Orgel. *Nagel : Bärenreiter. £2.00* RPVK/AAY (B75-50218)
Festouverture = Solemn overture. Opus 73 : for orchestra. (Glazunov, Aleksandr Konstantinovich). *Belaieff : Peters. Unpriced* MMJ (B75-50144)
Fêtes de Terpsichore. *Selections: arr.* Air en forme de pavane. (Boisvallée, Francois de). *Chappell. Unpriced* TMK/AHVG (B75-50273)
Fetzer, John F. Romantic Orpheus : profiles of Clemens Brentano. *University of California Press. £6.85* A(ZD) (B75-07422) ISBN 0-520-02312-9
Ffinch, Michael. The selfish giant. *Vocal score.* The selfish giant : an opera for young people. (Shaw, Francis). *Chester : Hansen. Unpriced* CN (B75-50009)
ffolkes. Joseph Cooper's hidden melodies : six improvisations for piano. (Cooper, Joseph). *Paxton. Unpriced* QPJ (B75-51237)
Field, Eugene. Full fathom five. Sea Lullaby. Sea lullaby : unison or soprano solo. (Fraser, Shena). *Thames. Unpriced* JDW (B75-50527)
Field, John. Marche triomphale : for piano. *Helicon. Unpriced* QPGM (B75-50673)
Fievet, Paul. - D'in vieux manoir : pour hautbois et piano. *Chappell. Unpriced* VTPJ (B75-50341)
Finger, Godfrey.
Sonata for trumpet, oboe and basso continuo in C major. *Musica rara. Unpriced* NWNTE (B75-51190)
Sonata for trumpet, violin, oboe and basso continuo in C major. *Musica rara. Unpriced* NUNSE (B75-51174)
Finger, Gottfried.
A collection of Musick in two parts. *Selections.* Leichte Duette für Altblockflöten. *Heinrichshofen : Hinrichsen. Unpriced* VSSNU (B75-50880)
Sonata for treble recorder & harpsichord, no.6. in F major. Sonata in F : for treble recorder and harpsichord, (or flute or oboe and piano). *Piers Press. Unpriced* VSSPE (B75-50336)
Fink, Siegfried. Conga Brazil : Brazilian impression for percussion ensemble (8 players). *Simrock. £3.60* XNNHJNC (B75-51476)
Finlayson, Walter Alan. Bright eyes. *arr.* Bright eyes. *Boosey and Hawkes. £2.20* WMPWRNTK (B75-51433)
Fire maid : an opera for schools. (Long, Robert). *Oxford University Press. £2.50* CN (B75-50402) ISBN 0-19-337374-2
Fire maid. *Vocal score.* The fire maid : an opera for schools. (Long, Robert). *Oxford University Press. £2.50* CN (B75-50402) ISBN 0-19-337374-2
Fireworks for brass band : variations on a theme of W. Hogarth Lear. (Howarth, Elgar). *Paxton. Unpriced* WM/T (B75-50914)
First book of guitar solos. *Oxford University Press. Unpriced* TSPMK/AAY (B75-50812) ISBN 0-19-356727-x
First year flautist
Vol.2. *Ashdown. £1.20* VRPK/AAY (B75-50852)
Fišer, Luboš. Report : for wind instruments, piano and percussion. *Peters. Unpriced* NYF (B75-50173)
Fisher, Harry. Christ in competition. *Edwardian Music. Unpriced* JDM/AY (B75-51078) ISBN 0-551-05530-8
Fiske, Roger.
Reminiscences of Michael Kelly. (Kelly, Michael, *b.1762*) 2nd ed. reprinted with corrections. *Oxford University Press. £7.50* AKGH/E(P) (B75-20392) ISBN 0-19-255417-4
Sonatas of three parts (1683), for strings & basso continuo, nos 1-6, Z.790-5. Sonatas for three parts, nos.1-6. (Purcell, Henry). *Eulenburg. Unpriced* NXNTE (B75-51194)
Fitzwilliam Museum. French music and the Fitzwilliam : a collection of essays and a catalogue of an exhibition of French music in the Fitzwilliam Museum in May and June 1975 on the occasion of two concerts of French music. *Trumpington St., Cambridge : Fitzwilliam Museum. £1.00* A(YH/XEXK142/WJ) (B75-18363) ISBN 0-904454-01-0
Five American hymn tunes : for men's or mixed voices unaccompanied. *Oxford University Press. Unpriced* GEZDM/AYT (B75-50512)
Five beginner's pieces : for piano. (Kasschau, Howard). *Schirmer. Unpriced* QPJ (B75-51245)
Five dialogues. Op.7 : for two B flat clarinets. (Bavicchi, John). *Oxford University Press. Unpriced* VVNU (B75-50895)
Five eighteenth century piano sonatas. *Oxford University Press. Unpriced* QPE/AY (B75-51227) ISBN 0-19-373206-8
Five folk-songs. *Oxford University Press. £0.75* EZDW/AY (B75-50483) ISBN 0-19-343836-4
Five pieces for half-size violin and piano. *See* Jacob, Gordon.
Five portraits : for piano. (Rose, Michael). *British and Continental. Unpriced* QPJ (B75-51251)
Five short pieces for organ. Folk tune. *arr.* Folk tune. (Whitlock, Percy). *Emerson. Unpriced* UNNK (B75-50308)
Five short pieces for strings. (Křenek, Ernst). *Bärenreiter. Unpriced* RXNS (B75-50761)
Five songs on Japanese haiku : soprano, clarinet, in A, violin, violoncello. (Riley, Dennis). *Peters. Unpriced* KFLE/NVVQNTDW (B75-51125)
Five transcriptions for string orchestra, (with optional trumpet in C). (Binkerd, Gordon). *Boosey and Hawkes. £12.50* RXMK/AAY (B75-50228)
Flammarion, Camille. When I heard the learn'd astronomer : for tenor and wind band. (Bedford, David). *Universal. Unpriced* KGHE/UMDX (B75-51130)
Flanders, Michael. The Michael Flanders and Donald Swann song book. (Swann, Donald). *Chappell. Unpriced* KDW (B75-50114)
Fleming, Antony le. *See*
Le Fleming.
Le Fleming, Antony.
Fleming, Christopher le. *See* Le Fleming, Christopher.
Fleming, Jimmy. Sylvia. *arr.* Sylvia. *Studio Music. Unpriced* WMK/DW (B75-50926)
Fletcher, Stanley. Four violin duets. *Boosey and Hawkes. Unpriced* SNU (B75-50241)
Flight, fight and romance : eight folk songs for voices and guitar. *Oxford University Press. £0.35* JE/TSDW/G/AY (B75-50094) ISBN 0-19-330628-x
Flight of fancy. *arr.* Flight of fancy : duet for cornet and euphonium with piano. (Hanmer, Ronald). *R. Smith. Unpriced* NWXPNT (B75-50647)
Flight of fancy : duet for cornet and euphonium with brass band. (Hanmer, Ronald). *R. Smith. Unpriced* WMPWRPLWW (B75-50935)
Flight of fancy : duet for cornet and euphonium with piano. (Hanmer, Ronald). *R. Smith. Unpriced* NWXPNT (B75-50647)
Flor del campo : valzer venezuelano per chitarra. *Zanibon Hinrichsen. Unpriced* TSPMHW (B75-50279)
Flores negras : pasillo ecuatoriano, per chitarra. *Zanibon Hinrichsen. Unpriced* TSPMK (B75-50284)
Florilegium cantionum latinarum : melodiae veteres ad cantum clavibus
Carmina profana. *Zanibon : Hinrichsen. Unpriced* KDW (B75-50107)
Flute master : ausgewählte Stücke für Altblockflöte allein (auch Querflöte oder Oboe). *Schott. £1.75* VSSPM/AY (B75-51387)
Fly, Leslie. London pictures : piano solos. *Forsyth. Unpriced* QPJ (B75-51242)
Fly, envious time. Op.148 : song with piano accompaniment. (Rubbra, Edmund). *Lengnick. £0.35* KDW (B75-51112)
Focus on classics. *EMI. Unpriced* RSPMK/AAY (B75-51283)
Folk directory
1975. *The Society. £2.00(£1.00 to members)* A/G(BC) (B75-19082) ISBN 0-85418-107-5
Folk musical instruments of Turkey. (Picken, Laurence). *Oxford University Press. £38.50* BZCAL/B (B75-25557) ISBN 0-19-318102-9
Folk shop instrumental series. Brune, John A. Resonant rubbish. *2 Regent's Park Rd, NW1 7AY : English Folk Dance and Song Society. Unpriced* AL/BC (B75-08293) ISBN 0-85418-097-4
Folk song in England. (Lloyd, Albert Lancaster). *Paladin. £1.50* ADW/G(YD) (B75-10254) ISBN 0-586-08210-7
Folk songs from Sussex and other songs. (Butterworth, George). *Galliard. Unpriced* KDW (B75-50551) ISBN 0-85249-332-0
Folkish tune : for horn in F and piano. (Pitfield, Thomas). *British and Continental Music Agencies. Unpriced* WTPJ (B75-50957)
Folksongs of Britain and Ireland : a guidebook to the living tradition of folksinging in the British Isles and Ireland, containing 360 folksongs from field recordings sung in English, Lowland Scots, Scottish Gaelic, Irish Gaelic and Manx Gaelic, Welsh, Cornish, Channel Islands French, Romany and Tinkers' Cant, etc. *Cassell. £15.00* ADW/G(YC) (B75-50974) ISBN 0-304-93754-1
Follow the star. *Selections: arr.* Follow the star : song album from a new musical for Christmas. (Parker, Jim). *Chappell. Unpriced* KDW/LF (B75-51120)
Forbes, Sebastian. Capriccio : organ. *Oxford University Press. £1.30* RJ (B75-50731) ISBN 0-19-375382-0
Forbes, Watson.
A classical and romantic album : for trumpet in B flat and piano
2nd. *Oxford University Press. £0.90* WSPK/AAY (B75-50947) ISBN 0-19-356523-4
3rd. *Oxford University Press. £0.90* WSPK/AAY (B75-50948) ISBN 0-19-356525-0
Classical and romantic pieces for clarinet and piano
Book 1. *Oxford University Press. £1.25* VVPK/AAY (B75-51406) ISBN 0-19-356517-x
Book 2. *Oxford University Press. £1.25* VVPK/AAY (B75-51407) ISBN 0-19-356520-x
Ford, Peter Robert John. Wagner : a documentary study. *Thames and Hudson. £12.00* BWC(N) (B75-30568) ISBN 0-500-01137-0
Forsblad, Leland. Bunker hill. *arr.* Bunker hill : march. *Warner : Blossom. Unpriced* UMMK/AGM (B75-50307)
Forsyth descant recorder tutor. (Lambert, Cecily). *Forsyth. Unpriced* VSR/AC (B75-50869)
Forsyth descant recorder tutor. (Lambert, Cecily). *Forsyth. Unpriced* VSR/AC (B75-51380)
Fortescue, Margaret. Careers with music ... *Careers Centre, University of East Anglia, University Plain, Norwich NR4 7TJ : University of East Anglia. £0.15(£0.10 to university and polytechnic careers services)* A(MN/YD) (B75-15001)
Fortner, Wolfgang. Machaut-Balladen : für Gesang und Orchester. *Schott. £7.30* JNGHE/MDW (B75-51101)
Fortune, Nigel. The new Oxford history of music
Vol.5: Opera and church music, 1630-1750. *Oxford University Press. £12.50* A(X) (B75-29312) ISBN 0-19-316305-5
Foss, Peter. Great songs of World War II : with the Home Front in pictures. *Wise Publications; 78 Newman St., W.1 : Distributed by Music Sales Ltd. £3.95* ADW/GB(XU7) (B75-22844) ISBN 0-86001-041-4
Foster, Stephen. Stephen Foster song book : original sheet music of 40 songs. *Dover : Constable. £2.40* KDW (B75-50553)
Foster, Stephen Collins.
Come where my love lies dreaming : for four-part chorus of mixed voices a cappella. *Schirmer. Unpriced* EZDW (B75-50479)
Some folks : for four-part chorus of mixed voices with guitar or piano accompaniment. *Schirmer. Unpriced* ETSDW (B75-50455)
Four centuries of song, from the troubadour to the Elizabethan age : for voice and guitar. *Associated Music. Unpriced* KE/TSDW/AY (B75-50563)
Four folk duets. *Forsyth. Unpriced* QNVK/DW/G/AYC (B75-51219)
Four Japanese lyrics. Opus 47 for high voice, clarinet & piano. (Josephs, Wilfred). *Novello. £0.85* KFTE/VVPDW (B75-50581)
Four little foxes : for unaccompanied mixed chorus. (Furman, James). *Oxford University Press. Unpriced* EZDW (B75-50065)
Four little foxes : for unaccompanied mixed chorus. (Furman, James). *Oxford University Press. Unpriced* EZDW (B75-50480)
Four miniatures : for two B flat clarinets. (Blank, Allan). *Associated Music. £1.30* VVNU (B75-51403)
Four orchestral landscapes (Symphony no.3). (Allanbrook, Douglas). *Boosey and Hawkes. Unpriced* MME (B75-50602)
Four outings for brass. (Previn, André). *Chester. Unpriced* WNR (B75-51437)
Four ragamats, 1967-1970 : piano. (Camilleri, Charles).

Roberton. £2.00 QPJ (B75-51235)
Four settings : for soprano and string quartet. (Dinerstein, Norman). *Boosey and Hawkes. Unpriced* KFLE/RXNSDW (B75-50576)
Four simple songs : baritone and piano. (Glasser, Stanley). *Piers Press. £1.25* KGNDW (B75-51133)
Four things a man must learn to do : for mixed chorus and piano with optional bass and guitar. (Atkinson, Condit). *Galaxy : Galliard. Unpriced* DW (B75-50436)
Four Victorian carols : SATB unacc. *Banks. Unpriced* EZDP/LF/AY (B75-51044)
Foursome fantasy : for four cornets. (Hanmer, Ronald). *Studio Music. Unpriced* WRNS (B75-51451)
Fowler, Frederick.
Two trebles : nine pieces arranged for two treble recorders and piano. *Oxford University Press. £1.20* VSSNTQK/AAY (B75-50879) ISBN 0-19-355202-7
Volkskinderlieder. *Selections: arr.* Seven pieces. (Brahms, Johannes). *Oxford University Press. £1.00* RXMK (B75-50750) ISBN 0-19-361906-7
Fox, Fred. A heritage of spirituals : a collection of American spirituals, for mixed chorus and piano or organ. *Galaxy : Galliard. Unpriced* DW/LC/AY (B75-50447)
Fox, Lilla. Resonant rubbish. (Brune, John A.). *2 Regent's Park Rd, NW1 7AY : English Folk Dance and Song Society. Unpriced* AL/BC (B75-08293) ISBN 0-85418-097-4
Fradd, Dale. The guitar. *Teach Yourself Books. £1.50* ATS/E (B75-18373) ISBN 0-340-16197-3
Françaix, Jean.
Le Gay Paris. *arr.* Le Gay Paris : pour trompette et instruments à vent. *Schott. £2.25* WSPK (B75-51459)
Le Gay Paris : pour trompette, solo flute, 2 hautbois, 2 clarinettes, basson, contrebasson et 2 cors. *Schott. Unpriced* UMPWS (B75-51352)
Octet for wind instruments. Octuor pour clarinette en si bémol, cor en Fa, basson, 2 violons, alto, violoncello et contrebasse. *Schott. £5.80* NVNN (B75-50162)
Trio for flute, harp & cello. Trio pour flûte, harpe et violoncelle. *Schott. £10.00* NVRNT (B75-51186)
Francis, *Saint of Assisi.* Prayer of St. Francis of Assisi : for S.A.T.B. chorus and organ or piano. (Nelson, Ron). *Boosey and Hawkes. £0.30* DH (B75-51004)
Frank, Alan.
Classical and romantic pieces for clarinet and piano
Book 1. *Oxford University Press. £1.25* VVPK/AAY (B75-51406) ISBN 0-19-356517-x
Book 2. *Oxford University Press. £1.25* VVPK/AAY (B75-51407) ISBN 0-19-356520-x
Frank, Gerold. Judy. *W.H. Allen. £5.00* AKDW/GB/E(P) (B75-24858) ISBN 0-491-01735-9
Frank, Marcel Gustave. Six reflections : for percussion quartet. *Boosey and Hawkes. Unpriced* XNS (B75-50966)
Fraser, Shena. Full fathom five. Sea Lullaby. Sea lullaby : unison or soprano solo. *Thames. Unpriced* JDW (B75-50527)
Frederick Delius. (Beecham, *Sir* Thomas, *bart*). Revised ed. *Severn House. £5.25* BDL(N) (B75-27351) ISBN 0-7278-0073-6
Frederick Delius 1862-1934, a catalogue of the Music Archive of the Delius Trust, London. (Delius Trust). *Delius Trust : Distributed by Boosey and Hawkes. £7.50* BDL(TE) (B75-08382) ISBN 0-85162-023-x
Freedman, Hermann L. Satori : solo guitar. *Thames. Unpriced* TSPMJ (B75-50810)
French music and the Fitzwilliam : a collection of essays and a catalogue of an exhibition of French music in the Fitzwilliam Museum in May and June 1975 on the occasion of two concerts of French music. *Trumpington St., Cambridge : Fitzwilliam Museum. £1.00* A(YH/XEXK142/WJ) (B75-18363) ISBN 0-904454-01-0
French's musical library. Mowatt, Anna Cora. Fashion : a musical comedy. *French. £1.10* BPIACM (B75-20393) ISBN 0-573-68065-5
Frescoes 70 : for percussion quartet. (Hummel, Bertold). *Simrock. £5.95* XNS (B75-51477)
Friends of Wells Cathedral. *See* Wells Cathedral. *Friends of Wells Cathedral.*
Friends, relatives, parents. *arr.* Friends, relatives, parents : a program opener for two-part chorus of treble voices with piano and optional guitar. (Williams, Phyllis). *Frank Music. Unpriced* FLDW (B75-51070)
Frith, Simon. Rock file
3. *Panther. £0.75* ADW/GB (B75-21065) ISBN 0-586-04261-x
Fritsch, Helmut. Czech Christmas mass. *Vocal score.* Ceska mse vanocni = Böhmische Hirtenmesse = Czech Christmas Mass. (Ryba, Jakub Jan). *Supraphon Achauer. £5.60* DE/LF (B75-50999)
From notes to rhythm. (Hossack, Alfred). *Lutterworth Press. £0.75* A/M (B75-25556) ISBN 0-7188-2128-9
From Quasimodo Sunday : for unaccompanied double bass. (Felice, John). *Yorke. Unpriced* SSPMJ (B75-50781)
From Satchmo to Miles. (Feather, Leonard). *Quartet Books. £1.50* AMT(M) (B75-10770) ISBN 0-7043-1223-9
From the beginning : a collection of hymns. *Galliard. Unpriced* JDM/AY (B75-51079) ISBN 0-85249-306-1
From the diary of Virginia Woolf : for medium voice and piano. (Argento, Dominick). *Boosey and Hawkes. Unpriced* KFVDW (B75-50582)
From the steeples and mountains. Charles Ives : a portrait. (Wooldridge, David). *Faber. £6.00* BIV(N) (B75-15003) ISBN 0-571-10687-0
Froom, Jacqueline. Merry be man : a Christmas sequence. (Roe, Betty). *Thames. Unpriced* FEZDE/LF (B75-50499)
Frost, Robert. Three poems of Robert Frost : for voice and piano. (Carter, Elliott). *Associated Music. £1.30* KDW (B75-51103)
Fuga sopra 'l do re mi fa sol la' : für Streichquartett oder Streichorchester. (Schacht, Theodor von). *Bosse : Bärenreiter. Unpriced* RXNS/Y (B75-50763)
Fugue on fugue : for brass quintet, B flat trumpet I, B flat trumpet II, F horn, trombone, tuba. (Kaplan, Nathan Ivan). *Chappell. Unpriced* WNR/Y (B75-51438)
Full fathom five. Sea Lullaby. Sea lullaby : unison or soprano solo. (Fraser, Shena). *Thames. Unpriced* JDW (B75-50527)
Fuller, John.
Boys in a pie : two-part song with piano. (Kelly, Bryan). *Roberton. £0.12* FDW (B75-50490)
The spider monkey uncle king. *Vocal score.* The spider monkey uncle king : an opera pantomime for children. (Kelly, Bryan). *Novello. £1.10* CN (B75-50008)
Funck, Heinz. Her ich verkund euch neue Mar. Weihnachtsgesang : for four-part mixed choir. (Agricola, Martin). *Bärenreiter. £0.60* EZDP/LF (B75-50060)
Für Stimmen (... missa est) dt 31, 6 : Fassung für grossen Chor. (Schnebel, Dieter). *Schott. Unpriced* EZDX (B75-51051)
Furman, James.
Four little foxes : for unaccompanied mixed chorus. *Oxford University Press. Unpriced* EZDW (B75-50065)
Four little foxes : for unaccompanied mixed chorus. *Oxford University Press. Unpriced* EZDW (B75-50480)
Gabus, Monique.
Vocalise
No.1. *Chappell. Unpriced* CB/AFH (B75-50391)
No.2. *Chappell. Unpriced* CB/AFH (B75-50392)
No.3. *Chappell. Unpriced* CB/AFH (B75-50393)
Gade, Niels Vilhelm. Aquarelles. Op.19, no.4. *arr.* Humoreske. Op.19, no.4. *British and Continental Music. Unpriced* VVPK (B75-50902)
Gál, Hans. Johannes Brahms : his work and personality. *Severn House. £4.50* BBT(N) (B75-30567) ISBN 0-7278-0078-7
Gallo : danza venezuelana per chitarra. (Torres, Pedro Manuel). *Zanibon : Hinrichsen. Unpriced* TSPMH (B75-50275)
Gallus, Eustachius de Monte Regali. *See* Monte Regali Gallus, Eustachius de.
Galston, James. Gustav Mahler. (Walter, Bruno). *Severn House : Distributed by Hutchinson. £3.75* BME (B75-27349) ISBN 0-7278-0075-2
Game of dates : for piano. (Jenni, Donald). *Associated Music. Unpriced* QPJ (B75-50701)
Gammond, Peter.
Music hall song book : a collection of 45 of the best songs from 1890-1920. *David & Charles : EMI. £4.50* KDW/JV/AY (B75-51119) ISBN 0-7153-7115-0
Scott Joplin and the ragtime era. *Angus and Robertson. £3.00* BJRP (B75-18371) ISBN 0-207-95648-0
Gardner, David. New church praise. *Saint Andrew Press. Unpriced* DM/LSG/AY (B75-50428) ISBN 0-7152-0311-8
Gardner, Ward. Bo-peep : based on the traditional air and a fugue by Pachelbel. *Banks. Unpriced* EZDW (B75-51046)
Gardonyi, Zoltan. Davids Danklied : für Bariton, vierstimmigen gemischten Chor, Bläser und Orgel. *Bärenreiter. £3.20* EWSNSRDH (B75-50044)
Garland of carols : SATB a cappella settings. *Chappell. Unpriced* EZDP/LF/AY (B75-50470)
Gartenberg, Egon. Johann Strauss : the end of an era. *Pennsylvania State University Press. £7.00* BSQ(N) (B75-21067) ISBN 0-271-01131-9
Gary Glitter story. (Tremlett, George). *Futura Publications. £0.40* AKDW/GB/E(P) (B75-01177) ISBN 0-86007-094-8
Gavall, John. A first book of guitar solos. *Oxford University Press. Unpriced* TSPMK/AAY (B75-50812) ISBN 0-19-356727-x
Gay Paris. *arr.* Le Gay Paris : pour trompette et instruments à vent. (Françaix, Jean). *Schott. £2.25* WSPK (B75-51459)
Gay Paris : pour trompette, solo flute, 2 hautbois, 2 clarinettes, basson, contrebasson et 2 cors. (Françaix, Jean). *Schott. Unpriced* UMPWS (B75-51352)
Gay señorita : brass band. (Heath, Reginald). *R. Smith. Unpriced* WMJ (B75-50921)
Gayfer, James McDonald. Canadian landscape : tone poem concert band. *Boosey and Hawkes. Full band set £4.50, Symphonic band set £6.00, Score £1.50* UMMJ (B75-50831)
Gazzaniga, Guiseppe. Don Giovanni. Don Giovanni o sai Il Convitato di pietra : dramma giocoso in un atto di Giovanni Bertati. *Bärenreiter. Unpriced* CQC (B75-50404)
Geczy, Olga. Dioclesian. *Selections.* Suite für Streicher. (Purcell, Henry). *Litolff : Peters. Unpriced* RXM/JM (B75-50225)
Gedike, Aleksandr Fedorovich.
Sixty pieces for piano. Op.36. Sechzig Klavierstücke : für Anfänger
Heft 1. *Peters. Unpriced* QPJ (B75-50190)
Sixty pieces for piano. Op.36. Sechzig Klavierstücke : für Anfänger
Heft 2. *Peters. Unpriced* QPJ (B75-50191)
Gegenstimmen : für gemischten Chor und obligates Cembalo. (Kagel, Mauricio). *Universal. Unpriced* DX (B75-50449)
Gelobet seist du, Jesu Christ : Choralkonzert für Tenor (einstimmigen Chor), zwei Trompeten, vier Posaunen und Basso continuo (ad lib). (Hammerschmidt, Andreas). *Bärenreiter. Unpriced* JGHE/WNQDH (B75-50544)
Genzmer, Harald.
Concertino for clarinet & string orchestra. Concertino für Klarinette in B und Kammerorchester. *Peters. Unpriced* RXMPVVFL (B75-50756)
Deutsche Messe : für gemischten Chor und Orgel. *Litolff : Peters. Unpriced* DG (B75-50015)
Seven studies for oboe. Sieben Studien : Capriccios für Oboe. *Litolff : Peters. Unpriced* VTPMJ (B75-50343)
Sonata for bassoon. Sonate für Fagott. *Litolff : Peters. Unpriced* VWPME (B75-50351)
Zwolf Duos : für zwei Posaunen. *Litolff : Peters. Unpriced* WUNU (B75-50960)
George Formby : a biography. (Randall, Alan). *W.H. Allen. £2.50* AKDW/GB/E(P) (B75-01176) ISBN 0-491-01771-5
George Gershwin's two waltzes in C : piano solo. (Gershwin, George). *Warner : Blossom. Unpriced* QPHW (B75-50682)
Gerber, Heinrich Nicolaus. Inventions. *Selections.* Four inventions. *Novello. £0.65* RJ (B75-50206)
Gerhard, Roberto. The Akond of Swat : for voice and percussion. *Oxford University Press. Unpriced* KE/XDW (B75-50568) ISBN 0-19-345361-4
Gerle, Hans. Five pieces for four viols. *Oxford University Press. Unpriced* STNS/AY (B75-50786) ISBN 0-19-343241-2
Gerould, Alberta.
Lute music. *Selections : arr.* Two pieces. (Dowland, John). *Oxford University Press. £0.50* TSPMK (B75-50811) ISBN 0-19-356279-0
Three pieces from the Jane Pickeringe Lute Book (Egerton 2046). *Oxford University Press. £0.50* TSPMK/AAY (B75-50814) ISBN 0-19-356770-9
Gershwin, George.
George Gershwin's two waltzes in C : piano solo. *Warner : Blossom. Unpriced* QPHW (B75-50682)
Porgy and Bess. Summertime. *arr.* Summertime music. *Chappell. Unpriced* UMK/DW (B75-50825)
Gershwin, Ira. George Gershwin's two waltzes in C : piano solo. (Gershwin, George). *Warner : Blossom. Unpriced* QPHW (B75-50682)
Gervaise, Claude. Danceries. Selections. *arr.* Three dances. *Chester. Unpriced* WNSK/AH (B75-51450)
Gestalt 17 : für Harfe, Klavier, Schlagzeug und drei Posaunen. (Matsushita, Shin-Ichi). *Universal. Unpriced* NYDXU (B75-50172)
Geysen, Frans. Periferisch-Diagonaal-Concentrisch = Peripheral-Diagonal-Concentric : for recorder quartet. *Schott. Unpriced* VSNS (B75-50860)
Giant Wombles music book : containing words and music of 32 compositions. (Batt, Mike). *Chappell. Unpriced* KDW/JS (B75-50561)
Gibbons, Orlando.
Fantasias for treble recorder duet. Three fantasias : for two treble (alto) recorders. *Faber Music. Unpriced* VSSNU (B75-50881)
Lord we beseech thee = The collect for the Annunciation of the Blessed Virgin Mary : verse anthem for alto and chorus (SAATB) with accompaniment for viols or organ. *Novello. £0.20* ESTNRDK (B75-50040)
Giegling, Franz.
Concerto à 5 for oboe & string orchestra, op.9, no.11, in B flat major. Concerto à 5 in B flat. Op.9, no.11 : for oboe, strings and basso continuo. (Albinoni, Tommaso). *Musica rara. £6.50* RXMPVTF (B75-51286)
Concerto à 5 for oboe & string orchestra, op.9, no.11, in B flat major. *arr.* Concerto à 5 in B flat. Op.9, no.11 : for oboe, strings and basso continuo. (Albinoni, Tommaso). *Musica rara. £2.50* VTPK/LF (B75-51395)
Concerto à 5 for two oboes, strings & basso continuo, op.9, no.12, in D major. Concerto à 5 in D. Opus 9, no.12 : for 2 oboes, strings and basso continuo. (Albinoni, Tommaso). *Musica Rara. £5.00* RXMPVTNUF (B75-51287)
Gigi. *Vocal score.* Lerner and Loewe's Gigi. (Loewe, Frederick). *Chappell. Unpriced* CM (B75-50398)
Gilbert, Anthony.
Brighton piece. Op.9 : for percussion and instrumental ensemble. *Schott. Unpriced* NYE (B75-50654)
Regions. Op.6 : for orchestra. *Central Music Library : Schott. Unpriced* MMJ (B75-50614)
Gilbert, Jean. Musical activities with young children. *Ward Lock. £2.95* A/GR(VG) (B75-19508) ISBN 0-7062-3462-6
Gilbert, William Schwenck. The Mikado. *Choral score : arr.* The Mikado, or, The Town of Titipu. (Sullivan, *Sir* Arthur Seymour). *Cramer. £1.20* DACF (B75-50405)
Gilbert and Sullivan : a biography. (Pearson, Hesketh). *Macdonald and Jane's. £3.95* BSWACF(N) (B75-27958) ISBN 0-356-08034-x
Gilbert and Sullivan companion. (Ayre, Leslie). *Pan Books. £1.50* BSWACF(C) (B75-01796) ISBN 0-330-24138-9
Gilbert and Sullivan : lost chords and discords. (Brahms, Caryl). *Weidenfeld and Nicolson. £5.25* BSW(N) (B75-26088) ISBN 0-297-76936-7
Gillett, Charlie.
Making tracks : Atlantic Records and the growth of a multi-billion-dollar industry. *W.H. Allen. £3.50* ADW/GB/FD(YT/X) (B75-06240) ISBN 0-491-01152-0
Rock file
3. *Panther. £0.75* ADW/GB (B75-21065) ISBN 0-586-04261-x
Gillies, Douglas. Tinga layo : West Indian song. *Oxford University Press. Unpriced* JFDW (B75-51093) ISBN 0-19-342051-1
Gillis, Frank J. Oh, didn't he ramble : the life story of Lee Collins. (Collins, Lee). *University of Illinois Press. £5.50* AMT(P) (B75-01179) ISBN 0-252-00234-2
Giovanni Gabrieli. (Arnold, Denis). *Oxford University Press.*

£1.80 BG (B75-07792) ISBN 0-19-315231-2

Girl Guides Association. Help yourself to play the guitar. (Stevens, Susan). *Girl Guides Association. £0.35* ATS/E (B75-10255) ISBN 0-85260-002-x

Girl with the flaxen hair. (Debussy, Claude). *R. Smith. Unpriced* WMK (B75-51421)

Glasser, Stanley.
Four simple songs : baritone and piano. *Piers Press. £1.25* KGNDW (B75-51133)
Jabula : for solo flute. *Piers Press. £0.75* VRPMJ (B75-50325)

Glasunow, Alexander. *See* Glazunov, Aleksandr Konstantinovich.

Glazunov, Aleksandr Konstantinovich.
Solemn overture. Op.73. Festouverture = Solemn overture. Opus 73 : for orchestra. *Belaieff : Peters. Unpriced* MMJ (B75-50144)
Suite caracteristique = Characteristic suite. Opus 9 : for orchestra. *Belaieff : Peters. Unpriced* MMG (B75-50136)
Symphony, no.8, op.83, in E flat major. Eighth symphony, E flat major. Opus 83. *Belaieff : Peters. Unpriced* MME (B75-50130)

Glenn Miller and his Orchestra. (Simon, George Thomas). *W.H. Allen. £4.95* AMT(P) (B75-00202) ISBN 0-491-01501-1

Glinka, Mikhail Ivanovich. A life for the Tsar. *Selections.* Drei Tanze aus der Oper 'Ein Leben für den Zaren'. *Belaieff : Peters. Unpriced* MMH (B75-50137)

Glitter gang : a cassation for audience and orchestra (piano). (Williamson, Malcolm). *Weinberger. Unpriced* FDX (B75-50074)

Glitter gang. *Vocal score.* The glitter gang : a cassation for audience and orchestra (piano). (Williamson, Malcolm). *Weinberger. Unpriced* FDX (B75-50074)

Gloria : unaccompanied mixed chorus. (Argento, Dominick). *Boosey and Hawkes. £0.40* EZDH (B75-51034)

Gmür, Hanspeter. Symphony, Op.6, no.3, in E flat major. Sinfonia in E flat major. Op6/III. (Bach, Johann Christian). *Nagel : Bärenreiter. £2.40* MRE (B75-50155)

God be in my head : SSAATTBB (unacc.). (Radcliffe, Philip). *Oxford University Press. Unpriced* EZDH (B75-50460) ISBN 0-19-350354-9

God, Jehovah : mixed chorus and keyboard. (Chadwick, George Whitfield). *Galaxy : Galliard. Unpriced* DH (B75-51003)

Godefroy, Vincent. The dramatic genius of Verdi : studies of selected operas
Vol.1. *Gollancz. £6.00* BVEAC (B75-19731) ISBN 0-575-01979-4

Godfather, part 2. (Rota, Nino). *Charles Hansen : Chappell. Unpriced* KDW (B75-50113)

Godfather, part 2. Kay's theme. *arr.* Kay's theme : piano solo. (Rota, Nino). *Famous Music : Chappell. Unpriced* QPK/JR (B75-50198)

Godfather, part 2. Love said goodbye. *arr.* Love said goodbye. (Rota, Nino). *Famous Music : Chappell. Unpriced* GDW (B75-50082)

Godfather, part 2. Love said goodbye. *arr.* Love said goodbye : music by Nino Rota. (Rota, Nino). *Famous Music : Chappell. Unpriced* FDW (B75-50072)

Godfather, part 2. *Selections: arr.* The godfather, part 2. (Rota, Nino). *Charles Hansen : Chappell. Unpriced* KDW (B75-50113)

Godfather, part 2. Theme. *arr.* Theme from Godfather 2 : piano solo. (Rota, Nina). *Famous Music : Chappell. Unpriced* QPK/JR (B75-50197)

Godfather, part II. Theme. *arr.* Theme from Godfather II. (Rota, Nino). *Famous Music : Chappell. Unpriced* UMMK/JR (B75-50836)

God's grandeur. *Vocal score.* God's grandeur : for mixed chorus, brass and organ (or chorus and organ). (Paynter, John). *Oxford University Press. Unpriced* DE (B75-50998) ISBN 0-19-337781-0

Godwin, Joscelyn. Schirmer scores : a repertory of Western music. *Schirmer Books : Collier Macmillan. £6.50* A(X) (B75-28635) ISBN 0-02-870700-1

Goebels, Franzpeter. Bird-boogie : for harpsichord (piano). *Bärenreiter. £2.00* PWPJ (B75-50175)

Goedicke, Alexander. *See* Gedike, Aleksandr Fedorovich.

Goethe, Johann Wolfgang von.
Four songs for male voices
2: Ephiphanias. (Zelter, Carl). *Boosey and Hawkes. Unpriced* GEZDW (B75-50517)
3 & 4: Master and journeyman ; and, Song of the flea. (Zelter, Carl). *Boosey and Hawkes. Unpriced* GEZDW (B75-50518)

Going down with Janis. (Caserta, Peggy). *Talmy Franklin. £1.95* AKDW/GB/E(P) (B75-29317) ISBN 0-900735-40-6

Goldberger, David. Piano music. *Selections.* Kabalevsky for the young pianist. (Kabalevsky, Dmitry). *Schroeder and Gunther. Unpriced* QPJ (B75-51244)

Golden years of Irving Berlin : songs. (Berlin, Irving). *Chappell. Unpriced* KDW (B75-51102)

Golland, John. Relay : for 3 cornets, 3 trombones and brass band. *British and Continental : EMI. Unpriced* WMPWNQ (B75-51431)

Gombrosi, Marilyn P. Psalm of joy of the congregation in Salem, for the peace celebration, July 4, 1783 : the music of the first organized Independence Day celebration, for soli, chorus of mixed voices and organ music. *Boosey and Hawkes. Unpriced* DH/AYT (B75-51008)

Good earth : five folk songs for voices and guitar. *Oxford University Press. £0.35* JE/TSDW/G/AY (B75-50095) ISBN 0-19-330629-8

Goodliffe, Francis James. Kemp's music & recording industry year book (international) : a comprehensive reference source and marketing guide to the music and recording industry in Great Britain & overseas
1974-75. *Kemp's. £3.75* A/GB(YC/BC) (B75-02719) ISBN 0-901268-76-3

Goodman, Alfred.
Sonatina for oboe. Sonatine für Oboe. *Litolff : Peters. Unpriced* VTPMEM (B75-50890)
Two studies for bassoon. Zwei Studien : für Fagott. *Litolff : Peters. Unpriced* VWPMJ (B75-50352)

Goodman, Paul. Absalom. (Rorem, Ned). *Boosey and Hawkes. Unpriced* KDW (B75-51108)

Goodwin, Noël. The story of the Royal Opera House, Covent Garden. *Head Office, Poultry, EC2P 2BX : Midland Bank Ltd. Free* AC/E(YC/QB) (B75-50001) ISBN 0-9501576-2-7

Gordian knot untied. (Purcell, Henry). *Piers Press. Unpriced* VSNSK/JM (B75-50330)

Gordian knot untied. *Selections: arr.* The Gordian knot untied. (Purcell, Henry). *Piers Press. Unpriced* VSNSK/JM (B75-50330)

Got it in my soul. (Edmunds, John F). *Robbins. Unpriced* UMMJ (B75-50303)

Gotkovsky, Ida. Caractères : pièces de concert, pour violon et piano. *Chappell. Unpriced* SPJ (B75-50767)

Gott, wie dein Name, so ist auch dein Ruhm : Kantate für dreistimmigen Männerchor, drei Trompeten und Basso continuo, (Bläsersatz), Pauken (ad lib.). (Lübeck, Vincent). *Bärenreiter. Unpriced* GE/WNPDE (B75-50511)

Gottschalk, Louis Moreau. Ten compositions for pianoforte. *Chappell. Unpriced* QPJ (B75-50698)

Gould, Morton. Soundings : for orchestra. *Chappell. Unpriced* MMJ (B75-50145)

Goûts réunis or Nouveaux concerts : for instrumental ensemble
Volume 1: Concerts 5-8 : for flute or oboe or violin & basso continuo. (Couperin, François). *Musica rara. Unpriced* LNG (B75-51140)
Volume 2: Concerts 9-10, 12, 14 : for flute or oboe or violin and basso continuo. (Couperin, François). *Musica rara. Unpriced* LNG (B75-51141)
Volume 3: Concerts 10, 12-13 : for three violas da gamba or cellos or bassoons. (Couperin, François). *Musica rara. Unpriced* LNG (B75-51142)

Gowans, John. Spirit!. *Vocal score.* Spirit! : a musical. (Larsson, John). *Salvationist Publishing and Supplies. Unpriced* CM/LN (B75-50400)

Graded study duets : for two flutes or two oboes or flute and oboe with optional bassoon part. (Harvey, Paul). *Boosey and Hawkes. £0.85* VRNU (B75-50316)

Graham, Colin. King Arthur. *Choral score.* King Arthur. (Purcell, Henry). *Faber Music. Unpriced* DACB/JM (B75-50996)

Gramophone Company.
Gramophone records of the First World War : an HMV catalogue, 1914-1918. *David and Charles. £5.25* A/FD(WM) (B75-12385) ISBN 0-7153-6842-7
'His Master's Voice' recordings, plum label 'C' series (12 inch). *Old School House, Tarrant Hinton, Blandford, Dorset : Oakwood Press. £4.50* A/FD(T/WT) (B75-08384) ISBN 0-85361-166-1

Gramophone records of the First World War : an HMV catalogue, 1914-1918. (Gramophone Company). *David and Charles. £5.25* A/FD(WM) (B75-12385) ISBN 0-7153-6842-7

Grand Canyon galop : brass band by Edrich Siebert. (Siebert, Edrich). *Studio Music. Unpriced* WMHLF (B75-50361)

Grant, John, *fl.1899-1920.* The pipes of war : a record of the achievements of pipers of Scottish and overseas regiments in the war, 1914-1918. (Seton, *Sir* Bruce Gordon, *bart*) 1st ed. reprinted. *EP Publishing etc.. £5.00* AVY (B75-15172) ISBN 0-7158-1089-8

Grant, Laurence. Piano music by the great masters : the baroque era, the classic era, the romantic era. *Ashley Phoenix. Unpriced* QPK/AAY (B75-51256)

Grant, Lawrence.
Piano music. Selections. *arr.* Scott Joplin, king of ragtime : easy organ. (Joplin, Scott). *Lewis : Phoenix. Unpriced* RK/AHXJ (B75-51278)
Scott Joplin : the king of ragtime writers. (Joplin, Scott). *Lewis Music : Phoenix. Unpriced* RK/AHXJ/AY (B75-50216)
World's favorite popular classics : for piano. *Ashley Phoenix. Unpriced* QPK/AAY (B75-51257)
World's favourite more classic to contemporary piano music : early grade piano music in its original form. *Ashley : Phoenix. Unpriced* QP/AY (B75-51221)

Graves, Richard.
Anglican folk mass. An Anglican folk mass : unison. (Shaw, Martin). *Roberton. £0.30* JDGS (B75-51077)
The entertainer. *arr.* The entertainer : two-part song. (Joplin, Scott). *Ashdown. £0.12* FDW (B75-51056)
Four Victorian carols : SATB unacc. *Banks. Unpriced* EZDP/LF/AY (B75-51044)
Prince of Denmark's march. *arr.* Let the earth resound ('Lobt den Herrn der Welt'). (Clarke, Jeremiah). *Bosworth. Unpriced* JDH (B75-50522)
Three journeys : a carol. *Novello. £0.10* JDP/LFP (B75-50526)
Twentieth century carol : unison with optional 2nd part. *Bosworth. Unpriced* JDP/LF (B75-51081)

Gray, Andy. Great country music stars. *Hamlyn. £2.95* AKDW/GC/E(M) (B75-50975) ISBN 0-600-33979-3

Gray, Michael, *b.1946.* Song and dance man : the art of Bob Dylan. *Abacus. £0.75* AKDW/GB/E(P) (B75-18369) ISBN 0-349-11540-0

Gray, Vera. Knives and forks and spoons : 20 songs with rhymes. *24 Royston St., Potton : Lindsay Music. £0.55* JFDW/GR (B75-50536) ISBN 0-85957-006-1

Great Britain. *Army. Royal Irish Rangers.* The Royal Irish Rangers (27th Inniskilling), 83rd and 87th : standard settings of pipe music. *Paterson. Unpriced* VYT/KH/AYDT (B75-51415)

Great country music stars. (Gray, Andy). *Hamlyn. £2.95* AKDW/GC/E(M) (B75-50975) ISBN 0-600-33979-3

Great songs of World War II : with the Home Front in pictures. *Wise Publications; 78 Newman St., W.1 : Distributed by Music Sales Ltd. £3.95* ADW/GB(XU7) (B75-22844) ISBN 0-86001-041-4

Grechaninov, Aleksandr Tikhonovich. Kinderbuch. Op.98. Kinder-Album. Op.98 : für Klavier zweihändig. *Peters. Unpriced* QPJ (B75-50192)

Green, Elizabeth Adine Herkimer. The conductor and his score. *Prentice-Hall. £4.40* A/EC (B75-16405) ISBN 0-13-167312-2

Green, Stanley, *b.1923.* The world of musical comedy : the story of the American musical stage as told through the careers of its foremost composers and lyricists. 3rd ed. revised and enlarged. *Barnes : Yoseloff. £7.00* ACM/E(YT/X) (B75-29315) ISBN 0-498-01409-6

Green and pleasant : for chamber orchestra. (Chapple, Brian). *Chester. Unpriced* MRJ (B75-50632)

Green print for song : a book of carols. (Carter, Sydney). *Galliard. Unpriced* JDP/AY (B75-50088) ISBN 0-85249-284-7

Greenfield, Robert. A journey through America with the Rolling Stones. *Panther. £0.75* AKDW/GB/E)P/XQM) (B75-24849) ISBN 0-586-04195-8

Greenfield, Robert. Stones Touring Party. *See* Greenfield, Robert. A journey through America with the Rolling Stones.

Greenfield, Robert. STP. *See* Greenfield, Robert. A journey through America with the Rolling Stones.

Greening, Anthony. Twelve easy anthems. *Royal School of Church Music. Unpriced* DH/AY (B75-51007)

Greensleeves : for brass quartet. (Siebert, Edrich). *British and Continental. Unpriced* WNSK/DW (B75-50940)

Gregson, Edward.
Concerto for horn & brass band. *arr.* Concerto for horn and piano. *R. Smith. Unpriced* WTPK/LF (B75-50385)
Concerto grosso for brass band. *R. Smith. Unpriced* WMPWNSF (B75-50933)
Prelude and capriccio for cornet & band. *arr.* Prelude and capriccio for cornet and band. *R. Smith. Unpriced* WRPK (B75-50945)

Gresley Male Voice Choir : 70 years of music making, 1904-1974. *14 Vale Rd, Midway, Burton-on-Trent, Staffs. : J. Mason. £0.25* AD/E(QB/YDHWC/X) (B75-16406) ISBN 0-9504178-0-7

Gretschaninoff, Alexander. *See* Grechaninov, Aleksander Tikhonovich.

Grimm, Heinrich. Prodromos musicae ecclesiasticae. *Selections.* Hosianna dem Sohne David, und, Wohlauf wohlauf zu dieser Frist : zwei kleine Weihnachtskonzert, für zwei mittlere Stimmen und Basso continuo. *Bärenreiter. £1.20* JNFVEDH/LF (B75-50103)

Grimsey, John. La Périchole : operetta in three acts. *10 Rathbone St., W1P 2BJ : Josef Weinberger Ltd. £0.80* BOFACF (B75-19083) ISBN 0-902136-36-4

Grubel, J K. Four songs for male voices
3 & 4: Master and journeyman ; and, Song of the flea. (Zelter, Carl). *Boosey and Hawkes. Unpriced* GEZDW (B75-50518)

Gruber, Franz. Stille Nacht. *arr.* Stille Nacht = Silent night. *Oxford University Press. Unpriced* EZDP/LF (B75-51042) ISBN 0-19-343053-3

Grundman, Clare.
A colonial legend : for wind band. *Boosey and Hawkes. Unpriced* UMJ (B75-51333)
Nocturne : for harp and wind ensemble. *Boosey and Hawkes. £7.50* UMPTQ (B75-51351)
Nocturne for harp & wind ensemble. *arr.* Nocturne : for harp and wind ensemble, edition for harp and piano. *Boosey and Hawkes. Unpriced* TQPJ (B75-51314)

Gruss, Hans.
Suite for orchestra, no.1, in C major. S.1066. Ouverture (Orchestral suite), C major. (Bach, Johann Sebastian). *Bärenreiter. Unpriced* MRG (B75-50627)
Suite for orchestra, no.2, in B minor. S.1067. Ouverture = (Orchestral suite). B minor. (Bach, Johann Sebastian). *Cassel : Bärenreiter. Unpriced* MRG (B75-50628)
Suite for orchestra, no.3, in D major. S.1068. Ouverture = (Orchestral suite), D major. (Bach, Johann Sebastian). *Bärenreiter. Unpriced* MRG (B75-50629)
Suite for orchestra, no.4, in D major. S.1069. Ouverture = (Orchestral sutte), D major. (Bach, Johann Sebastian). *Bärenreiter. Unpriced* MRG (B75-50630)

Guarneri, Mozart Camargo. *See* Camargo Guarnieri, Mozart.

Guettler, Eugene. Canzonette. Hor va canzona mia. Hor va canzona mia = How freely flies my song : SATB a cappella. (Hassler, Hans Leo). *Warner : Blossom. Unpriced* EZDU (B75-51045)

Guglielmo, G. Trios for two violins & cello, nos, 1-6. Op.2. Sei trii per due violini e violoncello. Op.1a. (Boccherini, Luigi). *Zanibon : Hinrichsen. Unpriced* RXNT (B75-50239)

Guided sight-reading
Book 3. (Lockhart, Helen). *Forsyth. Unpriced* Q/EG (B75-51212)

Guignon, Jean Pierre. Sonatas for two cellos. Op.2, nos. 1, 4, 3. Sonates. Op.2, pour 2 violoncelles basses de violes (Gamben) ou bassons (fagotti). 1st ed. *Kneusslin Hinrichsen. Unpriced* SRNUE (B75-50260)

Guitar. (Fradd, Dale). *Teach Yourself Books. £1.50* ATS/E (B75-18373) ISBN 0-340-16197-3

Guitar book : a handbook for electric and acoustic guitarists.

(Wheeler, Tom). *Macdonald and Jane's. £5.50* ATS/B (B75-25560) ISBN 0-356-08322-5
Guitar duets : music from four centuries. *Chester. Unpriced* TSNUK/AAY (B75-50800)
Guitarist's album for the young. (Cole, Keith R). *Ricordi. £1.50* TSPMJ (B75-50806)
Gulliver, Dorothy. The fire maid. *Vocal score.* The fire maid : an opera for schools. (Long, Robert). *Oxford University Press. £2.50* CN (B75-50402) ISBN 0-19-337374-2
Gupta, Punita. Maintenance of the sitar. *9 Ranelagh Rd, Southall, Middx : The author. Free* ATSX/BT (B75-20395) ISBN 0-9504319-0-7
Gustav Holst. (Rubbra, Edmund). *10E Prior Bolton St., N.1 : Triad Press. £2.40* BHP(D) **(B75-00200)** ISBN 0-902070-12-6
Gustav Holst (1874-1934) : a centenary documentation. (Short, Michael). *White Lion Publishers. £15.00* BHP(T) (B75-07086) ISBN 0-7285-0000-0
Gustav Mahler. (Walter, Bruno). *Severn House : Distributed by Hutchinson. £3.75* BME (B75-27349) ISBN 0-7278-0075-2
Gustav Mahler and the courage to be. (Holbrook, David). *Vision Press. £7.95* BME (B75-27350) ISBN 0-85478-243-5
Gustav Mahler
The Wunderhorn years : chronicles and commentaries. (Mitchell, Donald). *Faber. £15.00* BME (B75-30566) ISBN 0-571-10674-9
Gutche, Gene. Symphony no.6. Op.45. Symphony VI. Opus 45. *Highgate Press : Galliard. Unpriced* MME (B75-51149)
Habash, John Mitri. Concerto for harpsichord in A major. Rondeau. *arr.* Christmas is coming. (Dittersdorf, Carl Ditters von). *Robbins. Unpriced* DW/LF (B75-50031)
Haieff, Alexei. Orthodox Holy Week Music : SATB a cappella. *Boosey and Hawkes. £1.75* EZDGTC/LH/AYM (B75-50459)
Hail all hail to the queen : SATB. (Berlioz, Hector). *Oxford University Press. £0.08* DW (B75-50028) ISBN 0-19-343046-0
Hail! bright Cecilia. Ode on St Cecilia's day, 1692. Z.328. *Vocal score.* Ode on St Cecilia's day, 1692 : Hail! bright Cecilia : for soprano, two altos, tenor and two basses soli, SSAATB and instruments. (Purcell, Henry). *Novello. £1.20* DX (B75-51025)
Hajdu, Mihály.
Hungarian children's songs : for two violoncellos. *Boosey and Hawkes : Editio Musica. £0.75* SRNUK/DW/GJ/AYG (B75-50261)
Hungarian children's songs : for violoncello and piano. *Boosey and Hawkes : Editio Musica. £0.75* SRPK/DW/GJ/AYG (B75-50263)
Hale, Charles T. Hexachordum Apollinis. Chaconne in C major. *arr.* Chaconne in C. (Pachelbel, Johann). *Tomus. Unpriced* VSNTK/AHJN (B75-50864)
Halevy, Ludovic. La Périchole : operetta in three acts. (Grimsey, John). *10 Rathbone St., W1P 2BJ : Josef Weinberger Ltd. £0.80* BOFACF (B75-19083) ISBN 0-902136-36-4
Halffter, Cristóbal. Tiempo para espacios : for harpsichord and string orchestra. *Universal. Unpriced* RXMPQR (B75-50751)
Hall, Alan. The second book of solos for the classical guitar. *Scratchwood Music. Unpriced* TSPMK/AAY (B75-50813)
Hall, John. Sonatina for organ, no.1. Op.46. Sonatina no.1. Op.46 : for organ manual. *Chappell. Unpriced* RE (B75-51270)
Hambledon cricket song of the Rev Reynell Cotton. (Knight, Ronald David). *40A Abbotsbury Rd, Weymouth, Dorset DT4 0AE : R.D. Knight. £0.30* BCMTADW (B75-12697) ISBN 0-903769-00-x
Hambledon's cricket glory. Knight, Ronald David. The Hambledon cricket song of the Rev Reynell Cotton. *40A Abbotsbury Rd, Weymouth, Dorset DT4 0AE : R.D. Knight. £0.30* BCMTADW (B75-12697) ISBN 0-903769-00-x
Hamilton, Iain. Dialogues on lines of Chateaubriand : for high soprano, flute, trumpet, violoncello, percussion, piano and celesta. *Central Music Library : Schott. Unpriced* KFLE/NYDNQDX (B75-50574)
Hammar, Bonnie. Quartet for wind & piano in E flat major. Quartet in E flat major for piano and wind instruments. (Berwald, Franz). *Bärenreiter. £4.80* NWNS (B75-50166)
Hammerschmidt, Andreas. Kirchen - und Tafelmusik, no.21. Gelobet seist du, Jesu Christ : Choralkonzert für Tenor (einstimmigen Chor), zwei Trompeten, vier Posaunen und Basso continuo (ad lib). *Bärenreiter. Unpriced* JGHE/WNQDH (B75-50544)
Ha'nacker Mill : song. (Plumstead, Mary). *Roberton. Unpriced* KDW (B75-50556)
Handel, George Frideric.
Atalanta. Overture. Overture for trumpet, oboes, strings and basso continuo. *Musica rara. Unpriced* MRJ (B75-51171)
Atalanta. Overture. *arr.* Overture for trumpet. oboes, strings and basso continuo. *Musica rara. Unpriced* WSPK (B75-51460)
Faramondo. Overture. Ouverture für Streicher, 2 Oboi (Fl.), Fagotti ad lib, und Cembalo. *Kneusslin Hinrichsen. Unpriced* MRJ (B75-50159)
Keyboard works
Vol.1: First set of 1720, The eight great suites. *Bärenreiter. £3.00* QRP/AZ (B75-50202)
Messiah. *Selections.* Messiah ornamented : an ornamented edition of the solos from the oratorio. *Stainer and Bell. Unpriced* DADD (B75-50013) ISBN 0-85249-318-5
Selections. Complete trumpet repertoire
Volume 1: The operas. *Musica rara. £4.50* WS (B75-51452)
Selections. Complete trumpet repertoire
Volume 2: The sacred oratorios. *Musica rara. Unpriced* WS (B75-51453)
Selections. Complete trumpet repertoire
Volume 3: The church music. *Musica rara. £4.50* WS (B75-51454)
Selections. Complete trumpet repertoire
Volume 4: Miscellaneous. *Musica rara. £4.50* WS (B75-51455)
Sonata for violin & continuo, Op.1, no.1, in D minor. Sonata in D minor for violin and basso continuo. *Oxford University Press. £1.50* SPE (B75-50247) ISBN 0-19-356979-5
Suites de pièces. 1st collection. No.5. Aria con variazioni. *arr.* Aria con variazioni 'The harmonious blacksmith'. *Oxford University Press. £0.65* TQPMK/AT (B75-50794) ISBN 0-19-356993-0
Handel. (Young, Percy Marshall). Revised ed.. *Dent. £3.95* BHC (B75-13734) ISBN 0-460-03161-9
Handel before England. (Bell, Arnold Craig). *Darley, Harrogate, N. Yorkshire : Grian-Aig Press. £4.10* BHC(N/XEZE28) (B75-31189) ISBN 0-9500714-5-5
Handel Opera Society. The story of the Handel Opera Society. *Flat 3, 26 Medway St., S.W.1 : The Society. £0.75* AC/E(YC/QB/X) (B75-08736) ISBN 0-901175-02-1
Handl, Jacob. Quartus tomus musici operis. In nomine Jesu. In nomine Jesu : motet for five voices, SAATB, for the Feast of the Holy Name and general use. *Chester. Unpriced* EZDGKHL (B75-51032)
Hanmer, Richard. Famous Puccini arias
7-8: Oh my beloved father (O mio babbino caro), from Gianni Schicchi ; They call me Mimi (Mi chiamano Mimi), from La Bohème. (Puccini, Giacomo). *Studio Music. Unpriced* WMK/DW (B75-50931)
Hanmer, Ronald.
Cuckoo quartet : 2 flutes and 2 clarinets. *Emerson. Unpriced* VNS (B75-51361)
Famous Puccini arias
1-2: One fine day (Un bel di vedremo), from Madame Butterfly ; Love and music (Vissi d'arte), from Tosca. (Puccini, Giacomo). *Studio Music. Unpriced* WMK/DW (B75-50928)
3-4: Love duet (Oh! quanti occhi fissi attenti), from Madame Butterfly ; Your tiny hand is frozen (Che gelida manina), from La Bohème. (Puccini, Giacomo). *Studio Music. Unpriced* WMK/DW (B75-50929)
5-6: Musetta's waltz song (Quando me'n vu'), from La Bohème ; Stars are brightly shining (E lucetan le stelle), from Tosca. (Puccini, Giacomo). *Studio Music. Unpriced* WMK/DW (B75-50930)
Flight of fancy. *arr.* Flight of fancy : duet for cornet and euphonium with piano. *R. Smith. Unpriced* NWXPNT (B75-50647)
Flight of fancy : duet for cornet and euphonium with brass band. *R. Smith. Unpriced* WMPWRPLWW (B75-50935)
Foursome fantasy : for four cornets. *Studio Music. Unpriced* WRNS (B75-51451)
Latin-Americana : brass band. *Studio Music. Unpriced* WMJ (B75-50920)
Operettas. *Selections : arr.* The Johann Strauss song book : containing twelve songs for solo voice and piano. (Strauss, Johann, *b.1825*). *Weinberger. Unpriced* KDW (B75-51113)
Over hill, over dale : based on an American march. *Studio Music. Unpriced* WMK/AGM (B75-51426)
La Périchole : operetta in three acts. (Grimsey, John). *10 Rathbone St., W1P 2BJ : Josef Weinberger Ltd. £0.80* BOFACF (B75-19083) ISBN 0-902136-36-4
Praeludium and allegro for trombone & brass band. *arr.* Praeludium and allegro : trombone solo with piano accompaniment. *R. Smith. Unpriced* WUPK (B75-51471)
Praeludium and allegro : trombone solo with band accompaniment. *R. Smith. Unpriced* WMPWU (B75-51435)
Prelude and rondo : for brass septet. *R. Smith. Unpriced* WNP/W (B75-50375)
A runaway girl. Soldiers in the park. *arr.* Oh! listen to the band. (Monckton, Lionel). *Studio Music. Unpriced* WMK/DW (B75-50927)
Songs. *Selections. arr.* Victor Herbert memories. (Herbert, Victor). *Studio Music. Unpriced* WMK/DW (B75-50374)
Two contrasts : oboe and piano. *Emerson. Unpriced* VTPJ (B75-50342)
The wild wild west. Conductor. The wild wild west : an American medley for military band. *Studio Music. Unpriced* UMMJ (B75-50306)
Hans Andersen : souvenir song book. (Loesser, Frank). *Edwin H. Morris. Unpriced* KDW (B75-50108)
'Hans Christian Andersen'. Anywhere I wander. *arr.* Anywhere I wander : for mixed chorus (SATB) and piano with optional rhythm guitar, bass guitar and drums. (Loesser, Frank). *Frank Music. Unpriced* DW (B75-51019)
Hans Christian Andersen. *Selections : arr.* Songs from Frank Loesser's Hans Andersen. (Loesser, Frank). *Edwin H. Morris. Unpriced* VSNSQK/DW/JR (B75-50862)
Hans Christian Andersen. *Selections : arr.* Songs from Frank Loesser's Hans Andersen. (Loesser, Frank). *Edwin H. Morris. Unpriced* VSRNRK/DW/JR (B75-50871)
Hans Christian Andersen. *Selections : arr.* Songs from Frank Loesser's Hans Andersen. (Loesser, Frank). *Edwin H. Morris. Unpriced* VSSNRK/DW/JR (B75-50878)
Hans Christian Andersen. *Selections : arr.* Songs from Frank Loesser's Hans Andersen. (Loesser, Frank). *Edwin H. Morris. Unpriced* VSTNTK/DW/JR (B75-50885)
Hans Christian Andersen. *Selections: arr.* Hans Andersen : souvenir song book. (Loesser, Frank). *Edwin H. Morris. Unpriced* KDW (B75-50108)
'Hans Christian Andersen'. The inch worm. *arr.* The inch worm : for mixed chorus (SATB) and piano with optional rhythm guitar, bass guitar and drums. (Loesser, Frank). *Frank Music. Unpriced* DW (B75-51020)
'Hans Christian Andersen'. The ugly duckling. *arr.* The ugly duckling : for two-part chorus of treble voices with piano. (Loesser, Frank). *Frank Music. Unpriced* FLDW (B75-51068)
'Hans Christian Andersen'. Wonderful Copenhagen. *arr.* Wonderful Copenhagen : for two-part chorus of treble voices with piano. (Loesser, Frank). *Frank Music. Unpriced* FLDW (B75-51069)
Hanson, Byron. Litaniae Lauretanae. K.109. *Vocal score.* Litaniae Lauretanae. K.109 (Marien sic litany) : for four-part chorus of mixed voices and soprano, alto, tenor and bass solos. (Mozart, Wolfgang Amadeus). *Schirmer. Unpriced* DS/LDB (B75-50435)
Harding, James. Erik Satie. *Secker and Warburg. £5.75* BSCT(N) (B75-24234) ISBN 0-436-19106-7
Hare, Ian. Symphony no.9, op.125, in D minor, 'Choral'. Freude schöne Gotterfunken. *arr.* Hymn to joy. (Beethoven, Ludwig van). *Oxford University Press. £0.40* RK/DW (B75-50736) ISBN 0-19-375294-8
Harf, Jost. A collection of Musick in two parts. *Selections.* Leichte Duette für Altblockflöten. (Finger, Gottfried). *Heinrichshofen : Hinrichsen. Unpriced* VSSNU (B75-50880)
Harland, Peter. Sonata à 5 for two violins, trumpet, bassoon, viola da gamba and basso continuo. (Schmelzer, Johann Heinrich). *Musica rara. Unpriced* NUNQE (B75-51172)
Harmony. (Schenker, Heinrich). *M.I.T. Press. £2.00* A/R (B75-02996) ISBN 0-262-69044-6
Harmony of Maine. *Selections.* Deep North Spirituals, 1794 : mixed or male voices in three and four parts. (Belcher, Supply). *Peters. Unpriced* EZDM (B75-50058)
Harper, John. Psalm 150 : two-part. *Oxford University Press. £0.08* FDR (B75-50069) ISBN 0-19-351120-7
Harris, Karen. Sounds like folk
No.4: Victorian tear jerkers. *E.F.D.S. Unpriced* JE/TSDW/G/AY (B75-50092)
Harrison, Max. Modern jazz, the essential records : a critical selection. *Aquarius Books; Station Rd, Kings Langley, Herts. : Distributed by Argus Books. £2.90* AMT/FD(XPE26) (B75-21669) ISBN 0-904619-01-x
Hartley, Geoffrey. Round the mulberry bush : a fugal trio for three bassoons. *Emerson. Unpriced* VWNT/Y (B75-51412)
Hartzell, Eugene. Beethoven : a documentary study. Abridged ed. *Thames and Hudson. £3.00* BBJ (B75-03644) ISBN 0-500-18146-2
Harvey, Eddie. Jazz piano. *English Universities Press. £0.95* AQPHX/E (B75-09744) ISBN 0-340-12456-3
Harvey, Jean. Eighteenth-century violin sonatas
Book 1. *Associated Board of the Royal Schools of Music. Unpriced* SPE/AY (B75-51294)
Harvey, Jonathan.
The music of Stockhausen : an introduction. *Faber. £6.50* BSNK (B75-11222) ISBN 0-571-10251-4
Quantumplation : flute, clarinet in B flat, violin, cello, piano, tam tam. *Central Music Library : Novello. Unpriced* NYDPNQ (B75-50649)
Transformations of 'Love bade me welcome' : for clarinet and piano. *Novello. £3.00* VVPJ (B75-51404)
Harvey, Paul.
Graded study duets : for two flutes or two oboes or flute and oboe with optional bassoon part. *Boosey and Hawkes. £0.85* VRNU (B75-50316)
Three etudes on themes of Gershwin : for unaccompanied clarinet. *Chappell. Unpriced* VVPMJ (B75-51410)
Harvey, Roger. Camptown races : traditional. *R. Smith. Unpriced* WMK/DW (B75-51429)
Hashirim asher li Sh'lomo, no.32. Psalm 92. *arr.* Psalm 92. (Rossi, Salomone). *Schirmer. Unpriced* WMK/DR (B75-50925)
Hassler, Hans Leo. Canzonette. Hor va canzona mia. Hor va canzona mia = How freely flies my song : SATB a cappella. *Warner : Blossom. Unpriced* EZDU (B75-51045)
Hautus, Loek. Selve caverne e monti : cantata for soprano and basso continuo. (Scarlatti, Domenico). 1st ed. *Bärenreiter. £1.80* KFLDX (B75-50117)
Have a blow (on descant recorder) : a graded tune book for beginners, 50 tunes arranged in order of difficulty. *British and Continental. Unpriced* VSRPMK/DW/AY (B75-50877)
Hawkins, Martin. Catalyst : the Sun Records story. (Escott, Colin). *Aquarius Books; Station Rd, Kings Langley, Herts. : Distributed by Argus Books. £2.90* A/FD(Q) (B75-21384) ISBN 0-904619-00-1
Hawthorne, Alice. Listen to the mocking bird : for four-part chorus of mixed voices with optional tenor and bass solos and optional flute or violin and piano accompaniment. *Schirmer. Unpriced* DW (B75-50440)
Haydn, Joseph.
Divertimento for flute, violin, strings & continuo in D major. Hob IV/D2. Cassation, D-dur, für Flöte, Violine, Streicher und Basso continuo. *Litolff : Peters. Unpriced* RXMPVRPLS (B75-50231)
Divertimento for two clarinets & two horns in C major. Hob II/14. *arr.* Divertimento in C. *Banks. Unpriced* VVNSK (B75-50893)
Divertimento for two violins, cello & keyboard in C major. Hob. XIV, 8. Divertimento, C-dur : für Cembalo (Klavier), 2 Violinen und Violocello. Hoboken XIV, 8.

Zum ersten Mal herausgegeben von Gyorgy Balla. *Litolff : Peters. Unpriced* NXNS (B75-50169)
Piano music. *Selections.* Haydn. *Oxford University Press. £1.50* QPJ (B75-51243) ISBN 0-19-372782-x
Symphony, no.99, in E flat major. Symphony in E flat major, (London Symphony no.7). *Bärenreiter. £1.80* MME (B75-50131)
Symphony, no.100, in G major, 'Military'. Symphony in G major, 'Military' (London Symphony no.9). *Bärenreiter. £2.40* MME (B75-50132)
Symphony, no.101, in D major, 'The clock'. Symphony in D major, 'The clock' (London Symphony no.8). *Bärenreiter. £2.40* MME (B75-50133)
Twelve pieces for the musical clock (Flötenuhr, 1773). *Universal. Unpriced* VRPK/B/FK (B75-51372)
Haydn, Michael. Six menuets for keyboard, nos. 1, 2, 3, 5. Perger 70. Four minuets. *Novello. £0.30* VNTK/AHR (B75-50313)
Haydn. (Hughes, Rosemary). Revised ed. *Dent. £2.95* BHE (B75-01175) ISBN 0-460-03160-0
Hays, Will Shakespeare. Put the right man at the wheel : for four-part chorus of mixed voices with piano accompaniment. *Schirmer. Unpriced* DW (B75-50441)
Hazelgrove, Bernard.
Terpsichore. *Selections: arr.* Four dances
Set 1. (Praetorius, Michael). *Ricordi. Unpriced* WNRH (B75-50376)
Terpsichore. *Selections: arr.* Four dances
Set 2. (Praetorius, Michael). *Ricordi. Unpriced* WNRH (B75-50377)
Head, Michael. Siciliana : oboe and harpsichord or piano. *Emerson. Unpriced* VTPHVQ (B75-51392)
Heake, Horts. Trio for two clarinets & bassoon in E flat major. Trio für zwei Klarinetten und Fagott, Es-dur. (Pleyel, Ignaz). *Litolff : Peters. Unpriced* VNT (B75-50311)
Hear my prayer, O Lord : SATB. (Kroeger, Karl). *Boosey and Hawkes. Unpriced* EZDK (B75-50057)
Heart's music : TTBB (unacc.). (Noble, Harold). *Banks. Unpriced* GEZDW (B75-50515)
Heath, Reginald. Gay señorita : brass band. *R. Smith. Unpriced* WMJ (B75-50921)
Heavy band blues : for concert band. (Cacavas, John). *Chappell. Unpriced* UM/HHW (B75-50820)
Hebräische Melodien. Op.9. Hebrew melodies. Impressions of Byron's poems. Op.9 : for viola and piano. (Joachim, Joseph). *Musica rara. Unpriced* SQPJ (B75-51302)
Hebrew melodies. Impressions of Byron's poems. Op.9 : for viola and piano. (Joachim, Joseph). *Musica rara. Unpriced* SQPJ (B75-51302)
Hebrew University. *Jewish Music Research Centre. See* Jewish Music Research Centre.
Hedges, Anthony.
Psalm 104. Op.52. *Vocal score.* Psalm 104. Opus 52 : for S.S.S.S. and piano. *Chappell. Unpriced* FLDR (B75-50080)
A Rameau suite : keyboard pieces by Rameau. (Rameau, Jean Philippe). *Chappell. Unpriced* MK (B75-50128)
Hei dyma ni : a chaneuon eraill i'r plant lleiaf. *Christopher Davies. Unpriced* JFDW/G/AYDK (B75-50535)
Heiden, Bernhard. Inventions for two violoncelli. *Associated Music. Unpriced* SRNU (B75-50774)
Heider, Werner.
Kunst-Stoff : für Elektro-Klarinette, präpariertes Klavier und Tonband. *Litolff : Peters. Unpriced* VVPJ (B75-50349)
Pyramide für Igor Strawinsky : für Kammerensemble. *Litolff : Peters. Unpriced* MRJ (B75-50160)
Stundenbuch : für 12 Stimmen und 12 Bläser. *Litolff : Peters. Unpriced* EUMDX (B75-50041)
Heilbut, Peter. Erstes Zusammenspiel : für vier Sopranblockflöten und Klavier. *Heinrichshofen Hinrichsen. Unpriced* VSRNRQ (B75-50872)
Heiss, John C. Four short pieces : for piano. *Boosey and Hawkes. Unpriced* QPJ (B75-50699)
Heissenbüttel, Helmut. Nr 17 = Mikrophonie 2 : für Chor, Hammondorgel und 4 Ringmodulatoren. (Stockhausen, Karlheinz). *Universal. Unpriced* EPVDX (B75-50038)
Help yourself to play the guitar. (Stevens, Susan). *Girl Guides Association. £0.35* ATS/E (B75-10255) ISBN 0-85260-002-x
Helyer, Marjorie. Two dance duets : for piano. *Novello. £0.55* QNVH (B75-51217)
Henneberg, Claus. Death in Venice. *Vocal score.* Death in Venice. Op.88 : an opera in two acts. (Britten, Benjamin). *Faber Music. Unpriced* CC (B75-50988)
Her ich verkund euch neue Mar. Weihnachtsgesang : for four-part mixed choir. (Agricola, Martin). *Bärenreiter. £0.60* EZDP/LF (B75-50060)
Herbert, George. God's grandeur. *Vocal score.* God's grandeur : for mixed chorus, brass and organ (or chorus and organ). (Paynter, John). *Oxford University Press. Unpriced* DE (B75-50998) ISBN 0-19-337781-0
Herbert, Victor. Songs. *Selections. arr.* Victor Herbert memories. *Studio Music. Unpriced* WMK/DW (B75-50374)
Hercl, Josef. Czech Christmas mass. *Vocal score.* Ceska mse vanocni = Böhmische Hirtenmesse = Czech Christmas Mass. (Ryba, Jakub Jan). *Supraphon : Achauer. £5.60* DE/LF (B75-50999)
Here on a bed of straw : carol for unison voices, SAB or SATB. (Parfrey, Raymond). *Thames. Unpriced* JFDP/LF (B75-50533)
Heriot, Angus. The castrati in opera. *Calder and Boyars. £5.75* AKGGC/E(M) (B75-26087) ISBN 0-7145-0153-0
Heritage of spirituals : a collection of American spirituals, for mixed chorus and piano or organ. *Galaxy : Galliard. Unpriced* DW/LC/AY (B75-50447)
Herr, der ewige Gott und Vater unser : für gemischten Chor. (Schwarz-Schilling, Reinhard). *Bärenreiter. £1.20* EZDH (B75-50051)
Herrick, Robert. The mad maid's song : for SSAA and piano. (Crawford, John). *Oxford University Press. Unpriced* FDW (B75-50070)
Herrmann, William. Praise the Lord, O Jerusalem. *Vocal score.* Praise the Lord, O Jerusalem : verse anthem for five-part chorus of mixed voices and optional solo group. (Purcell, Henry). *Schirmer. Unpriced* DK (B75-51009)
Hervig, Richard.
Les Goûts réunis or Nouveaux concerts : for instrumental ensemble
Volume 1: Concerts 5-8 : for flute or oboe or violin & basso continuo. (Couperin, François). *Musica rara. Unpriced* LNG (B75-51140)
Volume 2: Concerts 9-10, 12, 14 : for flute or oboe or violin and basso continuo. (Couperin, François). *Musica rara. Unpriced* LNG (B75-51141)
Volume 3: Concerts 10, 12-13 : for three violas da gamba or cellos or bassoons. (Couperin, François). *Musica rara. Unpriced* LNG (B75-51142)
Sonata for flute, oboe & basso continuo in G major. Trio sonata in G, for flute, oboe and basso continuo. (Platti, Giovanni). *Musica rara. Unpriced* NWPNTE (B75-51191)
Herzogenberg, Heinrich von.
Legenden. Op.62. Legends for viola and piano. *Musica rara. £2.00* SQPJ (B75-51301)
Vier Choral-Motetten = Four chorale motets. Op.102 : for unaccompanied four-part chorus. *Bärenreiter. £1.20* EZDH (B75-50049)
He's got the whole world. (Sansom, Clive A). *Studio Music. Unpriced* GDW (B75-50509)
Hesse, Hermann. Leb wohl, Frau welt. Op:43 : Liederzyklus für mittlere Singstimme und Klavier. (Einem, Gottfried von). *Boosey and Hawkes. £3.00* KFVDW (B75-50586)
Hettrick, William E. Fasciculus sacrarum harmoniarum. Ricercars nos.1-3. Three ricercars. (Aichinger, Gregor). *Galaxy : Galliard. Unpriced* VSNS (B75-50858)
Heulyn, Meinir. Telyn y werin : harpCyfrol 1. *Adlais. Unpriced* TQPMK/DW/AYDK (B75-50793)
Hevingham, Henry. If music be the food of love (3rd setting). Z.379C. (Purcell, Henry). *Oxford University Press. £0.50* KDW (B75-50557) ISBN 0-19-345707-5
Hewitt-Jones, Anita. Das wohltemperirte Clavier, Tl. 1. S.867. *arr.* Prelude and fugue. (Bach, Johann Sebastian). *Oxford University Press. Score, £0.75 ; Parts, Unpriced* SRNRK/Y (B75-50773) ISBN 0-19-355238-8
Hexachordum Apollinis. Chaconne in C major. *arr.* Chaconne in C. (Pachelbel, Johann). *Tomus. Unpriced* VSNTK/AHJN (B75-50864)
Hibbard, William. Variations 3 : viola alone. (Riley, Dennis). *Peters. Unpriced* SQPMJ (B75-50258)
Hickman, David. Concerto for trumpet & string orchestra in E flat major. *arr.* Concerto in E flat for trumpet and strings. (Neruda, Johann Baptist Georg). *Musica rara. Unpriced* WSPK/LF (B75-51467)
Hill, Anthony Herschel.
Child in the manger : carol for SATB. *Thames. Unpriced* EZDP/LF (B75-50468)
The magi : carol for SATB, piano and double bass (optional). *Thames. Unpriced* DP/LFP (B75-50431)
Hiller, Wilfried. Katalog für Schlagzeug II = Catalogue for percussion II : 2 players. *Schott. Unpriced* XPQNU (B75-51481)
Hilty, Everett Jay. You are the temple of God : for treble choir in two parts and organ. *Oxford University Press. Unpriced* FLDK (B75-50079)
Hilty, Jay. The Booke of Common Praier noted. The Lord's Praier. *arr.* The Lord's Prayer : for unison choir or solo voice and piano or organ. (Merbecke, John). *Oxford University Press. Unpriced* JDTF (B75-51084)
Hip-hip Horatio : an 'oratorio' for narrator (tenor), chorus (high and low voices) and piano. (Hurd, Michael). *Novello. £0.90* FDX (B75-50498)
Hirsch, Hans Ludwig.
Concerto for oboe, bassoon & string orchestra. Konzert : für Oboe, Fagott und Streicher. *Litolff : Peters. Unpriced* RXMPVTPLVWF (B75-50233)
Correa nel seno amato : cantata for soprano, two violins and basso continuo. (Scarlatti, Alessandro). First edition. *Bärenreiter. £6.00* KFLE/SNTPWDX (B75-50119)
Drei Monodien : für Fagott. *Litolff : Peters. Unpriced* VWPMJ (B75-50353)
'His Master's Voice' recordings, plum label 'C' series (12 inch). (Gramophone Company). *Old School House, Tarrant Hinton, Blandford, Dorset : Oakwood Press. £4.50* A/FD(T/WT) (B75-08384) ISBN 0-85361-166-1
History and art of change ringing. (Morris, Ernest). 1st ed. reprinted. *EP Publishing. £8.00* AXSR/E(X) (B75-18374) ISBN 0-85409-995-6
History of the organ in the United States. (Ochse, Orpha). *Indiana University Press. £11.25* AR/B(YT/X) (B75-17690) ISBN 0-253-32830-6
HMV plum label catalogue. *See* Gramophone Company.
Hoare, Ian. The soul book. *Eyre Methuen. £1.50* AKDW/GB/E(YTLD/M) (B75-29984) ISBN 0-413-32150-9
Hoddinott, Alun.
The beach of Falesa. *Vocal score.* The beach of Falesa : opera in three acts. *Oxford University Press. £8.50* CC (B75-50394)
The silver swimmer. Opus 84 : for mixed chorus, SATB and piano duet. *Oxford University Press. £1.20* DX (B75-50032) ISBN 0-19-336840-4
Symphony no.5. Opus 81. *Oxford University Press. £6.75* MME (B75-50604) ISBN 0-19-364590-4
Hoddinott, Rhiannon. Four Welsh songs. *Oxford University Press. £0.60* GDW/G/AYDK (B75-50510) ISBN 0-19-343653-1
Hofbauer, Friedl. Opus number zoo : children's play for wind quintet (1951, rev. 1970). (Berio, Luciano). *Universal. Unpriced* CQN (B75-50994)
Hoffmeister, Franz Anton. Concerto for clarinet in B major. *arr.* Concerto in B flat for clarinet and orchestra. *Schott. £1.50* VVPK/LF (B75-51409)
Hofmann, Klaus.
Sonata for flute, oboe & continuo in E minor. Sonata in E minor : for flute, oboe (violin) and basso continuo. (Telemann, Georg Philipp). 1st ed. *Bärenreiter. £2.40* NWPNTE (B75-50167)
Sonatina for oboe, violin & basso continuo in E minor. Sonatine in E minor : for oboe, violin and basso continuo. (Telemann, Georg Philipp). First ed. *Bärenreiter. Unpriced* NUTNT (B75-50635)
Hofmann, Wolfgang.
Adagio : für Orgel and Streicher. *Litolff : Peters. Unpriced* RXMPR (B75-50753)
Divertimento for flute, violin, strings & continuo in D major. Hob IV/D2. Cassation, D-dur, für Flöte, Violine, Streicher und Basso continuo. (Haydn, Joseph). *Litolff : Peters. Unpriced* RXMPVRPLS (B75-50231)
Divertimento for strings. Divertimento. *Litolff : Peters. Unpriced* RXMJ (B75-50226)
Fünf Inventionen : für zwei Klarinetten. *Litolff : Peters. Unpriced* VVNU (B75-50897)
Mobile : fünf Skizzen für Sopran und Altblockflöte. *Litolff : Peters. Unpriced* VSNU (B75-50866)
Hofmannsthal, Hugo von. Ariadne auf Naxos : opera in one act with a prelude. *Boosey and Hawkes. £1.50* BSUAC (B75-08737) ISBN 0-85162-026-4
Hogner, Friedrich. Fantasia super H.C. : für Orgel. *Litolff : Peters. Unpriced* RJ (B75-51273)
Hogwood, Christopher.
Complete harpsichord works of William Croft
Vol.1. (Croft, William). *Stainer and Bell. Unpriced* QRP/AZ (B75-50200)
Vol.2. (Croft, William). *Stainer and Bell. Unpriced* QRP/AZ (B75-50201)
Holbrook, David. Gustav Mahler and the courage to be. *Vision Press. £7.95* BME (B75-27350) ISBN 0-85478-243-5
Holbrook, David. Studies in the psychology of culture. Holbrook, David. Gustav Mahler and the courage to be. *Vision Press. £7.95* BME (B75-27350) ISBN 0-85478-243-5
Holcombe, Bill. The three musketeers. *Selections: arr.* Themes from 'The three musketeers'. (Legrand, Michel). *Chappell. Unpriced* UMK/JR (B75-50301)
Hold, Trevor.
Early one morning : five poems of Edward Thomas, for tenor and guitar. *Thames Music. Unpriced* KGHE/TSDW (B75-50590)
Rutterkin : an overture for recorders, (descant, 2 trebles, 2 tenors, 2 basses), after a song by Peter Warlock, (from 1st set of Peterisms). *Tomus. Unpriced* VSNP (B75-51376)
Holiday overture : for brass band. (Ball, Eric). *Boosey and Hawkes. £6.00* WMJ (B75-51418)
Hollis, Helen Rice. The piano : a pictorial account of its ancestry and development. *David and Charles. £4.50* APW/B(X) (B75-13169) ISBN 0-7153-6559-2
Holmboe, Vagn. Vagn Holmboe : a catalogue of his music, discography, bibliography, essays. (Rapoport, Paul). *10E Prior Bolton St., N.1 : Triad Press. £2.50* BHO(N) (B75-04505) ISBN 0-902070-13-4
Holst, Gustav. The planets. Mars. *arr.* Mars. *Boosey and Hawkes. Unpriced* UMMK (B75-50833)
Holy son of God : carol for SATB. (Copley, Ian Alfred). *Thames. Unpriced* EZDP/LF (B75-50467)
Holzbauer, Ignas. Concerto for oboe & string orchestra in D minor. Konzert, d-moll, für Oboe und Streicher. Zum ersten Mal herausgegeben von Walter Lebermann. *Litolff : Peters. Unpriced* RXMPVTF (B75-50232)
Holzbauer, Ignaz. Concerto for oboe & string orchestra in D minor. *arr.* Konzert, D-moll für Oboe und Streicher. 1st ed. *Litolff : Peters. Unpriced* VTPK/LF (B75-51396)
Holzer, Gerhard. Concerto for trumpet & string orchestra. Concerto für Trompete und Streicher. *Litolff : Peters. Unpriced* RXMPWSF (B75-51289)
Homage to John Stanley : voluntary for organ manuals. (Wills, Arthur). *Chappell. Unpriced* RJ (B75-51276)
Hombe : Kenya (Luo) folk song, for 4-part mixed choir and contralto solo unaccompanied. (Ekwueme, Laz). *Roberton. Unpriced* EZDW (B75-50477)
Home on the range : traditional tune. (Siebert, Edrich). *455 Brighton Rd, South Croydon : Paul. Unpriced* WUNSK/DW (B75-50959)
Homer. Epilogue after Homer's 'The Odyssey' : for mezzosoprano, narrator, oboe, horn, guitar, piano, percussion and doublebass. (Antoniou, Theodor). *Bärenreiter. Unpriced* KFNE/NYDNQDX (B75-50578)
Hommage à Haydn : piano. (Debussy, Claude). *Peters. Unpriced* QPJ (B75-50689)
Hongkong anniversary overture. Op.99. (Arnold, Malcolm). *Central Music Library : Faber. Unpriced* MMJ (B75-50608)
Honolka, Kurt. Festival chorus. Slavnostní sbor = Festlicher Chor = Festival chorus : for four male voices, women's and men's chorus and piano. (Janacek, Leos). *Bärenreiter. £1.20* DX (B75-50033)
Honulka, Kurt. Drei slowakische Volkslieder : für Männerchor. *Bärenreiter. £2.00* GEZDW/G/AYFS (B75-50085)
Hook, James. Sonatas for flute & piano. Op.99, nos.3, 2. *arr.* Two sonatas. *Boosey and Hawkes. £1.25* WSPK/AE (B75-51461)

Hoosen, I D. Morys y Gwynt : can ddwy-ran ar gyfer ysgolion cynradd gyda chyfeiliant piano a recorder. (Owen, Elfed). *University of Wales Press. Unpriced* KFQE/VSPDW (B75-50123)
Hooson, I D. Morys y Gwyat : can ddwy-ran ar gyfer ysgolion cynradd gyda chyfeiliant piano a recorder. (Owen, Elfed). *University of Wales Press. Unpriced* KFE/VSPDW (B75-50570)
Hopkins, Gerard Manley. God's grandeur. *Vocal score.* God's grandeur : for mixed chorus, brass and organ (or chorus and organ). (Paynter, John). *Oxford University Press. Unpriced* DE (B75-50998) ISBN 0-19-337781-0
Hor va canzona mia = How freely flies my song : SATB a cappella. (Hassler, Hans Leo). *Warner : Blossom. Unpriced* EZDU (B75-51045)
Hora novissima. Urbs Syon unica. City of high renown = Urbs Syon unica : unaccompanied mixed chorus. (Parker, Horatio). *Galaxy : Galliard. Unpriced* EZDH (B75-51035)
Horovitz, Joseph.
Three choral songs from 'As you like it' : SATB. *Novello. £0.50* EZDW (B75-51047)
Variations on a theme of Paganini : for brass quartet, or saxophone quartet, or woodwind quartet. *R. Smith. Unpriced* WNS/T (B75-50379)
Horsfall, Jean. Teaching the cello to groups. *Oxford University Press. £2.75* ASR/E(VC) (B75-01178) ISBN 0-19-318510-5
Horticultural wife : (written by a celebrated English gardener after disappointment in love) : for four-part chorus of mixed voices with tenor (or baritone) solo and piano accompaniment. (Hutchinson Family). *Schirmer. Unpriced* DW (B75-50442)
Horton, John. A book of Christmas music. *Schott. Unpriced* CB/LF/AY (B75-50987) ISBN 0-901938-56-4
Hosianna dem Sohne David, und, Wohlauf wohlauf zu dieser Frist : zwei kleine Weihnachtskonzert, für zwei mittlere Stimmen und Basso continuo. (Grimm, Heinrich). *Bärenreiter. £1.20* JNFVEDH/LF (B75-50103)
Hossack, Alfred.
From notes to rhythm. *Lutterworth Press. £0,75* A/M (B75-25556) ISBN 0-7188-2128-9
Major and minor scales. *Lutterworth Press. £0.75* A/PF (B75-25555) ISBN 0-7188-2129-7
Hotteterre, Jacques.
Sonatas for two recorders & basso continuo. Op.3. Trio sonatas. Opus 3 : for 2 treble (alto) recorders and basso continuo
Nos.1-3. *Musica rara. Unpriced* VSSNTPWE (B75-51383)
Sonatas for two recorders & basso continuo. Op.3. Trio sonatas. Opus 3 : for 2 treble (alto) recorders and basso continuo
Nos.4-6. *Musica rara. Unpriced* VSSNTPWE (B75-51384)

Hovhaness, Alan.
Komachi. Opus 240 : piano solo. *Peters. Unpriced* QPJ (B75-50193)
Saris : violin and piano. *Peters. Unpriced* SPJ (B75-50250)

Symphony no.23, 'Ani'. City of a thousand and one cathedrals : for large band with antiphonal second brass choir ad lib. *Peters. Unpriced* UMME (B75-50827)
Hovhaness, Naru. Komachi. Opus 240 : piano solo. (Hovhaness, Alan). *Peters. Unpriced* QPJ (B75-50193)
How can it be? : for unison, SA or SAB chorus and piano. (Rocherolle, Eugenie R). *Warner : Blossom. Unpriced* DP/LF (B75-51012)
How do you open a show without a curtain?. *arr.* How do you open a show without a curtain? : a program opener, for two-part chorus of treble voices with piano and optional guitar. (Williams, Phyllis). *Frank Music. Unpriced* FLDW (B75-51071)
Howarth, Elgar.
Fireworks for brass band : variations on a theme of W. Hogarth Lear. *Paxton. Unpriced* WM/T (B75-50914)
Keyboard music. *Selections: arr.* Fancies, toyes and dreames. (Farnaby, Giles). *Chester. Unpriced* WNRK (B75-51445)
Howat, Roy. Sonata for violin & continuo, Op.1, no.1, in D minor. Sonata in D minor for violin and basso continuo. (Handel, George Frideric). *Oxford University Press. £1.50* SPE (B75-50247) ISBN 0-19-356979-5
Howden, Bruce. Requiem. Op.48. *Vocal score.* Requiem. Op.48 : for four-part chorus of mixed voices with soprano and baritone soli. (Fauré, Gabriel). *Schirmer. Unpriced* DGKAV (B75-51001)
Howe, Hubert S. Electronic music synthesis : concepts, facilities, techniques. *Dent. £6.50* APV/B (B75-07344) ISBN 0-460-04251-3
Hoyland, Vic. Jeux-thème : for mezzo-soprano and chamber orchestra. *Universal. Unpriced* KFNE/MRDW (B75-51127)
Hubbard, Paul. Sonata for treble recorder & harpsichord, no.6. in F major. Sonata in F : for treble recorder and harpsichord, (or flute or oboe and piano). (Finger, Gottfried). *Piers Press. Unpriced* VSSPE (B75-50336)
Hube, Max. Boris Godunov : opera in four acts with a prologue. (Mussorgsky, Modest). *Oxford University Press. Unpriced* CQC (B75-50993) ISBN 0-19-337699-7
Huber, Klaus. ' - inwending voller figur - ' : for chorus, loudspeakers, tape and large orchestra (1970/71). *Ars Viva : Schott. £6.00* EMDE (B75-50035)
Huddersfield Glee and Madrigal Society. Huddersfield Glee & Madrigal Society, 1875-1975. *Princess Alexandra Walk, Huddersfield HD1 2SU : Kirklees Libraries and Museums Service. £0.50* AD/E(YDJGH/QB) (B75-07343) ISBN 0-9502568-1-1
Hufschmidt, Wolfgang. Der barmherzige Samariter : für gemischten Chor und Sprecher. *Bärenreiter. £1.00* EZDH (B75-50050)
Hughes, David. The widow of Ephesus. *Vocal score.* The widow of Ephesus : chamber opera in one act. (Hurd, Michael). *Novello. £2.10* CC (B75-50395)
Hughes, Edward. Christ in competition. *Edwardian Music. Unpriced* JDM/AY (B75-51078) ISBN 0-551-05530-8
Hughes, Eric. Carambina : Spanish dance, for brass band. *Studio Music. Unpriced* WMH (B75-50917)
Hughes, Rosemary. Haydn. Revised ed. *Dent. £2.95* BHE (B75-01175) ISBN 0-460-03160-0
Hughes, Ted. The new world. Op.26 : set for medium voice and piano. (Crosse, Gordon). *Oxford University Press. £2.50* KFVDW (B75-50584) ISBN 0-19-345275-8
Humble, Keith.
Arcade II : for piano solo. *Universal. Unpriced* QPJ (B75-50700)
Arcade IIIa : solo flute. *Universal. Unpriced* VRPMJ (B75-50854)
Arcade IV : for guitar and percussion. *Universal. Unpriced* TSPLX (B75-50802)
Arcade V : for orchestra. *Universal. Unpriced* MMJ (B75-50615)
Trois poèmes à crier et à danser
Chant 1. *Universal. Unpriced* XNS (B75-50967)
Chant 2. *Universal. Unpriced* XNS (B75-50968)
Chant 3. *Universal. Unpriced* XNS (B75-50969)
Hummel, Bertold. Frescoes 70 : for percussion quartet. *Simrock. £5.95* XNS (B75-51477)
Hummel, Johann Nepomak.
Sonatas for piano. *Collections.* Complete piano sonatas Vol.1. *Musica rara. £6.00* QPE/AZ (B75-51228)
Sonatas for piano. *Collections.* Complete piano sonatas Vol.2. *Musica rara. £6.00* QPE/AZ (B75-51229)
Hummel, Johann Nepomuk. Concerto for bassoon in F major. *arr.* Bassoon concerto. *Boosey and Hawkes. £2.00* VWPK/LF (B75-50906)
Humoreske. Op.19, no.4. (Gade, Niels Vilhelm). *British and Continental Music. Unpriced* VVPK (B75-50902)
Hundred years of music. (Abraham, Gerald). 4th ed. *Duckworth. £6.95* A(YB/XHN141) (B75-12695) ISBN 0-7156-0703-0
Hungarian children's songs : for flute and piano. *Boosey and Hawkes. £1.00* VRPK/DW/GJ/AYG (B75-51373)
Hungarian children's songs : for two violoncellos. *Boosey and Hawkes : Editio Musica. £0.75* SRNUK/DW/GJ/AYG (B75-50261)
Hungarian children's songs : for violoncello and piano. *Boosey and Hawkes : Editio Musica. £0.75* SRPK/DW/GJ/AYG (B75-50263)
Hungarian march. (Berlioz, Hector). *Novello. £1.50* MGM (B75-51147)
Hunt, Edgar.
The bass recorder : a concise method for the bass in F and great bass in C. *Schott. £1.00* VSU/AF (B75-51388) ISBN 0-901938-49-1
The crumhorn : a concise method for the crumhorn and other wind-cap instruments. *Schott. £1.20* VSUS/AF (B75-51389) ISBN 0-901938-52-1
Hunt, Reginald. Little suite : for two descant recorders and piano. *Ashdown. £0.50* VSRNTQG (B75-50332)
Hunt, Reginald Heber. Rigadoon : piano solo. *Ashdown. Unpriced* QPHVK (B75-50679)
Hunter, Hilda. Music for today's children. (Ingley, William Stevens). *63 Highfield Rd, Rowley Regis, Warley, West Midlands : H. Hunter. £1.50* A(VC) (B75-50000) ISBN 0-9503936-0-6
Hurd, Michael.
Hip-hip Horatio : an 'oratorio' for narrator (tenor), chorus (high and low voices) and piano. *Novello. £0.90* FDX (B75-50498)
Invitation to the partsong
No.2: Part songs for SATB : a selection of four-part works. *Stainer and Bell. Unpriced* EZDW/AY (B75-50067) ISBN 0-85249-288-x
The widow of Ephesus. *Vocal score.* The widow of Ephesus : chamber opera in one act. *Novello. £2.10* CC (B75-50395)
Hurford, Peter. Sunny bank : carol, SATB. *Oxford University Press. £0.10* DP/LF (B75-50430) ISBN 0-19-343051-7
Hurry, little pony : Spanish traditional song. (Bonsor, Brian). *Oxford University Press. Unpriced* JFE/NYFSDW (B75-51097) ISBN 0-19-344836-x
Husa, Karel.
Apotheosis of this earth : for orchestra and chorus. *Associated Music. Unpriced* EMDX (B75-50450)
Divertimento for brass quintet. *Associated Music. £6.25* WNR (B75-51436)
Huscroft, John.
And when I am entombed : for voices, guitar & piano. *27 Donald Way, Chelmsford : John Huscroft. Unpriced* KE/TSPDW (B75-50567)
Jeykll sic and Hyde : solo for harpsichord or piano. *27 Donald Way, Chelmsford : John Huscroft. Unpriced* PWPJ (B75-50655)
Hutchinson Family. The horticultural wife : (written by a celebrated English gardener after disappointment in love) : for four-part chorus of mixed voices with tenor (or baritone) solo and piano accompaniment. *Schirmer. Unpriced* DW (B75-50442)
Huw Jones, Sheila. Caneuon Lili Lon. *Christopher Davies. £0.90* JFEZDW/JS (B75-51099) ISBN 0-7154-0167-x
Hyde, Derek.
Babylon's falling : a jazz spiritual for junior band and optional voices in two parts. (Wastall, Peter). *Boosey and Hawkes. £2.05* UMJ (B75-51338)
Joshua fought the battle of Jericho : a jazz spiritual for junior wind band and optional voices in two parts. (Wastall, Peter). *Boosey and Hawkes. £2.05* UMJ (B75-51340)
Sonatina for violin & harpsichord, no.6, in C major. *arr.* Sonatina no.3. (Telemann, Georg Philipp). *Boosey and Hawkes. £0.65* VVPK/AEM (B75-51408)
Hyde, Douglas. O King of the Friday : SATB unacc. (Nelson, Havelock). *Banks. Unpriced* EZDH/LK (B75-51038)
Hymn of St Columba (Regis regum rectissimi) : SATB and organ. (Britten, Benjamin). *Boosey and Hawkes. £0.20* DH (B75-50418)
Hymn to joy. (Beethoven, Ludwig van). *Oxford University Press. £0.40* RK/DW (B75-50736) ISBN 0-19-375294-8
Hymnos : wind orchestra and percussion. (Loudová, Ivana). *Peters. Unpriced* UMJ (B75-51334)
Hyslop, Graham. Musical instruments of East Africa
1: Kenya. *Nelson. £0.80* BZNCWAL/B (B75-26086) ISBN 0-17-511250-9
I can't sing pretty! (But I shore sing loud!) : for unison or SA chorus and piano. (Artman, Ruth). *Warner Blossom. Unpriced* FDW (B75-50488)
I could be happy : an autobiography. (Wilson, Sandy). *Joseph. £6.00* BWNTM(N) (B75-50389) ISBN 0-7181-1370-5
I hunger and I thirst : anthem for SATB with divisions and organ. (Wills, Arthur). *Novello. Unpriced* DH (B75-50421)
I saw a stranger yester'en : for mixed chorus and violin or piano. (Avshalomov, Jacob). *Galaxy : Galliard. Unpriced* ESDW (B75-50454)
I sing of a Maiden : two-part. (Wills, Arthur). *Oxford University Press. £0.10* FLDP/LF (B75-50507) ISBN 0-19-341510-0
I was glad when they said unto me : a paraphrase of Psalm 122, for two equal voices. (Coombes, Douglas). *28 Knolls Way, Clifton, Beds. : Lindsay Music. £0.12* FDR (B75-50487)
Iadone, Joseph. Four centuries of song, from the troubadour to the Elizabethan age : for voice and guitar. *Associated Music. Unpriced* KE/TSDW/AY (B75-50563)
Iadone, Norma Verrilli. Four centuries of song, from the troubadour to the Elizabethan age : for voice and guitar. *Associated Music. Unpriced* KE/TSDW/AY (B75-50563)
Ich spiele vom Blatt : Schule des Prima-Vista-Spiels : für Klavier und andere Tasteninstrumente
Band 2. (Keilmann, Wilhelm). *Litolff : Peters. Unpriced* Q/EG (B75-50658)
If music be the food of love (3rd setting). Z.379C. (Purcell, Henry). *Oxford University Press. £0.50* KDW (B75-50557) ISBN 0-19-345707-5
Ikos. Ikos : für zwei Soprane, zwei Alte, zwei Tenore, zwei Basse, with Katawassia : für zwei Soprane, Alt, zwei Tenore, Bariton. (Terzakis, Dimitri). *Bärenreiter. Unpriced* EZDW (B75-50482)
Ikos : für zwei Soprane, zwei Alte, zwei Tenore, zwei Basse, with Katawassia : für zwei Soprane, Alt, zwei Tenore, Bariton. (Terzakis, Dimitri). *Bärenreiter. Unpriced* EZDW (B75-50482)
Images : piano solo
Book I. (Debussy, Claude). *Peters. Unpriced* QPJ (B75-50690)
Book II. (Debussy, Claude). *Peters. Unpriced* QPJ (B75-50691)
Impressions : for recorder ensemble, descant, treble/sopranino, treble 2, tenors. (Kear, Warrick). *Tomus. Unpriced* VSNR (B75-51377)
Improvisation no.1 : valse pour accordeon. (Balta, Freddy). *Chappell. Unpriced* RSPMHW (B75-50744)
Improvisation no.V : piano. (Balta, Freddy). *Chappell. Unpriced* QPJ (B75-50685)
Improvviso da concerto : per chitarra. (Pizzini, Carlo Alberto). *Zanibon : Hinrichsen. Unpriced* TSPMJ (B75-50283)
In defence of Hanslick. (Deas, Stewart). Revised ed. *Gregg. £3.00* A/CC(P) (B75-02991) ISBN 0-576-28242-1
In dulci jubilo : for four-part chorus of mixed voices a cappella. (Najera, Edmund). *Schirmer. Unpriced* EZDP/LF (B75-50469)
In nomine : for two treble, two tenor and bass viols. (Parsley, Osbert). *Oxford University Press. Score £0.20, Parts unpriced* STNR (B75-50783) ISBN 0-19-341211-x
In nomine Jesu : motet for five voices, SAATB, for the Feast of the Holy Name and general use. (Handl, Jacob). *Chester. Unpriced* EZDGKHL (B75-51032)
Ina Boyle : an appreciation : with a select list of her music. (Maconchy, Elizabeth). *Trinity College Dublin, Library. Unpriced* BBSL (B75-50003) ISBN 0-904720-00-4
Incorporated Society of Musicians. Handbook and register of members
1974-75. *48 Gloucester Place, W1H 3HJ : The Society. £4.00* A(YC/Q/MM) (B75-00738) ISBN 0-902900-06-4
Ingley, William Stevens. Music for today's children. *63 Highfield Rd, Rowley Regis, Warley, West Midlands : H. Hunter. £1.50* A(VC) (B75-50000) ISBN 0-9503936-0-6
Ingman, Nicholas. What instrument shall I play? *Ward Lock. £2.95* AL/B (B75-29314) ISBN 0-7063-1988-5
Inness, Peter. Balulalow : carol for SAATB with divisions unaccompanied. *Novello. £0.10* EZDP/LF (B75-50061)
Interferences I : pour basson et piano. (Boutry, Roger). *Chappell. Unpriced* VWPJ (B75-50905)
International who's who in music and musicians' directory. *For earlier issues of this publication see* Who's who in

music, and musicians' international directory.
International who's who in music and musicians' directory
7th ed. : 1975. *Cambridge CB2 3QP : International Who's Who in Music. £15.00* A(N/BC) (B75-27957)
ISBN 0-900332-31-x
Introduction and tarantella : trio for flute, percussion and piano. (Bamert, Matthias). *Schirmer. £1.55* NYFRHVS (B75-51197)
Introduction et mascarade : pour trompette en ut (C) et piano. (Marischal, Louis). *Chappell. Unpriced* WSPJ (B75-51458)
'Introduction to the 12 button reed and electronic chord organ. (Bolton, Cecil). *Robbins Music : EMI. Unpriced* RPVC/AC (B75-51280)
Inventions for piano. Opus 2. (Tchaikowsky, André). *Novello. £1.00* QPJ (B75-50712)
Inventions for two violoncelli. (Heiden, Bernhard). *Associated Music. Unpriced* SRNU (B75-50774)
Invitation to the partsong
No.2: Part songs for SATB : a selection of four-part works. *Stainer and Bell. Unpriced* EZDW/AY (B75-50067) ISBN 0-85249-288-x
Invocation and toccata : orchestra. (Ward, Robert). *Highgate Press : Galliard. Unpriced* MMJ (B75-50618)
Ireland, John. Songs. *Selections.* The land of lost content and other songs. *Stainer and Bell. Unpriced* KDW (B75-51104) ISBN 0-85249-320-7
Iron man : English occupational songs. *Galliard : Stainer and Bell. Unpriced* JE/TSDW/GM/AYD (B75-50097)
ISBN 0-85249-294-4
Irvine, John. By winding roads : fifteen unison songs of the Irish countryside. (Parke, Dorothy). *Roberton. £1.00* JFDW (B75-51094)
It's time for music : a quick progress course for the piano class. (Kirkby-Mason, Barbara). *Faber Music. £0.75* Q/AC (B75-50656)
Ives, Charles.
Crossing the bar : anthem for solo quartet or mixed choir and organ. *Associated Music. Unpriced* DH (B75-50419)
March, Omega Lambda Chi. *arr.* March, Omega Lambda Chi : for band. *Associated Music. Unpriced* UMMK/AGM (B75-50835)
Variations on 'Jerusalem the golden'. *arr.* Variations on 'Jerusalem the golden'. *Associated Music. £1.30* UMK (B75-51341)
Ives, Grayston. Jubilate = (O be joyful in the Lord) : anthem for SATB and organ. *Novello. £0.25* DGNT (B75-50413)
Iveson, John. The Prince of Denmark's march. *arr.* Trumpet voluntary. (Clarke, Jeremiah). *Chester. Unpriced* WMK/AGM (B75-51424)
Ivor Novello : man of the theatre. (Noble, Peter). *White Lion Publishers. £3.75* BNO(N) (B75-19084)
ISBN 0-85617-769-5
Jabula : for solo flute. (Glasser, Stanley). *Piers Press. £0.75* VRPMJ (B75-50325)
Jack L'Eventreur. (Rorem, Ned). *Boosey and Hawkes. Unpriced* KDW (B75-51109)
Jackson, Richard. Stephen Foster song book : original sheet music of 40 songs. (Foster, Stephen). *Dover : Constable. £2.40* KDW (B75-50553)
Jacob, Gordon.
5 pieces for half-size violin and piano. *Chappell. Unpriced* SPJ (B75-51296)
Concerto for double bass & string orchestra. *arr.* A little concerto for double bass and string orchestra. *Yorke. Unpriced* SSPK/LF (B75-50269)
On a summer evening : flute and piano. *Jane Emerson. Unpriced* VRPJ (B75-50322)
Sonatina for piano or harpsichord. *Chappell. Unpriced* PWPE (B75-51199)
Sonatina for two violas. *Oxford University Press. Unpriced* SQNUEM (B75-50770) ISBN 0-19-357357-1
Swansea town : folk song, theme and variations, for wind quintet. *Emerson. Unpriced* UNR/T (B75-50840)
Swansea town : wind quintet. *Emerson. Unpriced* UNR/T (B75-51358)
Jacobs, Arthur. British music yearbook : a survey and directory with statistics and reference articles
1975. *Bowker. £7.50* A(YC/BC) (B75-16403)
ISBN 0-85935-024-x
James, John. Two trumpet voluntaries. *Oxford University Press. £0.50* RJ (B75-50732) ISBN 0-19-375490-8
James Thomson's Music Book. *Selections.* Twenty-one Scots tunes from James Thomson's music book (1702). *Forsyth. Unpriced* VSSPMJ (B75-50884)
Janacek, Leos.
Festival chorus. Slavnostní sbor = Festlicher Chor = Festival chorus : for four male voices, women's and men's chorus and piano. *Bärenreiter. £1.20* DX (B75-50033)
Mass in E flat major. Mass, E flat major (unfinished Mass). *Bärenreiter. £2.10* DG (B75-50016)
Jandl, Ernst. 'Mit Musik'. 5 Gedichte von Ernst Jandl : für einen Sprecher und Instrumente, (2 Trompeten in C-oder Klarinetten, Flöten, Blockflöten-, Violoncello, Kontrabass, Schlagzeug und Klavier). (Regner, Hermann). *Schott. £3.50* HYE/NYDNQ (B75-51076)
Janski, Stefan.
The snowman of Kashmir : a workshop opera for children. (Kay, Peter). *Universal. Unpriced* CQN (B75-50995)
The snowman of Kashmir. *Vocal score.* The snowman of Kashmir : a workshop opera for children. (Kay, Peter). *Universal. Unpriced* CN (B75-50401)
Jasper, Tony.
Jesus in a pop culture. *Fontana. £2.00* A/GB/L(XR5) (B75-06415) ISBN 0-00-215371-8
Simply pop. *Queen Anne Press. £0.95* AKDW/GB/E(M) (B75-27955) ISBN 0-362-00247-9
Jay, Dave. Jolsonography : the world's greatest reference work on the world's greatest entertainer. 2nd ed. *70 Southcote Rd, Bournemouth, Hants. : Barrie Anderton. £15.00* AKDW/GB/E(P) (B75-03647)
ISBN 0-9501412-1-6
Jazz piano. (Harvey, Eddie). *English Universities Press. £0.95* AQPHX/E (B75-09744) ISBN 0-340-12456-3
Jeans, Susi, *Lady.* Inventions. *Selections.* Four inventions. (Gerber, Heinrich Nicolaus). *Novello. £0.65* RJ (B75-50206)
Jefferson, Alan. Richard Strauss. *Macmillan. £3.75* BSU(N) (B75-15005) ISBN 0-333-14649-2
Jefferson, Thomas. We hold these truths : bicentennial ode, for chorus and symphonic band with optional strings. (Washburn, Robert). *Boosey and Hawkes. £15.00* EUMDX (B75-51029)
Jenkins, Jean. Eighteenth century musical instruments, France and Britain = Les Instruments de musique au XVIIIe Siecle, France et Grande-Bretagne : catalogue of an exhibition. (Thibault, G). *Victoria and Albert Museum. £2.50* AL/B(YH/XF101) (B75-03646)
ISBN 0-901486-71-x
Jenkinson, Philip. Celluloid rock : twenty years of movie rock. *Lorrimer. £1.95* A/GB/JR(XPP21) (B75-06416)
ISBN 0-85647-046-5
Jenni, Donald.
Ad te levavi : for full chorus of mixed voices a cappella. *Associated Music. Unpriced* EZDH/LEZ (B75-50464)
Cucumber music : 'Metamorphosis' for 4 players, 9 instruments. *Associated Music. Unpriced* NYDPNS (B75-50652)
Death, be not proud : for four-part chorus of mixed voices with chimes and piano accompaniment. *Associated Music. Unpriced* EXTPRPDW (B75-50458)
Early spring : for four part chorus of mixed voices a cappella. *Associated Music. £0.20* EZDW (B75-51048)
A game of dates : for piano. *Associated Music. Unpriced* QPJ (B75-50701)
Musique printanière : for flute and piano. *Associated Music. Unpriced* VRPJ (B75-50850)
Tympanorum musices : for four timpani and three bongos. *Associated Music. Unpriced* XQNP (B75-50971)
Jergenson, Dale. Bric-a-Bach (constructed from five different compositions by J.S. Bach) : for full chorus of mixed voices with optional guitar, bass and drums accompaniment. *Schirmer. Unpriced* EZDX (B75-50484)
Jerry Silverman's folk song encyclopaedia : with over 1,000 favorite songs arranged for voice and guitar
Vol.1. *Chappell. Unpriced* KE/TSDW/G/AY (B75-50564)
Vol.2. *Chappell. Unpriced* KE/TSDW/G/AY (B75-50565)
Jesu dulcissime : motet for six voices. (Schütz, Heinrich). First edition. *Bärenreiter. £1.40* EZDJ (B75-50054)
Jesus in a pop culture. (Jasper, Tony). *Fontana. £2.00* A/GB/L(XR5) (B75-06415) ISBN 0-00-215371-8
Jesus, Jesus, rest your head : Southern Appalachian carol. (Dinham, Kenneth J). *Banks. Unpriced* EZDP/LF (B75-51041)
Jesus, Jesus, rest your head : Southern Appalachian carol. (Dinham, Kenneth J). *Banks. Unpriced* GEZDP/LF (B75-51074)
Jeux. Op.22 : for violoncello and string orchestra. (Antoniou, Theodore). *Bärenreiter. £2.80* RXMPSR (B75-50230)
Jeux-thème : for mezzo-soprano and chamber orchestra. (Hoyland, Vic). *Universal. Unpriced* KFNE/MRDW (B75-51127)
Jewish Music Research Centre. Yuval : studies of the Jewish Music Research Centre
Vol.3. *Magnes Press : Distributed by Oxford University Press. £10.25* A(YBU/D) (B75-08735)
ISBN 0-19-647920-7
Jeykll sic and Hyde : solo for harpsichord or piano. (Huscroft, John). *27 Donald Way, Chelmsford : John Huscroft. Unpriced* PWPJ (B75-50655)
Joachim, Joseph.
Hebräische Melodien. Op.9. Hebrew melodies. Impressions of Byron's poems. Op.9 : for viola and piano. *Musica rara. Unpriced* SQPJ (B75-51302)
Variations for viola and piano. Op.10. *Musica rara. Unpriced* SQP/T (B75-51300)
Joffe, Judah Achilles. My musical life. (Rimsky-Korsakoff, Nikolai). *48 Great Marlborough St., W.1 : Ernst Eulenberg Ltd. £6.25* BRI(N) (B75-24236)
ISBN 0-903873-13-3
Johann Sebastian Bach : Leben und Werk in Dokumenten. *32 Great Titchfield St., W.1 : Bärenreiter-Verlag etc.. £1.56* BBC(N)
Johann Strauss song book : containing twelve songs for solo voice and piano. (Strauss, Johann, *b.1825*). *Weinberger. Unpriced* KDW (B75-51113)
Johann Strauss : the end of an era. (Gartenberg, Egon). *Pennsylvania State University Press. £7.00* BSQ(N) (B75-21067) ISBN 0-271-01131-9
Johannes Brahms : his work and personality. (Gál, Hans). *Severn House. £4.50* BBT(N) (B75-30567)
ISBN 0-7278-0078-7
John Foulds : his life in music : with a detailed catalogue of his works, a discography, a bibliographical note, and with music examples and illustrations. (MacDonald, Malcolm, *b.1948*). *22 Pheasants Way, Rickmansworth, Herts. : Triad Press. £4.75* BFS(N) (B75-28637)
ISBN 0-902070-15-0
Johnson, Brenda. The adventures of Paddington Bear. Paddington Bear. *arr.* Paddington Bear : song. (Chappell, Herbert). *Music Sales. £0.25* KDW (B75-50106)
Johnson, David.
James Thomson's Music Book. *Selections.* Twenty-one Scots tunes from James Thomson's music book (1702). *Forsyth. Unpriced* VSSPMJ (B75-50884)
Sonata for violin & continuo. Op.1, no.2 in G minor. Sonata in G minor for violin and basso continuo. (McLean, Charles). *Oxford University Press. £1.30* SPE (B75-50249) ISBN 0-19-357679-1
Sonatas for flute & continuo. Op.1, nos 9,10. Two sonatas for flute & basso continuo. (McLean, Charles). *Oxford University Press. £2.00* VRPE (B75-50318)
ISBN 0-19-357681-3
Johnson, Derek. The Armada pop quiz book. (Kinn, Maurice). *Armada Books. £0.35* A(DE) (B75-05789)
ISBN 0-00-690953-1
Johnson, Robert. Complete works for solo lute. *Oxford University Press. £2.75* TW/AZ (B75-50291)
ISBN 0-19-357390-3
Johnson, Robert, *b.1582.* Songs. *Collections.* Ayres, songs and dialogues. 2nd revised ed. *Stainer and Bell. Unpriced* KE/TWDW/AZ (B75-51123)
Johnson, Robert Sherlaw.
Messiaen. *Dent. £6.95* BMKS (B75-17689)
ISBN 0-460-04198-3
Triptych : for flute, clarinet, violin, cello, piano and percussion. *Oxford University Press. £2.50* NYDPNQ (B75-50650) ISBN 0-19-357331-8
Johnson, Stuart. Three carols for brass. *British and Continental Music. Unpriced* WMK/DP/LF/AYC (B75-50924)
Johnson, Thomas Arnold.
Gavotte : for descant recorder, oboe or B flat clarinet and piano. *Bosworth. Unpriced* VSRPHM (B75-50875)
Gigue : for descant recorder, oboe or clarinet in B flat or A and piano. *Bosworth. Unpriced* VSRPHP (B75-50876)
Horn pipe (Allegro moderato) : for oboe (or clarinet) and piano. *British and Continental Music. Unpriced* VTPHN (B75-50889)
Johnson, Val. Tell me what month : an American Christmas folk song. (Bune, Robert). *Warner : Blossom. Unpriced* ENVSNRDW/LF (B75-50451)
Johnston, Peter Fyfe. Three Scottish folk tunes. *Oxford University Press. Unpriced* QNVK/DW/G/AYDL (B75-51220) ISBN 0-19-372985-7
Johnstone, Harry Diack.
My heart is ev'ry beauty's prey : tenor solo, harpsichord and cello (ad lib.). (Croft, William). *Roberton. Unpriced* KGHDW (B75-50589)
Two trumpet voluntaries. (James, John). *Oxford University Press. £0.50* RJ (B75-50732) ISBN 0-19-375490-8
Joio, Norman dello. *See* Dello Joio, Norman.
Jokers wild : cornet or trumpet trio (based on a theme by Mozart from 'Ein musikalischer Spass'. K.522. (Siebert, Edrich). *Studio Music. Unpriced* WMPWRNT (B75-50934)
Jolivet, René. Viva Napoli. *Vocal score.* Viva Napoli : operette à grand spectacle en 2 actes et 12 tableaux. (Lopez, Francis). *Chappell. Unpriced* CF (B75-50990)
Jolsonography : the world's greatest reference work on the world's greatest entertainer. (Jay, Dave). 2nd ed. *70 Southcote Rd, Bournemouth, Hants. : Barrie Anderton. £15.00* AKDW/GB/E(P) (B75-03647)
ISBN 0-9501412-1-6
Jon Raven, nos 1-8. Contemporary life : eight folk-songs for voices and guitar. *Oxford University Press. £0.35* JE/TSDW/G/AY (B75-50091) ISBN 0-19-330627-1
Jonas, Oswald. Harmony. (Schenker, Heinrich). *M.I.T. Press. £2.00* A/R (B75-02996) ISBN 0-262-69044-6
Jones, Anita Hewitt-. *See* Hewitt-Jones, Anita.
Jones, David Lloyd-. *See* Lloyd-Jones, David.
Jones, E Olwen. Hei dyma ni : a chaneuon eraill i'r plant lleiaf. *Christopher Davies. Unpriced* JFDW/G/AYDK (B75-50535)
Jones, Glyn. The beach of Falesa. *Vocal score.* The beach of Falesa : opera in three acts. (Hoddinott, Alun). *Oxford University Press. £8.50* CC (B75-50394)
Jones, Maimie Noel. Caneuon Lili Lon. (Huw Jones, Sheila). *Christopher Davies. £0.90* JFEZDW/JS (B75-51099)
ISBN 0-7154-0167-x
Jones, Philip. Paduana, galliarda, etc. quaternis et quinis vocibus cum basso continuo. Selections. *arr.* Battle suite. (Scheidt, Samuel). *Chester. Unpriced* WNRK (B75-51446)
Jones, Sheila Huw. *See* Huw Jones, Sheila.
Joplin, Scott.
Bethena. *arr.* Bethena. *Chappell. Unpriced* WMK/AHXJ (B75-50372)
The entertainer. *arr.* The entertainer. *Rubank : Novello. Unpriced* VQPK/AHXJ (B75-51365)
The entertainer. *arr.* The entertainer. *Rubank : Novello. Unpriced* VRNTK/AHXJ (B75-51366)
The entertainer. *arr.* The entertainer. *Rubank : Novello. Unpriced* VVNTK/AHXJ (B75-51402)
The entertainer. *arr.* The entertainer. *Rubank : Novello. Unpriced* VVRPK/AHXJ (B75-51411)
The entertainer. *arr.* The entertainer ; with, Maple leaf rag. *Paxton. Unpriced* WMK/AHXJ (B75-50373)
The entertainer. *arr.* The entertainer : two-part song. *Ashdown. £0.12* FDW (B75-51056)
Piano music. Selections. *arr.* Scott Joplin, king of ragtime : easy organ. *Lewis : Phoenix. Unpriced* RK/AHXJ (B75-51278)
Rags. *Oxford University Press. £1.75* VVNSK/AHXJ (B75-50894) ISBN 0-19-357320-2
Scott Joplin ragtime rags
Book 1. *Bosworth. Unpriced* QPHXJ (B75-50683)
Book 2. *Bosworth. Unpriced* QPHXJ (B75-50684)
Scott Joplin : the king of ragtime writers. *Lewis Music Phoenix. Unpriced* RK/AHXJ/AY (B75-50216)

The best of Scott Joplin. *Chappell. Unpriced* WMK/AHXJ (B75-50371)
Treemonisha. *Selections: arr.* Treemonisha. *Fanfare Press : Chappell : Chappell. Unpriced* KDW (B75-51105)
Joseph and the amazing technicolour dreamcoat. (Webber, Andrew Lloyd). Revised and enlarged ed. *Novello. £2.00* CM/L (B75-50399)
Joseph and the amazing technicolour dreamcoat. *Vocal score.* Joseph and the amazing technicolour dreamcoat. (Webber, Andrew Lloyd). Revised and enlarged ed. *Novello. £2.00* CM/L (B75-50399)
Joseph Cooper's hidden melodies : six improvisations for piano. (Cooper, Joseph). *Paxton. Unpriced* QPJ (B75-51237)
Josephs, Wilfred.
Four Japanese lyrics. Opus 47 for high voice, clarinet & piano. *Novello. £0.85* KFTE/VVPDW (B75-50581)
Octet for string & wind instruments. Octet. Opus 43 : for strings & winds, B flat clarinet, F horn, bassoon, violin I, violin II, viola, violoncello, contrabass. *Chappell. Unpriced* NVPNN (B75-51183)
Siesta. Op.8 : for violin and piano. *Chappell. Unpriced* SPJ (B75-51297)
Sonata for cello solo. Opus 73. *Novello. £1.00* SRPME (B75-50265)
Joshua fought the battle of Jericho : a jazz spiritual for junior wind band and optional voices in two parts. (Wastall, Peter). *Boosey and Hawkes. £2.05* UMJ (B75-51340)
Joshua fought the battle of Jericho : traditional. (Smith-Masters, Stanley). *Studio Music. Unpriced* WMK/DW/LC (B75-50932)
Josquin des Prés. Qui belles amours : ATTB. *Oxford University Press. Unpriced* EZDW (B75-51049) ISBN 0-19-341222-5
Journey into space travelogue : an antiscore. (Wishart, Trevor). *2 Fareham St., W.1 : Distributed by Alfred A. Kalmus. Unpriced* BWNVAPV (B75-31194) ISBN 0-9504561-0-1
Journey through America with the Rolling Stones. (Greenfield, Robert). *Panther. £0.75* AKDW/GB/E)P/XQM) (B75-24849) ISBN 0-586-04195-8
Joy of music. (Bernstein, Leonard). *White Lion Publishers. £3.25* A/C (B75-04502) ISBN 0-85617-717-2
Joyce, James. Syzygy : for soprano, French horn and chamber orchestra. (Del Tredici, David). *Boosey and Hawkes. £9.00* KFLE/MPWTDX (B75-50118)
Jubilate Domino : Solokantate für Alt, Viola da gamba (Violoncello) und Basso continuo. (Buxtehude, Dietrich). *Bärenreiter. £1.80* KFQE/SRPDE (B75-50122)
Judd, Margaret.
Spring dances : for pianoforte. *Bosworth. Unpriced* QPH (B75-50675)
The witches : for piano. *Bosworth. Unpriced* QPJ (B75-50702)
The witches : for piano. *Bosworth. Unpriced* QPJ (B75-50703)
Judith. God. Jehovah. God, Jehovah : mixed chorus and keyboard. (Chadwick, George Whitfield). *Galaxy Galliard. Unpriced* DH (B75-51003)
Judy. (Frank, Gerold). *W.H. Allen. £5.00* AKDW/GB/E(P) (B75-24858) ISBN 0-491-01735-9
Judy, with love : the story of 'Miss Show Business'. (Smith, Lorna). *Hale. £3.80* AKDW/GB/E(P) (B75-24859) ISBN 0-7091-5257-4
Julian, V M. Mr Squirrel : SSA. (Williams, Patrick). *Bosworth. Unpriced* FLDW (B75-50081)
Juliana : valzer venezuelano per chitarra. (Belasco, Lionel). *Zanibon : Hinrichsen. Unpriced* TSPMHW (B75-50276)
Jungk, Klaus. Esquisses experimentales : für Flöte. *Litolff : Peters. Unpriced* VRPMJ (B75-50326)
Just a song at twilight : the second parlour song book. *Michael Joseph. £8.50* KDW/GB/AY(XHS64) (B75-51115) ISBN 0-7181-1339-x
K-Rhapsodie. Souvenir. Souvenir : für Violine und Klavier. (Kupkovič, Ladislav). *Universal. Unpriced* SPJ (B75-50768)
Kabalevsky, Dmitry. Piano music. *Selections.* Kabalevsky for the young pianist. *Schroeder and Gunther. Unpriced* QPJ (B75-51244)
Kabalevsky for the young pianist. (Kabalevsky, Dmitry). *Schroeder and Gunther. Unpriced* QPJ (B75-51244)
Kachamba Brothers' Band : a study of neo-traditional music in Malaŵi. (Kubik, Gerhard). *Manchester University Press for University of Zambia Institute for African Studies. £2.25* BZNNALN(P) (B75-15002) ISBN 0-7190-1408-5
Kagel, Mauricio.
Aus Zungen Stimmen : für Akkordeonquintett. *Universal. Unpriced* RSNR (B75-50743)
Exotica : für aussereuropäische Instrumente, 1971-72. *Universal. Unpriced* LN (B75-50126)
Gegenstimmen : für gemischten Chor und obligates Cembalo. *Universal. Unpriced* DX (B75-50449)
Mirum : für Tuba, 1965. *Universal. Unpriced* WVPMJ (B75-50386)
Vom Hönensagen : für Frauenstimmen und obligates Harmonium. *Universal. Unpriced* FDE (B75-50485)
Kalisch, Alfred. Ariadne auf Naxos : opera in one act with a prelude. (Hofmannsthal, Hugo von). *Boosey and Hawkes. £1.50* BSUAC (B75-08737) ISBN 0-85162-026-4
Kaminsky, Heinrich. Andante für Orgel und Orgelchoral 'Meine Seele ist stille'. *Bärenreiter. £1.20* RJ (B75-50207)
Kaplan, Nathan Ivan. Fugue on fugue : for brass quintet, B flat trumpet I, B flat trumpet II, F horn, trombone, tuba. *Chappell. Unpriced* WNR/Y (B75-51438)
Karas, Anton. The third man. Harry Lime theme. *arr.* The third man. *Chappell. Unpriced* UMK/JR (B75-50826)
Karpeles, Maud.
The crystal spring : English folk songs
Book 1. *Oxford University Press. Unpriced* JE/TSDW/G/AYD (B75-51088) ISBN 0-19-330516-x
Book 2. *Oxford University Press. Unpriced* JE/TSDW/G/AYD (B75-51089) ISBN 0-19-330517-8
Kasschau, Howard.
Five beginner's pieces : for piano. *Schirmer. Unpriced* QPJ (B75-51245)
Seven recital pieces : for piano. *Schirmer. Unpriced* QPJ (B75-51246)
Six easy pieces : for piano. *Schirmer. Unpriced* QPJ (B75-51247)
Katalog für Schlagzeug II = Catalogue for percussion II : 2 players. (Hiller, Wilfried). *Schott. Unpriced* XPQNU (B75-51481)
Kay, Ernest. International who's who in music and musicians' directory
7th ed. : 1975. *Cambridge CB2 3QP : International Who's Who in Music. £15.00* A(N/BC) (B75-27957) ISBN 0-900332-31-x
Kay, Peter.
The snowman of Kashmir : a workshop opera for children. *Universal. Unpriced* CQN (B75-50995)
The snowman of Kashmir. *Vocal score.* The snowman of Kashmir : a workshop opera for children. *Universal. Unpriced* CN (B75-50401)
Kay's theme : piano solo. (Rota, Nino). *Famous Music : Chappell. Unpriced* QPK/JR (B75-50198)
Kear, Warrick. Impressions : for recorder ensemble, descant, treble/sopranino, treble 2, tenors. *Tomus. Unpriced* VSNR (B75-51377)
Keeping, Charles. Cockney ding dong. *Kestrel Books : EMI. £3.95* KE/TSDW/AYDB (B75-51122) ISBN 0-7226-5061-2
Keilmann, Wilhelm. Ich spiele vom Blatt : Schule des Prima-Vista-Spiels : für Klavier und andere Tasteninstrumente
Band 2. *Litolff : Peters. Unpriced* Q/EG (B75-50658)
Kelemen, Milko.
Abecedarium : für Streicher. *Litolff : Peters. Unpriced* RXMJ (B75-50227)
Fabliau : für Orgel. *Litolff : Peters. Unpriced* RJ (B75-50208)
Olifant : für einen Solisten (Posaune, Trombita Bali-Flöten Zurla, Buchel, Alphorn) und zwei Kammerensembles. *Litolff : Peters : Hinrichsen. Unpriced* MRJ (B75-50161)
Kelkel, Manfred. Zagreber concerto for guitar. Op.19. *arr.* Zagreber Konzert : für Gitarre und Orchester. Op.19. *Schott. Unpricd* TSPMK/LF (B75-50290)
Keller, Hans. Death in Venice. *Vocal score.* Death in Venice. Op.88 : an opera in two acts. (Britten, Benjamin). *Faber Music. Unpriced* CC (B75-50988)
Keller, Hermann. Recercares for organ, nos.1-4. Four recercars : for organ. (Steigleder, Johann Ulrich). New ed. *Bärenreiter. Unpriced* RJ (B75-50734)
Kelly, Bryan.
Boys in a pie : two-part song with piano. *Roberton. £0.12* FDW (B75-50490)
Seasonal sentences suitable for the Series 3 communion service or as independent anthems. *Oxford University Press. £0.90* DGSKAD (B75-50416) ISBN 0-19-395242-4
The spider monkey uncle king. *Vocal score.* The spider monkey uncle king : an opera pantomime for children. *Novello. £1.10* CN (B75-50008)
Kelly, Michael, *b.1762.* Reminiscences of Michael Kelly. 2nd ed. reprinted with corrections. *Oxford University Press. £7.50* AKGH/E(P) (B75-20392) ISBN 0-19-255417-4
Kelterborn, Rudolf.
Changements : pour grand orchestre. *Bärenreiter. Unpriced* MMJ (B75-50616)
Drei Fragmente : für Chor, SATB 1973. *Bärenreiter. £3.00* EZDW (B75-50066)
Kember, John. Wind band book : seven pieces, for woodwind and brass instruments with optional percussion. *Oxford University Press. £2.75* UMK/AAY (B75-50298) ISBN 0-19-369800-5
Kemp, David. The Armada pop quiz book. (Kinn, Maurice). *Armada Books. £0.35* A(DE) (B75-05789) ISBN 0-00-690953-1
Kemp's music & recording industry year book (international) : a comprehensive reference source and marketing guide to the music and recording industry in Great Britain & overseas
1974-75. *Kemp's. £3.75* A/GB(YC/BC) (B75-02719) ISBN 0-901268-76-3
Kennedy, John Brodbin.
April and May : two songs. *Boosey and Hawkes. Unpriced* KDW (B75-51106)
The look, the kiss and joy : three madrigals with coda, SSA unaccompanied. *Boosey and Hawkes. Unpriced* FEZDW (B75-51065)
Kennerley, Peter.
The bells : a carol for S.S.A. and piano. (Walters, Edmund). *Boosey and Hawkes. £0.15* FDP/LF (B75-51054)
Born in Bethlehem : a carol for treble voices with optional S.A. or S.A.T.B. chorus. (Walters, Edmund). *Boosey and Hawkes. £0.10* FDP/LF (B75-51055)
Kenny, Terry.
Trombone rockanova. *Studio Music. Unpriced* WMJ (B75-50922)
Trombone rockanova : brass band. *Studio Music. Unpriced* WMH (B75-50918)
Kenyon, Nicholas. Sing the Mass : a new source-book of liturgical music for cantor, choir and congregation. *Chapman. Unpriced* JDG/AY (B75-50521) ISBN 0-225-65984-0
Kern, Jerome. The best of Jerome Kern. *Chappell. Unpriced* KDW (B75-50554)
Keyboard interpretation from the 14th to the 19th century : an introduction. (Ferguson, Howard). *Oxford University Press. £2.95* APW/E(XCX601) (B75-21076) ISBN 0-19-318419-2
Keyper, Franz. Romance and rondo for double bass & orchestra. *arr.* Romance and rondo : for double bass and orchestra. *Yorke. Unpriced* SSPK/W (B75-50780)
Keyper, Franz Anton Leopold Joseph. Rondo solo : for double bass and violoncello or viola. *Yorke. Unpriced* SRPLSS/W (B75-50264)
Killmayer, Wilhelm.
Salvum me fac : Bariton und Klavier. *Schott. Unpriced* KGNDR (B75-51131)
Symphony no.3, 'Menschen-Los'. *Schott. £4.50* MME (B75-51150)
Kinder-Album. Op.98 : für Klavier zweihändig. (Grechaninov, Aleksandr Tikhonovich). *Peters. Unpriced* QPJ (B75-50192)
Kinderbuch. Op.98. Kinder-Album. Op.98 : für Klavier zweihändig. (Grechaninov, Aleksandr Tikhonovich). *Peters. Unpriced* QPJ (B75-50192)
King, Janet.
Christmas carols made easy : for piano with guitar chords. *M.S.M. Unpriced* QPK/DP/LF/AY (B75-51261)
Time to play : for piano. *M.S.M. Unpriced* QPJ (B75-51248)
King, Jeffrey. A wind has blown the rain away : SATB and piano. *Boosey and Hawkes. Unpriced* DW (B75-51018)
King Arthur. *Choral score.* King Arthur. (Purcell, Henry). *Faber Music. Unpriced* DACB/JM (B75-50996)
Kinn, Maurice. The Armada pop quiz book. *Armada Books. £0.35* A(DE) (B75-05789) ISBN 0-00-690953-1
Kirchen - und Tafelmusik, no.21. Gelobet seist du, Jesu Christ : Choralkonzert für Tenor (einstimmigen Chor), zwei Trompeten, vier Posaunen und Basso continuo (ad lib). (Hammerschmidt, Andreas). *Bärenreiter. Unpriced* JGHE/WNQDH (B75-50544)
Kirchner, Leon. Fanfare for brass trio (2 trumpets and horn). *Associated Music. Unpriced* WNTGN (B75-50944)
Kirk, H L. Pablo Casals : a biography. *Hutchinson. £5.50* ASR/E(P) (B75-13171) ISBN 0-09-122230-3
Kirkby-Mason, Barbara.
Eight Jamaican folk-songs. *Oxford University Press. £0.50* QPK/DW/G/AYULD (B75-50720) ISBN 0-19-373273-4
It's time for music : a quick progress course for the piano class. *Faber Music. £0.75* Q/AC (B75-50656)
My first collection : containing interesting examples of works by composers through the ages for the developing pianist. *Bosworth. Unpriced* QPK/AAY (B75-50716)
My second collection : containing interesting examples of works by composers through the ages for the developing pianist. *Bosworth. Unpriced* QPK/AAY (B75-50717)
My third collection containing interesting examples of works by composers through the ages for the developing pianist. *Bosworth. Unpriced* QPK/AAY (B75-50718)
Kirklees Libraries and Museums Service. Huddersfield Glee & Madrigal Society, 1875-1975. (Huddersfield Glee and Madrigal Society). *Princess Alexandra Walk, Huddersfield HD1 2SU : Kirklees Libraries and Museums Service. £0.50* AD/E(YDJGH/QB) (B75-07343) ISBN 0-9502568-1-1
Kirkpatrick, John. Crossing the bar : anthem for solo quartet or mixed choir and organ. (Ives, Charles). *Associated Music. Unpriced* DH (B75-50419)
Kiss me goodnight, Sergeant Major : the songs and ballads of World War II. *Panther. £0.60* ADW/KG(YC/XNU7) (B75-29320) ISBN 0-586-04152-4
Kittredge, Walter. Tenting on the old camp ground : for four-part mixed voices with piano or guitar (and optional oboe, flute, or violin). *Schirmer. Unpriced* DW (B75-50443)
Klein, Maynard. Litaniae Lauretanae. K.109. *Vocal score.* Litaniae Lauretanae. K.109 (Marien sic litany) : for four-part chorus of mixed voices and soprano, alto, tenor and bass solos. (Mozart, Wolfgang Amadeus). *Schirmer. Unpriced* DS/LDB (B75-50435)
Klein, Theodor. Sonatas for viola d'amore & continuo, 'Stockholm'. 'Stockholm sonatas' : for viola d'amore (viola) and basso continuo
1: Sonatas in F major, A minor, G major. (Ariosti, Attilio). *Bärenreiter. £2.80* SQQPE (B75-50259)
Kleine Stücke grosser Meister : für Sopran-und Altblockflöte. *Noetzel : Hinrichsen. Unpriced* VSNUK/AAY (B75-50867)
Kleine Tänze grosser Meister : für Sopran-und Altblockflöte. *Noetzel : Hinrichsen. Unpriced* VSNUK/AH/AY (B75-50868)
Klempererisms : a few of Dr Klemperer's lighter moments. (Beavan, Peter). *15 Dungarvan Ave., S.W.15 : Cock Robin Press. Free* A/EC(P) (B75-09268) ISBN 0-9500594-2-0
Klima tis apussias = Stimmung der Abwesenheit = Sense of absence : for voice and chamber orchestra. (Antoniou, Theodore). *Bärenreiter. £2.40* KE/MRDW (B75-50116)
Klima tis apussias = Stimmung der Abwesenheit = Sense of absence : for voice and piano. (Antoniou, Theodore). *Bärenreiter. £2.40* KDW (B75-50104)
Klima tis apussias. *Vocal score.* Klima tis apussias = Stimmung der Abwesenheit = Sense of absence : for voice and piano. (Antoniou, Theodore). *Bärenreiter. £2.40* KDW (B75-50104)
Klocker, Dieter. Trio for two clarinets & bassoon in E flat

major. Trio für zwei Klarinetten und Fagott, Es-dur. (Pleyel, Ignaz). *Litolff : Peters. Unpriced* VNT (B75-50311)
Klopčič, Rok. Rondo for violin & piano in G major. K-H 41. Rondo for violin & piano. (Beethoven, Ludwig van). *Schirmer. Unpriced* SP/W (B75-50764)
Klotz, Hans.
Sechzehn Vorspiele zu evangelischen Kirchenliedern : für die Orgel. *Bärenreiter. £3.26* RJ (B75-50209)
Über die Orgelkunst der Gotik, der Renaissance und des Barock : Musik, Disposition, Mixturen, Mensuren, Registrierung, Gebrauch der Klaviere. 2., völlig neubearb. Aufl. *32 Great Titchfield St., W.1 : Bärenreiter. £31.50* AR/B(XCL431)
Knapp, Dan. Going down with Janis. (Caserta, Peggy). *Talmy Franklin. £1.95* AKDW/GB/E(P) (B75-29317) ISBN 0-900735-40-6
Kneale, Peter. Quartet for brass. *R. Smith. Unpriced* WNS (B75-50939)
Knechtel, Ried.
Forsyth descant recorder tutor. (Lambert, Cecily). *Forsyth. Unpriced* VSR/AC (B75-50869)
Forsyth descant recorder tutor. (Lambert, Cecily). *Forsyth. Unpriced* VSR/AC (B75-51380)
Kneusslin, Fritz. Faramondo. Overture. Ouverture für Streicher, 2 Oboi (Fl.), Fagotti ad lib, und Cembalo. (Handel, George Frideric). *Kneusslin : Hinrichsen. Unpriced* MRJ (B75-50159)
Knight, Ronald David. The Hambledon cricket song of the Rev Reynell Cotton. *40A Abbotsbury Rd, Weymouth, Dorset DT4 0AE : R.D. Knight. £0.30* BCMTADW (B75-12697) ISBN 0-903769-00-x
Knives and forks and spoons : 20 songs with rhymes. (Gray, Vera). *24 Royston St., Potton : Lindsay Music. £0.55* JFDW/GR (B75-50536) ISBN 0-85957-006-1
Knott, Joshua Robert. A study of Brindley and Foster, organ builders of Sheffield, 1854-1939. *101 Highcroft Cres., Bognor Regis, Sussex PO22 8DT : The author. £1.15* AR/BC(Q/YDJGS) (B75-50002) ISBN 0-9503869-0-1
Koblitz, David. Nomos : for unaccompanied double bass. *Yorke. Unpriced* SSPMJ (B75-50782)
Kohaut, Karl. Sonata for lute in D major. *arr.* Sonata in D. *Oxford University Press. Unpriced* TSPMK/AE (B75-50815) ISBN 0-19-357428-4
Komachi. Opus 240 : piano solo. (Hovhaness, Alan). *Peters. Unpriced* QPJ (B75-50193)
Konrad of the mountains : a pageant for voice and instruments. (Blyton, Carey). *Belwin-Mills. Unpriced* JFE/NYEDX (B75-50538)
Korsakoff, Nikolai Rimsky-. *See* Rimsky-Korsakoff, Nikolai.
Korsakov, Nikolai Rimsky-. *See* Rimsky-Korsakov, Nikolai.
Kovács, Béla. Duets for two clarinets. Op.74. Sechs Duos für zwei Klarinetten. Opus 74. (Devienne, Francois). *Litolff : Peters. Unpriced* VVNU (B75-50896)
Krapf, Gerhard.
Les Goûts réunis or Nouveaux concerts : for instrumental ensemble
Volume 1: Concerts 5-8 : for flute or oboe or violin & basso continuo. (Couperin, François). *Musica rara. Unpriced* LNG (B75-51140)
Volume 2: Concerts 9-10, 12, 14 : for flute or oboe or violin and basso continuo. (Couperin, François). *Musica rara. Unpriced* LNG (B75-51141)
Volume 3: Concerts 10, 12-13 : for three violas da gamba or cellos or bassoons. (Couperin, François). *Musica rara. Unpriced* LNG (B75-51142)
Kraus, Eberhard. Fuga sopra 'l do re mi fa sol la' : für Streichquartett oder Streichorchester. (Schacht, Theodor von). *Bosse : Bärenreiter. Unpriced* RXNS/Y (B75-50763)
Krebs, Johann Ludwig. Orgelwerke
Bd.2. *Litolff : Peters. Unpriced* RJ (B75-50210)
Kreidler, Dieter. Picking Blues : leichte Blues - Sätze nach alten und neuen Melodien, für Gitarre. *Schott. Unpriced* TSPMK/DW/HHW/AY (B75-51329)
Křenek, Ernst. Five short pieces for strings. *Bärenreiter. Unpriced* RXNS (B75-50761)
Kreutzer, Konradin. Quintet for flute, clarinet, viola, cello and piano in A major. *Musica rara. Unpriced* NURNR (B75-51175)
Krishna Govinda's rudiments of tabla playing. (Baily, John). *Llan-fynydd, Carmarthen, Dyfed SA32 7TT : Unicorn Bookshop. £2.50* BZFLAXQ/AC (B75-04510) ISBN 0-85659-018-5
Kroatische Suite nach Volksweisen aus Medjimurje : für Gitarre. (Miletić, Miroslav). *Schott. £0.90* TSPMG (B75-51322)
Kroeger, Karl. Hear my prayer, O Lord : SATB. *Boosey and Hawkes. Unpriced* EZDK (B75-50057)
Krommer, Franz.
Quartet for clarinet, violin, viola & cello, op.82, in D major. Quartet in D. Opus 82 : for clarinet, violin, viola and cello. *Musica rara. £3.00* NVVNS (B75-51188)
Quartet for clarinet, violin, viola & cello, op.83, in B flat major. Quartet in B flat. Opus 83 : for clarinet, violin, viola and cello. *Musica rara. £3.00* NVVNS (B75-51189)
Quintet for clarinet & strings, op.95, in B flat major. Quintet in B flat. Opus 95 : for clarinet and strings. *Musica rara. Unpriced* NVVNR (B75-51187)
Kubik, Gerhard. The Kachamba Brothers' Band : a study of neo-traditional music in Malaŵi. *Manchester University Press for University of Zambia Institute for African Studies. £2.25* BZNNALN(P) (B75-15002) ISBN 0-7190-1408-5
Kucera, Karel. Festival chorus. Slavnostní sbor = Festlicher Chor = Festival chorus : for four male voices, women's and men's chorus and piano. (Janacek, Leos). *Bärenreiter. £1.20* DX (B75-50033)
Kuhlau, Friedrich Daniel Rudolph. Three fantasias. Opus 38 : for flute solo. *Universal. Unpriced* VRPMJ (B75-50855)
Kummerling, Harald. Biblische Motetten für das Kirchenjahr. Band 2: Darstellung des Herrn bis Trinitas. *Selections.* Spruchmotten
3: Motetten. *Bärenreiter. £1.40* EZDJ/AYE (B75-50056)
Kunst-Stoff : für Elektro-Klarinette, präpariertes Klavier und Tonband. (Heider, Werner). *Litolff : Peters. Unpriced* VVPJ (B75-50349)
Kunze, Stefan. Don Giovanni. Don Giovanni o sai Il Convitato di pietra : dramma giocoso in un atto di Giovanni Bertati. (Gazzaniga, Guiseppe). *Bärenreiter. Unpriced* CQC (B75-50404)
Kupkovič, Ladislav. K-Rhapsodie. Souvenir. Souvenir : für Violine und Klavier. *Universal. Unpriced* SPJ (B75-50768)
Kusik, Larry.
The godfather, part 2. Love said goodbye. *arr.* Love said goodbye. (Rota, Nino). *Famous Music : Chappell. Unpriced* GDW (B75-50082)
The godfather, part 2. Love said goodbye. *arr.* Love said goodbye : music by Nino Rota. (Rota, Nino). *Famous Music : Chappell. Unpriced* FDW (B75-50072)
Labyrinth : for piano. (Roxburgh, Edwin). *United Music. Unpriced* QPJ (B75-50708)
Lachrimae, nos 8, 1, 12. *arr.* Three dances. (Dowland, John). *Novello. £0.75* TSNSK/AH (B75-51319)
Laderman, Ezra. Songs from Michelangelo : for baritone and piano. *Oxford University Press. Unpriced* KGNDW (B75-51134)
Laing, Dave. The electric muse : the story of folk into rock. *Eyre Methuen. £1.70* A/HK(ZF) (B75-21664) ISBN 0-413-31860-5
Lam, Basil.
Beethoven string quartets
1. *British Broadcasting Corporation. £0.70* BBJARXNS (B75-30569) ISBN 0-563-10166-0
2. *British Broadcasting Corporation. £0.70* BBJARXNS (B75-30570) ISBN 0-563-12675-2
Lambert, Cecily.
Forsyth descant recorder tutor. *Forsyth. Unpriced* VSR/AC (B75-50869)
Forsyth descant recorder tutor. *Forsyth. Unpriced* VSR/AC (B75-51380)
Set of five : piano duets. *Forsyth. Unpriced* QNVG (B75-50181)
Set of five piano duets. *Forsyth. Unpriced* QNV (B75-51214)
Lancen, Serge.
Concert à six : 1 petite clarinette E bémol, 2 clarinettes B bémol, 1 clarinette alto E bémol (ou 3 ème clarinette B bémol), 1 clarinette basse B bémol, 1 clarinette contrabasse E bémol (ou 2 ème clarinette, basse B bémol. *Chappell. Unpriced* VVNQF (B75-51400)
Duo concertant pour flûte et harpe ou flûte et piano et orchestre à cordes non oblige : edition pour flûte et harpe. *Chappell. Unpriced* VRPLTQF (B75-51375)
Quatre flûtes en balade : pour quatre flûtes. *Chappell. Unpriced* VRNS (B75-50314)
Land of lost content and other songs. (Ireland, John). *Stainer and Bell. Unpriced* KDW (B75-51104) ISBN 0-85249-320-7
Land of the mountain and the flood. *Selections : arr.* Sutherland's law. (MacCunn, Hamish). *Ambleside Music : EMI. Unpriced* WMK (B75-51422)
Landon, Howard Chandler Robbins.
Beethoven : a documentary study. Abridged ed. *Thames and Hudson. £3.00* BBJ (B75-03644) ISBN 0-500-18146-2
Mass, no.12, in C major. K.258. *Vocal score.* Piccolomini mass. (Missa brevis in C) : mixed chorus. (Mozart, Wolfgang Amadeus). *Schirmer. Unpriced* DG (B75-50410)
Mass, no.13, in C major. K.259. *Vocal score.* Organ solo mass. (Missa brevis in C) : mixed chorus. (Mozart, Wolfgang Amadeus). *Schirmer. Unpriced* DG (B75-50411)
Lane, Edith M. Six Irish tunes. *Lengnick. Unpriced* NYDSK/DW/AYDM (B75-50653)
Lane, Joan. Three more songs for two-part choir. (Dale, Mervyn). *Ashdown. £0.15* FDW (B75-50071)
Lane, Philip.
A babe is born : SSA unacc. *Banks. Unpriced* FEZDP/LF (B75-51061)
A spotless rose : S.A. unacc. *Banks. Unpriced* FEZDP/LF (B75-51062)
Langley, Robin.
Concerto for harpsichord & string orchestra, op.2, no.2, in A major. Concerto in A major : for harpsichord, two violins and violoncello. (Chilcot, Thomas). *Oxford University Press. £2.60* RXMPQRF (B75-50752) ISBN 0-19-362290-4
Concerto for harpsichord, op.2, no.5, in F major. Concerto in F major : for harpsichord, two oboes, bassoon and strings. (Chilcot, Thomas). *Oxford University Press. Unpriced* MPQRF (B75-50622) ISBN 0-19-362296-3
Lantern festival : S.S.A. unacc. (Burtch, Mervyn). *Banks. Unpriced* FEZDW (B75-51064)
Lantier, Pierre. Diptyque pour alto et piano. *Chappell. Unpriced* SQPJ (B75-50257)
Lanza, Alcides.
Acúfenos II (1971-IV) : for chamber ensemble, electronic sounds and electronic extensions. *Boosey and Hawkes. Unpriced* NYD (B75-51195)
Eidesis III (1971-II) : for one or two orchestras and electronic sounds. *Boosey and Hawkes. Unpriced* MPPV (B75-51161)
Large, Brian. Martinu. *Duckworth. £9.50* BMFMN(N) (B75-22839) ISBN 0-7156-0770-7
Largo religioso : pour orchestra à cordes et clavecin avec orgue ad lib. (Boisvalée, François de). *Chappell. Unpriced* RXMJ (B75-50748)
Lark in the clear air : Irish air. (Deale, Edgar Martin). *Banks. Unpriced* DW (B75-50439)
Larsson, John. Spirit!. *Vocal score.* Spirit! : a musical. *Salvationist Publishing and Supplies. Unpriced* CM/LN (B75-50400)
LASER. *See* London and South Eastern Library Region.
LASER manual for cataloguing monographs and music. (London and South Eastern Library Region). *9 Alfred Place, WC1E 7EB : L.A.S.E.R. £1.25* A(UM) (B75-13384) ISBN 0-903764-04-0
Lasocki, David.
Concerto for flute, strings & basso continuo, in B flat major. Wq.167. Concerto in B flat major. Wq.167 : for flute, strings and basso continuo. (Bach, Carl Philipp Emanuel). *Musica rara. Unpriced* RXMPVRF (B75-51285)
Concerto for flute, strings & basso continuo in B flat major. Wq.167. *arr.* Concerto in B flat major. Wq.167 : for flute, strings and basso continuo. (Bach, Carl Philipp Emanuel). *Musica rara. Unpriced* VRPK/LF (B75-51374)
Concerto for oboe, bassoon & string orchestra in G major. P.129. Concerto in G major for oboe, bassoon, strings and basso continuo. P.129. (Vivaldi, Antonio). *Musica rara. £5.50* RXMPVTPLVWF (B75-51288)
Concerto for oboe, bassoon & string orchestra in G major. P.129. *arr.* Concerto in G major for oboe, bassoon, strings and basso continuo. P.129. (Vivaldi, Antonio). *Musica rara. Unpriced* NWPNTK/LF (B75-51193)
Les Goûts réunis or Nouveaux concerts : for instrumental ensemble
Volume 1: Concerts 5-8 : for flute or oboe or violin & basso continuo. (Couperin, François). *Musica rara. Unpriced* LNG (B75-51140)
Volume 2: Concerts 9-10, 12, 14 : for flute or oboe or violin and basso continuo. (Couperin, François). *Musica rara. Unpriced* LNG (B75-51141)
Volume 3: Concerts 10, 12-13 : for three violas da gamba or cellos or bassoons. (Couperin, François). *Musica rara. Unpriced* LNG (B75-51142)
Sonata for flute, cello & piano, op.65, in F major. Grand sonata in F major. Opus 65 : for flute (or violin) and piano. (Dussek, Jan Ladislav). *Musica rara. £3.80* NURNTE (B75-51176)
Sonata for flute, oboe & basso continuo in C minor. Trio sonata in C minor for flute, oboe and basso continuo. (Quantz, Johann Joachim). *Musica rara. Unpriced* NWPNTE (B75-51192)
Sonatas for two recorders & basso continuo. Op.3. Trio sonatas. Opus 3 : for 2 treble (alto) recorders and basso continuo
Nos.1-3. (Hotteterre, Jacques). *Musica rara. Unpriced* VSSNTPWE (B75-51383)
Sonatas for two recorders & basso continuo. Op.3. Trio sonatas. Opus 3 : for 2 treble (alto) recorders and basso continuo
Nos.4-6. (Hotteterre, Jacques). *Musica rara. Unpriced* VSSNTPWE (B75-51384)
Symphonie concertante for two flutes, op.76, in G major. *arr.* Symphonie concertante in G. Op.76 : for 2 flutes and orchestra. (Devienne, François). *Musica rara. £3.00* VRNTQK/LE (B75-51368)
Lassus, Victoria, Palestrina : three-part vocal compositions. *Ricordi. Unpriced* VSNTK/CB/AY (B75-50865)
Last, Joan.
The day's play : piano. *Forsyth. Unpriced* QPJ (B75-51249)
Two of a kind : 8 short inventions, for piano, introducing contrapuntal style. *Forsyth. Unpriced* QP/RM (B75-51224)
Two of a kind : 8 short inventions introducing contrapuntal style. *Forsyth. Unpriced* QP/RM (B75-50665)
Village pictures : piano. *Forsyth. Unpriced* QPJ (B75-50704)
Village pictures : piano pieces. *Forsyth. Unpriced* QPJ (B75-51250)
Latham, Peter, *b.1894.* Brahms. Revised ed.. *Dent. £2.95* BBT (B75-27352) ISBN 0-460-03158-9
Latin-Americana : brass band. (Hanmer, Ronald). *Studio Music. Unpriced* WMJ (B75-50920)
Latouche, John. Candide. *Selections: arr.* Candide : vocal selections. (Bernstein, Leonard). *Schirmer. Unpriced* KDW (B75-50550)
Lauber, Joseph. Quartet for double basses. *Yorke. Unpriced* SSNS (B75-50776)
Laure, Mary. Jack L'Eventreur. (Rorem, Ned). *Boosey and Hawkes. Unpriced* KDW (B75-51109)
Lavagne, Andre. Etude baroque : grand étude de concert pour piano. *Chappell. Unpriced* QPJ (B75-50194)
Law, Leslie G. A little impromptu. A little impromptu, and, Dance time. *Charnwood Music. Unpriced* RSPMJ (B75-51282)
Lawrence, Ian. Music and the teacher. *Pitman. £2.50* A(VC) (B75-19078) ISBN 0-273-00354-2
Lawrence, Vera Brodsky. Treemonisha. *Selections: arr.* Treemonisha. (Joplin, Scott). *Fanfare Press : Chappell Chappell. Unpriced* KDW (B75-51105)
Lawton, Sidney. Wind band book : seven pieces, for woodwind and brass instruments with optional percussion. *Oxford University Press. £2.75* UMK/AAY (B75-50298) ISBN 0-19-369800-5
Le Fleming, Antony.
Pop moods for young duettists : piano. *Chappell. Unpriced*

QNV (B75-51215)

Suite : for junior orchestra. *Chappell. Unpriced* RXMG (B75-50747)

Le Fleming, Christopher. The Mikado. *Choral score : arr.* The Mikado, or, The Town of Titipu. (Sullivan, *Sir* Arthur Seymour). *Cramer. £1.20* DACF (B75-50405)

Leach, John. Suite for unaccompanied double bass. *Yorke. Unpriced* SSPMG (B75-50270)

Lead guitar. (Owen, Tom). *Chappell. Unpriced* TS/AF (B75-51315)

Leadbitter, Mike. Blues records, January, 1943 to December, 1966. *Music Sales Ltd, 78 Newman St., W.1 : Oakwood Publications. Unpriced* AKDW/HHW/FD(WT/XPC18) (B75-50977) ISBN 0-86001-089-9

Lear, Edward. The Akond of Swat : for voice and percussion. (Gerhard, Roberto). *Oxford University Press. Unpriced* KE/XDW (B75-50568) ISBN 0-19-345361-4

Lear, W Hogarth.

Fireworks for brass band : variations on a theme of W. Hogarth Lear. (Howarth, Elgar). *Paxton. Unpriced* WM/T (B75-50914)

Pel mel : for brass band. *Paxton Music. £1.75* WMJ (B75-50365)

Pop goes the posthorn : for brass band. *Paxton. £1.50* WMJ (B75-50366)

Leb wohl, Frau welt. Op:43 : Liederzyklus für mittlere Singstimme und Klavier. (Einem, Gottfried von). *Boosey and Hawkes. £3.00* KFVDW (B75-50586)

Lebermann, Walter.

8 Capricen für Flöte. (Stamitz, Anton). *Litolff : Peters. Unpriced* VRPMJ (B75-50327)

Concerto for oboe & string orchestra in D minor. Konzert, d-moll, für Oboe und Streicher. (Holzbauer, Ignas). Zum ersten Mal herausgegeben von Walter Lebermann. *Litolff : Peters. Unpriced* RXMPVTF (B75-50232)

Concerto for oboe & string orchestra in D minor. *arr.* Konzert, D-moll für Oboe und Streicher. (Holzbauer, Ignaz). 1st ed. *Litolff : Peters. Unpriced* VTPK/LF (B75-51396)

Concerto for three violins & string orchestra in F major. P.278. *arr.* Concerto F-Dur. P.V.278 : für drei Violinen, Streichorchester und Basso continuo. (Vivaldi, Antonio). *Schott. £3.00* SNSQK/LF (B75-51292)

Concerto for viola & string orchestra, no.4, in D major. Concerto no.4 in D major : for viola and strings. (Stamitz, Anton). *Nagel : Bärenreiter. £3.60* RXMPSQF (B75-50229)

Ledger, Philip.

King Arthur. *Choral score.* King Arthur. (Purcell, Henry). *Faber Music. Unpriced* DACB/JM (B75-50996)

Six carols with descants. *Oxford University Press. Unpriced* DP/LF/AY (B75-51016) ISBN 0-19-353244-1

Ledward, James. Concert-Stück for oboe and orchestra. Op.33. *arr.* Concert piece : for oboe and orchestra. Op.33. (Rietz, Julius). *Musica rara. Unpriced* VTPK (B75-51394)

Lee, Clifford. Romance and rondo for double bass & orchestra. *arr.* Romance and rondo : for double bass and orchestra. (Keyper, Franz). *Yorke. Unpriced* SSPK/W (B75-50780)

Lees, Benjamin.

Sonata for violin and piano, no.2. *Boosey and Hawkes. £4.00* SPE (B75-50248)

Symphony no.3. *Boosey and Hawkes. Unpriced* MME (B75-50605)

Lefevre, Jean Xavier. Méthode de clarinette. Sonata for clarinet & piano, no.1, in B flat major. Sonata no.1 : for clarinet in B flat and piano. *Schott. £0.70* VVPE (B75-50348)

Legacy of the blues : a glimpse into the art and the lives of twelve great bluesmen : an informal study. (Charters, Samuel Barclay). *Calder and Boyars. £3.95* AKDW/HHW/E(M) (B75-50976) ISBN 0-7145-1098-x

Legend : for oboe and strings. (Luening, Otto). *Highgate Press : Galliard. Unpriced* RXMPVT (B75-50755)

Legenden. Op.62. Legends for viola and piano. (Herzogenberg, Heinrich von). *Musica rara. £2.00* SQPJ (B75-51301)

Legends for viola and piano. (Herzogenberg, Heinrich von). *Musica rara. £2.00* SQPJ (B75-51301)

Legrand, Michel. The three musketeers. *Selections: arr.* Themes from 'The three musketeers'. *Chappell. Unpriced* UMK/JR (B75-50301)

Legrenzi, Giovanni. Sonatas in five parts for various instruments. *Selections: arr.* Two sonatas in five parts : five recorders. *Universal. Unpriced* VSNRK/AE (B75-50857)

Leichte Duette für Altblockflöten. (Finger, Gottfried). *Heinrichshofen : Hinrichsen. Unpriced* VSSNU (B75-50880)

Leitch, Michael. Great songs of World War II : with the Home Front in pictures. *Wise Publications; 78 Newman St., W.1 : Distributed by Music Sales Ltd. £3.95* ADW/GB(XU7) (B75-22844) ISBN 0-86001-041-4

Lennon, John. Songs. *Selections : arr.* The Beatles for classical guitar. *Wise, Music Sales. Unpriced* TSPMK/DW (B75-50818)

Lenski, Karl.

Quartet for flute, violin, viola & cello, no.1, in D major. Quartet no.1 in D : for flute, violin, viola and cello. (Cimarosa, Domenico). *Musica rara. £2.00* NVRNS (B75-51184)

Quartet for flute, violin, viola & cello, no.2, in F major. Quarter no.2 in F : for flute, violin, viola and cello. (Cimarosa, Domenico). *Musica rara. £2.00* NVRNS (B75-51185)

Leonard, Stanley.

Fanfare and allegro : for trumpet and solo timpani. *Simrock. Unpriced* WSPLXR (B75-50383)

Notenbuch der Anna Magdalena Bach, 1725. *Selections: arr.* Bachiana for percussion : four pieces. (Bach, Johann Sebastian). *Simrock. Unpriced* XNQK (B75-50965)

Leppard, Raymond. La Calisto. *Vocal score.* La Calisto : opera in two acts with a prologue. (Cavalli, Francesco). *Faber Music. Unpriced* CC (B75-50989)

Lerner, Alan Jay.

Gigi. *Vocal score.* Lerner and Loewe's Gigi. (Loewe, Frederick). *Chappell. Unpriced* CM (B75-50398)

The little prince. Little prince. *arr.* Little prince : song. (Loewe, Frederick). *Famous Chappell. Unpriced* KDW/JR (B75-51118)

Showstoppers : the great songs of Lerner and Loewe. (Loewe, Frederick). *Chappell. Unpriced* RK/DW (B75-50737)

Lerner and Loewe's Gigi. (Loewe, Frederick). *Chappell. Unpriced* CM (B75-50398)

Let the earth resound ('Lobt den Herrn der Welt'). (Clarke, Jeremiah). *Bosworth. Unpriced* JDH (B75-50522)

Let's play drums. (Manne, Shelly). *Chappell. Unpriced* XQ/AC (B75-50387)

Levine, Rhoda. Opus number zoo : children's play for wind quintet (1951, rev. 1970). (Berio, Luciano). *Universal. Unpriced* CQN (B75-50994)

Lewin, Olive.

Beeny Bud : 12 Jamaican folk-songs for children. *Oxford University Press. Unpriced* FEZDW/G/AYULD (B75-51066) ISBN 0-19-330543-7

Dandy Shandy : 12 Jamaican folk-songs for children. *Oxford University Press. £0.40* FEZDW/G/AYULD (B75-50504) ISBN 0-19-330545-3

Lewis, Anthony, *b.1915.* The new Oxford history of music

Vol.5: Opera and church music, 1630-1750. *Oxford University Press. £12.50* A(X) (B75-29312) ISBN 0-19-316305-5

Liberace. Liberace : an autobiography. *44 Hill St., W1X 8LB : Star Books. £0.60* AQ/E(P) (B75-02999) ISBN 0-352-30010-8

Libro primo de canzoni da sonare. Canzona 'La Girella'. Canzona 'La Girella' : for four instruments. (Maschera, Florentio). *Oxford University Press. £0.55* LNS (B75-51146) ISBN 0-19-341206-3

Liddell, Claire. A Scottish carol : for 3-part treble voices with optional solo. *Roberton. £0.10* FLDP/LF (B75-51067)

Liedermagazin : für die Sekundarstufen. *Cassel : Bärenreiter. Unpriced* JDW/AY (B75-50528)

Life for the Tsar. *Selections.* Drei Tanze aus der Oper 'Ein Leben für den Zaren'. (Glinka, Mikhail Ivanovich). *Belaieff : Peters. Unpriced* MMH (B75-50137)

Liferman, Georges.

Nymphes et driades : pour orchestre. *Chappell. Unpriced* MMJ (B75-51154)

Sicilienne : pour flûte et piano. *Chappell. Unpriced* VRPHVQ (B75-50320)

Ligeti, György. Ballade und Tanz = Ballad and dance : after Roumanian folk songs, for school orchestra. *Schott. £2.90* MH (B75-50127)

Ligeti, György. Concerto for flute, oboe & orchestra (1972). Double concerto for flute, oboe and orchestra (1972). *Schott. Unpriced* MPVRPLVTF (B75-50154)

Like as the hart : soprano solo and mixed chorus. (Roe, Betty). *Thames. Unpriced* DH (B75-51005)

Lincoln, Stoddard. Five eighteenth century piano sonatas. *Oxford University Press. Unpriced* QPE/AY (B75-51227) ISBN 0-19-373206-8

Linde, Hans Martin. Musica da camera (1972) : for recorder (treble recorder and bass recorder) and guitar. *Schott. Unpriced* VSPLTS (B75-50331)

Lindsay, Vachel. The Congo jive : for choir, percussion and piano. (Paviour, Paul). *Boosey and Hawkes. £3.60* ENYLNTDW (B75-50037)

Lindsley, Charles Edward. Five American hymn tunes : for men's or mixed voices unaccompanied. *Oxford University Press. Unpriced* GEZDM/AYT (B75-50512)

Linike, Johann Georg. Mortorium à 5. Sonata (Mortorium) à 5 (1737) : for trumpet, oboe, flute, violin and basso continuo. *Musica rara. Unpriced* NUNR (B75-51173)

Linley, Dora. Sechs geistliche Lieder = Six sacred songs : for four-part chorus of mixed voices. (Wolf, Hugo). *Bärenreiter. £1.60* EZDH (B75-50053)

Listen to the blues. (Cook, Bruce). *Robson Books. £4.35* AKDW/HHW(X) (B75-21070) ISBN 0-903895-47-1

Listen to the mocking bird : for four-part chorus of mixed voices with optional tenor and bass solos and optional flute or violin and piano accompaniment. (Hawthorne, Alice). *Schirmer. Unpriced* DW (B75-50440)

Listeners. *Vocal score.* The listeners : a dramatic cantata for soprano solo, male speaker and small soprano chorus, with chamber orchestra. (Young, Douglas). *Faber Music. Unpriced* FLDX (B75-51073)

Liszt, Franz.

Liszt Society publications

Vol.6: Selected songs. *Schott. Unpriced* C/AZ (B75-50390)

Piano works

Vol.7: Années de pélerinage II. *Bärenreiter. Unpriced* QP/AZ (B75-50664)

Liszt. (Perényi, Eleanor). *Weidenfeld and Nicolson. £8.50* BLJ(N) (B75-11755) ISBN 0-297-76910-3

Liszt. (Wilkinson, Anthony). *Macmillan. £3.75* BLJ(N) (B75-14335) ISBN 0-333-15064-3

Liszt Society publications

Vol.6: Selected songs. (Liszt, Franz). *Schott. Unpriced* C/AZ (B75-50390)

Litaniae Lauretanae. K.109 (Marien sic litany) : for four-part chorus of mixed voices and soprano, alto, tenor and bass solos. (Mozart, Wolfgang Amadeus). *Schirmer. Unpriced* DS/LDB (B75-50435)

Little circus : orchestral suite. (Cohn, James). *Boosey and Hawkes. Unpriced* MMG (B75-51152)

Little concerto for double bass and string orchestra. (Jacob, Gordon). *Yorke. Unpriced* SSPK/LF (B75-50269)

Little impromptu. A little impromptu, and, Dance time. (Law, Leslie G). *Charnwood Music. Unpriced* RSPMJ (B75-51282)

Little negro = Le petit Negre : piano solo. (Debussy, Claude). *Peters. Unpriced* QPJ (B75-50692)

Little nigar. The little negro = Le petit Negre : piano solo. (Debussy, Claude). *Peters. Unpriced* QPJ (B75-50692)

Little nigar. *arr.* Le petit negre. (Debussy, Claude). *Emerson. Unpriced* WNRK (B75-51444)

Little night music. A little night music. *arr.* A little night music : piano. (Sondheim, Stephen). *Chappell. Unpriced* QPK/CM (B75-51260)

Little night music. *Selections : arr.* A little night music : souvenir song folio. (Sondheim, Stephen). *Chappell. Unpriced* KDW (B75-50559)

Little night music : souvenir song folio. (Sondheim, Stephen). *Chappell. Unpriced* KDW (B75-50559)

Little prince. Little prince. *arr.* Little prince : song. (Loewe, Frederick). *Famous Chappell. Unpriced* KDW/JR (B75-51118)

Little senorita : for piano solo. (Parke, Dorothy). *Banks. Unpriced* QPJ (B75-50706)

Little suite : for two descant recorders and piano. (Hunt, Reginald). *Ashdown. £0.50* VSRNTQG (B75-50332)

Livermore, Ann. A short history of Spanish music. *Duckworth. £2.95* A(YK/X) (B75-21071) ISBN 0-7156-0886-x

Livingstone, Wayne. Bunker hill. *arr.* Bunker hill : march. (Forsblad, Leland). *Warner : Blossom. Unpriced* UMMK/AGM (B75-50307)

Lloyd, Albert Lancaster. Folk song in England. *Paladin. £1.50* ADW/G(YD) (B75-10254) ISBN 0-586-08210-7

Lloyd, Richard. Preces and responses : for SATB with divisions (unaccompanied). *Novello. £0.15* EZDGMM (B75-50046)

Lloyd, Stephen. Gustav Holst. (Rubbra, Edmund). *10E Prior Bolton St., N.1 : Triad Press. £2.40* BHP(D) (B75-00200) ISBN 0-902070-12-6

Lloyd-Jones, David. Boris Godunov : opera in four acts with a prologue. (Mussorgsky, Modest). *Oxford University Press. Unpriced* CQC (B75-50993) ISBN 0-19-337699-7

Lobet den Namen des Herrn : vierstimmiger gemischter Chor und Orgel. (Schweizer, Rolf). *Bärenreiter. £0.20* DH (B75-50022)

Locke, Matthew. Consort of four parts. *Stainer and Bell. Unpriced* STNSG (B75-51309)

Lockhart, Helen. Guided sight-reading

Book 3. *Forsyth. Unpriced* Q/EG (B75-51212)

Loeffelholz, Klaus von. Choralbearbeitungen : für Blechbläser und Orgel. *Bärenreiter. Unpriced* NWXPNR (B75-50645)

Loesser, Frank.

'Hans Christian Andersen'. Anywhere I wander. *arr.* Anywhere I wander : for mixed chorus (SATB) and piano with optional rhythm guitar, bass guitar and drums. *Frank Music. Unpriced* DW (B75-51019)

Hans Christian Andersen. *Selections : arr.* Songs from Frank Loesser's Hans Andersen. *Edwin H. Morris. Unpriced* VSNSQK/DW/JR (B75-50862)

Hans Christian Andersen. *Selections : arr.* Songs from Frank Loesser's Hans Andersen. *Edwin H. Morris. Unpriced* VSRNRK/DW/JR (B75-50871)

Hans Christian Andersen. *Selections : arr.* Songs from Frank Loesser's Hans Andersen. *Edwin H. Morris. Unpriced* VSSNRK/DW/JR (B75-50878)

Hans Christian Andersen. *Selections : arr.* Songs from Frank Loesser's Hans Andersen. *Edwin H. Morris. Unpriced* VSTNTK/DW/JR (B75-50885)

Hans Christian Andersen. *Selections: arr.* Hans Andersen : souvenir song book. *Edwin H. Morris. Unpriced* KDW (B75-50108)

'Hans Christian Andersen'. The inch worm. *arr.* The inch worm : for mixed chorus (SATB) and piano with optional rhythm guitar, bass guitar and drums. *Frank Music. Unpriced* DW (B75-51020)

'Hans Christian Andersen'. The ugly duckling. *arr.* The ugly duckling : for two-part chorus of treble voices with piano. *Frank Music. Unpriced* FLDW (B75-51068)

'Hans Christian Andersen'. Wonderful Copenhagen. *arr.* Wonderful Copenhagen : for two-part chorus of treble voices with piano. *Frank Music. Unpriced* FLDW (B75-51069)

Loewe, Frederick.

Gigi. *Vocal score.* Lerner and Loewe's Gigi. *Chappell. Unpriced* CM (B75-50398)

The little prince. Little prince. *arr.* Little prince : song. *Famous Chappell. Unpriced* KDW/JR (B75-51118)

Showstoppers : the great songs of Lerner and Loewe. *Chappell. Unpriced* RK/DW (B75-50737)

Lolly too dum. (Miller, Carl). *Chappell. Unpriced* FDW (B75-50492)

Lombardo, Mario.

Sounds I prefer. *arr.* Sounds I prefer : for mixed chorus (SATB). *Chappell. Unpriced* DW (B75-51021)

Variations in a mod mood : for concert band. *Chappell. Unpriced* UM/T (B75-50294)

Volcanic rock : for concert band. *Chappell. Unpriced* UMMJ (B75-51344)

London and South Eastern Library Region. LASER manual for cataloguing monographs and music. *9 Alfred Place, WC1E 7EB : L.A.S.E.R. £1.25* A(UM) (B75-13384) ISBN 0-903764-04-0

London College of Music. Examinations in pianoforte

playing and singing, sight reading tests, sight singing tests, as set throughout 1972, grades 1-8 and diplomas. *Ashdown. £0.35* Q/EG (B75-50176)
London pictures : piano solos. (Fly, Leslie). *Forsyth. Unpriced* QPJ (B75-51242)
London Welsh Male Voice Choir. Take me home part-songs. *Chappell. Unpriced* DW/AY (B75-51022)
Lonesome valley : spiritual, SATB. (Cumming, Richard). *Boosey and Hawkes. Unpriced* DW/LC (B75-50446)
Long, Martin. Selected works for lute. (Bacheler, Daniel). *Oxford Universuty Press. £4.50* TWPMJ (B75-50292) ISBN 0-19-355305-8
Long, Robert. The fire maid. *Vocal score.* The fire maid : an opera for schools. *Oxford University Press. £2.50* CN (B75-50402) ISBN 0-19-337374-2
Long long ago : for four-part female chorus, unaccompanied. (Beaumont, Adrian). *Roberton. £0.08* FEZDP/LF (B75-51059)
Longmire, John. Four folk duets. *Forsyth. Unpriced* QNVK/DW/G/AYC (B75-51219)
Look, the kiss and joy : three madrigals with coda, SSA unaccompanied. (Kennedy, John Brodbin). *Boosey and Hawkes. Unpriced* FEZDW (B75-51065)
Lopez, Anja.
Maria. *arr.* Maria. *Chappell. Unpriced* TMK/DW (B75-51310)
Viva Napoli. *Vocal score.* Viva Napoli : operette à grand spectacle en 2 actes et 12 tableaux. (Lopez, Francis). *Chappell. Unpriced* CF (B75-50990)
Lopez, Francis. Viva Napoli. Maria. *arr.* Maria. (Lopez, Anja). *Chappell. Unpriced* TMK/DW (B75-51310)
Lopez, Francis.
Viva Napoli. La Mandoline a du bon. *arr.* La Mandoline a du bon. *Chappell. Unpriced* TMK/DW (B75-51311)
Viva Napoli. Ma sérénade. *arr.* Ma sérénade. *Chappell. Unpriced* TMK/DW (B75-51312)
Viva Napoli. Viva Napoli. *arr.* Viva Napoli. *Chappell. Unpriced* TMK/DW (B75-51313)
Viva Napoli. *Vocal score.* Viva Napoli : operette à grand spectacle en 2 actes et 12 tableaux. *Chappell. Unpriced* CF (B75-50990)
Lorca, Federico Garcia.
Epitaffio no. 1, 2 & 3. (Nono, Luigi). *Ars Viva : Schott. £11.60* HYE/M (B75-50086)
Songs, drones and refrains of death : a cycle of poems by Federico Garcia Lorca for baritone, electric guitar, electric contrabass, electric piano, (electric harpsichord), percussion (2 players). (Crumb, George). *Peters. Unpriced* KGNE/PVDW (B75-51136)
Lord is my shepherd : anthem for two sopranos, chorus and organ. (Wise, Michael). *Novello. £0.20* DK (B75-51010)
Lord of the dance. (Carter, Sydney). *Galaxy : Galliard. Unpriced* DP (B75-50429)
Lord of the dance. (Carter, Sydney). *Galaxy : Galliard. Unpriced* FLDP (B75-50506)
Lord, walk with me : for SATB chorus and piano. (Artman, Ruth). *Warner : Blossom. Unpriced* DH (B75-50417)
Lord we beseech thee = The collect for the Annunciation of the Blessed Virgin Mary : verse anthem for alto and chorus (SAATB) with accompaniment for viols or organ. (Gibbons, Orlando). *Novello. £0.20* ESTNRDK (B75-50040)
Lorenzen, Hermann. Prodromos musicae ecclesiasticae. *Selections.* Hosianna dem Sohne David, und, Wohlauf wohlauf zu dieser Frist : zwei kleine Weihnachtskonzert, für zwei mittlere Stimmen und Basso continuo. (Grimm, Heinrich). *Bärenreiter. £1.20* JNFVEDH/LF (B75-50103)
Lorimer, Michael. Suite espagnole. Bolero de los picaros. *arr.* Bolero de los picaros. (Surinach, Carlos). *Associated Music. Unpriced* TSPMK/AHJK (B75-50816)
Lotz, Hans Georg. Quartett nach einer Intrade aus dem 16. Jahrhundert : für Blockflöten-Quartett (Sopran, Alt, Tenor, Bass). *Schott. £1.20* VSNS (B75-51379)
Loudová, Ivana. Hymnos : wind orchestra and percussion. *Peters. Unpriced* UMJ (B75-51334)
Love in a life. (Rorem, Ned). *Boosey and Hawkes. Unpriced* KDW (B75-51110)
Love said goodbye. (Rota, Nino). *Famous Music : Chappell. Unpriced* GDW (B75-50082)
Love said goodbye : music by Nino Rota. (Rota, Nino). *Famous Music : Chappell. Unpriced* FDW (B75-50072)
Lovely Scouse song : unison modern comedy folk song, with chorus, words and music. (Davies, Laurence Hector). *Ashdown. £0.07* JFDW (B75-50534)
Lowe, Rachel. Frederick Delius 1862-1934, a catalogue of the Music Archive of the Delius Trust, London. (Delius Trust). *Delius Trust : Distributed by Boosey and Hawkes. £7.50* BDL(TE) (B75-08382) ISBN 0-85162-023-x
Lowinsky, Edward E. Musica duorum, Rome, 1521. (Romano, Eustachio). *Chicago University Press. Unpriced* C/AZ (B75-50983) ISBN 0-226-22646-8
Lübeck, Vincent. Gott, wie dein Name, so ist auch dein Ruhm : Kantate für dreistimmigen Männerchor, drei Trompeten und Basso continuo, (Bläsersatz), Pauken (ad lib.). *Bärenreiter. Unpriced* GE/WNPDE (B75-50511)
Luening, Otto.
The bells of Bellagio : 2 or 3 players at 1,2 or 3 pianos. *Peters. Unpriced* QN (B75-50177)
Legend : for oboe and strings. *Highgate Press : Galliard. Unpriced* RXMPVT (B75-50755)
Meditation : violin solo. *Peters. Unpriced* SPMJ (B75-50256)
Sonata for violin, no.1. Sonata no.1 : violin solo. *Peters. Unpriced* SPME (B75-50255)
Sonata for violin, no.2. Sonata II : violin solo. *Peters. Unpriced* SPME (B75-50769)
Suite for cello & piano. Suite for cello (or viola) and piano. *Highgate Press : Galliard. Unpriced* SRPG (B75-51305)
Trio trumpet in C, horn in F and trombone. *Peters. Unpriced* WNT (B75-50943)
Luke, Ray. Concerto for bassoon. *arr.* Concerto for bassoon and orchestra. *Oxford University Press. Unpriced* VWPK/LF (B75-50350)
Lumsdaine, David. Annotations of Auschwitz : soprano, flute (bass flute), trumpet, horn, violin, cello, piano. *Universal. Unpriced* KFLE/NUNQDX (B75-51124)
Lute music. *Selections : arr.* Two pieces. (Dowland, John). *Oxford University Press. £0.50* TSPMK (B75-50811) ISBN 0-19-356279-0
Lyall, John. Maintenance of the sitar. (Gupta, Punita). *9 Ranelagh Rd, Southall, Middx : The author. Free* ATSX/BT (B75-20395) ISBN 0-9504319-0-7
Lyle, Emily Buchanan. Andrew Crawfurd's collection of ballads and songs
Vol.1. *27 George Sq., Edinburgh EH8 9LD : The Scottish Text Society. Unpriced* **ADW/G(YDL) B75-29319)** ISBN 0-9500245-4-6
Lyons, Graham.
Pastoral : for two flutes and four clarinets. *British and Continental Music. Unpriced* VNQ (B75-50841)
Three piece suite : for four clarinets. *British and Continental Music. Unpriced* VVNSG (B75-50892)
Lyric suite : for euphonium and piano with treble clef and bass clef parts. (White, Donald H). *Schirmer. Unpriced* WWPG (B75-51474)
Lyric suite : for piano duet. (Tate, Phyllis). *Oxford University Press. £2.50* QNVG (B75-50661) ISBN 0-19-373807-4
M, J.C. A Scottish carol : for 3-part treble voices with optional solo. (Liddell, Claire). *Roberton. £0.10* FLDP/LF (B75-51067)
Ma sérénade. (Lopez, Francis). *Chappell. Unpriced* TMK/DW (B75-51312)
McCabe, John.
Bartók orchestral music. *British Broadcasting Corporation. £0.55* BBGAM (B75-02998) ISBN 0-563-12674-4
The Chagall windows : for orchestra. *Novello. Unpriced* MMJ (B75-50617)
McCartney, Paul. Songs. *Selections : arr.* The Beatles for classical guitar. (Lennon, John). *Wise, Music Sales. Unpriced* TSPMK/DW (B75-50818)
McClelland-Young, Thomas. Bow down thine ear : short anthem for baritone or bass solo, SATB and organ, suitable for Lent or general use. *Novello. £0.15* DK (B75-50425)
MacCunn, Hamish. The land of the mountain and the flood. *Selections : arr.* Sutherland's law. *Ambleside Music : EMI. Unpriced* WMK (B75-51422)
MacDermot, Galt. Mass in F. *Vocal score.* Mass in F for choir with instrumental accompaniment. *Chappell. Unpriced* DG (B75-50017)
MacDonald, Malcolm, *b.1948.* John Foulds : his life in music : with a detailed catalogue of his works, a discography, a bibliographical note, and with music examples and illustrations. *22 Pheasants Way, Rickmansworth, Herts. : Triad Press. £4.75* BFS(N) (B75-28637) ISBN 0-902070-15-0
Macdonald, Mary. Child in the manger : carol for SATB. (Hill, Anthony Herschel). *Thames. Unpriced* EZDP/LF (B75-50468)
Machaut, Guillaume de. Machaut-Balladen : für Gesang und Orchester. (Fortner, Wolfgang). *Schott. £7.30* JNGHE/MDW (B75-51101)
Machaut-Balladen : für Gesang und Orchester. (Fortner, Wolfgang). *Schott. £7.30* JNGHE/MDW (B75-51101)
Mack, Dietrich. Wagner : a documentary study. *Thames and Hudson. £12.00* BWC(N) (B75-30568) ISBN 0-500-01137-0
McKay, David Phares. William Billings of Boston : eighteenth-century composer. *Princeton University Press. £8.40* BBNS (B75-50980) ISBN 0-691-09118-8
Mackerness, Eric David. Somewhere further north : a history of music in Sheffield. *Northend. £3.00* A(YDCGS/X) (B75-16404) ISBN 0-901100-13-7
MacKinnon, Doris Livingstone. Beethoven's sketches : an analysis of his style based on a study of his sketch-books. (Mies, Paul). *Dover Publications etc. : Constable. £1.40* BBJ/D (B75-25553) ISBN 0-486-23042-2
McLean, Charles.
Sonata for violin & continuo. Op.1, no.2 in G minor. Sonata in G minor for violin and basso continuo. *Oxford University Press. £1.30* SPE (B75-50249) ISBN 0-19-357679-1
Sonatas for flute & continuo. Op.1, nos 9,10. Two sonatas for flute & basso continuo. *Oxford University Press. £2.00* VRPE (B75-50318) ISBN 0-19-357681-3
McMillan, Fiona. Three dances for piano duet. *Forsyth. Unpriced* QNVH (B75-51218)
Maconchy, Elizabeth.
Ina Boyle : an appreciation : with a select list of her music. *Trinity College Dublin, Library. Unpriced* BBSL (B75-50003) ISBN 0-904720-00-4
Quartet for strings, no.10. String quartet no.10. *Chappell. Unpriced* RXNS (B75-50762)
Mad maid's song : for SSAA and piano. (Crawford, John). *Oxford University Press. Unpriced* FDW (B75-50070)
Madden, John. Make we joy now in this feast : SATB. *Oxford University Press. Unpriced* DP/LF (B75-51011) ISBN 0-19-343054-1
Magi : carol for SATB, piano and double bass (optional). (Hill, Anthony Herschel). *Thames. Unpriced* DP/LFP (B75-50431)
Magic clarinet : for clarinet and piano. (Simpson, John). *Rahter. Unpriced* VVPJ (B75-50901)
Magic of music. (Baker, Richard, *b.1925*). *Hamilton. £3.95* A(X) (B75-11220) ISBN 0-241-89194-9
Maher, James T. American popular song : the great innovators, 1900-1950. (Wilder, Alec). *Oxford University Press. £3.25* ADW/GB(YT/XM51) (B75-18368) ISBN 0-19-284009-6
Mahler, Gustav. Symphony no.1 in D major. 3rd movement. *arr.* 'Bruder Martin'. *Bosworth. Unpriced* MJ (B75-50595)
Mahler. (Raynor, Henry). *Macmillan. £3.75* BME(N) (B75-14333) ISBN 0-333-18137-9
Mahrenholz, Christhard. The calculation of organ pipe scales from the middle ages to the mid-nineteenth century. *130 Southfield Rd, Oxford OX4 1PA : Positif Press. £2.50* AR/BPPG (B75-31193) ISBN 0-9503892-2-6
Maiden's prayer. (Bądarzewska, Thécla). *Boosey and Hawkes. £1.00* WMK (B75-51420)
Mailman, Martin. Shouts, hymns and praises. Op.52 : for wind band with vocal part for the audience. *Boosey and Hawkes. Unpriced* JE/UMDX (B75-51090)
Mainero, Gloria. Canzonette. Hor va canzona mia. Hor va canzona mia = How freely flies my song : SATB a cappella. (Hassler, Hans Leo). *Warner : Blossom. Unpriced* EZDU (B75-51045)
Maintenance of the sitar. (Gupta, Punita). *9 Ranelagh Rd, Southall, Middx : The author. Free* ATSX/BT (B75-20395) ISBN 0-9504319-0-7
Major and minor scales. (Hossack, Alfred). *Lutterworth Press. £0.75* A/PF (B75-25555) ISBN 0-7188-2129-7
Make we joy now in this feast : SATB. (Madden, John). *Oxford University Press. Unpriced* DP/LF (B75-51011) ISBN 0-19-343054-1
Maker of man : plainsong melody, faburden verses SATB. (Tunnard, Thomas). *Banks. Unpriced* EZDH (B75-50461)
Makin, Ena. Letters of Giacomo Puccini : mainly connected with the composition and production of his operas. (Puccini, Giacomo). New ed. *Harrap. £4.00* BPU(N) (B75-05793) ISBN 0-245-52422-3
Making electronic music : a course for schools
Book 1. (Dwyer, Terence). *Oxford University Press. £1.50* **APV/D (B75-24850)** ISBN 0-19-321071-1
Book 2. (Dwyer, Terence). *Oxford University Press. £1.50* APV/D (B75-24851) ISBN 0-19-321072-x
Teacher's book. (Dwyer, Terence). *Oxford University Press. £2.50* APV/D (B75-24852) ISBN 0-19-321070-3
Making tracks : Atlantic Records and the growth of a multi-billion-dollar industry. (Gillett, Charlie). *W.H. Allen. £3.50* ADW/GB/FD(YT/X) (B75-06240) ISBN 0-491-01152-0
Malko, Nicolai. The conductor and his score. (Green, Elizabeth Adine Herkimer). *Prentice-Hall. £4.40* A/EC (B75-16405) ISBN 0-13-167312-2
Man who gave the Beatles away. (Williams, Allan). *Elm Tree Books. £3.50* AKDW/GB/E(P/XPU4) (B75-16094) ISBN 0-241-89204-x
Mancini, Francesco. Sonata no.1 for treble recorder & continuo in D minor. Sonata in D minor for treble recorder and basso continuo. *Bärenreiter. £2.00* VSSPE (B75-50335)
Mandoline a du bon. (Lopez, Francis). *Chappell. Unpriced* TMK/DW (B75-51311)
Manège. (Bonneau, Paul). *Chappell. Unpriced* TMK (B75-50788)
Mangore, Agustin Barrios.
Danza paraguaya : per chitarra. *Zanibon : Hinrichsen. Unpriced* TSPMH (B75-50274)
Oración : valzer popolare venezuelano, per chitarra. *Zanibon : Hinrichsen. Unpriced* TSPMHW (B75-50280)
Mann, Adrian. Adagio and rondo for double bass & string quartet in C major. *arr.* Adagio and rondo in C major. (Dragonetti, Domenico). *Yorke. Unpriced* SSPK/W (B75-50779)
Mann, Michael A. Two psalms : unison. *Chappell. Unpriced* JDR (B75-51082)
Mann, Peter Henry. The audience for orchestral concerts : a report on surveys in Birmingham, Bournemouth, Glasgow, Liverpool and Manchester. *Arts Council of Great Britain. £0.50* AM(W) (B75-13446) ISBN 0-7287-0059-x
Manne, Shelly. Let's play drums. *Chappell. Unpriced* XQ/AC (B75-50387)
Manual for cataloguing monographs and music. *See* London and South Eastern Library Region.
Maori action songs. *Reed. £3.45* BZWYADW/GR (B75-50981) ISBN 0-589-00777-7
Marcello, Alessandro. Concerto grosso in F major. Concerto in fa magg : per archi con due oboi (o flauti) e fagotto ad libitum oppure 2 violini e violoncello ad libitum e cembalo. *Zanibon : Peters. Unpriced* MRF (B75-50156)
March for the piano. (Alt, Hansi). *Oxford University Press. Unpriced* QPGM (B75-50671)
March, Omega Lambda Chi. *arr.* March, Omega Lambda Chi : for band. (Ives, Charles). *Associated Music. Unpriced* UMMK/AGM (B75-50835)
March, Omega Lambda Chi : for band. (Ives, Charles). *Associated Music. Unpriced* UMMK/AGM (B75-50835)
Marche triomphale : for piano. (Field, John). *Helicon. Unpriced* QPGM (B75-50673)
Mare, Walter de la. *See* De la Mare, Walter.
Margaretten, Bill. Sounds I prefer. *arr.* Sounds I prefer : for mixed chorus (SATB). (Lombardo, Mario). *Chappell. Unpriced* DW (B75-51021)
Margoni, Alain. Quatre personnages de Calderon : pour guitare. *Chappell. Unpriced* TSPMJ (B75-51324)
Maria. *arr.* Maria. (Lopez, Anja). *Chappell. Unpriced* TMK/DW (B75-51310)
Mario of the Cross, *Sister.* Blessed be that maid Mary :

Christmas carol, SATB and organ. *Oxford University Press. Unpriced* FDP/LF (B75-51052)
Marischal, Louis.
Introduction et mascarade : pour trompette en ut (C) et piano. *Chappell. Unpriced* WSPJ (B75-51458)
Promenade. *arr.* Promenade : pour cor et orchestre à cordes. *Chappell. Unpriced* WTPK (B75-51469)
Marks, J. Mick Jagger : the singer, not the song. *Abacus. £0.60* AKDW/GB/E(P) (B75-02369) ISBN 0-349-12288-1
Marquis, Don. Six Mehitabel magpies : for soprano and double bass. (Seamarks, Colin). *Yorke. Unpriced* KFLE/SSPMDW (B75-50120)
Mars. (Holst, Gustav). *Boosey and Hawkes. Unpriced* UMMK (B75-50833)
Marshall, Nicholas.
Partita : for guitar. *Thames. Unpriced* TSPMG (B75-50805)
Suite for guitar, flute, clarinet, violin and cello. *Schott. £1.00* NVPNRG (B75-50642)
Marshall, Robert L. Studies in Renaissance and baroque music in honour of Arthur Mendel. *32 Great Titchfield St., W.1 : Bärenreiter-Verlag etc.. £20.70* A(XD251/D)
Marshall, William, *b.1926.* The man who gave the Beatles away. (Williams, Allan). *Elm Tree Books. £3.50* AKDW/GB/E(P/XPU4) (B75-16094) ISBN 0-241-89204-x
Martin Shaw : a centenary appreciation. (Routley, Erik). *77 Archway St., SW13 0AN : E.M. Campbell. £0.45* BSGP(N) (B75-21068) ISBN 0-9504306-0-9
Martini, Ulrich. Die Orgeldispositionssammlungen bis zur Mitte des 19. Jahrhunderts. *32 Great Titchfield St., W.1 : Bärenreiter. £7.36* AR/BC(XCRR420)
Martinu. (Large, Brian). *Duckworth. £9.50* BMFMN(N) (B75-22839) ISBN 0-7156-0770-7
Marvell, Andrew. The Bermudas : for chorus and orchestra. (Bennett, Richard Rodney). *Universal. Unpriced* EMDX (B75-51026)
Mary and Joseph : a Christmas calypso, unison. (Ager, Laurence). *Ashdown. £0.08* JDP/LF (B75-51080)
Mary Jones : a musical play for young people. (Warren, Norman). *Maplewell Press. Unpriced* CM/L (B75-50991) ISBN 0-9504473-0-7
Marz, Karl Robert.
La Calisto. *Vocal score.* La Calisto : opera in two acts with a prologue. (Cavalli, Francesco). *Faber Music. Unpriced* CC (B75-50989)
King Arthur. *Choral score.* King Arthur. (Purcell, Henry). *Faber Music. Unpriced* DACB/JM (B75-50996)
Maschera, Florentio. Libro primo de canzoni da sonare. Canzona 'La Girella'. Canzona 'La Girella' : for four instruments. *Oxford University Press. £0.55* LNS (B75-51146) ISBN 0-19-341206-3
Mason, Barbara Kirkby-. *See* Kirkby-Mason, Barbara.
Masonic funeral music. (Mozart, Wolfgang Amadeus). *Oxford University Press. £0.50* RK/KDN (B75-50740) ISBN 0-19-375582-3
Masque of angels. Gloria. *arr.* Gloria : unaccompanied mixed chorus. (Argento, Dominick). *Boosey and Hawkes. £0.40* EZDH (B75-51034)
Masques : piano. (Debussy, Claude). *Peters. Unpriced* QPJ (B75-50693)
Master musicians series.
Arnold, Denis. Monteverdi. Revised ed. *Dent. £3.95* BMN (B75-27353) ISBN 0-460-03155-4
Blom, Eric. Mozart. Revised ed. *Dent. £3.15* BMS (B75-04504) ISBN 0-460-03157-0
Hughes, Rosemary. Haydn. Revised ed. *Dent. £2.95* BHE (B75-01175) ISBN 0-460-03160-0
Latham, Peter, *b.1894.* Brahms. Revised ed.. *Dent. £2.95* BBT (B75-27352) ISBN 0-460-03158-9
Routh, Francis. Stravinsky. *Dent. £4.50* BSV (B75-24847) ISBN 0-460-03138-4
Watson, Derek. Bruckner. *Dent. £2.95* BBUE (B75-21066) ISBN 0-460-03144-9
Westrup, *Sir* Jack Allan. Purcell. 7th ed.. *Dent. £3.60* BPV (B75-24233) ISBN 0-460-03150-3
Young, Percy Marshall. Handel. Revised ed.. *Dent. £3.95* BHC (B75-13734) ISBN 0-460-03161-9
Masters, Stanley Smith-. *See* Smith-Masters, Stanley.
Mathias, William.
Ceremony after a fire raid. Op.63 : for mixed voices (SATB Bar B), piano and percussion. *Oxford University Press. £1.50* ENYLDX (B75-50452) ISBN 0-19-337434-x
Jubilate. Op.67, no.2 : organ. *Oxford University Press. £0.75* RJ (B75-50733) ISBN 0-19-375553-x
This worlde's joie. *Vocal score.* This worlde's joie : a cantata for soprano, tenor and baritone soloists, mixed chorus, boys' (or girls') choir, and orchestra. *Oxford University Press. £3.95* DE (B75-50408) ISBN 0-19-337437-4
Matsushita, Shin-Ichi. Gestalt 17 : für Harfe, Klavier, Schlagzeug und drei Posaunen. *Universal. Unpriced* NYDXU (B75-50172)
Matthaus-Passion = St Matthew Passion. (Bach, Johann Sebastian). *Bärenreiter. £4.40* EMDD/LK (B75-50034)
Matthei, Karl.
Jubilate Domino : Solokantate für Alt, Viola da gamba (Violoncello) und Basso continuo. (Buxtehude, Dietrich). *Bärenreiter. £1.80* KFQE/SRPDE (B75-50122)
Mein Herz ist bereit. (57. Psalm Davids) : Solokantate für Bass, drei Violinen, Violoncello und Basso continuo. (Buxtehude, Dietrich). *Bärenreiter. £2.40* KGXE/NXNRDR (B75-50125)
Matthes, Eric.
Hans Christian Andersen. *Selections : arr.* Songs from Frank Loesser's Hans Andersen. (Loesser, Frank). *Edwin H. Morris. Unpriced* VSNSQK/DW/JR (B75-50862)
Hans Christian Andersen. *Selections : arr.* Songs from Frank Loesser's Hans Andersen. (Loesser, Frank). *Edwin H. Morris. Unpriced* VSNRK/DW/JR (B75-50871)
Hans Christian Andersen. *Selections : arr.* Songs from Frank Loesser's Hans Andersen. (Loesser, Frank). *Edwin H. Morris. Unpriced* VSSNRK/DW/JR (B75-50878)
Hans Christian Andersen. *Selections : arr.* Songs from Frank Loesser's Hans Andersen. (Loesser, Frank). *Edwin H. Morris. Unpriced* VSTNTK/DW/JR (B75-50885)
Matthews, Colin. Death in Venice. *Vocal score.* Death in Venice. Op.88 : an opera in two acts. (Britten, Benjamin). *Faber Music. Unpriced* CC (B75-50988)
Matthews, Denis. Sonata for piano, no.16, in B flat major. K.570. Sonata in B flat. K.570. (Mozart, Wolfgang Amadeus). *Associated Board of the Royal Schools of Music. Unpriced* QPE (B75-51225)
Matthews, Nibs. 8 Morris dances of England and Flamborough sword dance. *English Folk Dance and Song Society. Unpriced* LH/G/AYD (B75-51137) ISBN 0-85418-108-3
Matthews, S A. Dances from the Yorkshire dales. *English Folk Dance and Song Society. Unpriced* LH/H/G/AYDJG (B75-50593)
Maughan, Jean. Tommy Thumb : ten songs for young singers and players, for unison voices with tuned and untuned percussion (and guitar symbols). *Oxford University Press. £0.65* JFE/XMDW/AY (B75-50101) ISBN 0-19-330558-5
Maurerische Trauermusik, K.477. *arr.* Masonic funeral music. (Mozart, Wolfgang Amadeus). *Oxford University Press. £0.50* RK/KDN (B75-50740) ISBN 0-19-375582-3
Maw, Nicholas. Te Deum : treble and tenor soli, chorus, congregation and organ. *Boosey and Hawkes. £2.00* DGNQ (B75-51002)
Mayr, Johann Simon. Suite for harp. Suite für Harfe. Zum ersten Mal herausgegeben von Heinrich Bauer. *Litolff : Peters. Unpriced* TQPMG (B75-50790)
Mays, Spike. The band rats. *P. Davies. £4.50* AUMM (B75-24238) ISBN 0-432-09230-7
Meale, Richard.
Coruscations : piano. *Universal. Unpriced* QPJ (B75-50705)
Quintet for winds. *Universal. Unpriced* UNR (B75-50838)

Soon it will die : for orchestra. *Universal. Unpriced* MMJ (B75-51155)
Mechem, Kirke. Symphony no.1. Op.16. *Boosey and Hawkes. Unpriced* MME (B75-50134)
Meditation : violin solo. (Luening, Otto). *Peters. Unpriced* SPMJ (B75-50256)
Meilhac, Henri. La Périchole : operetta in three acts. (Grimsey, John). *10 Rathbone St., W1P 2BJ : Josef Weinberger Ltd. £0.80* BOFACF (B75-19083) ISBN 0-902136-36-4
Mein Gott und Herr : concerto for two sopranos and bass, (chorus or soloists), two violins and basso continuo. (Capricornus, Samuel). *Bärenreiter. £2.40* ESNTPWDH (B75-50039)
Mein Herz ist bereit. (57. Psalm Davids) : Solokantate für Bass, drei Violinen, Violoncello und Basso continuo. (Buxtehude, Dietrich). *Bärenreiter. £2.40* KGXE/NXNRDR (B75-50125)
Melodies of Robert Burns. *Warren and Phillips. Unpriced* QPK/DW/G/AYDL (B75-50719)
'Melody Maker' specials. Rock life. *Hamlyn. £1.95* AKDW/HK/E(M) (B75-03642) ISBN 0-600-38708-9
Memento vitae : a concerto in homage to Beethoven, for solo string quartet & orchestra. (Musgrave, Thea). *Chester. Unpriced* MPRXNSF (B75-51163)
Menashe, Samuel. April and May : two songs. (Kennedy, John Brodbin). *Boosey and Hawkes. Unpriced* KDW (B75-51106)
Mendel, Arthur. Studies in Renaissance and baroque music in honour of Arthur Mendel. *32 Great Titchfield St., W.1 : Bärenreiter-Verlag etc.. £20.70* A(XD251/D)
Mendelssohn, Felix. 'The Hebrides'. Op.26. Overture, 'The Hebrides'. Op.26. *Eulenburg. Unpriced* MMJ (B75-51156)
Mendoza, Anne.
A festival for autumn : for dramatic presentation or concert performance, for voices, recorder, guitar, piano and percussion. *Novello. £0.50* JFE/NYDSDX (B75-50537)
The monkey's hornpipe, and other pieces : for school music ensemble. *Chappell. Unpriced* LN (B75-51138)
Sociable songs
Book 3, part 1 : for unison or part-singing with optional instrumental parts. *Oxford University Press. Unpriced* JDW/AY (B75-51085) ISBN 0-19-330590-9
Mentor music books.
Hossack, Alfred. From notes to rhythm. *Lutterworth Press. £0.75* A/M (B75-25556) ISBN 0-7188-2128-9
Hossack, Alfred. Major and minor scales. *Lutterworth Press. £0.75* A/PF (B75-25555) ISBN 0-7188-2129-7
Mentor Textbooks.
From notes to rhythm. (Hossack, Alfred). *Lutterworth Press. £0.75* A/M (B75-25556) ISBN 0-7188-2128-9
Major and minor scales. (Hossack, Alfred). *Lutterworth Press. £0.75* A/PF (B75-25555) ISBN 0-7188-2129-7
Merbecke, John. The Booke of Common Praier noted. The Lord's Praier. *arr.* The Lord's Prayer : for unison choir or solo voice and piano or organ. *Oxford University Press. Unpriced* JDTF (B75-51084)
Merka, Ivan. Quintet for clarinet & strings. Op.107, in F major. Quintetto in fa maggiore. Op.107 : per clarinetto, due violini, viola e violoncello. (Reicha, Anton). *Zanibon : Hinrichsen. Unpriced* NVVNR (B75-50164)
Merkel, Gustav. Sonata for organ, op.30, in D minor. Fugue. Fugue for organ duet. *Oxford University Press. £0.75* R/Y (B75-50204) ISBN 0-19-375561-0
Merry be man : a Christmas sequence. (Roe, Betty). *Thames. Unpriced* FEZDE/LF (B75-50499)
Messiaen. (Johnson, Robert Sherlaw). *Dent. £6.95* BMKS (B75-17689) ISBN 0-460-04198-3
Messiaen. (Nichols, Roger). *Oxford University Press. £2.50* BMKS (B75-15004) ISBN 0-19-315428-5
Messiah ornamented : an ornamented edition of the solos from the oratorio. (Handel, George Frideric). *Stainer and Bell. Unpriced* DADD (B75-50013) ISBN 0-85249-318-5
Messiah. *Selections.* Messiah ornamented : an ornamented edition of the solos from the oratorio. (Handel, George Frideric). *Stainer and Bell. Unpriced* DADD (B75-50013) ISBN 0-85249-318-5
Messiter, Arthur. Rejoice ye pure in heart : for mixed chorus and keyboard, based on a hymn by Arthur Messiter. (Wilson, Don). *Galaxy : Galliard. Unpriced* DH (B75-50023)
Metodo practico di canto italiano. Practical method of Italian singing. (Vaccai, Nicolo). New ed. *Schirmer. Unpriced* K/AFH (B75-50547)
Metzger, Hans-Arnold. Recercares for organ, nos.1-4. Four recercars : for organ. (Steigleder, Johann Ulrich). New ed. *Bärenreiter. Unpriced* RJ (B75-50734)
Meyer, Jean. Bavardages : cinq pièces brèves en canon pour quintette a vent (flute, hautbois, clarinette, B bémol, cor F, basson). *Chappell. Unpriced* UNR (B75-51357)
Meyer, Krysztof. Concerto da camera : per oboe, percussione ed archi. *Litolff : Peters. Unpriced* MPVTF (B75-50625)
Mezö, Imré. Piano works
Vol.7: Années de pèlerinage II. (Liszt, Franz). *Bärenreiter. Unpriced* QP/AZ (B75-50664)
Mező, László. Hungarian children's songs : for two violoncellos. *Boosey and Hawkes : Editio Musica. £0.75* SRNUK/DW/GJ/AYG (B75-50261)
Miall, Antony. Just a song at twilight : the second parlour song book. *Michael Joseph. £8.50* KDW/GB/AY(XHS64) (B75-51115) ISBN 0-7181-1339-x
Michael Flanders and Donald Swann song book. (Swann, Donald). *Chappell. Unpriced* KDW (B75-50114)
Michelangelo. Songs from Michelangelo : for baritone and piano. (Laderman, Ezra). *Oxford University Press. Unpriced* KGNDW (B75-51134)
Mick Jagger : the singer, not the song. (Marks, J.). *Abacus. £0.60* AKDW/GB/E(P) (B75-02369) ISBN 0-349-12288-1
Middleton, James. Orphée aux Enfers. Galop infernal. *arr.* Offenbach's can-can. (Offenbach, Jacques). *Piers Press. £1.50(for 3 performing scores)* VSNRK/AHJMP (B75-51378)
Midland Bank. The story of the Royal Opera House, Covent Garden. (Goodwin, Noël). *Head Office, Poultry, EC2P 2BX : Midland Bank Ltd. Free* AC/E(YC/QB) (B75-50001) ISBN 0-9501576-2-7
Midnight carol. Op.21 : two-part. (Platts, Kenneth). *Ashdown. Unpriced* FDW (B75-50495)
Mies, Paul. Beethoven's sketches : an analysis of his style based on a study of his sketch-books. *Dover Publication etc. : Constable. £1.40* BBJ/D (B75-25553) ISBN 0-486-23042-2
Mikado. *Choral score : arr.* The Mikado, or, The Town of Titipu. (Sullivan, *Sir* Arthur Seymour). *Cramer. £1.20* DACF (B75-50405)
Mikado, or, The Town of Titipu. (Sullivan, *Sir* Arthur Seymour). *Cramer. £1.20* DACF (B75-50405)
Miletić, Miroslav. Kroatische Suite nach Volksweisen aus Medjimurje : für Gitarre. *Schott. £0.90* TSPMG (B75-51322)
Millar, Bill. The Coasters. *44 Hill St., W1X 8LB : Star Books. £0.60* AKDW/GB/E(P) (B75-04508) ISBN 0-352-30020-5
Miller, Ashley. Showstoppers : the great songs of Lerner and Loewe. (Loewe, Frederick). *Chappell. Unpriced* RK/DW (B75-50737)
Miller, Carl.
The Eddystone light. *Chappell. Unpriced* FDW (B75-50491)
Lolly too dum. *Chappell. Unpriced* FDW (B75-50492)
A musical voyage with two guitars : 64 duets from 34 countries. *Collier Macmillan. £3.50* TSNUK/AAY (B75-51321) ISBN 0-02-060150-6
Simple gifts : traditional Shaker song. *Chappell. Unpriced* FDW (B75-50493)
The willow song. *Chappell. Unpriced* FDW (B75-50494)
Miller, Carl S. Sing, children, sing : songs, dances and singing games of many lands and peoples. *Chappell. Unpriced* JFDW/AY (B75-51095)
Miller, James. A heritage of spirituals : a collection of American spirituals, for mixed chorus and piano or organ. *Galaxy : Galliard. Unpriced* DW/LC/AY (B75-50447)
Milner, Anthony. Quintet for wind instruments. *Central Music Library : Novello. Unpriced* UNR (B75-50839)
Milton, John. Fly, envious time. Op.148 : song with piano accompaniment. (Rubbra, Edmund). *Lengnick. £0.35* KDW (B75-51112)
Miner, John W. Oh, didn't he ramble : the life story of Lee Collins. (Collins, Lee). *University of Illinois Press. £5.50* AMT(P) (B75-01179) ISBN 0-252-00234-2
Miniature. (Betti, Henri). *Chappell. Unpriced* TMK (B75-50787)
Miniature. *arr.* Miniature. (Betti, Henri). *Chappell. Unpriced* TMK (B75-50787)
Miniature scores:.
Bach, Johann Sebastian. St Matthew passion S.244.

Matthaus-Passion = St Matthew Passion. *Bärenreiter. £4.40* EMDD/LK (B75-50034)
Bach, Johann Sebastian. Suite for orchestra, no.1, in C major. S.1066. Ouverture (Orchestral suite), C major. *Bärenreiter. Unpriced* MRG (B75-50627)
Bach, Johann Sebastian. Suite for orchestra, no.2, in B minor. S.1067. Ouverture = (Orchestral suite). B minor. *Cassel : Bärenreiter. Unpriced* MRG (B75-50628)
Bach, Johann Sebastian. Suite for orchestra, no.3, in D major. S.1068. Ouverture = (Orchestral suite), D major. *Bärenreiter. Unpriced* MRG (B75-50629)
Bach, Johann Sebastian. Suite for orchestra, no.4, in D major. S.1069. Ouverture = (Orchestral sutte), D major. *Bärenreiter. Unpriced* MRG (B75-50630)
Baird, Tadeusz. Elegeia : für Orchester. *Litolff : Peters. Unpriced* MMJ (B75-51153)
Balakirev, Mily. Tamara : symphonic poem. *Eulenburg. £2.50* MMJ (B75-50609)
Berlioz, Hector. Les Troyens. *Eulenburg. Unpriced* CQC (B75-50010)
Britten, Benjamin. Quartet for strings in D major (1931). String quartet in D major (1931). *Faber Music. Unpriced* RXNS (B75-50759)
Del Tredici, David. Syzygy : for soprano, French horn and chamber orchestra. *Boosey and Hawkes. £9.00* KFLE/MPWTDX (B75-50118)
Glazunov, Aleksandr Konstantinovich. Solemn overture. Op.73. Festouverture = Solemn overture. Opus 73 : for orchestra. *Belaieff : Peters. Unpriced* MMJ (B75-50144)
Glazunov, Aleksandr Konstantinovich. Suite caracteristique = Characteristic suite. Opus 9 : for orchestra. *Belaieff : Peters. Unpriced* MMG (B75-50136)

Glazunov, Aleksandr Konstantinovich. Symphony, no.8, op.83, in E flat major. Eighth symphony, E flat major. Opus 83. *Belaieff : Peters. Unpriced* MME (B75-50130)
Glinka, Mikhail Ivanovich. A life for the Tsar. *Selections.* Drei Tanze aus der Oper 'Ein Leben für den Zaren'. *Belaieff : Peters. Unpriced* MMH (B75-50137)
Haydn, Joseph. Symphony, no.99, in E flat major. Symphony in E flat major, (London Symphony no.7). *Bärenreiter. £1.80* MME (B75-50131)
Haydn, Joseph. Symphony, no.100, in G major, 'Military'. Symphony in G major, 'Military' (London Symphony no.9). *Bärenreiter. £2.40* MME (B75-50132)
Haydn, Joseph. Symphony, no.101, in D major, 'The clock'. Symphony in D major, 'The clock' (London Symphony no.8). *Bärenreiter. £2.40* MME (B75-50133)
Holzer, Gerhard. Concerto for trumpet & string orchestra. Concerto für Trompete und Streicher. *Litolff : Peters. Unpriced* RXMPWSF (B75-51289)
Kelemen, Milko. Olifant : für einen Solisten (Posaune, Trombita Bali-Flöten Zurla, Buchel, Alphorn) und zwei Kammerensembles. *Litolff : Peters : Hinrichsen. Unpriced* MRJ (B75-50161)
Lees, Benjamin. Symphony no.3. *Boosey and Hawkes. Unpriced* MME (B75-50605)
Mendelssohn, Felix. 'The Hebrides'. Op.26. Overture, 'The Hebrides'. Op.26. *Eulenburg. Unpriced* MMJ (B75-51156)
Mozart, Wolfgang Amadeus. Concerto for piano, no.17, in G major. K.453. Concerto in G major for pianoforte and orchestra, KV453. *Bärenreiter. Unpriced* MPQF (B75-50620)
Purcell, Henry. Sonatas of three parts (1683), for strings & basso continuo, nos 1-6, Z.790-5. Sonatas for three parts, nos.1-6. *Eulenburg. Unpriced* NXNTE (B75-51194)
Rimsky-Korsakoff, Nikolai. Russian Easter overture. Op.36 : for orchestra. *Belaieff : Peters. Unpriced* MMJ (B75-50146)
Rimsky-Korsakoff, Nikolai. Sinfonietta on Russian themes. Op.31. *Belaieff : Hinrichsen. Unpriced* MMEM (B75-50135)
Schumann, Gerhard. Audiogramme : für vier Klarinetten. *Heinrichshofen : Hinrichsen. Unpriced* VVNS (B75-50891)
Skriabin, Aleksandr Nikolaevich. Le Poeme de l'extase = The poem of ecstasy. Op.54. *Belaieff : Hinrichsen. Unpriced* MMJ (B75-51157)
Tchaikovsky, Peter. The storm. Op.76. L'Orage : Ouverture für Orchester nach dem Drama von A.N. Ostrowsky. *Belaieff : Hinrichsen. £8.00* MMJ (B75-50147)
Tcherepnin, Nikolai. Destiny. Op.59. Le Destin = Destiny. Opus 59 : three symphonic fragments on a ballad by Edgar Allan Poe. *Belaieff : Peters. Unpriced* MMJ (B75-50148)
Miniatures for wind band
Set 1, nos 1-5. (Walton, *Sir* William). *Oxford University Press. £2.50* UMK/AG (B75-50299) ISBN 0-19-368267-2
Set 2, nos 6-10. (Walton, *Sir* William). *Oxford University Press. £3.00* UMK/AG (B75-50300) ISBN 0-19-368507-8
Minter, Robert.
Mortorium à 5. Sonata (Mortorium) à 5 (1737) : for trumpet, oboe, flute, violin and basso continuo. (Linike, Johann Georg). *Musica rara. Unpriced* NUNR (B75-51173)
Sinfonia concertante for trumpet & wind band in D major. MWV VIII, 1. Sinfonia concertante. MWV VIII, 1 : for solo trumpet, (clarino), 2 oboes, 2 horns and bassoon. (Molter, Johann Melchior). *Musica rara. Unpriced* UMPWSE (B75-51353)
Sinfonia concertante for trumpet & wind band in D major. MWV VIII, 2. Sinfonia concertante. MWV VIII, 2 : for solo trumpet (clarino), 2 oboes, 2 horns and bassoon. (Molter, Johann Melchior). *Musica rara. Unpriced* UMPWSE (B75-51354)

Minter, Robert L.
Selections. Complete trumpet repertoire
Volume 1: The operas. (Handel, George Frideric). *Musica rara. £4.50* WS (B75-51452)
Selections. Complete trumpet repertoire
Volume 2: The sacred oratorios. (Handel, George Frideric). *Musica rara. Unpriced* WS (B75-51453)
Selections. Complete trumpet repertoire
Volume 3: The church music. (Handel, George Frideric). *Musica rara. £4.50* WS (B75-51454)
Selections. Complete trumpet repertoire
Volume 4: Miscellaneous. (Handel, George Frideric). *Musica rara. £4.50* WS (B75-51455)
Sonata à 7 for six trumpets, timpani & organ. Sonata à 7 (1688) for 6 trumpets, timpani and organ. (Biber, Heinrich Ignaz Franz). *Musica rara. Unpriced* NYFXSNNE (B75-51198)
Sonata for trumpet, oboe and basso continuo in C major. (Finger, Godfrey). *Musica rara. Unpriced* NWNTE (B75-51190)
Sonata for trumpet, violin, oboe and basso continuo in C major. (Finger, Godfrey). *Musica rara. Unpriced* NUNSE (B75-51174)
Miranda, Sharon Moe. American fanfare : for brass ensemble and timpani. *Chappell. Unpriced* WMGN (B75-50359)
Miroglio, Francis. Tremplins : voices and orchestra. *Universal. Unpriced* JNCE/MDX (B75-50545)
Mirum : für Tuba, 1965. (Kagel, Mauricio). *Universal. Unpriced* WVPMJ (B75-50386)
Mister Czerny : solo d'accordeon d'aprés une étude de la grande velocité de Carl Czerny. (Balta, Freddy). *Chappell. Unpriced* RSPMJ (B75-50745)
'Mit Musik'. 5 Gedichte von Ernst Jandl : für einen Sprecher und Instrumente, (2 Trompeten in C-oder Klarinetten, Flöten, Blockflöten-, Violoncello, Kontrabass, Schlagzeug und Klavier). (Regner, Hermann). *Schott. £3.50* HYE/NYDNQ (B75-51076)
Mitchell, Donald. Gustav Mahler
The Wunderhorn years : chronicles and commentaries. *Faber. £15.00* BME (B75-30566) ISBN 0-571-10674-9
Mobile : fünf Skizzen für Sopran und Altblockflöte. (Hofmann, Wolfgang). *Litolff : Peters. Unpriced* VSNU (B75-50866)
Model housekeeper : nine rounds and canons for women's voices. (Beeson, Jack). *Boosey and Hawkes. Unpriced* FEZDW/XC (B75-50505)
Modern jazz, the essential records : a critical selection. *Aquarius Books; Station Rd, Kings Langley, Herts. : Distributed by Argus Books. £2.90* AMT/FD(XPE26) (B75-21669) ISBN 0-904619-01-x
Moderne Rhythmen : für Jazz-Gitarre. *Schott. £1.75* TSPMK (B75-51327)
Modeste Mignon : d'après une valse d'Honoré de Balzac, i.e. par Daniel Auber, pour dix instruments à vent. (Sutermeister, Heinrich). *Schott. Unpriced* UMJ (B75-51335)
Moehn, Heinz. Don Giovanni. K 527. *Vocal score.* Don Giovanni. KV 527. (Mozart, Wolfgang Amadeus). *Cassel : Bärenreiter. Unpriced* CC (B75-50396)
Mohr, Joseph. Stille Nacht. *arr.* Stille Nacht = Silent night. (Gruber, Franz). *Oxford University Press. Unpriced* EZDP/LF (B75-51042) ISBN 0-19-343053-3
Molter, Johann Melchior.
Sinfonia concertante for trumpet & wind band in D major. MWV VIII, 1. Sinfonia concertante. MWV VIII, 1 : for solo trumpet, (clarino), 2 oboes, 2 horns and bassoon. *Musica rara. Unpriced* UMPWSE (B75-51353)
Sinfonia concertante for trumpet & wind band in D major. MWV VIII, 2. Sinfonia concertante. MWV VIII, 2 : for solo trumpet (clarino), 2 oboes, 2 horns and bassoon. *Musica rara. Unpriced* UMPWSE (B75-51354)
Monckton, Lionel. A runaway girl. Soldiers in the park. *arr.* Oh! listen to the band. *Studio Music. Unpriced* WMK/DW (B75-50927)
Monkey's hornpipe, and other pieces : for school music ensemble. (Mendoza, Anne). *Chappell. Unpriced* LN (B75-51138)
Monody : for piano with live electronic modulation (1 player). (Smalley, Roger). *Faber Music. £3.00* QPVJ (B75-50722)
Monsell, J S B. I hunger and I thirst : anthem for SATB with divisions and organ. (Wills, Arthur). *Novello. Unpriced* DH (B75-50421)
Monte Regali Gallus, Eustachius de. Musica duorum, Rome, 1521. (Romano, Eustachio). *Chicago University Press. Unpriced* C/AZ (B75-50983) ISBN 0-226-22646-8
Monteverdi. (Arnold, Denis). Revised ed. *Dent. £3.95* BMN (B75-27353) ISBN 0-460-03155-4
Moods and movement : piano. (Slack, Roy). *Keith Prowse Music. Unpriced* QP/GR (B75-51222)
Moon, sea and stars : nocturnes for tenor horn and strings. (Cowie, Edward). *Chester : Hansen. Unpriced* KGHE/RXMPWTDX (B75-50124)
Moore, Gerald, *b.1899.* The Schubert song cycles : with thoughts on performance. *Hamilton. £6.95* BSFADW (B75-07794) ISBN 0-241-89082-9
Moore, Jack.
An introduction to the 12 button reed and electronic chord organ. (Bolton, Cecil). *Robbins Music : EMI. Unpriced* RPVC/AC (B75-51280)
Any time's children's time : for chord organ. *EMI. Unpriced* RPVCK/DW/AY (B75-51281)
Sunday songs for chord organs. *EMI Music. Unpriced* RPVCK/DM/AY (B75-50741)
Moore, Jerrold Northrop. Elgar on record : the composer and the gramophone. *Oxford University Press. £5.00* BEP(N/XM21) (B75-06901) ISBN 0-19-315434-x
More, Henry. The holy son of God : carol for SATB. (Copley, Ian Alfred). *Thames. Unpriced* EZDP/LF (B75-50467)
Morehen, John.
In nomine : for two treble, two tenor and bass viols. (Parsley, Osbert). *Oxford University Press. Score £0.20, Parts unpriced* STNR (B75-50783) ISBN 0-19-341211-x
Maurerische Trauermusik, K.477. *arr.* Masonic funeral music. (Mozart, Wolfgang Amadeus). *Oxford University Press. £0.50* RK/KDN (B75-50740) ISBN 0-19-375582-3
Parsley's clock a 5 : for two treble, two tenor, and bass viols. (Parsley, Osbert). *Oxford University Press. Score, £0.20 ; Parts, Unpriced* STNR (B75-50784) ISBN 0-19-341213-6
Spes nostra : for two treble, two tenor and bass viols. (Parsley, Osbert). *Oxford University Press. £0.30* STNR (B75-50785) ISBN 0-19-341212-8
Morlaix, Bernard de. Hora novissima. Urbs Syon unica. City of high renown = Urbs Syon unica : unaccompanied mixed chorus. (Parker, Horatio). *Galaxy : Galliard. Unpriced* EZDH (B75-51035)
Morris, Ernest. The history and art of change ringing. 1st ed. reprinted. *EP Publishing. £8.00* AXSR/E(X) (B75-18374) ISBN 0-85409-995-6
Morris, Reginald Owen. The Oxford harmony
Vol.1. *Oxford University Press. £1.20* A/R (B75-12696) ISBN 0-19-317315-8
Morrow, Michael. Five pieces for four viols. *Oxford University Press. Unpriced* STNS/AY (B75-50786) ISBN 0-19-343241-2
Mortorium à 5. Sonata (Mortorium) à 5 (1737) : for trumpet, oboe, flute, violin and basso continuo. (Linike, Johann Georg). *Musica rara. Unpriced* NUNR (B75-51173)
Morys y Gwyat : can ddwy-ran ar gyfer ysgolion cynradd gyda chyfeiliant piano a recorder. (Owen, Elfed). *University of Wales Press. Unpriced* KFE/VSPDW (B75-50570)
Morys y Gwynt : can ddwy-ran ar gyfer ysgolion cynradd gyda chyfeiliant piano a recorder. (Owen, Elfed). *University of Wales Press. Unpriced* KFQE/VSPDW (B75-50123)
Moscheles, Ignaz. Introduction et rondeau écossais. Op.63. Duo. Op.63 : for horn and piano. *Musica rara. £1.50* WTPJ (B75-51468)
Motettorum liber tertius. Surge, illuminare Jerusalem. Surge, illuminare Jerusalem : a motet for two four-part choirs (SATB SATB for the feast of the Epiphany). (Palestrina, Giovanni Pierluigi da). *Chester. Unpriced* EZDJ/LFP (B75-51040)
Mouret, Jean Joseph.
Sonatas for flute duet, nos.1-6. 6 Sonaten für zwei Querflöten
Heft 1: Sonatas 1-3. *Heinrichshofen : Hinrichsen. Unpriced* VRNUE (B75-50846)
Sonatas for flute duet, nos.1-6. 6 Sonaten für zwei Querflöten
Heft 2: Sonatas 4-6. *Heinrichshofen : Hinrichsen. Unpriced* VRNUE (B75-50847)
Moving up : a first set of violin pieces in the second position, violin and piano. (Nelson, Sheila M). *Boosey and Hawkes. £1.45* SPJ (B75-50251)
Mowatt, Anna Cora. Fashion : a musical comedy. *French. £1.10* BPIACM (B75-20393) ISBN 0-573-68065-5
Mozart, Franz Xavier. Quatre Polonaises mélancoliques. Op.22. Four polonaises : for piano. 1st ed. reprinted. *Oxford University Press. £1.20* QPHVHM (B75-50678) ISBN 0-19-373410-9
Mozart, Wolfgang Amadeus.
Concerto for piano, no.17, in G major. K.453. Concerto in G major for pianoforte and orchestra, KV453. *Bärenreiter. Unpriced* MPQF (B75-50620)
Don Giovanni. K 527. *Vocal score.* Don Giovanni. KV 527. *Cassel : Bärenreiter. Unpriced* CC (B75-50396)
Fantasy for mechanical organ in F minor. K.608. *arr.* Fantasy for mechanical organ. K.608. *Schirmer. Unpriced* QNVK (B75-50662)
Jokers wild : cornet or trumpet trio (based on a theme by Mozart from 'Ein musikalischer Spass'. K.522. (Siebert, Edrich). *Studio Music. Unpriced* WMPWRNT (B75-50934)
Litaniae Lauretanae. K.109. *Vocal score.* Litaniae Lauretanae. K.109 (Marien sic litany) : for four-part chorus of mixed voices and soprano, alto, tenor and bass solos. *Schirmer. Unpriced* DS/LDB (B75-50435)
Mass, no.12, in C major. K.258. *Vocal score.* Piccolomini mass. (Missa brevis in C) : mixed chorus. *Schirmer. Unpriced* DG (B75-50410)
Mass, no.13, in C major. K.259. *Vocal score.* Organ solo mass. (Missa brevis in C) : mixed chorus. *Schirmer. Unpriced* DG (B75-50411)
Maurerische Trauermusik, K.477. *arr.* Masonic funeral music. *Oxford University Press. £0.50* RK/KDN (B75-50740) ISBN 0-19-375582-3
Mozart's greatest hits. *Chappell. Unpriced* RK (B75-50735)
Quartet for strings, op.6, no.82, in B flat major, 'Figaro-Quartett'. String quartet in B flat major 'Figaro-Quartett'. Op.6, no.2. (Danzi, Franz). *Bärenreiter. Unpriced* RXNS (B75-50760)
Rondo for violin & orchestra in C major. K.373. *arr.* Rondo für Solo-Violine, Streicher, zwei Oboen und zwei Hörner. K.V.373. *Schott. £1.75* SPK/LW (B75-51299)
Sonata for piano, no.16, in B flat major. K.570. Sonata in B flat. K.570. *Associated Board of the Royal Schools of Music. Unpriced* QPE (B75-51225)
Mozart. (Blom, Eric). Revised ed. *Dent. £3.15* BMS (B75-04504) ISBN 0-460-03157-0

Mozart's greatest hits. (Mozart, Wolfgang Amadeus). *Chappell. Unpriced* RK (B75-50735)
Mr Squirrel : SSA. (Williams, Patrick). *Bosworth. Unpriced* FLDW (B75-50081)
Muczynski, Robert. Duos for flutes. Op.34. *Schirmer. Unpriced* VRNU (B75-50845)
Mud songs and Blighty : a scarpbook of the first World War. *Hutchinson : EMI. £3.50* KDW/GB/AYC(XMP5) (B75-51116) ISBN 0-09-124421-8
Mueller, Carl Frank. An anthem of faith 'Lord increase our faith' : for four-part chorus of mixed voices with piano or organ accompaniment. *Associated Music. Unpriced* DK (B75-50426)
Muhlenberg, William Augustus. Shout the glad tidings. Op.12 : for mixed choir and organ, with optional instruments. (Thomas, Paul Lindsley). *Oxford University Press. Unpriced* DH (B75-51006)
Munday, Ann. Great songs of World War II : with the Home Front in pictures. *Wise Publications; 78 Newman St., W.1 : Distributed by Music Sales Ltd. £3.95* ADW/GB(XU7) (B75-22844) ISBN 0-86001-041-4
Mundy, John. Sing joyfully : SSATB and strings (or organ) with verses for bass solo. Revised ed. *Oxford University Press. £0.40* ERXNRDK (B75-50453) ISBN 0-19-352184-9
Murrells, Joseph. The book of golden discs. *Barrie and Jenkins. £9.95* A/GB/FD(X) (B75-14337) ISBN 0-214-20032-9
Musgrave, Thea.
Concerto for viola. *Novello. Unpriced* MPSQF (B75-50623)
Impromptu no.2 : for flute, oboe and clarinet. *Chester. Unpriced* VNT (B75-50843)
Memento vitae : a concerto in homage to Beethoven, for solo string quartet & orchestra. *Chester. Unpriced* MPRXNSF (B75-51163)
Space play : a concerto for nine instruments. *Novello. Unpriced* NVNMF (B75-51180)
Music. *Holt, Rinehart and Winston. £7.00* A (B75-29313) ISBN 0-03-012681-9
Music. (Politoske, Daniel Theodore). *Prentice-Hall. £5.10* A(X) (B75-02367) ISBN 0-13-607465-0
Music alphabet : piano, four hands
Vol.1. (Stravinsky, Soulima). *Peters. Unpriced* QNV (B75-50179)
Vol.2. (Stravinsky, Soulima). *Peters. Unpriced* QNV (B75-50180)
Music and language with young children. (Chacksfield, Kathleen Merle). *Blackwell. £4.50* A/GR(VG) (B75-22597) ISBN 0-631-15330-6
Music & recording industry year book (international). *See* Kemp's music & recording industry year book (international).
Music and the teacher. (Lawrence, Ian). *Pitman. £2.50* A(VC) (B75-19078) ISBN 0-273-00354-2
Music as stimulus in secondary assembly and RE ... (Tillman, June). *2 Chester House, Pages La., N10 1PR : Christian Education Movement, Religious Education Service. £0.40* A/FD(VK/WT) (B75-15228) ISBN 0-905022-00-9
Music Box Society. News Letter
No.1- ; Aug. 1974-. *42 Dumgoyne Drive, Bearsden, Dunbartonshire : The Society. Free to members* A/FH/B(B) (B75-19736)
Music for beginners.
Hossack, Alfred. From notes to rhythm. *Lutterworth Press. £0,75* A/M (B75-25556) ISBN 0-7188-2128-9
Hossack, Alfred. Major and minor scales. *Lutterworth Press. £0.75* A/PF (B75-25555) ISBN 0-7188-2129-7
Music for the Maltings. Opus 22 : for orchestra. (Platts, Kenneth). *Ashdown. Unpriced* MJ (B75-50597)
Music for today's children. (Ingley, William Stevens). *63 Highfield Rd, Rowley Regis, Warley, West Midlands : H. Hunter. £1.50* A(VC) (B75-50000) ISBN 0-9503936-0-6
Music hall song book : a collection of 45 of the best songs from 1890-1920. *David & Charles : EMI. £4.50* KDW/JV/AY (B75-51119) ISBN 0-7153-7115-0
Music in American life. Collins, Lee. Oh, didn't he ramble : the life story of Lee Collins. *University of Illinois Press. £5.50* AMT(P) (B75-01179) ISBN 0-252-00234-2
Music in education : a point of view. (Bentley, Arnold). *NFER. £2.95* A(V) (B75-26085) ISBN 0-85633-066-3
Music in the medieval world. (Seay, Albert). 2nd ed. *Prentice-Hall. £5.50* A(XA1420) (B75-24232) ISBN 0-13-608133-9
Music of Africa. (Nketia, Joseph Hanson Kwabena). *Gollancz. £4.00* BZK (B75-05792) ISBN 0-575-01842-9
Music of Stockhausen : an introduction. (Harvey, Jonathan). *Faber. £6.50* BSNK (B75-11222) ISBN 0-571-10251-4
Music quiz. (Butterworth, Neil). *139 Holgate Rd, York : Banks Music Publications. £0.45* A(DE) (B75-27348) ISBN 0-9503337-0-0
Music reference and research materials : an annotated bibliography. (Duckles, Vincent). 3rd ed. *Free Press : Collier Macmillan. £5.50* A(T) (B75-00957) ISBN 0-02-907700-1
Music therapy. (Alvin, Juliette). *Hutchinson. £4.25* A(ZD) (B75-08620) ISBN 0-09-120320-1
Music through the ages. (Alberti, Luciano). *Cassell. £7.50* A(X) (B75-02995) ISBN 0-304-29420-9
Music through the recorder : a course in musicianship
Vol.1. (Simpson, Kenneth). *Nelson. Unpriced* VS/AC (B75-50856) ISBN 0-17-436081-9
Music today. *See* Boulez, Pierre.
'Music Week' industry yearbook
No.6 : 1975-76. *7 Carnaby St., W1V 1PG : Billboard Publications Ltd. £2.50* A/FD(BC) (B75-12986) ISBN 0-902285-01-7
Music workshop : an approach to music for the non-specialist teacher. (Witham, June). *Macmillan. £4.75* A/C(VG) (B75-04501) ISBN 0-333-14455-4
Music yearbook. *For later issues of this yearbook see* British music yearbook.
Musica Britannica : a national collection of music
Vol.22: Consort songs. 2nd revised ed. *Stainer and Bell. Unpriced* C/AYD (B75-50006)
Vol.36: Early Tudor songs and carols; transcribed and edited by John Stevens. *Stainer and Bell. Unpriced* C/AYD (B75-50982)
Musica da camera (1972) : for recorder (treble recorder and bass recorder) and guitar. (Linde, Hans Martin). *Schott. Unpriced* VSPLTS (B75-50331)
Musica duorum, Rome, 1521. (Romano, Eustachio). *Chicago University Press. Unpriced* C/AZ (B75-50983) ISBN 0-226-22646-8
Musical activities with young children. (Gilbert, Jean). *Ward Lock. £2.95* A/GR(VG) (B75-19508) ISBN 0-7062-3462-6
Musical Europe : an illustrated guide to musical life in 18 European countries. *Paddington Press. £3.50* A(YB/WE) (B75-01174) ISBN 0-8467-0031-x
Musical instrument recipe book. (Education Development Center). *Penguin Education. £0.50* AY/BC (B75-08294) ISBN 0-14-081185-0
Musical instruments of East Africa
1: Kenya. *Nelson. £0.80* BZNCWAL/B (B75-26086) ISBN 0-17-511250-9
Musical plays. *Selections : arr.* Rodgers and Hammerstein guitar book. (Rodgers, Richard). *Williamson Music. Unpriced* TSPMK/DW (B75-50819)
Musical plays. *Selections: arr.* Rogers and Hammerstein 'Showtime'
Vol.1. (Rodgers, Richard). *Williamson. Unpriced* KDW (B75-50112)
Musical voyage with two guitars : 64 duets from 34 countries. *Collier Macmillan. £3.50* TSNUK/AAY (B75-51321) ISBN 0-02-060150-6
Musicians.
Jefferson, Alan. Richard Strauss. *Macmillan. £3.75* BSU(N) (B75-15005) ISBN 0-333-14649-2
Raynor, Henry. Mahler. *Macmillan. £3.75* BME(N) (B75-14333) ISBN 0-333-18137-9
Wilkinson, Anthony. Liszt. *Macmillan. £3.75* BLJ(N) (B75-14335) ISBN 0-333-15064-3
Musique printanière : for flute and piano. (Jenni, Donald). *Associated Music. Unpriced* VRPJ (B75-50850)
Musorgsky, Modest. Pictures at an exhibition. *arr.* Pictures at an exhibition. *Henmar Press : Peters. Unpriced* MMK (B75-50619)
Mussorgsky, Modest. Boris Godunov : opera in four acts with a prologue. *Oxford University Press. Unpriced* CQC (B75-50993) ISBN 0-19-337699-7
Mussorgsky, Modest. *See* Musorgsky, Modest.
Muston, Jeff. The myths and legends of King Arthur and the Knights of the Round Table. *Vocal score.* The myths and legends of King Arthur and the Knights of the Round Table : cantata. (Wakeman, Rick). *Rondor Music. Unpriced* JDX (B75-51087)
My first collection : containing interesting examples of works by composers through the ages for the developing pianist. *Bosworth. Unpriced* QPK/AAY (B75-50716)
My friend Androcles : musical play for voices, piano and percussion. (Arch, Gwyn). *British and Continental Music : EMI Music. Unpriced* CQN (B75-50012)
My heart is ev'ry beauty's prey : tenor solo, harpsichord and cello (ad lib.). (Croft, William). *Roberton. Unpriced* KGHDW (B75-50589)
My musical life. (Rimsky-Korsakoff, Nikolai). *48 Great Marlborough St., W.1 : Ernst Eulenberg Ltd. £6.25* BRI(N) (B75-24236) ISBN 0-903873-13-3
My second collection : containing interesting examples of works by composers through the ages for the developing pianist. *Bosworth. Unpriced* QPK/AAY (B75-50717)
My third collection containing interesting examples of works by composers through the ages for the developing pianist. *Bosworth. Unpriced* QPK/AAY (B75-50718)
Myslik, Antonin. Divertimento for two oboes & cor anglais in B flat major. Divertimento, B-dur : für 2 Oboi und Corno inglese B-dur. (Wenth, Johann). 1st ed. *Kneusslin : Hinrichsen. Unpriced* VNT (B75-50312)
Myths and legends of King Arthur and the Knights of the Round Table. *Vocal score.* The myths and legends of King Arthur and the Knights of the Round Table : cantata. (Wakeman, Rick). *Rondor Music. Unpriced* JDX (B75-51087)
Najera, Edmund.
Exultate Deo : for four-part chorus of mixed voices with piano accompaniment. *Schirmer. Unpriced* DJ (B75-50423)
In dulci jubilo : for four-part chorus of mixed voices a cappella. *Schirmer. Unpriced* EZDP/LF (B75-50469)
National anthems of the world. 4th and revised ed. *Blandford Press. £5.80* JDW/KM/AY (B75-50529) ISBN 0-7137-0679-1
National Foundation for Educational Research in England and Wales. Music in education : a point of view. (Bentley, Arnold). *NFER. £2.95* A(V) (B75-26085) ISBN 0-85633-066-3
Naylor, Frank.
Annen-Polka. Op.117. *arr.* Annen-Polka. Op.117 : polka française. (Strauss, Johann, *b.1825*). *Bosworth. Unpriced* MK/AHVH (B75-50129)
Concertino for violin & piano. Op.13. *arr.* Concertino for four violins. Op.13. (Portnoff, Leo). *Bosworth. Unpriced* RXMPSNSK/LFL (B75-50754)
Persischer Marsch. Op.289. *arr.* Persian march. Op.289. (Strauss, Johann, *b.1825*). *Bosworth. Unpriced* MK/AGM (B75-50600)
Radetzky march. Op.228. *arr.* Radetzky march. Op.228. (Strauss, Johann, *b.1805*). *Bosworth. Unpriced* MK/AGM (B75-50599)
Twelve days of Christmas : traditional song. *Bosworth. Unpriced* QPK/DW/LF (B75-51263)
Neale, John Mason. Bell carol : based on the tune 'Puer nobis', for junior choir, mixed choir, and organ, with optional bells. (Wichmann, Russell G). *Oxford University Press. Unpriced* DP/LF (B75-51013)
Negro Spirituals für Gitarre solo. *Schott. £1.75* TSPMK/DW/LC (B75-51330)
Neill, David. Armalita. *arr.* Armalita : tango. *Swan. Unpriced* QPHVR (B75-50680)
Nelson, Havelock.
The enchanted valley : traditional Irish air. *Roberton. £0.12* FEZDW (B75-50502)
O King of the Friday : SATB unacc. *Banks. Unpriced* EZDH/LK (B75-51038)
Oh! I am come to the Low Countrie : traditional melody. *Elkin. £0.15* EZDW (B75-50481)
Peggy, my love : Uist boat song, traditional Scottish melody. *Elkin. £0.15* GEZDW (B75-51075)
Nelson, Ron.
Prayer of St. Francis of Assisi : for S.A.T.B. chorus and organ or piano. *Boosey and Hawkes. £0.30* DH (B75-51004)
Psalm 95 - Come let us praise Yaweh : for mixed chorus and organ with optional instrumental accompaniment. *Boosey and Hawkes. Unpriced* DR (B75-50434)
Nelson, Sheila M.
Moving up : a first set of violin pieces in the second position, violin and piano. *Boosey and Hawkes. £1.45* SPJ (B75-50251)
Two in one : violin duets in the first finger position. *Boosey and Hawkes. £1.00* SNU (B75-50242)
Nenia. The death of Orpheus : for soprano solo, crotales, two pianos and three clarinets. (Birtwistle, Harrison). *Universal. Unpriced* KFLE/NYFVNQDX (B75-50575)
Neruda, Johann Baptist Georg. Concerto for trumpet & string orchestra in E flat major. *arr.* Concerto in E flat for trumpet and strings. *Musica rara. Unpriced* WSPK/LF (B75-51467)
Neruda, Pablo. Epitaffio no. 1, 2 & 3. (Nono, Luigi). *Ars Viva : Schott. £11.60* HYE/M (B75-50086)
Neuzeitliches Spielbuch : für Altblockflöte und Klavier. *Schott. £3.00* VSSP/AY (B75-51385)
Neville, Paul. Shrewsbury fair : quick march, for military band. *Boosey and Hawkes. £1.00* UMMGM (B75-51342)
New church praise. *Saint Andrew Press. Unpriced* DM/LSG/AY (B75-50428) ISBN 0-7152-0311-8
New hymns for young people : twelve hymns chosen from the Southern Television network competition. *Weinberger. £0.60* JDM/JS/AY (B75-50087)
New look scales for piano. (Pasfield, William Reginald). *Ashdown. Unpriced* Q/AF (B75-50657)
New music : the avant-garde since 1945. (Brindle, Reginald Smith). *Oxford University Press. £3.95* A(XPE30) (B75-27956) ISBN 0-19-315424-2
New music vocabulary : a guide to notational signs for contemporary music. (Risatti, Howard). *University of Illinois Press. £2.75* A(QU/XPL25) (B75-21069) ISBN 0-252-00406-x
New Oxford history of music
Vol.5: Opera and church music, 1630-1750. *Oxford University Press. £12.50* A(X) (B75-29312) ISBN 0-19-316305-5
New world. Op.26 : set for medium voice and piano. (Crosse, Gordon). *Oxford University Press. £2.50* KFVDW (B75-50584) ISBN 0-19-345275-8
Newe auserlesene Branden, Intraden, Mascheraden, Baletten, Allmanden, Couranten, Volten, Auffzuge und frembde Tantze (1617)
Volume 1 : for 2 cornetti (trumpets in C) and 3 trombones. *Musica rara. £4.00* WNRH/AY (B75-51441)

Volume 2 : for 2 cornetti (trumpets in C) and 3 trombones. *Musica rara. £4.00* WNRH/AY (B75-51442)

Volume 3 : for 3 cornetti and 2 trombones. *Musica rara. £4.00* WNRH/AY (B75-51443)
Newe ausserlesene liebliche Branden, Intraden. Newe auserlesene Branden, Intraden, Mascheraden, Baletten, Allmanden, Couranten, Volten, Auffzuge und frembde Tantze (1617)
Volume 1 : for 2 cornetti (trumpets in C) and 3 trombones. *Musica rara. £4.00* WNRH/AY (B75-51441)

Newe ausserlesene liebliche Branden, Intraden. Newe auserlesene Branden, Intraden, Mascheraden, Baletten, Allmanden, Couranten, Volten, Auffzuge und frembde Tantze (1617)
Volume 2 : for 2 cornetti (trumpets in C) and 3 trombones. *Musica rara. £4.00* WNRH/AY (B75-51442)

Newe ausserlesene liebliche Branden, Intraden. Newe auserlesene Branden, Intraden, Mascheraden, Baletten, Allmanden, Couranten, Volten Auffzuge und frembde Tantze (1617)
Volume 3 : for 3 cornetti and 2 trombones. *Musica rara. £4.00* WNRH/AY (B75-51443)
Newley, Anthony. Quilp. *Selections : arr.* Quilp : a musical adaptation of Charles Dickens 'The old curiosity shop'.

Edwin H. Morris. Unpriced KDW (B75-51107)
New/rediscovered musical instruments
Vol.1. *15 Bayonne Rd, W.6 : Mirliton Publications. £0.75* AY/B (B75-04507) ISBN 0-904414-03-5
Ngata, Reupena. Maori action songs. *Reed. £3.45* BZWYADW/GR (B75-50981) ISBN 0-589-00777-7
Nichols, Roger. Messiaen. *Oxford University Press. £2.50* BMKS (B75-15004) ISBN 0-19-315428-5
Nine by six : suite for wind instruments, flute (picc.), oboe (eng. horn), clarinet (bs. cl.), trumpet, horn, bassoon. (Read, Gardner). *Peters. Unpriced* UNQG (B75-50309)
Nine folk song preludes : for piano. (Berkowitz, Sol). *Frank Music. Unpriced* QPJ (B75-50686)
Nketia, Joseph Hanson Kwabena. The music of Africa. *Gollancz. £4.00* BZK (B75-05792) ISBN 0-575-01842-9
Noble, Harold.
Arietta : for horn and piano. *British and Continental. Unpriced* WTPJ (B75-50956)
Heart's music : TTBB (unacc.). *Banks. Unpriced* GEZDW (B75-50515)
The road of evening : song with piano accompaniment. *Lengnick. £0.35* KDW (B75-50555)
A Welshman can't help singing = Mae'r Cymro'n canu heunydd : chorus for male voices (TTBB) and piano. *Bosworth. Unpriced* GDW (B75-50508)
Noble, Peter. Ivor Novello : man of the theatre. *White Lion Publishers. £3.75* BNO(N) (B75-19084) ISBN 0-85617-769-5
Noble numbers : based on organ music of the 17th and 18th centuries, by Frescobaldi, Pachelbel, Zachau, Vetter, and Walther, for wind ensemble. *Boosey and Hawkes. Unpriced* UMK/AAY (B75-50297)
Nocturne : for harp and wind ensemble. (Grundman, Clare). *Boosey and Hawkes. £7.50* UMPTQ (B75-51351)
Noël : for horn and piano. (Brightmore, C Victor). *British and Continental. Unpriced* WTP/LF (B75-50953)
Noel X. (Daquin, Louis Claude). *Chappell. Unpriced* RSPMK (B75-50746)
Nomos : for unaccompanied double bass. (Koblitz, David). *Yorke. Unpriced* SSPMJ (B75-50782)
Nono, Luigi. Epitaffio no. 1, 2 & 3. *Ars Viva : Schott. £11.60* HYE/M (B75-50086)
Norfolk rhapsody. *arr.* Norfolk rhapsody. (Vaughan Williams, Ralph). *Oxford University Press. Unpriced* UMMK (B75-51348)
Norton, Mary Dows Herter. Renaissance and Baroque music : a comprehensive survey. (Blume, Friedrich). *Faber. £1.25* A(XCQ351) (B75-08734) ISBN 0-571-10719-2
Notenbuch der Anna Magdalena Bach, 1725. *Selections: arr.* Bachiana for percussion : four pieces. (Bach, Johann Sebastian). *Simrock. Unpriced* XNQK (B75-50965)
Nouveau livre de noëls. Noel 10. *arr.* Noel X. (Daquin, Louis Claude). *Chappell. Unpriced* RSPMK (B75-50746)

Novak, Jan.
Florilegium cantionum latinarum : melodiae veteres ad cantum clavibus
Carmina profana. *Zanibon : Hinrichsen. Unpriced* KDW (B75-50107)
Panisci fistula : tre preludi per tre flauti. *Zanibon Hinrichsen. Unpriced* VRNT (B75-50315)
Schola cantans. *Vocal score.* Schola cantans : graves auctores latini, leviter decantandi, cantus ad claves. *Zanibon : Hinrichsen. Unpriced* KDW (B75-50109)
Novello band book. (Rivers, Patrick). *Novello. £2.50* WM/AF (B75-50355)
Novello short biographies. Sharp, Geoffrey Brinsley. Byrd ; &, Victoria. *Novello. £0.20* BBX(N) (B75-03643) ISBN 0-85360-060-0
Now the holly bears a berry : unison song with descant. (Toplis, Gloria). *Ricordi. Unpriced* FDP/LF (B75-51053)
Nr 17 = Mikrophonie 2 : für Chor, Hammondorgel und 4 Ringmodulatoren. (Stockhausen, Karlheinz). *Universal. Unpriced* EPVDX (B75-50038)
Nugent, Maud. Sweet Rosie O'Grady. *arr.* Sweet Rosie O'Grady. *455 Brighton Rd, South Croydon : Paul. Unpriced* WUNSK/DW (B75-50958)
Numerical listing of Edison Bell 'Winner'. *19 Glendale Rd, Bournemouth BH6 4JA : 'Talking Machine Review'. £2.00* A/FD(T/WT) (B75-19333) ISBN 0-902338-17-x
Nuovi ricercari : per flauto dolce contralto. (Dolci, Amico). *Heinrichshofen : Hinrichsen. Unpriced* VSSPMJ (B75-50883)
Nymphes et driades : pour orchestre. (Liferman, Georges). *Chappell. Unpriced* MMJ (B75-51154)
O altitudo : soprano solo, flute solo, violin, violoncello, harp, celesta, percussion, women's chorus. (Stout, Alan). *Peters. Unpriced* FE/NYERNQDH (B75-50075)
O how amiable : anthem for mixed chorus (SATB) and band or organ. (Vaughan Williams, Ralph). *Oxford University Press. Unpriced* EUMDK (B75-51028)
O how amiable. *arr.* O how amiable : anthem for mixed chorus (SATB) and band or organ. (Vaughan Williams, Ralph). *Oxford University Press. Unpriced* EUMDK (B75-51028)
O King of the Friday : SATB unacc. (Nelson, Havelock). *Banks. Unpriced* EZDH/LK (B75-51038)
O sweet Jesu : SATB. (Binkerd, Gordon). *Boosey and Hawkes. Unpriced* EZDH (B75-50048)
Oboist's companion
Volume 1. (Rothwell, Evelyn). *Oxford University Press. £3.25* VT/AC (B75-51390) ISBN 0-19-322335-x
O'Brien, Robert.
Norfolk rhapsody. *arr.* Norfolk rhapsody. (Vaughan Williams, Ralph). *Oxford University Press. Unpriced* UMMK (B75-51348)
Street corner overture. *arr.* Street corner overture. (Rawsthorne, Alan). *Oxford University Press. Unpriced* UMMJ (B75-51345)
Ochse, Orpha. The history of the organ in the United States. *Indiana University Press. £11.25* AR/B(YT/X) (B75-17690) ISBN 0-253-32830-6
October songs : SSA unacc. (Benger, Richard). *Banks. Unpriced* FEZDW (B75-50500)
Ode on St Cecilia's day, 1692. Z.328. *Vocal score.* Ode on St Cecilia's day, 1692 : Hail! bright Cecilia : for soprano, two altos, tenor and two basses soli, SSAATB and instruments. (Purcell, Henry). *Novello. £1.20* DX (B75-51025)
Of a feather : five songs for high and low voices and piano. (Bacon, Ernst). *Novello. Unpriced* FDW (B75-50489)
Offenbach, Jacques.
Orphée aux Enfers. Galop infernal. *arr.* Offenbach's can-can. *Piers Press. £1.50(for 3 performing scores)* VSNRK/AHJMP (B75-51378)
La Périchole : operetta in three acts. (Grimsey, John). *10 Rathbone St., W1P 2BJ : Josef Weinberger Ltd. £0.80* BOFACF (B75-19083) ISBN 0-902136-36-4
Offenbach's can-can. (Offenbach, Jacques). *Piers Press. £1.50(for 3 performing scores)* VSNRK/AHJMP (B75-51378)
Official book of scales and arpeggios for double bass, (Grades III, IV, V, VI, and VIII). (Associated Board of the Royal Schools of Music). *Associated Board of the Royal Schools of Music. £0.45* SS/AF (B75-50267)
O'Gorman, Denis. Advent to Easter : short musical plays for junior and middle schools. *Grail Publications. £1.00* BOFGACN/L (B75-18364) ISBN 0-901829-25-0
Oh! dem golden slippers : for brass quartet. (Siebert, Edrich). *British and Continental. Unpriced* WNSK/DW (B75-50941)
Oh, didn't he ramble : the life story of Lee Collins. (Collins, Lee). *University of Illinois Press. £5.50* AMT(P) (B75-01179) ISBN 0-252-00234-2
Oh! I am come to the Low Countrie : traditional melody. (Nelson, Havelock). *Elkin. £0.15* EZDW (B75-50481)
Oh! listen to the band. (Monckton, Lionel). *Studio Music. Unpriced* WMK/DW (B75-50927)
Old English music : for oboe, clarinet and bassoon (or two clarinets and bassoon). *Oxford University Press. Unpriced* VNTK/AYD (B75-51364) ISBN 0-19-359203-7
Olifant : für einen Solisten (Posaune, Trombita Bali-Flöten Zurla, Buchel, Alphorn) und zwei Kammerensembles. (Kelemen, Milko). *Litolff : Peters : Hinrichsen. Unpriced* MRJ (B75-50161)
Olsen, Mark. Experimenting with electronic music. (Brown, Robert, *b.1943*). *Foulsham-Tab. £1.50* APV/B (B75-05798) ISBN 0-7042-0129-1
Oltremari, Giorgio.
Fantasia, fuga, tombeau, capriccio : per chitarra dalla intavolatura per liuto. (Weiss, Sylvius Leopold). *Zanibon : Hinrichsen. Unpriced* TSPMK (B75-50285)
Suite for lute, no.18, in A major. Suite in la maggiore : per chitarra dalla intavolatura per linto. (Weiss, Sylvius Leopold). *Zanibon : Hinrichsen. Unpriced* TSPMK/AG (B75-50289)
Olympic fanfares : for marching band. (Ellis, Ray). *Unichappell. Unpriced* UMMGM (B75-50829)
On a summer evening : flute and piano. (Jacob, Gordon). *Jane Emerson. Unpriced* VRPJ (B75-50322)
On parade : quick march. (Elms, Albert). *Boosey and Hawkes. Unpriced* UMMGM (B75-50830)
One man went to Mo-zart : piano solo. (Duke, Henry). *Feldman. Unpriced* QPJ (B75-50188)
Opella nova. Tl. 1,2. *Selections.* Sechs Choral konzerte : für zwei gleiche Stimmen und Basso continuo. (Schein, Johann Hermann). *Bärenreiter. £2.00* JNEDH (B75-50102)
Opera. Air. Air : for soprano and orchestra. (Berio, Luciano). *Universal. Unpriced* KFLE/MDW (B75-50572)
Opera. Air. *arr.* Air : for soprano and 4 instruments. (Berio, Luciano). *Universal. Unpriced* KFLE/NXNSDW (B75-50573)
Opera library. Heriot, Angus. The castrati in opera. *Calder and Boyars. £5.75* AKGGC/E(M) (B75-26087) ISBN 0-7145-0153-0
Opera production
2 : a handbook. (Eaton, Quaintance). *University of Minnesota Press : Oxford University Press. £7.25* AC (B75-26794) ISBN 0-8166-0689-7
Operette : elektronische Orgel. *Nagel : Bärenreiter. £2.00* RPVK/DW/AY (B75-50220)
Opus newer Paduanen, Galliarden, Intraden, Canzonen (1617) : for 3 cornetti (trumpets in C) and 2 trombones
Volume 1. (Simpson, Thomas). *Musica rara. Unpriced* WNRH (B75-51439)
Volume 2. (Simpson, Thomas). *Musica rara. Unpriced* WNRH (B75-51440)
Opus number zoo : children's play for wind quintet (1951, rev. 1970). (Berio, Luciano). *Universal. Unpriced* CQN (B75-50994)
Oración : valzer popolare venezuelano, per chitarra. (Mangore, Agustin Barrios). *Zanibon : Hinrichsen. Unpriced* TSPMHW (B75-50280)
Orage : Ouverture für Orchester nach dem Drama von A.N. Ostrowsky. (Tchaikovsky, Peter). *Belaieff : Hinrichsen. £8.00* MMJ (B75-50147)
Orff, Carl. Von der Freundlichkeit der Welt = The world's welcome (1930/1973) : choral settings on texts by Bert Brecht for mixed chorus, three pianos and percussion instruments. *Schott. Unpriced* ENYLDW (B75-51027)
Organ & organists. (Smith, William Joseph Thomas). *Boreham Vicarage, Chelmsford, Essex CM3 3EG : The author. £0.25* AR/B(YDDB) (B75-21667) ISBN 0-9504312-0-6
Organ music for manuals
Book 5. *Oxford University Press. Unpriced* R/AY (B75-51267) ISBN 0-19-375852-0
Book 6. *Oxford University Press. Unpriced* R/AY (B75-51268) ISBN 0-19-375853-9
Organ solo mass. (Missa brevis in C) : mixed chorus. (Mozart, Wolfgang Amadeus). *Schirmer. Unpriced* DG (B75-50411)
Organs and organists of Wells Cathedral. (Bowers, Roger). *22 Vicars' Close, Wells, Somerset BA5 2UJ : The Friends of Wells Cathedral. £0.20* AR/B(YDFGWB) (B75-00741) ISBN 0-902321-12-9
Orgeldispositionssammlungen bis zur Mitte des 19. Jahrhunderts. (Martini, Ulrich). *32 Great Titchfield St., W.1 : Bärenreiter. £7.36* AR/BC(XCRR420)
Orgenwissenschaftliche Forschungsstelle, *Westfälische Wilhelmsuniversität.* Veröffentlichungen. Martini, Ulrich. Die Orgeldispositionssammlungen bis zur Mitte des 19. Jahrhunderts. *32 Great Titchfield St., W.1 : Bärenreiter. £7.36* AR/BC(XCRR420)
Orphée aux Enfers. Galop infernal. *arr.* Offenbach's can-can. (Offenbach, Jacques). *Piers Press. £1.50(for 3 performing scores)* VSNRK/AHJMP (B75-51378)
Orrego-Salas, Juan. Four centuries of song, from the troubadour to the Elizabethan age : for voice and guitar. *Associated Music. Unpriced* KE/TSDW/AY (B75-50563)
Orthodox Holy Week Music : SATB a cappella. *Boosey and Hawkes. £1.75* EZDGTC/LH/AYM (B75-50459)
Ottolenghi, Vittoria. Opus number zoo : children's play for wind quintet (1951, rev. 1970). (Berio, Luciano). *Universal. Unpriced* CQN (B75-50994)
Our chalet song book. *Our Chalet Committee. Unpriced* JFE/TSDW/AY (B75-50100)
Ouseley, Frederick Arthur Gore. The works of Henry Purcell
Vol.2: Timon of Athens originally edited by Frederick Arthur Gore Ouseley ; revised by Jack Westrup ; words by Thomas Shadwell. (Purcell, Henry). 2nd ed. *Novello. £3.00* C/AZ (B75-50007)
Out of his head : the sound of Phil Spector. (Williams, Richard, *b.1947*). *Abacus. £0.65* A/FD/E(P) (B75-22851) ISBN 0-349-13723-4
Ouvre feu : oboe and piano. (Barthe, Adrian). *Emerson. Unpriced* VTPJ (B75-51393)
Over hill, over dale : based on an American march. (Hanmer, Ronald). *Studio Music. Unpriced* WMK/AGM (B75-51426)
Over the sticks : galop. (Siebert, Edrich). *Studio Music. Unpriced* WMHLF (B75-51417)
Overture, The court of Henry VIII : for concert band. (Cacavas, John). *Chappell. Unpriced* UMJ (B75-50822)
Owen, Elfed.
Morys y Gwyat : can ddwy-ran ar gyfer ysgolion cynradd gyda chyfeiliant piano a recorder. *University of Wales Press. Unpriced* KFE/VSPDW (B75-50570)
Morys y Gwynt : can ddwy-ran ar gyfer ysgolion cynradd gyda chyfeiliant piano a recorder. *University of Wales Press. Unpriced* KFQE/VSPDW (B75-50123)
Owen, Tom.
Lead guitar. *Chappell. Unpriced* TS/AF (B75-51315)
Tenor banjo chord coloring book : chords and how to use them. *Chappell. Unpriced* TTV/RC (B75-51331)
Oxford English memoirs and travels. Kelly, Michael, *b.1762.* Reminiscences of Michael Kelly. 2nd ed. reprinted with corrections. *Oxford University Press. £7.50* AKGH/E(P) (B75-20392) ISBN 0-19-255417-4
Oxford harmony
Vol.1. *Oxford University Press. £1.20* A/R (B75-12696) ISBN 0-19-317315-8
Oxford studies of composers.
Arnold, Denis. Giovanni Gabrieli. *Oxford University Press. £1.80* BG (B75-07792) ISBN 0-19-315231-2
Nichols, Roger. Messiaen. *Oxford University Press. £2.50* BMKS (B75-15004) ISBN 0-19-315428-5
Oyageur. L'Avenir. *arr.* L'Avenir : pour baryton. (Duclos, Pierre). *Chappell. Unpriced* KGNDW (B75-50592)
Pablo Casals : a biography. (Kirk, H L). *Hutchinson. £5.50* ASR/E(P) (B75-13171) ISBN 0-09-122230-3
Pachelbel, Johann.
Bo-peep : based on the traditional air and a fugue by Pachelbel. (Gardner, Ward). *Banks. Unpriced* EZDW (B75-51046)
Hexachordum Apollinis. Chaconne in C major. *arr.* Chaconne in C. *Tomus. Unpriced* VSNTK/AHJN (B75-50864)
Selected organ works
6. *Bärenreiter. £2.40* RJ (B75-50211)
Paddington Bear : song. (Chappell, Herbert). *Music Sales. £0.25* KDW (B75-50106)
Padley, Kenneth.
Making electronic music : a course for schools
Book 1. (Dwyer, Terence). *Oxford University Press. £1.50* **APV/D (B75-24850)** ISBN 0-19-321071-1
Book 2. (Dwyer, Terence). *Oxford University Press. £1.50* APV/D (B75-24851) ISBN 0-19-321072-x
Teacher's book. (Dwyer, Terence). *Oxford University Press. £2.50* APV/D (B75-24852) ISBN 0-19-321070-3
Paduana, galliarda, etc. quaternis et quinis vocibus cum basso continuo. Selections. *arr.* Battle suite. (Scheidt, Samuel). *Chester. Unpriced* WNRK (B75-51446)
Paean : for piano. (Payne, Anthony). *Chester. Unpriced* QPJ (B75-50707)
Paganini, Nicolò. Sonata for viola & orchestra. *arr.* Sonata per la grand'viola e orchestra. *Schott. Unpriced* **SQPK/LE (B75-51303)**
Page, Martin, *b.1938.* Kiss me goodnight, Sergeant Major : the songs and ballads of World War II. *Panther. £0.60*

ADW/KG(YC/XNU7) (B75-29320)
ISBN 0-586-04152-4
Palestrina, Giovanni Pierluigi da.
Stabat mater : for double choir. *Eulenburg. Unpriced* EZDGKADD/LK (B75-50045)
Surge, illuminare Jerusalem : a motet for two four-part choirs (SATB SATB for the feast of the Epiphany). *Chester. Unpriced* EZDJ/LFP (B75-51040)
Palm Beach : barcarolle for brass band. (Siebert, Edrich). *Studio Music. Unpriced* WMJ (B75-50369)
Panisci fistula : tre preludi per tre flauti. (Novak, Jan). *Zanibon : Hinrichsen. Unpriced* VRNT (B75-50315)
Panther rock series. Rock file
3. *Panther. £0.75* ADW/GB (B75-21065)
ISBN 0-586-04261-x
Panufnik, Andrzej.
Concerto for piano and orchestra. *Boosey and Hawkes. £7.00* MPQ (B75-50149)
Concerto for piano. *arr.* Concerto for piano and orchestra (recomposed 1972). *Boosey and Hawkes. £3.00* QNUK/LF (B75-50178)
Pardini, Enrico. Quintets for wind & strings. Op.8, 9. Sei quintetti. Op.8 & op.9 : per flauto, oboe, violino, viola e basso. (Cambini, Giovanni Giuseppe). *Hinrichsen. Unpriced* NVPNR (B75-50163)
Parfrey, Raymond. Here on a bed of straw : carol for unison voices, SAB or SATB. *Thames. Unpriced* JFDP/LF (B75-50533)
Park, Phil. La Périchole : operetta in three acts. (Grimsey, John). *10 Rathbone St., W1P 2BJ : Josef Weinberger Ltd. £0.80* BOFACF (B75-19083)
ISBN 0-902136-36-4
Parke, Dorothy.
By winding roads : fifteen unison songs of the Irish countryside. *Roberton. £1.00* JFDW (B75-51094)
The little senorita : for piano solo. *Banks. Unpriced* QPJ (B75-50706)
Parker, Horatio. Hora novissima. Urbs Syon unica. City of high renown = Urbs Syon unica : unaccompanied mixed chorus. *Galaxy : Galliard. Unpriced* EZDH (B75-51035)

Parker, Isabella G. Hora novissima. Urbs Syon unica. City of high renown = Urbs Syon unica : unaccompanied mixed chorus. (Parker, Horatio). *Galaxy : Galliard. Unpriced* EZDH (B75-51035)
Parker, Jim. Follow the star. *Selections: arr.* Follow the star : song album from a new musical for Christmas. *Chappell. Unpriced* KDW/LF (B75-51120)
Parsley, Osbert.
In nomine : for two treble, two tenor and bass viols. *Oxford University Press. Score £0.20, Parts unpriced* STNR (B75-50783) ISBN 0-19-341211-x
Parsley's clock a 5 : for two treble, two tenor, and bass viols. *Oxford University Press. Score, £0.20 ; Parts, Unpriced* STNR (B75-50784) ISBN 0-19-341213-6
Spes nostra : for two treble, two tenor and bass viols. *Oxford University Press. £0.30* STNR (B75-50785)
ISBN 0-19-341212-8
Parsley's clock a 5 : for two treble, two tenor, and bass viols. (Parsley, Osbert). *Oxford University Press. Score, £0.20 ; Parts, Unpriced* STNR (B75-50784)
ISBN 0-19-341213-6
Parsons, Denys. The directory of tunes and musical themes. *Spencer Brown. £6.00* A(TD) (B75-13381)
ISBN 0-904747-00-x
Pasfield, William Reginald. New look scales for piano. *Ashdown. Unpriced* Q/AF (B75-50657)
Pastoral : for two flutes and four clarinets. (Lyons, Graham). *British and Continental Music. Unpriced* VNQ (B75-50841)
Paton, John Glenn. Metodo practico di canto italiano. Practical method of Italian singing. (Vaccai, Nicolo). New ed. *Schirmer. Unpriced* K/AFH (B75-50547)
Paton, Tam. The Bay City Rollers. *Everest. £0.45* AKDW/GB/E(P) (B75-29316) ISBN 0-903925-60-5
Patterns : for saxophone quartet. (Cordell, Frank). *Novello. £3.75* VUNS (B75-51397)
Patterson, Paul.
Conversations : for clarinet B flat and piano. *Weinberger. Unpriced* VVPJ (B75-50900)
Count down : brass band. *Weinberger. Unpriced* WMJ (B75-50923)
Country search. Theme. *arr.* Country search : piano. *Weinberger. £0.30* QPK/JS (B75-51264)
Requiem. *Vocal score.* Requiem for chorus and orchestra. *Weinberger. Unpriced* DGKAV (B75-50019)
Paul Hindemith : the man behind the music : a biography. (Skelton, Geoffrey). *Gollancz. £6.00* BHM(N) (B75-22841) ISBN 0-575-01988-3
Paul McCartney story. (Tremlett, George). *Futura Publications. £0.50* AKDW/GB/E(P) (B75-19734)
ISBN 0-86007-200-2
Pavey, Sidney.
Clog dance : for orchestra. *Bosworth. Unpriced* MH (B75-50594)
Windmills : for orchestra. *Bosworth. Unpriced* MJ (B75-50596)
Paviour, Paul. The Congo jive : for choir, percussion and piano. *Boosey and Hawkes. £3.60* ENYLNTDW (B75-50037)
Pavlakis, Christopher. The American music handbook. *Free Press : Collier Macmillan. £10.00* A(YT) (B75-11221)
ISBN 0-02-925180-x
Payne, Anthony. Paean : for piano. *Chester. Unpriced* QPJ (B75-50707)
Paynter, John.
God's grandeur. *Vocal score.* God's grandeur : for mixed chorus, brass and organ (or chorus and organ). *Oxford University Press. Unpriced* DE (B75-50998)
ISBN 0-19-337781-0
A temporary diversion. *Vocal score.* A temporary diversion : (or the monumental photographic and zoological umbrella show). *Universal. Unpriced* CN (B75-50992)
Paysage ibérique. (Duclos, Pierre). *Chappell. Unpriced* TMK (B75-50271)
Paysage suedois. (Duclos, Pierre). *Chappell. Unpriced* TMK (B75-50272)
Peacock, Alan. The composer in the market place. *Faber. £5.50* A(JC/K/YC/XM70) (B75-18726)
ISBN 0-571-10011-2
Pearsall, Robert Lucas. Duetto buffo di due gatti = Comic duet for two cats. (Berthold, G). *28 Knolls Way, Clifton, Beds. : Lindsay Music. £0.15* JNFEDW (B75-50546)
ISBN 0-85957-005-3
Pearsall, Ronald. Edwardian popular music. *David and Charles. £4.95* ADW/GB(YC/XMA14) (B75-11753)
ISBN 0-7153-6814-1
Pearson, Hesketh. Gilbert and Sullivan : a biography. *Macdonald and Jane's. £3.95* BSWACF(N) (B75-27958)
ISBN 0-356-08034-x
Pearson, L R. Le Roi s'amuse. Passepied. *arr.* Passepied. (Delibes, Leo). *Oxford University Press. Unpriced* TSPMK/AHU (B75-50817) ISBN 0-19-356159-x
Peggy, my love : Uist boat song, traditional Scottish melody. (Nelson, Havelock). *Elkin. £0.15* GEZDW (B75-51075)
Pehkonen, Elis. Who killed Lawless Lean? : for voices, 4 melody instruments, percussion and piano. *Universal. Unpriced* JFE/LNRPXDW (B75-51096)
Pel mel : for brass band. (Lear, W Hogarth). *Paxton Music. £1.75* WMJ (B75-50365)
Penguin book of Italian madrigals for four voices. *Penguin Books. £1.00* EZDU/AYJ (B75-50063)
ISBN 0-14-070843-x
Penguin education. Education Development Center. The musical instrument recipe book. *Penguin Education. £0.50* AY/BC (B75-08294) ISBN 0-14-081185-0
Perchance to dream : the world of Ivor Novello. (Rose, Richard, *b.1902*). *Frewin. £4.95* BNO(N) (B75-50005)
ISBN 0-85632-120-6
Percussion instruments and their history. (Blades, James). New and revised ed. *Faber. £15.00* **AX/B(X)** (B75-13738) ISBN 0-571-04832-3
Perényi, Eleanor. Liszt. *Weidenfeld and Nicolson. £8.50* BLJ(N) (B75-11755) ISBN 0-297-76910-3
Perera, Ronald Christopher. The development and practice of electronic music. *Prentice-Hall. £8.80* APV (B75-15702) ISBN 0-13-207605-5
Périchole : operetta in three acts. (Grimsey, John). *10 Rathbone St., W1P 2BJ : Josef Weinberger Ltd. £0.80* BOFACF (B75-19083) ISBN 0-902136-36-4
Periferisch-Diagonaal-Concentrisch = Peripheral-Diagonal-Concentric : for recorder quartet. (Geysen, Frans). *Schott. Unpriced* VSNS (B75-50860)
Periodicals:, *New periodicals and those issued with changed titles.*
Music Box Society. News Letter
No.1- ; Aug. 1974-. *42 Dumgoyne Drive, Bearsden, Dunbartonshire : The Society. Free to members* A/FH/B(B) (B75-19736)
Traditional Music
No.1- ; mid 1975-. *90 St Julian's Farm Rd, SE27 0RS : Traditional Music. £0.35(£1.20 yearly)* A/G(YC/B)
Vintage Light Music : for the enthusiast of light music on 78 r.p.m. records
No.1- ; Jan. 1975-. *c/o Hon. Secretary, 4 Harvest Bank Rd, West Wickham, Kent : Vintage Light Music Society. £0.25(£1.00 yearly)* A/GB/FD(B) (B75-15703)
Perle, George. Serial composition and atonality : an introduction to the music of Schoenberg, Berg and Webern. 2nd ed. revised and enlarged. *Faber. £2.60* A/PN (B75-13735) ISBN 0-571-10700-1
Perlis, Vivian. Charles Ives remembered : an oral history. *Yale University Press. £6.25* BIV(N) (B75-05791)
ISBN 0-300-01758-8
Perrin, Geoffrey. Careers with music ... (Fortescue, Margaret). *Careers Centre, University of East Anglia, University Plain, Norwich NR4 7TJ : University of East Anglia. £0.15(£0.10 to university and polytechnic careers services)* A(MN/YD) (B75-15001)
Persian march. Op.289. (Strauss, Johann, *b.1825*). *Bosworth. Unpriced* MK/AGM (B75-50600)
Persischer Marsch. Op.289. *arr.* Persian march. Op.289. (Strauss, Johann, *b.1825*). *Bosworth. Unpriced* MK/AGM (B75-50600)
Peter, Johann Friedrich. Psalm of joy of the congregation in Salem, for the peace celebration, July 4, 1783 : the music of the first organized Independence Day celebration, for soli, chorus of mixed voices and organ music. *Boosey and Hawkes. Unpriced* DH/AYT (B75-51008)
Petit negre. (Debussy, Claude). *Emerson. Unpriced* WNRK (B75-51444)
Petit Trianon suite : ten easy pieces on 18th century style dance melodies, for piano. (Agay, Denes). *Schirmer. Unpriced* QPG (B75-50668)
Petrassi, Goffedro. Concerto no.1 for orchestra. Primo concerto per orchestra. *Eulenberg. Unpriced* MMF (B75-51151)
Petrie, Gavin.
Black music. *Hamlyn. £1.95* AKDW/GB/E(YTLD/M) (B75-03641) ISBN 0-600-31343-3
Pop today. *Hamlyn. £1.95* AKDW/GB/E(M) (B75-02994) ISBN 0-600-37080-1
Rock life. *Hamlyn. £1.95* AKDW/HK/E(M) (B75-03642)
ISBN 0-600-38708-9
Petrovics, Emil. Hungarian children's songs : for flute and piano. *Boosey and Hawkes. £1.00* VRPK/DW/GJ/AYG (B75-51373)
Petrzelka, Vilem. Mass in E flat major. Mass, E flat major (unfinished Mass). (Janacek, Leos). *Bärenreiter. £2.10* DG (B75-50016)
Petti, Anthony Gaetano.
Cantiones sacrae. Alma redemptoris. Alma redemptoris : antiphon of the Blessed Virgin, for five voices, S.S.A.T.B. (Philips, Peter). *Chester. Unpriced* EZDGKJ (B75-51033)
Quartus tomus musici operis. In nomine Jesu. In nomine Jesu : motet for five voices, SAATB, for the Feast of the Holy Name and general use. (Handl, Jacob). *Chester. Unpriced* EZDGKHL (B75-51032)
Surge, illuminare Jerusalem : a motet for two four-part choirs (SATB SATB for the feast of the Epiphany). (Palestrina, Giovanni Pierluigi da). *Chester. Unpriced* EZDJ/LFP (B75-51040)
Philipp, Günter. Piano music. *Selections.* Selected piano works
Vol.6: Sonatas nos 6-10. (Skriabin, Aleksandr Nikolaevich). *Peters. Unpriced* QPJ (B75-50195)
Philips, Peter.
Cantiones sacrae. Alma redemptoris. Alma redemptoris : antiphon of the Blessed Virgin, for five voices, S.S.A.T.B. *Chester. Unpriced* EZDGKJ (B75-51033)
Les Rossignols spirituels. *Selections.* Eleven Christmas carols. *Oxford University Press. Unpriced* EZDP/LF (B75-51043) ISBN 0-19-353346-4
Piano : a pictorial account of its ancestry and development. (Hollis, Helen Rice). *David and Charles. £4.50* APW/B(X) (B75-13169) ISBN 0-7153-6559-2
Piano makers. (Wainwright, David, *b.1929*). *Hutchinson. £6.00* AQ/B(K/X) (B75-50979) ISBN 0-09-122950-2
Piano music by the great masters : the baroque era, the classic era, the romantic era. *Ashley : Phoenix. Unpriced* QPK/AAY (B75-51256)
Piano music. *Selections.* Selected piano works
Vol.6: Sonatas nos 6-10. (Skriabin, Aleksandr *Peters. Unpriced* QPJ (B75-50195)
Piccolomini mass. (Missa brevis in C) : mixed chorus. (Mozart, Wolfgang Amadeus). *Schirmer. Unpriced* DG (B75-50410)
Picken, Laurence. Folk musical instruments of Turkey. *Oxford University Press. £38.50* BZCAL/B (B75-25557)
ISBN 0-19-318102-9
Pickeringe, Jane.
Lute music. *Selections : arr.* Two pieces. (Dowland, John). *Oxford University Press. £0.50* TSPMK (B75-50811)
ISBN 0-19-356279-0
Three pieces from the Jane Pickeringe Lute Book (Egerton 2046). *Oxford University Press. £0.50* TSPMK/AAY (B75-50814) ISBN 0-19-356770-9
Picking Blues : leichte Blues - Sätze nach alten und neuen Melodien, für Gitarre. *Schott. Unpriced* TSPMK/DW/HHW/AY (B75-51329)
Pictures at an exhibition. (Musorgsky, Modest). *Henmar Press : Peters. Unpriced* MMK (B75-50619)
Pictures at an exhibition. *arr.* Pictures at an exhibition. (Musorgsky, Modest). *Henmar Press : Peters. Unpriced* MMK (B75-50619)
Pieces for Anya : for piano solo. (Camilleri, Charles). *Roberton. £0.50* QPJ (B75-51236)
Pierce, Richard. Music through the ages. (Alberti, Luciano). *Cassell. £7.50* A(X) (B75-02995) ISBN 0-304-29420-9
Pike, Lionel. Les Rossignols spirituels. *Selections.* Eleven Christmas carols. (Philips, Peter). *Oxford University Press. Unpriced* EZDP/LF (B75-51043)
ISBN 0-19-353346-4
Pinkham, Daniel. Wedding cantata. Set me as a seal. *arr.* Wedding song : high voice and organ. *Peters. Unpriced* KFTDH/KDD (B75-51128)
Piot, Paul. Cornouailles march : piano. (Blot, André). *Chappell. Unpriced* QPGM (B75-50672)
Piper, Myfanwy. Death in Venice. *Vocal score.* Death in Venice. Op.88 : an opera in two acts. (Britten, Benjamin). *Faber Music. Unpriced* CC (B75-50988)
Pipes of war : a record of the achievements of pipers of Scottish and overseas regiments in the war, 1914-1918. (Seton, *Sir* Bruce Gordon, *bart*). 1st ed. reprinted. *EP Publishing etc.. £5.00* AVY (B75-15172)
ISBN 0-7158-1089-8
Pippin, Don. Fashion : a musical comedy. (Mowatt, Anna Cora). *French. £1.10* BPIACM (B75-20393)
ISBN 0-573-68065-5
Pishnetto : recital étude no.5, for cello and piano. (Tortelier, Paul). *Chester. Unpriced* SRPJ (B75-51306)
Pitfield, Thomas. A folkish tune : for horn in F and piano. *British and Continental Music Agencies. Unpriced* WTPJ (B75-50957)
Pitman education library. Lawrence, Ian. Music and the teacher. *Pitman. £2.50* A(VC) (B75-19078)
ISBN 0-273-00354-2
Pizzini, Carlo Alberto.
Capriccio napoletano : per chitarra. *Zanibon : Hinrichsen. Unpriced* TSPMJ (B75-50282)
Improvviso da concerto : per chitarra. *Zanibon Hinrichsen. Unpriced* TSPMJ (B75-50283)
Planets. Mars. *arr.* Mars. (Holst, Gustav). *Boosey and Hawkes. Unpriced* UMMK (B75-50833)
Plath, Wolfgang. Sonata for violin & piano, op.3, no.3, in B flat major. Sonata in B flat major : for violin and piano. Op.3, no.3. (Sarti, Giuseppe). *Nagel : Bärenreiter. Unpriced* SPE (B75-50765)
Platt, Norman. Von der Freundlichkeit der Welt = The world's welcome (1930/1973) : choral settings on texts by Bert Brecht for mixed chorus, three pianos and percussion instruments. (Orff, Carl). *Schott. Unpriced* ENYLDW (B75-51027)
Platt, Peter. Cantica sacra, 1618. (Dering, Richard). *Stainer & Bell. Unpriced* DJ (B75-50025)
Platt, Richard. Sonatas for flute & continuo, nos 4,7. Two

sonatas for flute and basso continuo. (Roseingrave, Thomas). *Oxford University Press. £2.00* VRPE (B75-50319) ISBN 0-19-358642-8
Platti, Giovanni. Sonata for flute, oboe & basso continuo in G major. Trio sonata in G, for flute, oboe and basso continuo. *Musica rara. Unpriced* NWPNTE (B75-51191)

Platts, Kenneth.
A midnight carol. Op.21 : two-part. *Ashdown. Unpriced* FDW (B75-50495)
Music for the Maltings. Opus 22 : for orchestra. *Ashdown. Unpriced* MJ (B75-50597)
Play at sight : a graded sight reading course
Part 6. (Brown, Christine). *EMI. Unpriced* Q/EG (B75-51211)
Play the trombone, treble clef. (Bright, Clive). *Chappell. Unpriced* WU/AC (B75-51470)
Playing & composing on the recorder. (Etkin, Ruth). *Sterling etc. : Distributed by Ward Lock. £1.95* AVS/E (B75-28638) ISBN 0-7061-2080-9
Pleasure and practice music cards : songs
Set 1. *E.J. Arnold. Unpriced* LNK/DW/AY (B75-51143) ISBN 0-560-00487-7
Set 2. *E.J. Arnold. Unpriced* LNK/DW/AY (B75-51144) ISBN 0-560-00488-5
Set 3. *E.J. Arnold. Unpriced* LNK/DW/AY (B75-51145) ISBN 0-560-00489-3
Pleyel, Ignaz.
Sextet for wind instruments in E flat major. Sextet in E flat major : for 2 clarinets, 2 bassoons and 2 horns. *Musica rara. £6.50* UNQ (B75-51355)
Trio for two clarinets & bassoon in E flat major. Trio für zwei Klarinetten und Fagott, Es-dur. *Litolff : Peters. Unpriced* VNT (B75-50311)
Pleyel, Ignaz.Trio for two clarinets & bassoon, op.20, no.2, in E flat major. Trio in E flat. Op.20, no.2, for 2 clarinets and bassoon. *Musica rara. Unpriced* VNT (B75-51363)
Plomley, Roy. 'Desert Island Discs'. *Kimber. £2.95* A/FD/JT(P/X) (B75-50973) ISBN 0-7183-0024-6
Ploughboy : traditional, solo for E flat or B flat bass and brass band. (Shield, William). *455 Brighton Rd, South Croydon : Paul. Unpriced* WMPWUU (B75-50936)
Plumstead, Mary. Ha'nacker Mill : song. *Roberton. Unpriced* KDW (B75-50556)
Plumtre, Edward H. Rejoice ye pure in heart : for mixed chorus and keyboard, based on a hymn by Arthur Messiter. (Wilson, Don). *Galaxy : Galliard. Unpriced* DH (B75-50023)
Pocaterra, A. Trios for two violins & cello, nos, 1-6. Op.2. Sei trii per due violini e violoncello. Op.1a. (Boccherini, Luigi). *Zanibon : Hinrichsen. Unpriced* RXNT (B75-50239)
Pocaterra, Antonio. Concerto for violin & cello in D minor. Concerto in re minore : per violino, violoncello e orchestra. (Donizetti, Gaetano). *Zanibon : Peters. Unpriced* MPSPLSRF (B75-50153)
Poeme de l'extase = The poem of ecstasy. Op.54. (Skriabin, Aleksandr *Belaieff : Hinrichsen. Unpriced* MMJ (B75-51157)
Poet's song : for four-part chorus of mixed voices with piano accompaniment. (Dello Joio, Norman). *Associated Music. £0.25* DW (B75-51017)
Politoske, Daniel Theodore. Music. *Prentice-Hall. £5.10* A(X) (B75-02367) ISBN 0-13-607465-0
Ponte, Lorenzo da. Don Giovanni. K 527. *Vocal score.* Don Giovanni. KV 527. (Mozart, Wolfgang Amadeus). *Cassel : Bärenreiter. Unpriced* CC (B75-50396)
Poos, Heinrich. Das ist ein kestlich Ding, dem Herren danken : Motette für vier gleiche Stimmen und zweistimmige Kinderchor. *Bärenreiter. £0.20* FEZDJ (B75-50076)
Pop goes the posthorn : for brass band. (Lear, W Hogarth). *Paxton. £1.50* WMJ (B75-50366)
Pop moods for young duettists : piano. (Le Fleming, Antony). *Chappell. Unpriced* QNV (B75-51215)
Pop quiz book. *See* Kinn, Maurice.
Pop today. *Hamlyn. £1.95* AKDW/GB/E(M) (B75-02994) ISBN 0-600-37080-1
Porgy and Bess. Summertime. *arr.* Summertime music. (Gershwin, George). *Chappell. Unpriced* UMK/DW (B75-50825)
Porter, Peter.
Annotations of Auschwitz : soprano, flute (bass flute), trumpet, horn, violin, cello, piano. (Lumsdaine, David). *Universal. Unpriced* KFLE/NUNQDX (B75-51124)
Konrad of the mountains : a pageant for voice and instruments. (Blyton, Carey). *Belwin-Mills. Unpriced* JFE/NYEDX (B75-50538)
Portnoff, Leo. Concertino for violin & piano. Op.13. *arr.* Concertino for four violins. Op.13. *Bosworth. Unpriced* RXMPSNSK/LFL (B75-50754)
Poupée de porcelaine. *arr.* Poupée de porcelaine : musique de Pierre Max Dubois et Paul Bonneau. (Dubois, Pierre Max). *Chappell. Unpriced* TMK (B75-50789)
Poupée de porcelaine : musique de Pierre Max Dubois et Paul Bonneau. (Dubois, Pierre Max). *Chappell. Unpriced* TMK (B75-50789)
Pour le piano : piano solo. (Debussy, Claude). *Peters. Unpriced* QPG (B75-51230)
Powers, William J. Blossom's a possum : for mixed chorus, SATB. (Cassey, Charles R). *Chappell. Unpriced* DW (B75-50437)
Practical method of Italian singing. (Vaccai, Nicolo). New ed. *Schirmer. Unpriced* K/AFH (B75-50547)
Praeludiana : for organ. (Chapple, Brian). *Chester. Unpriced* RJ (B75-50730)
Praetorius, Jacob. Choral bearbeitungen : für Orgel. *Bärenreiter. £3.60* RJ (B75-50212)
Praetorius, Michael.
Terpsichore. *Selections: arr.* Four dances
Set 1. *Ricordi. Unpriced* WNRH (B75-50376)
Terpsichore. *Selections: arr.* Four dances
Set 2. *Ricordi. Unpriced* WNRH (B75-50377)
Praise the Lord, O Jerusalem. *Vocal score.* Praise the Lord, O Jerusalem : verse anthem for five-part chorus of mixed voices and optional solo group. (Purcell, Henry). *Schirmer. Unpriced* DK (B75-51009)
Praise the Lord, O my soul : anthem for unison voices or SATB and organ, suitable for Rogation, Harvest or general use. (Ferguson, Barry). *Novello. £0.10* JDK/LP (B75-50523)
Prayer of St. Francis of Assisi : for S.A.T.B. chorus and organ or piano. (Nelson, Ron). *Boosey and Hawkes. £0.30* DH (B75-51004)
Preamble for a solemn occasion. (Copland, Aaron). *Boosey and Hawkes. £9.00* UMK (B75-50296)
Preamble for a solemn occasion. *arr.* Preamble for a solemn occasion. (Copland, Aaron). *Boosey and Hawkes. £9.00* UMK (B75-50296)
Preces and responses : for SATB with divisions (unaccompanied). (Lloyd, Richard). *Novello. £0.15* EZDGMM (B75-50046)
Prelude and capriccio for cornet and band. (Gregson, Edward). *R. Smith. Unpriced* WRPK (B75-50945)
Prelude and capriccio for cornet & band. *arr.* Prelude and capriccio for cornet and band. (Gregson, Edward). *R. Smith. Unpriced* WRPK (B75-50945)
Prelude and fugue. (Bach, Johann Sebastian). *Oxford University Press. Score, £0.75 ; Parts, Unpriced* SRNRK/Y (B75-50773) ISBN 0-19-355238-8
Prentice-Hall history of music series. Seay, Albert. Music in the medieval world. 2nd ed. *Prentice-Hall. £5.50* A(XA1420) (B75-24232) ISBN 0-13-608133-9
Previn, André. Four outings for brass. *Chester. Unpriced* WNR (B75-51437)
Prière d'une vierge. *arr.* A maiden's prayer. (Bądarzewska, Thécla). *Boosey and Hawkes. £1.00* WMK (B75-51420)
'Primo libro di madrigali. *Selections.* Three madrigals : for 4 voices or instruments. (Arcadelt, Jacques). *Antico. Unpriced* EZDU (B75-50473)
Prince of Denmark's march. *arr.* Let the earth resound ('Lobt den Herrn der Welt'). (Clarke, Jeremiah). *Bosworth. Unpriced* JDH (B75-50522)
Prince of Denmark's march. *arr.* Trumpet voluntary. (Clarke, Jeremiah). *Chester. Unpriced* WMK/AGM (B75-51424)
Princess, sedate and merry : for string orchestra. (Branson, David). *Helicon. Unpriced* RXMJ (B75-50749)
Principles and problems of music education. (Regelski, Thomas A). *Prentice-Hall. £6.05* A(VF) (B75-20389) ISBN 0-13-709840-5
Prizer, William. Qui belles amours : ATTB. (Josquin des Prés). *Oxford University Press. Unpriced* EZDW (B75-51049) ISBN 0-19-341222-5
Prodromos musicae ecclesiasticae. *Selections.* Hosianna dem Sohne David, und, Wohlauf wohlauf zu dieser Frist : zwei kleine Weihnachtskonzert, für zwei mittlere Stimmen und Basso continuo. (Grimm, Heinrich). *Bärenreiter. £1.20* JNFVEDH/LF (B75-50103)
Programmed texts:.
Hossack, Alfred. From notes to rhythm. *Lutterworth Press. £0,75* A/M (B75-25556) ISBN 0-7188-2128-9
Hossack, Alfred. Major and minor scales. *Lutterworth Press. £0.75* A/PF (B75-25555) ISBN 0-7188-2129-7
Regelski, Thomas A. Principles and problems of music education. *Prentice-Hall. £6.05* A(VF) (B75-20389) ISBN 0-13-709840-5
Progressive reading for guitarists. (Dodgson, Stephen). *Ricordi. £3.00* TS/AF (B75-50795)
Prokofiev, Sergei. Quintet for oboe, clarinet, violin, viola & double bass. Op.39. Quintet. Opus 39 : for oboe, clarinet, violin, viola and double bass. *Boosey and Hawkes. £1.25* NVPNR (B75-50640)
Promenade. *arr.* Promenade : pour cor et orchestre à cordes. (Marischal, Louis). *Chappell. Unpriced* WTPK (B75-51469)
Prophecy : SSAA unaccompanied. (Diemer, Emma Lou). *Boosey and Hawkes. Unpriced* FEZDK (B75-50077)
Providence of God : a sequence of readings, hymns and anthems to celebrate the harvest. *Novello. £0.60* DF/LP (B75-50409)
Psalm 98 : for men's chorus (TBB), accompanied by brass quintet and piano, or by organ and piano alone. (Crawford, John). *Oxford University Press. Unpriced* GE/NWXPNQDR (B75-50083)
Psalm of joy of the congregation in Salem, for the peace celebration, July 4, 1783 : the music of the first organized Independence Day celebration, for soli, chorus of mixed voices and organ music. *Boosey and Hawkes. Unpriced* DH/AYT (B75-51008)
Psalm-Tripychon : für gemischten Chor und Bläserchor. (Wenzel, Eberhard). *Bärenreiter. £2.40* EWMDR (B75-50042)
Psychodrama : für Orchester. (Baird, Tadeusz). *Litolff : Peters. Unpriced* MMJ (B75-50141)
Psychology for musicians. (Buck, *Sir* Percy Carter). *Oxford University Press. £1.25* A/CS (B75-18003) ISBN 0-19-311914-5

Puccini, Giacomo.
Famous Puccini arias
1-2: One fine day (Un bel di vedremo), from Madame Butterfly ; Love and music (Vissi d'arte), from Tosca. *Studio Music. Unpriced* WMK/DW (B75-50928)
3-4: Love duet (Oh! quanti occhi fissi attenti), from Madame Butterfly ; Your tiny hand is frozen (Che gelida manina), from La Bohème. *Studio Music. Unpriced* WMK/DW (B75-50929)
5-6: Musetta's waltz song (Quando me'n vu'), from La Bohème ; Stars are brightly shining (E lucetan le stelle), from Tosca. *Studio Music. Unpriced* WMK/DW (B75-50930)
7-8: Oh my beloved father (O mio babbino caro), from Gianni Schicchi ; They call me Mimi (Mi chiamano Mimi), from La Bohème. *Studio Music. Unpriced* WMK/DW (B75-50931)
Letters of Giacomo Puccini : mainly connected with the composition and production of his operas. New ed. *Harrap. £4.00* BPU(N) (B75-05793) ISBN 0-245-52422-3
Puijenbroeck, Victor van.
Partita for lute in C minor. S.997. *arr.* Partita. (Bach, Johann Sebastian). *Uitgave Metropolis : Hinrichsen. £1.00* TSPMK/AG (B75-50288)
Partita for violin, no.2. S.1064. Chaconne. *arr.* Chaconne. (Bach, Johann Sebastian). *Uitgave Metropolis Hinrichsen. Unpriced* RSPMK/AHJN (B75-50224)
Sonata for lute in B minor, London no.16. Sonate (London nr 16). (Weiss, Sylvius Leopold). *Uitgave Metropolis Hinrichsen. Unpriced* TSPMK/AE (B75-50287)
Purcell, Henry.
Dioclesian. *Selections.* Suite für Streicher. *Litolff : Peters. Unpriced* RXM/JM (B75-50225)
The Gordian knot untied. *Selections: arr.* The Gordian knot untied. *Piers Press. Unpriced* VSNSK/JM (B75-50330)
If music be the food of love (3rd setting). Z.379C. *Oxford University Press. £0.50* KDW (B75-50557) ISBN 0-19-345707-5
King Arthur. *Choral score.* King Arthur. *Faber Music. Unpriced* DACB/JM (B75-50996)
Ode on St Cecilia's day, 1692. Z.328. *Vocal score.* Ode on St Cecilia's day, 1692 : Hail! bright Cecilia : for soprano, two altos, tenor and two basses soli, SSAATB and instruments. *Novello. £1.20* DX (B75-51025)
Praise the Lord, O Jerusalem. *Vocal score.* Praise the Lord, O Jerusalem : verse anthem for five-part chorus of mixed voices and optional solo group. *Schirmer. Unpriced* DK (B75-51009)
Prince of Denmark's march. *arr.* Let the earth resound ('Lobt den Herrn der Welt'). (Clarke, Jeremiah). *Bosworth. Unpriced* JDH (B75-50522)
Sonatas of three parts (1683), for strings & basso continuo, nos 1-6, Z.790-5. Sonatas for three parts, nos.1-6. *Eulenburg. Unpriced* NXNTE (B75-51194)
The works of Henry Purcell
Vol.2: Timon of Athens originally edited by Frederick Arthur Gore Ouseley ; revised by Jack Westrup ; words by Thomas Shadwell. 2nd ed. *Novello. £3.00* C/AZ (B75-50007)
Purcell. (Westrup, *Sir* Jack Allan). 7th ed.. *Dent. £3.60* BPV (B75-24233) ISBN 0-460-03150-3
Put the right man at the wheel : for four-part chorus of mixed voices with piano accompaniment. (Hays, Will Shakespeare). *Schirmer. Unpriced* DW (B75-50441)
Pyramide für Igor Strawinsky : für Kammerensemble. (Heider, Werner). *Litolff : Peters. Unpriced* MRJ (B75-50160)
Quantumplation : flute, clarinet in B flat, violin, cello, piano, tam tam. (Harvey, Jonathan). *Central Music Library : Novello. Unpriced* NYDPNQ (B75-50649)
Quantz, Johann Joachim.
Sonata for flute, oboe & basso continuo in C minor. Trio sonata in C minor for flute, oboe and basso continuo. *Musica rara. Unpriced* NWPNTE (B75-51192)
Sonata for oboe, cello & basso continuo in G major. Trio sonata in G major : for oboe (or flute, violin, descant or tenor recorder), violoncello or bassoon, and harpsichord (or piano), with a second violoncello or basson ad lib. *Schott. £2.00* NUTNTE (B75-50636)
Quartet no.1 for brass, Op.22. (Bavicchi, John). *Oxford University Press. Unpriced* WNS (B75-50938)
Quartet romantic : 2 flutes, violin, viola, and, Quartet euphometric : 2 violins, viola, violoncello. (Cowell, Henry). *Peters. Unpriced* NVRNS (B75-50643)
Quartus tomus musici operis. In nomine Jesu. In nomine Jesu : motet for five voices, SAATB, for the Feast of the Holy Name and general use. (Handl, Jacob). *Chester. Unpriced* EZDGKHL (B75-51032)
Quatre flûtes en balade : pour quatre flûtes. (Lancen, Serge). *Chappell. Unpriced* VRNS (B75-50314)
Quatre personnages de Calderon : pour guitare. (Margoni, Alain). *Chappell. Unpriced* TSPMJ (B75-51324)
Quatre Polonaises mélancoliques. Op.22. Four polonaises : for piano. (Mozart, Franz Xavier). 1st ed. reprinted. *Oxford University Press. £1.20* QPHVHM (B75-50678) ISBN 0-19-373410-9
Qui belles amours : ATTB. (Josquin des Prés). *Oxford University Press. Unpriced* EZDW (B75-51049) ISBN 0-19-341222-5
Quilp. *Selections : arr.* Quilp : a musical adaptation of Charles Dickens 'The old curiosity shop'. (Newley, Anthony). *Edwin H. Morris. Unpriced* KDW (B75-51107)
Quine, Hector.
Progressive reading for guitarists. (Dodgson, Stephen). *Ricordi. £3.00* TS/AF (B75-50795)
Suites de pièces. 1st collection. No.5. Aria con variazioni. *arr.* Aria con variazioni 'The harmonious blacksmith'. (Handel, George Frideric). *Oxford University Press. £0.65* TQPMK/AT (B75-50794) ISBN 0-19-356993-0
Rabbits : unison song. (Deacon, Helen). *Roberton. £0.10* JFDW (B75-51092)
Radcliffe, Philip. God be in my head : SSAATTBB (unacc.). *Oxford University Press. Unpriced* EZDH (B75-50460) ISBN 0-19-350354-9
Radeke, Winfried. Divertimento for flute, violin, strings &

continuo in D major. Hob IV/D2. Cassation, D-dur, für Flöte, Violine, Streicher und Basso continuo. (Haydn, Joseph). *Litolff : Peters. Unpriced* RXMPVRPLS (B75-50231)
Radetzky march. Op.228. (Strauss, Johann, *b.1805*). *Bosworth. Unpriced* MK/AGM (B75-50599)
Radetzky march. Op.228. *arr.* Radetzky march. Op.228. (Strauss, Johann, *b.1805*). *Bosworth. Unpriced* MK/AGM (B75-50599)
Rag 'n' bone : trombone solo and brass band. (Brand, Michael). *R. Smith. Unpriced* WMPWU (B75-51434)
Rags. (Joplin, Scott). *Oxford University Press. £1.75* VVNSK/AHXJ (B75-50894) ISBN 0-19-357320-2
Ragtime for guitar ensemble. *Chappell. Unpriced* TSNK/AHXJ/AY (B75-51318)
Raine, Kathleen. Spells. *Vocal score.* Spells : soprano solo, mixed chorus & orchestra. (Bennett, Richard Rodney). *Novello. £1.00* DX (B75-50448)
Rameau, Jean Philippe. A Rameau suite : keyboard pieces by Rameau. *Chappell. Unpriced* MK (B75-50128)
Rameau suite : keyboard pieces by Rameau. (Rameau, Jean Philippe). *Chappell. Unpriced* MK (B75-50128)
Randall, Alan. George Formby : a biography. *W.H. Allen. £2.50* AKDW/GB/E(P) (B75-01176) ISBN 0-491-01771-5
Rands, Bernard.
As all get out (after an idea by Bruno Maderna) : for instrumental ensemble. *Universal. Unpriced* MRJ (B75-50633)
Ballad 2 : music/theatre piece for voice and piano. *Universal. Unpriced* CB/J (B75-50986)
Déjà : for flute, clarinet, viola, cello, piano and percussion. *Universal. Unpriced* NYDPNQ (B75-50651)
Rapoport, Paul. Vagn Holmboe : a catalogue of his music, discography, bibliography, essays. *10E Prior Bolton St., N.1 : Triad Press. £2.50* BHO(N) (B75-04505) ISBN 0-902070-13-4
Ratcliffe, Desmond.
The providence of God : a sequence of readings, hymns and anthems to celebrate the harvest. *Novello. £0.60* DF/LP (B75-50409)
Requiem. Op.48. *Vocal score.* Requiem. Opus 48 : for soprano and baritone soli, SATB and orchestra. (Fauré, Gabriel). *Novello. £0.75* DGKAV (B75-50018)
Requiem. Opus 48. *Vocal score: arr.* Requiem. Opus 48. (Fauré, Gabriel). *Novello. £1.00* DGKAV (B75-51000)
Raven, Jon.
Jon Raven, nos 1-8. Contemporary life : eight folk-songs for voices and guitar. *Oxford University Press. £0.35* JE/TSDW/G/AY (B75-50091) ISBN 0-19-330627-1
Turpin hero, nos. 9-16. Flight, fight and romance : eight folk songs for voices and guitar. *Oxford University Press. £0.35* JE/TSDW/G/AY (B75-50094) ISBN 0-19-330628-x
Turpin hero, nos. 17-21. Good earth : five folk songs for voices and guitar. *Oxford University Press. £0.35* JE/TSDW/G/AY (B75-50095) ISBN 0-19-330629-8
Turpin hero, nos. 22-30. Bravado and travellers all : nine folk songs for voices and guitar. *Oxford University Press. £0.35* JE/TSDW/G/AY (B75-50096) ISBN 0-19-330630-1
Rawsthorne, Alan.
Elegy for guitar. *Oxford University Press. Unpriced* TSPMJ (B75-51325) ISBN 0-19-358510-3
Street corner overture. *arr.* Street corner overture. *Oxford University Press. Unpriced* UMMJ (B75-51345)
Raynor, Henry. Mahler. *Macmillan. £3.75* BME(N) (B75-14333) ISBN 0-333-18137-9
Razorback reel. (Davis, Allan). *Oxford University Press. Unpriced* UMMHVJ (B75-50302)
Read, Gardner. Nine by six : suite for wind instruments, flute (picc.), oboe (eng. horn), clarinet (bs. cl.), trumpet, horn, bassoon. *Peters. Unpriced* UNQG (B75-50309)
Reaks, Brian. As fit as a fiddle
Book 2: Six health education songs for younger children. *British and Continental. Unpriced* JFDW (B75-50098)
Receveur, Roland. Le Voyageur. L'Avenir. *arr.* L'Avenir : pour baryton. (Duclos, Pierre). *Chappell. Unpriced* KGNDW (B75-50592)
Recital for handbells : ten classical pieces. *Schirmer. Unpriced* XSQMK/AAY (B75-50972)
Recital hors-d'oevre. Opus 51 : for 2 trumpets, horn and trombone. (Dale, Gordon). *British and Continental : EMI. Unpriced* WNS (B75-51447)
Recorder playing in colour : for descant recorders
Book 1: Junior. (Davey, Brian). *Chappell. Unpriced* VSR/AF (B75-50870)
Reda, Siegfried. Sechs Intonationen und Cantus-firmus. Sechs Intonationen und Cantus-firmus-Stücke zu Adventsliedern des EKG (1959), with Anhang Anbetung des Kindes Jesus (1965) : für Orgel. *Bärenreiter. Unpriced* R/LEZ (B75-50729)
Reed, Will. Christ in competition. *Edwardian Music. Unpriced* JDM/AY (B75-51078) ISBN 0-551-05530-8
Rees, Terence. The zoo. *Vocal score.* The zoo : a musical folly. (Sullivan, *Sir* Arthur Seymour). *Cramer. Unpriced* CF (B75-50397)
Reeve, Peter. Danceries. Selections. *arr.* Three dances. (Gervaise, Claude). *Chester. Unpriced* WNSK/AH (B75-51450)
Reflection : for organ. (Watson, Walter). *Oxford University Press. Unpriced* RJ (B75-51275)
Reflections on Paris : symphonic band. (Tull, Fisher). *Boosey and Hawkes. £20.50* UMJ (B75-51336)
Regali Gallus, Eustachius de Monte. *See* Monte Regali Gallus, Eustachius de.
Regelski, Thomas A. Principles and problems of music education. *Prentice-Hall. £6.05* A(VF) (B75-20389) ISBN 0-13-709840-5
Regions. Op.6 : for orchestra. (Gilbert, Anthony). *Central Music Library : Schott. Unpriced* MMJ (B75-50614)
Regner, Hermann.
'Mit Musik'. 5 Gedichte von Ernst Jandl : für einen Sprecher und Instrumente, (2 Trompeten in C-oder Klarinetten, Flöten, Blockflöten-, Violoncello, Kontrabass, Schlagzeug und Klavier). *Schott. £3.50* HYE/NYDNQ (B75-51076)
Sechs leichte Schlagzeugtrios. *Schott. £2.00* XNT (B75-51478)
Reicha, Anton.
36 fugues for the piano. Op.36
Vol.1: Nos. 1-13. *Bärenreiter. £3.20* QP/Y (B75-50184)
Vol.2: Nos. 14-24. *Bärenreiter. £3.20* QP/Y (B75-50185)
Vol.3: Nos. 25-36. *Bärenreiter. £3.20* QP/Y (B75-50186)
Quintet for clarinet & strings. Op.107, in F major. Quintetto in fa maggiore. Op.107 : per clarinetto, due violini, viola e violoncello. *Zanibon : Hinrichsen. Unpriced* NVVNR (B75-50164)
Reimann, Aribert. Wolkenloses Christfest : Requiem für Bariton, Violoncello und Orchester. *Schott. £11.00* KGNE/MPSRDE (B75-51135)
Reiser, Ekkehard.
Spielheft Klassik : für drei Gitarren. *Schott. Unpriced* TSNTK/AAY (B75-50799)
Spielheft Klassik : für zwei Gitarren. *Schott. Unpriced* TSNUK/AAY (B75-50801)
Rejcha, Antonin. *See* Reicha, Anton.
Rejoice ye pure in heart : for mixed chorus and keyboard, based on a hymn by Arthur Messiter. (Wilson, Don). *Galaxy : Galliard. Unpriced* DH (B75-50023)
Relay : for 3 cornets, 3 trombones and brass band. (Golland, John). *British and Continental : EMI. Unpriced* WMPWNQ (B75-51431)
Renaissance and Baroque music : a comprehensive survey. (Blume, Friedrich). *Faber. £1.25* A(XCQ351) (B75-08734) ISBN 0-571-10719-2
Rennert, Jonathan. William Crotch, 1775-1847 : composer, artist, teacher. *Dalton. £3.20* BCT(N) (B75-20390) ISBN 0-900963-61-1
Report : for wind instruments, piano and percussion. (Fišer, Luboš). *Peters. Unpriced* NYF (B75-50173)
Resonant rubbish. (Brune, John A.). *2 Regent's Park Rd, NW1 7AY : English Folk Dance and Song Society. Unpriced* AL/BC (B75-08293) ISBN 0-85418-097-4
Retford centenary exhibition. *4 Station Parade, Uxbridge Rd, W5 3LD : Ealing Strings. £12.50* ARXT/BC(P/WJ) (B75-22849) ISBN 0-9504357-0-8
Rêverie : piano. (Debussy, Claude). *Peters. Unpriced* QPJ (B75-50695)
Reyne, Gerard. Sonata for lute in D major. *arr.* Sonata in D. (Kohaut, Karl). *Oxford University Press. Unpriced* TSPMK/AE (B75-50815) ISBN 0-19-357428-4
Rhapsodie : for guitar. (Dale, Mervyn). *Ashdown. £0.40* TSPMJ (B75-50807)
Rhapsody : for flute and organ. (Weaver, John). *Boosey and Hawkes. £2.25* VRPJ (B75-51371)
Rhode Island rag : brass band. (Siebert, Edrich). *Studio Music. Unpriced* WMK/AHXJ (B75-50364)
Rhodes, Phillip.
Autumn setting : soprano and string quartet. *Peters. Unpriced* KFLE/RXNSDX (B75-51126)
Duo : violin and violoncello. *Peters. Unpriced* SPLSR (B75-50254)
Ricci, Josiane Bran-. *See* Bran-Ricci, Josiane.
Rice, Tim. Joseph and the amazing technicolour dreamcoat. *Vocal score.* Joseph and the amazing technicolour dreamcoat. (Webber, Andrew Lloyd). Revised and enlarged ed. *Novello. £2.00* CM/L (B75-50399)
Rich, Ellis. Focus on classics. *EMI. Unpriced* RSPMK/AAY (B75-51283)
Richard Strauss. (Jefferson, Alan). *Macmillan. £3.75* BSU(N) (B75-15005) ISBN 0-333-14649-2
Richards, Goff. Bethena. *arr.* Bethena. (Joplin, Scott). *Chappell. Unpriced* WMK/AHXJ (B75-50372)
Richardson, Norman.
Bright eyes. *arr.* Bright eyes. (Finlayson, Walter Alan). *Boosey and Hawkes. £2.20* WMPWRNTK (B75-51433)
Concerto for bassoon in F major. *arr.* Bassoon concerto. (Hummel, Johann Nepomuk). *Boosey and Hawkes. £2.00* VWPK/LF (B75-50906)
The planets. Mars. *arr.* Mars. (Holst, Gustav). *Boosey and Hawkes. Unpriced* UMMK (B75-50833)
Richter, Clifford G. Sechs geistliche Lieder = Six sacred songs : for four-part chorus of mixed voices. (Wolf, Hugo). *Bärenreiter. £1.60* EZDH (B75-50053)
Riddell, Don. Have a blow (on descant recorder) : a graded tune book for beginners, 50 tunes arranged in order of difficulty. *British and Continental. Unpriced* VSRPMK/DW/AY (B75-50877)
Ridout, Alan.
Concertante for woodwind quartet. *Central Music Library : Chappell. Unpriced* VNSF (B75-50842)
Concerto for double bass & string orchestra. *arr.* Concerto for double bass and strings. *Yorke. Unpriced* SSPK/LF (B75-50778)
Dance suite : for organ. *Chappell. Unpriced* RHG (B75-51271)
Suite for oboe and piano. *Chappell. Unpriced* VTPG (B75-51391)
Rietz, Julius. Concert-Stück for oboe and orchestra. Op.33. *arr.* Concert piece : for oboe and orchestra. Op.33. *Musica rara. Unpriced* VTPK (B75-51394)
Rieu, E V. Creature conforts : a fantasy for voices and percussion. (Tomlinson, Geoffrey). *Boosey and Hawkes. 2.50* JFE/NYLDX (B75-50542)
Riley, Dennis.
Five songs on Japanese haiku : soprano, clarinet, in A, violin, violoncello. *Peters. Unpriced* KFLE/NVVQNTDW (B75-51125)
Variations 2 : trio, violin, viola, violoncello. *Peters. Unpriced* RXNT/T (B75-50240)
Variations 3 : viola alone. *Peters. Unpriced* SQPMJ (B75-50258)
Rilke, Rainer Maria. Drei Lieder. Op.16 : für Sopran und Klavier. (Spinner, Leopold). *Boosey and Hawkes. £1.50* KFLDW (B75-50571)
Rimsky-Korsakoff, Nikolai.
My musical life. *48 Great Marlborough St., W.1 : Ernst Eulenberg Ltd. £6.25* BRI(N) (B75-24236) ISBN 0-903873-13-3
Russian Easter overture. Op.36 : for orchestra. *Belaieff : Peters. Unpriced* MMJ (B75-50146)
Sinfonietta on Russian themes. Op.31. *Belaieff : Hinrichsen. Unpriced* MMEM (B75-50135)
Rimsky-Korsakov, Nikolai. *See* Rimsky-Korsakoff, Nikolai.
Rimsky-Korsakow, Nikolai. *See* Rimsky-Korsakoff, Nikolai.
Ringold, Daniel. Viva Napoli. *Vocal score.* Viva Napoli : operette à grand spectacle en 2 actes et 12 tableaux. (Lopez, Francis). *Chappell. Unpriced* CF (B75-50990)
Risatti, Howard. New music vocabulary : a guide to notational signs for contemporary music. *University of Illinois Press. £2.75* A(QU/XPL25) (B75-21069) ISBN 0-252-00406-x
Ritchie, Douglas. Fantasias for treble recorder duet. Three fantasias : for two treble (alto) recorders. (Gibbons, Orlando). *Faber Music. Unpriced* VSSNU (B75-50881)
Ritornelli and intermezzi : piano. (Saxton, Robert). *Chester. Unpriced* QPJ (B75-51252)
Rittmann, Trude. Gigi. *Vocal score.* Lerner and Loewe's Gigi. (Loewe, Frederick). *Chappell. Unpriced* CM (B75-50398)
Rivers, Patrick. The Novello band book. *Novello. £2.50* WM/AF (B75-50355)
Road of evening : song with piano accompaniment. (Noble, Harold). *Lengnick. £0.35* KDW (B75-50555)
Roberts, Don. Chordal solo technique for guitar. *EMI Music. Unpriced* TS/RC (B75-50797)
Robins, Vivien Mary. Music and language with young children. (Chacksfield, Kathleen Merle). *Blackwell. £4.50* A/GR(VG) (B75-22597) ISBN 0-631-15330-6
Roche, Jerome. The Penguin book of Italian madrigals for four voices. *Penguin Books. £1.00* EZDU/AYJ (B75-50063) ISBN 0-14-070843-x
Rocherolle, Eugenie R. How can it be? : for unison, SA or SAB chorus and piano. *Warner : Blossom. Unpriced* DP/LF (B75-51012)
Rock file
3. *Panther. £0.75* ADW/GB (B75-21065) ISBN 0-586-04261-x
Rock life. *Hamlyn. £1.95* AKDW/HK/E(M) (B75-03642) ISBN 0-600-38708-9
Rocking : for two voices, woodwind, keyboard and percussion. (Roe, Betty). *Thames. Unpriced* FE/NYFPNTDP/LF (B75-51057)
Rodgers, Richard.
50 super songs. *Williamson Music. Unpriced* RK/DW (B75-50738)
Musical plays. *Selections : arr.* Rodgers and Hammerstein guitar book. *Williamson Music. Unpriced* TSPMK/DW (B75-50819)
Musical plays. *Selections: arr.* Rogers and Hammerstein 'Showtime'
Vol.1. *Williamson. Unpriced* KDW (B75-50112)
Rogers and Hammerstein 'Showtime'
Vol.2. *Williamson. Unpriced* KDW (B75-50111)
Rogers and Hammerstein showtime
Vol.4. *Williamson Music. Unpriced* KDW (B75-50110)
Rodgers and Hammerstein guitar book. (Rodgers, Richard). *Williamson Music. Unpriced* TSPMK/DW (B75-50819)
Roe, Betty.
Like as the hart : soprano solo and mixed chorus. *Thames. Unpriced* DH (B75-51005)
Merry be man : a Christmas sequence. *Thames. Unpriced* FEZDE/LF (B75-50499)
Rocking : for two voices, woodwind, keyboard and percussion. *Thames. Unpriced* FE/NYFPNTDP/LF (B75-51057)
Sonatine for flute & piano. Sonatina flute/piano. *Thames. Unpriced* VRPEM (B75-51369)
Rogers, Eddie.
The alley cat song. *arr.* The alley cat song. (Bjorn, Frank). *Chappell. Unpriced* UMK/DW (B75-50824)
Porgy and Bess. Summertime. *arr.* Summertime music. (Gershwin, George). *Chappell. Unpriced* UMK/DW (B75-50825)
The third man. Harry Lime theme. *arr.* The third man. (Karas, Anton). *Chappell. Unpriced* UMK/JR (B75-50826)
Rogers, Elizabeth. Elizabeth Rogers hir virginall booke. *Dover : Constable. £3.00* QSQ/AY (B75-51265) ISBN 0-486-23138-0
Rogers and Hammerstein 'Showtime'
Vol.1. (Rodgers, Richard). *Williamson. Unpriced* KDW (B75-50112)
Vol.2. (Rodgers, Richard). *Williamson. Unpriced* KDW (B75-50111)
Rogers and Hammerstein showtime
Vol.4. (Rodgers, Richard). *Williamson Music. Unpriced* KDW (B75-50110)
Roi s'amuse. Passepied. *arr.* Passepied. (Delibes, Leo). *Oxford University Press. Unpriced* TSPMK/AHU (B75-50817) ISBN 0-19-356159-x
Rokos, Kurt W. Symphony no.1 in D major. 3rd movement. *arr.* 'Bruder Martin'. (Mahler, Gustav). *Bosworth. Unpriced* MJ (B75-50595)
Romano, Eustachio. Musica duorum, Rome, 1521. *Chicago University Press. Unpriced* C/AZ (B75-50983)

ISBN 0-226-22646-8

Romantic Orpheus : profiles of Clemens Brentano. (Fetzer, John F). *University of California Press. £6.85* A(ZD) (B75-07422) ISBN 0-520-02312-9

Romantik : elektronische Orgel. *Nagel : Bärenreiter. £2.00* RPVK/AAY (B75-50219)

Rooke, Pat.
The discontented man : musical play for voices, piano and percussion. (Arch, Gwyn). *British and Continental Music : EMI Music. Unpriced* CQN (B75-50011)
My friend Androcles : musical play for voices, piano and percussion. (Arch, Gwyn). *British and Continental Music : EMI Music. Unpriced* CQN (B75-50012)

Rorem, Ned.
14 songs on American poetry : voice and piano. *Peters. Unpriced* KDW (B75-50558)
Absalom. *Boosey and Hawkes. Unpriced* KDW (B75-51108)
Canticle of the Lamb : SATB unaccompanied. *Boosey and Hawkes. Unpriced* EZDH (B75-51036)
Jack L'Eventreur. *Boosey and Hawkes. Unpriced* KDW (B75-51109)
Love in a life. *Boosey and Hawkes. Unpriced* KDW (B75-51110)
To a young girl. *Boosey and Hawkes. Unpriced* KDW (B75-51111)

Rose, Bernard. Feast song for Saint Cecilia : for SATB with divisions (unaccompanied). *Novello. £0.20* EZDH (B75-51037)

Rose, Gregory.
The Camrose Lord's Prayer : SATB with optional accompaniment. *Boosey and Hawkes. £0.10* EZDTF (B75-50472)
Feast song for Saint Cecilia : for SATB with divisions (unaccompanied). (Rose, Bernard). *Novello. £0.20* EZDH (B75-51037)

Rose, Jon. Continuum : for two manual organ with three players. *United Music. Unpriced* RNVQ (B75-51279)

Rose, Michael. Five portraits : for piano. *British and Continental. Unpriced* QPJ (B75-51251)

Rose, Richard, *b.1902.* Perchance to dream : the world of Ivor Novello. *Frewin. £4.95* BNO(N) (B75-50005) ISBN 0-85632-120-6

Roseingrave, Thomas. Sonatas for flute & continuo, nos 4,7. Two sonatas for flute and basso continuo. *Oxford University Press. £2.00* VRPE (B75-50319) ISBN 0-19-358642-8

Rosen, Charles. Selections. *arr.* Bach. The fugue. (Bach, Johann Sebastian). *Oxford University Press. Unpriced* QPK (B75-51255) ISBN 0-19-372220-8

Rosenthal, Carl A. O how amiable. *arr.* O how amiable : anthem for mixed chorus (SATB) and band or organ. (Vaughan Williams, Ralph). *Oxford University Press. Unpriced* EUMDK (B75-51028)

Ross, Walter.
Concerto for tuba & military band. Tuba concerto : tuba solo and symphonic band. *Boosey and Hawkes. £20.00* UMMPWVF (B75-50837)
Concerto for tuba. *arr.* Tuba concerto. *Boosey and Hawkes. Unpriced* WVPK/LF (B75-50962)

Rossetti, Christina. O sweet Jesu : SATB. (Binkerd, Gordon). *Boosey and Hawkes. Unpriced* EZDH (B75-50048)

Rossi, Salomone. Hashirim asher li Sh'lomo, no.32. Psalm 92. *arr.* Psalm 92. *Schirmer. Unpriced* WMK/DR (B75-50925)

Rossignols spirituels. *Selections.* Eleven Christmas carols. (Philips, Peter). *Oxford University Press. Unpriced* EZDP/LF (B75-51043) ISBN 0-19-353346-4

Rostal, Max. Rondo for violin & orchestra in C major. K.373. *arr.* Rondo für Solo-Violine, Streicher, zwei Oboen und zwei Hörner. K.V.373. (Mozart, Wolfgang Amadeus). *Schott. £1.75* SPK/LW (B75-51299)

Rota, Nina. The godfather, part 2. Theme. *arr.* Theme from Godfather 2 : piano solo. *Famous Music : Chappell. Unpriced* QPK/JR (B75-50197)

Rota, Nino.
The godfather, part 2. Kay's theme. *arr.* Kay's theme : piano solo. *Famous Music : Chappell. Unpriced* QPK/JR (B75-50198)
The godfather, part 2. Love said goodbye. *arr.* Love said goodbye. *Famous Music : Chappell. Unpriced* GDW (B75-50082)
The godfather, part 2. Love said goodbye. *arr.* Love said goodbye : music by Nino Rota. *Famous Music Chappell. Unpriced* FDW (B75-50072)
The godfather, part 2. *Selections: arr.* The godfather, part 2. *Charles Hansen : Chappell. Unpriced* KDW (B75-50113)
The godfather, part II. Theme. *arr.* Theme from Godfather II. *Famous Music : Chappell. Unpriced* UMMK/JR (B75-50836)

Rothwell, Evelyn. The oboist's companion
Volume 1. *Oxford University Press. £3.25* VT/AC (B75-51390) ISBN 0-19-322335-x

Round the mulberry bush : a fugal trio for three bassoons. (Hartley, Geoffrey). *Emerson. Unpriced* VWNT/Y (B75-51412)

Routh, Francis. Stravinsky. *Dent. £4.50* BSV (B75-24847) ISBN 0-460-03138-4

Routley, Erik.
Behold your King : a devotion for choir and congregation devised by Erik Routley. *Royal School of Church Music. Unpriced* DP/LF/AY (B75-51015) ISBN 0-85402-059-4
Martin Shaw : a centenary appreciation. *77 Archway St., SW13 0AN : E.M. Campbell. £0.45* BSGP(N) (B75-21068) ISBN 0-9504306-0-9
New church praise. *Saint Andrew Press. Unpriced* DM/LSG/AY (B75-50428) ISBN 0-7152-0311-8

Rowe, Mike. Chicago breakdown. *2 Greycoat Place, S.W.1 : Eddison Press Ltd. £2.50* AKDW/HHW(YTKC/XNK43) (B75-03645) ISBN 0-85649-015-6

Rowntree, John Pickering. The classical organ in Britain, 1955-1974. *130 Southfield Rd, Oxford OX4 1PA : Positif Press. £2.95* AR/B(YC/XPQ20) (B75-13170) ISBN 0-9503892-1-8

Roxburgh, Edwin. Labyrinth : for piano. *United Music. Unpriced* QPJ (B75-50708)

Royal College of Organists. Year book
1974-1975. *Kensington Gore, SW7 2QS : The College. £0.75* AR(YC/VP/Q) (B75-05797) ISBN 0-902462-05-9

Royal Irish Rangers (27th Inniskilling), 83rd and 87th : standard settings of pipe music. (Great Britain. *Army. Royal Irish Rangers*). *Paterson. Unpriced* VYT/KH/AYDT (B75-51415)

Royal pageant. Op.11 : for recorder quartet, (2 descant treble tenor). (Touchin, Colin M). *Carne House, Parsons Lane, Bury, Lancs. : Tomus. Unpriced* VSNS (B75-50861)

Royal School of Church Music.
English church music : a collection of essays
1975. *Addington Palace, Croydon CR9 5AD : Royal School of Church Music. £1.00* AD/LD(YD/D) (B75-21074) ISBN 0-85402-060-8
Five anthems for today : SATB. *Royal School of Church Music. Unpriced* DH/AY (B75-50024)

Rubbra, Edmund.
Fly, envious time. Op.148 : song with piano accompaniment. *Lengnick. £0.35* KDW (B75-51112)
Gustav Holst. *10E Prior Bolton St., N.1 : Triad Press. £2.40* **BHP(D) (B75-00200)** ISBN 0-902070-12-6

Runaway girl. Soldiers in the park. *arr.* Oh! listen to the band. (Monckton, Lionel). *Studio Music. Unpriced* WMK/DW (B75-50927)

Russell, Armand. Facets : in four movements, for percussion solo, two timbales, tom-toms (or bongos), snare drum, two suspended cymbals, triangle, five temple blocks. *Schirmer. £1.30* XMG (B75-51475)

Russian Easter overture. Op.36 : for orchestra. (Rimsky-Korsakoff, Nikolai). *Belaieff : Peters. Unpriced* MMJ (B75-50146)

Rutherford, Robert. Six monologues for boys. (Wilcock, Frank). *Brown, Son and Ferguson. Unpriced* HYE/QP (B75-50520)

Rutter, John.
Donkey carol : two-part. *Oxford University Press. £0.20* FDP/LF (B75-50486) ISBN 0-19-341511-9
Down by the riverside : American traditional song. *Oxford University Press. Unpriced* DW/LC (B75-51023) ISBN 0-19-343049-5
Thy perfect love : SATB. *Oxford University Press. £0.10* DH (B75-50420) ISBN 0-19-351122-3
When icicles hang. *Vocal score.* When icicles hang : a cycle of choral settings (SATB) with small orchestra. *Oxford University Press. £1.50* DW (B75-50444) ISBN 0-19-338073-0

Rutterkin : an overture for recorders, (descant, 2 trebles, 2 tenors, 2 basses), after a song by Peter Warlock, (from 1st set of Peterisms). (Hold, Trevor). *Tomus. Unpriced* VSNP (B75-51376)

Ryba, Jakub Jan. Czech Christmas mass. *Vocal score.* Ceska mse vanocni = Böhmische Hirtenmesse = Czech Christmas Mass. *Supraphon : Achauer. £5.60* DE/LF (B75-50999)

Sadie, Stanley. Sonata for piano, no.16, in B flat major. K.570. Sonata in B flat. K.570. (Mozart, Wolfgang Amadeus). *Associated Board of the Royal Schools of Music. Unpriced* QPE (B75-51225)

Sadleir, Dick. Waltzes. *Selections: arr.* Waltz themes from Strauss. (Strauss, Johann, *b.1825*). *British and Continental. Unpriced* NVPK/AHW (B75-51182)

St Matthew passion S.244. Matthaus-Passion = St Matthew Passion. (Bach, Johann Sebastian). *Bärenreiter. £4.40* EMDD/LK (B75-50034)

Salas, Juan Orrego-. *See* Orrego-Salas, Juan.

Salt Lake City samba : brass band. (Siebert, Edrich). *Studio Music. Unpriced* WMHVKS (B75-50363)

Salter, Lionel. Eighteenth-century violin sonatas
Book 1. *Associated Board of the Royal Schools of Music. Unpriced* SPE/AY (B75-51294)

Salvation Army Brass Band Journal (Festival series)
Nos 357-360: The suppliant heart: meditation / by Brian Bowen. The warrior psalm: tone poem / by Ray Steadman-Allen. The swan: euphonium or trombone solo / by C. Saint-Saens; arr. Ray Steadman-Allen. Just like John: festival arrangement / by Norman Bearcroft. *Salvationist Publishing and Supplies. Unpriced* WM/AY (B75-50356)
Nos. 365-368: New frontier : selection / by William Himes. The high council : festival march / by Ray Steadman-Allen. The children's song : festival arrangement / by Robert Schramm. The great physician : song arrangement / by Dudley J. Bright. *Salvationist Publishing and Supplies. Unpriced* WM/AY (B75-50907)
Nos.361-364: I saw three ships : Christmas fantasy / by Brian Bowen. Selection from 'Jesus Folk' / by Ray Steadman-Allen ; songs John Larsson Ellers ; prelude by Robert Getz. Life's pageant : cornet solo / by Terry Camsey. *Salvationist Publishing and Supplies. Unpriced* WM/AY (B75-50908)

Salvation Army Brass Band Journal (General series)
Nos 1657-1660: Wigan citadel: march / by Charles Dove. A singing heart: selection / by Erik Silfverberg. In tune with thy divinity (Londonderry air) / arr. Robert Redhead. Nearer to thee: selection / by Ken James. *Salvationist Publishing and Supplies. Unpriced* WM/AY (B75-50357)
Nos 1661-1664: Long Point : march / by Norman Bearcroft. A Child's praises : selection / by Christopher Cole. The source of peace : transcription / by Ray Steadman-Allen. Wonder, wonderful Jesus : song arrangement / by Dean Goffin, with, Ask and it shall be given you : transcription / by Dean Goffin. *Salvationist Publishing & Supplies. Unpriced* WM/AY (B75-50909)
Nos.1665-1668: Harvest praise : selection / by Ray Steadman-Allen. We want the world to know : song transcription / by Philip Catelinet. The pure in heart : meditation / by R.E. Dorow. God's love : march / by Eiliv Herikstad. *Salvationist Publishing and Supplies. Unpriced* WM/AY (B75-50910)

Salvation Army Brass Band Journal (Triumph series)
Nos 765-768: St Gallen: march / by Paul Martin. Movements from 'Album for the young' / by Tchaikovsky; arr. Michael Kenyon. Hallelujah! Christ arose: song arrangement / by Ray Steadman-Allen. O sinner man: euphonium solo / by Robin Redhead. *Salvationist Publishing and Supplies. Unpriced* WM/AY (B75-50358)
Nos 777-780: Keep up the flag : march / by Philip Catelinet. Sailors' songs : selection / by Erik Silfverberg. Joy and gladness : trombone solo / by Ray Steadman-Allen. Congregational tunes / arr. Ray Steadman-Allen. *Salvationist Publishing and Supplies. Unpriced* WM/AY (B75-50911)
Nos. 781-784: Fighting onward : march / by Eiliv Herikstad. Mountain camp : march / by Donald Osgood. Beneath the Cross of Jesus : song arrangement / by Ira D. Sankey ; arr. Philip Catelinet. The happy warriors : cornet duet / by Erik Silfrerberg. *Salvationist Publishing and Supplies. Unpriced* WM/AY (B75-50912)
Nos.785-788: If Jesus keeps me polished : humouresque / by Terry Camsey. This I know : selection / by Ray F. Cresswell. Evening prayer (In the gloaming) : song arrangement / arr. Howard Davies. Harwich : march / by Charles Dove. *Salvationist Publishing and Supplies. Unpriced* WM/AY (B75-51416)

Salvator mundi : SATB. (Ashfield, Robert). *Banks. Unpriced* DGMS (B75-50412)

Salvum me fac : Bariton und Klavier. (Killmayer, Wilhelm). *Schott. Unpriced* KGNDR (B75-51131)

Sansom, Clive A.
The donkey : the Christmas story portrayed by the animals. *Studio Music. Unpriced* FDE/LF (B75-50068)
He's got the whole world. *Studio Music. Unpriced* GDW (B75-50509)
Tick-tock song : for SATB (or SA, SSA, TTB) with instrumental accompaniment. *Paterson. Unpriced* ENYLDW (B75-50036)

Santa Lucia : Neapolitan air, for brass quartet. (Siebert, Edrich). *British and Continental. Unpriced* WNSK/DW (B75-50942)

Sarett, Lew.
Four little foxes : for unaccompanied mixed chorus. (Furman, James). *Oxford University Press. Unpriced* EZDW (B75-50065)
Four little foxes : for unaccompanied mixed chorus. (Furman, James). *Oxford University Press. Unpriced* EZDW (B75-50480)

Saris : violin and piano. (Hovhaness, Alan). *Peters. Unpriced* SPJ (B75-50250)

Sarlin, Bob. Turn it up! (I can't hear the words). *Coronet. £0.50* ADW/GB(XQ14) (B75-07793) ISBN 0-340-17848-5

Sarti, Giuseppe. Sonata for violin & piano, op.3, no.3, in B flat major. Sonata in B flat major : for violin and piano. Op.3, no.3. *Nagel : Bärenreiter. Unpriced* SPE (B75-50765)

Satori : solo guitar. (Freedman, Hermann L). *Thames. Unpriced* TSPMJ (B75-50810)

Saturn V : wind band. (Washburn, Robert). *Boosey and Hawkes. £12.00* UMJ (B75-51337)

Saxton, Robert. Ritornelli and intermezzi : piano. *Chester. Unpriced* QPJ (B75-51252)

Scarlatti, Alessandro. Correa nel seno amato : cantata for soprano, two violins and basso continuo. First edition. *Bärenreiter. £6.00* KFLE/SNTPWDX (B75-50119)

Scarlatti, Domenico. Selve caverne e monti : cantata for soprano and basso continuo. 1st ed. *Bärenreiter. £1.80* KFLDX (B75-50117)

Scenes : for cello. (Blake, David). *Novello. £1.00* SRPMJ (B75-50266)

Schacht, Theodor von. Fuga sopra 'l do re mi fa sol la' : für Streichquartett oder Streichorchester. *Bosse : Bärenreiter. Unpriced* RXNS/Y (B75-50763)

Schade, Wernerfritz. Zweistimmige Orgelchorale : gemeinsame Lieder der deutschsprachigen Kirchen. *Schott. £4.50* RJ (B75-51274)

Schaum, John W.
Scott Joplin ragtime rags
Book 1. (Joplin, Scott). *Bosworth. Unpriced* QPHXJ (B75-50683)
Book 2. (Joplin, Scott). *Bosworth. Unpriced* QPHXJ (B75-50684)

Scheidt, Samuel. Paduana, galliarda, etc. quaternis et quinis vocibus cum basso continuo. Selections. *arr.* Battle suite. *Chester. Unpriced* WNRK (B75-51446)

Schein, Johann Hermann. Opella nova. Tl. 1,2. *Selections.* Sechs Choral konzerte : für zwei gleiche Stimmen und Basso continuo. *Bärenreiter. £2.00* JNEDH (B75-50102)

Schenker, Heinrich. Harmony. *M.I.T. Press. £2.00* A/R (B75-02996) ISBN 0-262-69044-6

Schifrin, Lalo. Variants on a madrigal by Gesualdo : for large chamber ensemble. *Associated Music. £3.25* MR/T (B75-50626)
Schilling, Reinhard Schwarz-. *See* Schwarz-Schilling, Reinhard.
Schingerlin, Rudolf. Fünf Studien für Schlagzeugtrio. *Schott. £2.00* XNT (B75-51479)
Schirmer scores : a repertory of Western music. (Godwin, Joscelyn). *Schirmer Books : Collier Macmillan. £6.50* A(X) (B75-28635) ISBN 0-02-870700-1
Schmelzer, Johann Heinrich. Sonata à 5 for two violins, trumpet, bassoon, viola da gamba and basso continuo. *Musica rara. Unpriced* NUNQE (B75-51172)
Schmidt, Gustavo Becerra-. *See* Becerra-Schmidt, Gustavo.
Schmierer, Johann Abraham. Zodiaci musici. Part 1. Nos 1, 2. Suites for four parts (strings or wind instruments and basso continuo). *Bärenreiter. £4.80* NXNRG (B75-50168)
Schnebel, Dieter.
Für Stimmen (... missa est) dt 31, 6 : Fassung für grossen Chor. *Schott. Unpriced* EZDX (B75-51051)
Schulmusik : Übungen mit Klangen, für 6 oder mehr Spieler (Langtoninstrumente und Stimmen ad lib.). *Schott. £2.50* LN/AF (B75-51139)
Schneider, Martin Gotthard. Der Weg der Barmherzigkeit. There's a road (which leads from Jerusalem) : hymn. *Bosworth. Unpriced* JDM (B75-50524)
Schneider, Max. St Matthew passion S.244. Matthaus-Passion = St Matthew Passion. (Bach, Johann Sebastian). *Bärenreiter. £4.40* EMDD/LK (B75-50034)
Schneider, Patricia V. Autumn setting : soprano and string quartet. (Rhodes, Phillip). *Peters. Unpriced* KFLE/RXNSDX (B75-51126)
Schoenberg, Arnold. Style and idea : selected writings of Arnold Schoenberg. *Faber. £17.50* A(D) (B75-11219) ISBN 0-571-09722-7
Schola cantans : graves auctores latini, leviter decantandi, cantus ad claves. (Novak, Jan). *Zanibon : Hinrichsen. Unpriced* KDW (B75-50109)
Schola cantans. *Vocal score.* Schola cantans : graves auctores latini, leviter decantandi, cantus ad claves. (Novak, Jan). *Zanibon : Hinrichsen. Unpriced* KDW (B75-50109)
School of English Church Music. *See* Royal School of Church Music.
School recorder book
Book 3: Advanced recorder technique. Revised ed. *Arnold. Unpriced* VS/AC (B75-50329) ISBN 0-560-00271-8
Schroeder, Felix. Concerto for two horns & string orchestra in F major. P.320. *arr.* Concerto, F major, for two horns solo, strings, bassoon ad lib. and basso continuo. (Vivaldi, Antonio). *Heinrichshofen : Hinrichsen. Unpriced* NUXTNSK/LF (B75-50638)
Schubert, Franz.
Piano music. *Selections.* Schubert. *Oxford University Press. £1.90* QPJ (B75-51253) ISBN 0-19-373653-5
Sonata for piano, no.5, op.147, in B major. Scherzo. *arr.* Scherzo and trio. *Emerson. Unpriced* VNPK (B75-51360)
Unaccompanied part-songs for men's voices. *Bärenreiter. £1.70* GEZDW (B75-50084)
Schubert song cycles . with thoughts on performance. (Moore, Gerald, *b.1899*). *Hamilton. £6.95* BSFADW (B75-07794) ISBN 0-241-89082-9
Schuhmacher, Gerhard. Traditionen und Reforman in der Kirchenmusik : Festschrift für Konrad Ameln zum 75. Geburstag am 6, Juli 1974. *32 Great Titchfield St., W.1 : Bärenreiter-Verlag. £13.80* AD/LD(YE/X)
Schule bläserische Gestaltung : eine Bläserschule, für Fortgeschrittene auch zum Selbst und Gruppenuntervicht. (Ehmann, Wilhelm). *Bärenreiter. £3.60* W/AC (B75-50354)
Schulmusik : Übungen mit Klangen, für 6 oder mehr Spieler (Langtoninstrumente und Stimmen ad lib.). (Schnebel, Dieter). *Schott. £2.50* LN/AF (B75-51139)
Schumann, Gerhard. Audiogramme : für vier Klarinetten. *Heinrichshofen : Hinrichsen. Unpriced* VVNS (B75-50891)
Schumann, Robert. Schumann. *Warren and Phillips. Unpriced* QPK (B75-50196)
Schumann. (Schumann, Robert). *Warren and Phillips. Unpriced* QPK (B75-50196)
Schurmann, Gerard. Contrasts : for piano. *Novello. Unpriced* QPJ (B75-50709)
Schurmann, Gerhard. Concerto for piano. Piano concerto. *Novello. £4.75* MPQF (B75-50621)
Schütz, Heinrich. Jesu dulcissime : motet for six voices. First edition. *Bärenreiter. £1.40* EZDJ (B75-50054)
Schwantner, Joseph. Consortium (I) : flute, B flat clarinet, violin, viola, violoncello. *Peters. Unpriced* NVPNR (B75-50641)
Schwartz, Gunter. Zehn Essays : für Gitarre solo. (Wanek, Friedrich). *Schott. £1.75* TSPMJ (B75-51326)
Schwarz-Schilling, Reinhard.
Exaudi Domine vocem meam : vier Psalm-Motetten, für gemischten Chor. *Bärenreiter. £1.20* EZDJ (B75-50055)
Der Herr, der ewige Gott und Vater unser : für gemischten Chor. *Bärenreiter. £1.20* EZDH (B75-50051)

Schweizer, Rolf.
Lobet den Namen des Herrn : vierstimmiger gemischter Chor und Orgel. *Bärenreiter. £0.20* DH (B75-50022)
Die Seligpreisungen : dreistimmiger gemischter Chor und Gemeinde (mit Tasteninstrument ad libitum). *Bärenreiter. £0.20* EZDH (B75-50052)
Spirituals : elektronische Orgel. *Nagel : Bärenreiter. £2.00* RPVK/DW/LC/AY (B75-50221)
Zehn Psalmspruche : für drei und vierstimmigen gemischten Chor und Orgel. *Bärenreiter. £2.00* DR (B75-50027)

Scott, David. Sing joyfully : SSATB and strings (or organ) with verses for bass solo. (Mundy, John). Revised ed. *Oxford University Press. £0.40* ERXNRDK (B75-50453) ISBN 0-19-352184-9
Scott Joplin and the ragtime era. (Gammond, Peter). *Angus and Robertson. £3.00* BJRP (B75-18371) ISBN 0-207-95648-0
Scott Joplin, king of ragtime : easy organ. (Joplin, Scott). *Lewis : Phoenix. Unpriced* RK/AHXJ (B75-51278)
Scott Joplin ragtime rags
Book 1. (Joplin, Scott). *Bosworth. Unpriced* QPHXJ (B75-50683)
Book 2. (Joplin, Scott). *Bosworth. Unpriced* QPHXJ (B75-50684)
Scott Joplin : the king of ragtime writers. (Joplin, Scott). *Lewis Music : Phoenix. Unpriced* RK/AHXJ/AY (B75-50216)
Scottish carol : for 3-part treble voices with optional solo. (Liddell, Claire). *Roberton. £0.10* FLDP/LF (B75-51067)
Scottish Text Society. Publications : 4th series. Andrew Crawfurd's collection of ballads and songs
Vol.1. *27 George Sq., Edinburgh EH8 9LD : The Scottish Text Society. Unpriced* **ADW/G(YDL) (B75-29319)** ISBN 0-9500245-4-6
Scriabin, Alexander. *See* Skriabin, Aleksandr Nikolaevich.
Scriven, R C. Songs for Naomi : unison voices, glockenspiel and/or chime bars, xylophone, descant recorder, triangle, tambourine, wood blocks, piano (one stave). (Burnett, Michael). *Ricordi. Unpriced* JFE/NYFSRDW (B75-50099)
Sea lullaby : unison or soprano solo. (Fraser, Shena). *Thames. Unpriced* JDW (B75-50527)
Seamarks, Colin. Six Mehitabel magpies : for soprano and double bass. *Yorke. Unpriced* KFLE/SSPMDW (B75-50120)
Seasonal sentences suitable for the Series 3 communion service or as independent anthems. (Kelly, Bryan). *Oxford University Press. £0.90* DGSKAD (B75-50416) ISBN 0-19-395242-4
Seaton, Ray, *b.1931.* George Formby : a biography. (Randall, Alan). *W.H. Allen. £2.50* AKDW/GB/E(P) (B75-01176) ISBN 0-491-01771-5
Seay, Albert. Music in the medieval world. 2nd ed. *Prentice-Hall. £5.50* A(XA1420) (B75-24232) ISBN 0-13-608133-9
Sechs Choral konzerte : für zwei gleiche Stimmen und Basso continuo. (Schein, Johann Hermann). *Bärenreiter. £2.00* JNEDH (B75-50102)
Sechs geistliche Lieder = Six sacred songs : for four-part chorus of mixed voices. (Wolf, Hugo). *Bärenreiter. £1.60* EZDH (B75-50053)
Sechs Intonationen und Cantus-firmus. Sechs Intonationen und Cantus-firmus-Stücke zu Adventsliedern des EKG (1959), with Anhang Anbetung des Kindes Jesus (1965) : für Orgel. (Reda, Siegfried). *Bärenreiter. Unpriced* R/LEZ (B75-50729)
Sechs Intonationen und Cantus-firmus-Stücke zu Adventsliedern des EKG (1959), with Anhang Anbetung des Kindes Jesus (1965) : für Orgel. (Reda, Siegfried). *Bärenreiter. Unpriced* R/LEZ (B75-50729)
Sechs leichte Schlagzeugtrios. (Regner, Hermann). *Schott. £2.00* XNT (B75-51478)
Second book of solos for the classical guitar. *Scratchwood Music. Unpriced* TSPMK/AAY (B75-50813)
Second easy album for organ : six pieces. *Oxford University Press. £0.90* R/AYC (B75-50728) ISBN 0-19-375129-1
Secret garden : an album for young pianists based on his music for the recording of Francis Hodgson Burnett's novel. (Clayton, Kenny). *United Music. Unpriced* QP/JM (B75-51223)
Selby, Philip. Suite for solo guitar. *Anthony Music. £0.60* TSPMG (B75-51323)
Selen, Ebbe. Mein Gott und Herr : concerto for two sopranos and bass, (chorus or soloists), two violins and basso continuo. (Capricornus, Samuel). *Bärenreiter. £2.40* ESNTPWDH (B75-50039)
Selfish giant. *Vocal score.* The selfish giant : an opera for young people. (Shaw, Francis). *Chester : Hansen. Unpriced* CN (B75-50009)
Seligpreisungen : dreistimmiger gemischter Chor und Gemeinde (mit Tasteninstrument ad libitum). (Schweizer, Rolf). *Bärenreiter. £0.20* EZDH (B75-50052)
Selve caverne e monti : cantata for soprano and basso continuo. (Scarlatti, Domenico). 1st ed. *Bärenreiter. £1.80* KFLDX (B75-50117)
Senaillié, Jean Baptiste. Premier livre de sonates a violon seul. Sonata for violin, no.5, in C minor. *arr.* Sonata 5 : treble recorder and keyboard in G minor. *Universal. Unpriced* VSSPK/AE (B75-50337)
Serial composition and atonality : an introduction to the music of Schoenberg, Berg and Webern. (Perle, George). 2nd ed. revised and enlarged. *Faber. £2.60* A/PN (B75-13735) ISBN 0-571-10700-1
Set of five : piano duets. (Lambert, Cecily). *Forsyth. Unpriced* QNVG (B75-50181)
Set of five piano duets. (Lambert, Cecily). *Forsyth. Unpriced* QNV (B75-51214)
Seton, *Sir* Bruce Gordon, *bart.* The pipes of war : a record of the achievements of pipers of Scottish and overseas regiments in the war, 1914-1918. 1st ed. reprinted. *EP Publishing etc.. £5.00* AVY (B75-15172) ISBN 0-7158-1089-8
Seven recital pieces : for piano. (Kasschau, Howard). *Schirmer. Unpriced* QPJ (B75-51246)
Seven space songs : music for voices, melodic instruments, percussion and piano. (Coombes, Douglas). *28 Knolls Way, Clifton, Beds. : Lindsay Music. £0.58* JFE/NYLDW (B75-50541)
Seven studies for oboe. Sieben Studien : Capriccios für Oboe. (Genzmer, Harald). *Litolff : Peters. Unpriced* VTPMJ (B75-50343)
Seymour, Peter. Beatus vir, Psalm 112 : SATB. (Carissimi, Giacomo). *Oxford University Press. Unpriced* DR (B75-50433) ISBN 0-19-350351-4
Seymour, William Kean. The magi : carol for SATB, piano and double bass (optional). (Hill, Anthony Herschel). *Thames. Unpriced* DP/LFP (B75-50431)
Shadwell, Thomas. The works of Henry Purcell
Vol.2: Timon of Athens originally edited by Frederick Arthur Gore Ouseley ; revised by Jack Westrup ; words by Thomas Shadwell. (Purcell, Henry). 2nd ed. *Novello. £3.00* C/AZ (B75-50007)
Shakespeare, William. Three choral songs from 'As you like it' : SATB. (Horovitz, Joseph). *Novello. £0.50* EZDW (B75-51047)
Sharp, Cecil.
The crystal spring : English folk songs
Book 1. *Oxford University Press. Unpriced* JE/TSDW/G/AYD (B75-51088) ISBN 0-19-330516-x
Book 2. *Oxford University Press. Unpriced* JE/TSDW/G/AYD (B75-51089) ISBN 0-19-330517-8
Sharp, Geoffrey Brinsley. Byrd ; &, Victoria. *Novello. £0.20* BBX(N) (B75-03643) ISBN 0-85360-060-0
Shaw, Francis. The selfish giant. *Vocal score.* The selfish giant : an opera for young people. *Chester : Hansen. Unpriced* CN (B75-50009)
Shaw, Martin.
Anglican folk mass. An Anglican folk mass : unison. *Roberton. £0.30* JDGS (B75-51077)
National anthems of the world. 4th and revised ed. *Blandford Press. £5.80* JDW/KM/AY (B75-50529) ISBN 0-7137-0679-1
Shaw, Pat. Sociable songs
Book 3, part 1 : for unison or part-singing with optional instrumental parts. *Oxford University Press. Unpriced* JDW/AY (B75-51085) ISBN 0-19-330590-9
Shaw, Watkins.
Cathedral music. Morning and Evening Service in D major. Magnificat and Nunc dimittis : for SATB and organ. (Walmisley, Thomas Attwood). *Oxford University Press. £0.50* DGPP (B75-50414) ISBN 0-19-395316-1
Two short Elizabethan anthems : for SATB unaccompanied or with organ. *Novello. Unpriced* EZDK (B75-50465)
Shealy, Alexander. World's favorite pure and simple pieces for flute solos, duets and trios : includes basic charts and playing principles with chords for accompaniment by piano, guitar, etc. *Ashley : Phoenix. Unpriced* VRPK/AAY (B75-50853)
Shenandoah : American folk song, for full chorus of mixed voices unaccompanied. (Erb, James). *Roberton. £0.12* EZDW (B75-50478)
Shield, William. The farmer. The ploughboy. *arr.* The ploughboy : traditional, solo for E flat or B flat bass and brass band. *455 Brighton Rd, South Croydon : Paul. Unpriced* WMPWUU (B75-50936)
Shield of faith : cantata for soprano and baritone soli, SATB and organ. (Bliss, *Sir* Arthur). *Novello. £1.00* DE (B75-50407)
Shifrin, Seymour. Duo : violin and piano. *Peters. Unpriced* SPJ (B75-50252)
Short, Michael.
Gustav Holst (1874-1934) : a centenary documentation. *White Lion Publishers. £15.00* BHP(T) (B75-07086) ISBN 0-7285-0000-0
Song's eternity : part-song for unaccompanied female voices (SSA). *Roberton. £0.14* FEZDW (B75-50503)
Short chorale preludes with and without pedals
Book 1. *Oxford University Press. £0.95* R/AY (B75-50726) ISBN 0-19-375843-1
Book 2. *Oxford University Press. £0.95* R/AY (B75-50727) ISBN 0-19-375844-x
Short history of Spanish music. (Livermore, Ann). *Duckworth. £2.95* A(YK/X) (B75-21071) ISBN 0-7156-0886-x
Shout the glad tidings. Op.12 : for mixed choir and organ, with optional instruments. (Thomas, Paul Lindsley). *Oxford University Press. Unpriced* DH (B75-51006)
Shouts, hymns and praises. Op.52 : for wind band with vocal part for the audience. (Mailman, Martin). *Boosey and Hawkes. Unpriced* JE/UMDX (B75-51090)
Show songs from 'The black crook' to 'The red mill' : original sheet music for 60 songs from 50 shows, 1866-1906. *Dover : Constable. £4.20* KDW/GB/AYT(XKF41) (B75-51117)
Showstoppers : the great songs of Lerner and Loewe. (Loewe, Frederick). *Chappell. Unpriced* RK/DW (B75-50737)
Shrewsbury fair : quick march, for military band. (Neville, Paul). *Boosey and Hawkes. £1.00* UMMGM (B75-51342)
Sieben Studien : Capriccios für Oboe. (Genzmer, Harald). *Litolff : Peters. Unpriced* VTPMJ (B75-50343)
Siebert, Edrich.
Blow the wind southerly. *Studio Music. Unpriced* WMK/DW (B75-51430)
Boston bounce : brass band. *Studio Music. Unpriced* WMJ (B75-50367)
Chatanooga cha-cha : brass band. *Studio Music. Unpriced* WMHJMR (B75-50360)
Connecticut capers : brass band. *Studio Music. Unpriced* WMJ (B75-50368)
El Paso : paso doble brass band. *Studio Music. Unpriced* WMHSW (B75-50362)

The farmer. The ploughboy. *arr.* The ploughboy : traditional, solo for E flat or B flat bass and brass band. (Shield, William). *455 Brighton Rd, South Croydon : Paul. Unpriced* WMPWUU (B75-50936)
Grand Canyon galop : brass band by Edrich Siebert. *Studio Music. Unpriced* WMHLF (B75-50361)
Greensleeves : for brass quartet. *British and Continental. Unpriced* WNSK/DW (B75-50940)
Home on the range : traditional tune. *455 Brighton Rd, South Croydon : Paul. Unpriced* WUNSK/DW (B75-50959)
Jokers wild : cornet or trumpet trio (based on a theme by Mozart from 'Ein musikalischer Spass'. K.522. *Studio Music. Unpriced* WMPWRNT (B75-50934)
Oh! dem golden slippers : for brass quartet. *British and Continental. Unpriced* WNSK/DW (B75-50941)
Over the sticks : galop. *Studio Music. Unpriced* WMHLF (B75-51417)
Palm Beach : barcarolle for brass band. *Studio Music. Unpriced* WMJ (B75-50369)
Rhode Island rag : brass band. *Studio Music. Unpriced* WMK/AHXJ (B75-50364)
Salt Lake City samba : brass band. *Studio Music. Unpriced* WMHVKS (B75-50363)
Santa Lucia : Neapolitan air, for brass quartet. *British and Continental. Unpriced* WNSK/DW (B75-50942)
Symphony no.9, op.125, in D minor, 'Choral'. Freude, schöner Gotterfunken. *arr.* Song of joy. (Beethoven, Ludwig van). *Studio Music. Unpriced* WMK/DW (B75-51427)
Les Vêpres siciliennes. Overture. *arr.* Overture, Sicilian vespers. (Verdi, Giuseppe). *Studio Music. Unpriced* WMK (B75-51423)
Siesta. Op.8 : for violin and piano. (Josephs, Wilfred). *Chappell. Unpriced* SPJ (B75-51297)
Silver swimmer. Opus 84 : for mixed chorus, SATB and piano duet. (Hoddinott, Alun). *Oxford University Press. £1.20* DX (B75-50032) ISBN 0-19-336840-4
Silverman, Jerry.
Jerry Silverman's folk song encyclopaedia : with over 1,000 favorite songs arranged for voice and guitar
Vol.1. *Chappell. Unpriced* KE/TSDW/G/AY (B75-50564)
Vol.2. *Chappell. Unpriced* KE/TSDW/G/AY (B75-50565)
Simeone, Harry.
The godfather, part 2. Love said goodbye. *arr.* Love said goodbye. (Rota, Nino). *Famous Music : Chappell. Unpriced* GDW (B75-50082)
The godfather, part 2. Love said goodbye. *arr.* Love said goodbye : music by Nino Rota. (Rota, Nino). *Famous Music : Chappell. Unpriced* FDW (B75-50072)
Simon, George Thomas. Glenn Miller and his Orchestra. *W.H. Allen. £4.95* AMT(P) (B75-00202) ISBN 0-491-01501-1
Simple gifts : traditional Shaker song. (Miller, Carl). *Chappell. Unpriced* FDW (B75-50493)
Simply pop. (Jasper, Tony). *Queen Anne Press. £0.95* AKDW/GB/E(M) (B75-27955) ISBN 0-362-00247-9
Simpson, John.
The magic clarinet : for clarinet and piano. *Rahter. Unpriced* VVPJ (B75-50901)
Symphony no.1 in D major. 3rd movement. *arr.* 'Bruder Martin'. (Mahler, Gustav). *Bosworth. Unpriced* MJ (B75-50595)
Simpson, Kenneth. Music through the recorder : a course in musicianship
Vol.1. *Nelson. Unpriced* VS/AC (B75-50856) ISBN 0-17-436081-9
Simpson, Lionel.
Andantino cantabile. Opus 69 : for flute and piano. *British and Continental. Unpriced* VRPJ (B75-50851)
Prelude for brass quartet. Op.105. *British and Continental : EMI. Unpriced* WNS (B75-51448)
Simpson, Robert. Quintet for clarinet in A and string quartet (1968). *Lengnick. Unpriced* NVVQNR (B75-50165)
Simpson, Thomas.
Opus newer Paduanen, Galliarden, Intraden, Canzonen (1617) : for 3 cornetti (trumpets in C) and 2 trombones
Volume 1. *Musica rara. Unpriced* WNRH (B75-51439)
Volume 2. *Musica rara. Unpriced* WNRH (B75-51440)
Sinfonia avanti l'opera, G.14 : for trumpet, strings and continuo. (Torelli, Giuseppe). *Musica rara. £1.50* WSPK/LE (B75-51462)
Sing a new song : twenty-three hymns and songs from Southern Television Hymn Contest, 1975. *Weinberger. £0.85* JDM/JS/AY (B75-50525)
Sing, children, sing : songs, dances and singing games of many lands and peoples. *Chappell. Unpriced* JFDW/AY (B75-51095)
Sing hosanna : hymns. *Holmes McDougall. £3.80* JFDM/AY (B75-51091) ISBN 0-7157-0934-8
Sing it in the morning : hymns. Teachers' ed. *Nelson. Unpriced* JFDM/AY (B75-50531) ISBN 0-17-428009-2
Sing joyfully : SSATB and strings (or organ) with verses for bass solo. (Mundy, John). Revised ed. *Oxford University Press. £0.40* ERXNRDK (B75-50453) ISBN 0-19-352184-9
Sing mortals! : a sonnet for the festival of St Cecilia, for SATB and organ. (Bliss, *Sir* Arthur). *Novello. Unpriced* DH (B75-50021)
Sing the Mass : a new source-book of liturgical music for cantor, choir and congregation. *Chapman. Unpriced* JDG/AY (B75-50521) ISBN 0-225-65984-0
Sinner man : folk hymn setting, for medium voice and piano with audience participation. (Boatwright, Howard). *Boosey and Hawkes. Unpriced* KFVDW (B75-50583)

Sitsky, Larry.
Apparitions for orchestra. *Boosey and Hawkes. £6.00* MJ (B75-50598)
Quartet for woodwind instruments. Woodwind quartet : for flute, oboe, clarinet and bassoon. *Boosey and Hawkes. £5.00* VNS (B75-50310)
Six carols with descants. *Oxford University Press. Unpriced* DP/LF/AY (B75-51016) ISBN 0-19-353244-1
Six Christmas carols : six easy carols from five countries, for easy wind and percussion. *Ricordi. Unpriced* JFE/NYHDP/LF/AYB (B75-51098)
Six easy pictures. Opus 5 : guitar solo. (Duarte, John William). *Novello. Unpriced* TSPMJ (B75-50809)
Six easy pieces : for piano. (Kasschau, Howard). *Schirmer. Unpriced* QPJ (B75-51247)
Six Irish tunes. *Lengnick. Unpriced* NYDSK/DW/AYDM (B75-50653)
Six Mehitabel magpies : for soprano and double bass. (Seamarks, Colin). *Yorke. Unpriced* KFLE/SSPMDW (B75-50120)
Six monologues for boys. (Wilcock, Frank). *Brown, Son and Ferguson. Unpriced* HYE/QP (B75-50520)
Six pieces for organ. Opus 33. (Steel, Christopher). *Novello. £0.85* RJ (B75-50213)
Six preludes for piano (in differing time signatures). (Branson, David). *David Branson. Unpriced* QPJ (B75-51233)
Six reflections : for percussion quartet. (Frank, Marcel Gustave). *Boosey and Hawkes. Unpriced* XNS (B75-50966)
Skelton, Geoffrey. Paul Hindemith : the man behind the music : a biography. *Gollancz. £6.00* BHM(N) (B75-22841) ISBN 0-575-01988-3
Skoda, Eva Badura-. *See* Badura-Skoda, Eva.
Skoda, Paul Badura-. *See* Badura-Skoda, Paul.
Skriabin, Aleksandr
Concerto for piano, in F sharp minor. Op.20. Concerto, F sharp minor, for piano and orchestra. Opus 20. *Eulenburg. Unpriced* MPQF (B75-51162)
Piano music. *Selections.* Selected piano works
Vol.6: Sonatas nos 6-10. *Peters. Unpriced* QPJ (B75-50195)
Le Poeme de l'extase = The poem of ecstasy. Op.54. *Belaieff : Hinrichsen. Unpriced* MMJ (B75-51157)
Skywatch (The Royal Observer Corps march past) : for military band. (Davies, Roy Edward Charles). *Boosey and Hawkes. £1.50* UMMGM/KH (B75-51343)
Slack, Roy.
Moods and movement : piano. *Keith Prowse Music. Unpriced* QP/GR (B75-51222)
Three little dances : for three clarinets. *British and Continental. Unpriced* VVNTH (B75-51401)
Slade story. (Tremlett, George). *Futura Publications. £0.40* AKDW/GB/E(P) (B75-13167) ISBN 0-86007-193-6
Slatford, Rodney.
Quartet for double basses. (Lauber, Joseph). *Yorke. Unpriced* SSNS (B75-50776)
Romance and rondo for double bass & orchestra. *arr.* Romance and rondo : for double bass and orchestra. (Keyper, Franz). *Yorke. Unpriced* SSPK/W (B75-50780)
Rondo solo : for double bass and violoncello or viola. (Keyper, Franz Anton Leopold Joseph). *Yorke. Unpriced* SRPLSS/W (B75-50264)
Works, double bass & piano. Yorke complete Bottesini : for double bass and piano
Volume 2. (Bottesini, Giovanni). *Yorke. Unpriced* SSP/AZ (B75-51308)
Yorke complete Bottesini : for double bass and piano
Vol.1. (Bottesini, Giovanni). *Yorke. Unpriced* SSP/AZ (B75-50268)
Slaven, Neil. Blues records, January, 1943 to December, 1966. (Leadbitter, Mike). *Music Sales Ltd, 78 Newman St., W.1 : Oakwood Publications. Unpriced* AKDW/HHW/FD(WT/XPC18) (B75-50977) ISBN 0-86001-089-9
Slavnostní sbor = Festlicher Chor = Festival chorus : for four male voices, women's and men's chorus and piano. (Janacek, Leos). *Bärenreiter. £1.20* DX (B75-50033)
Sleeping beauty. (Tchaikovsky, Peter). *Eulenberg. Unpriced* MM/HM (B75-50601)
Smalley, Roger. Monody : for piano with live electronic modulation (1 player). *Faber Music. £3.00* QPVJ (B75-50722)
Smet, Robin de. Selected pieces. (Fauré, Gabriel). *Cramer. Unpriced* QPJ (B75-50189)
Smet, Robin de. *See* De Smet, Robin.
Smetana on 3000 records. (Bennett, John Reginald). *Oakwood Press. £8.75* BSIM/FD (B75-14334) ISBN 0-85361-158-0
Smith, Bryan. Tango el Torro. *arr.* Tango el Torro : piano. *Swan. Unpriced* QPK/AHVR (B75-51258)
Smith, Elizabeth W.
Everyman's handyman : nine rounds and canons for men's voices. (Beeson, Jack). *Boosey and Hawkes. Unpriced* GEZDW/XC (B75-50519)
The model housekeeper : nine rounds and canons for women's voices. (Beeson, Jack). *Boosey and Hawkes. Unpriced* FEZDW/XC (B75-50505)
Smith, Gregg.
Come where my love lies dreaming : for four-part chorus of mixed voices a cappella. (Foster, Stephen Collins). *Schirmer. Unpriced* EZDW (B75-50479)
The horticultural wife : (written by a celebrated English gardener after disappointment in love) : for four-part chorus of mixed voices with tenor (or baritone) solo and piano accompaniment. (Hutchinson Family). *Schirmer. Unpriced* DW (B75-50442)

Listen to the mocking bird : for four-part chorus of mixed voices with optional tenor and bass solos and optional flute or violin and piano accompaniment. (Hawthorne, Alice). *Schirmer. Unpriced* DW (B75-50440)
Put the right man at the wheel : for four-part chorus of mixed voices with piano accompaniment. (Hays, Will Shakespeare). *Schirmer. Unpriced* DW (B75-50441)
Some folks : for four-part chorus of mixed voices with guitar or piano accompaniment. (Foster, Stephen Collins). *Schirmer. Unpriced* ETSDW (B75-50455)
Tenting on the old camp ground : for four-part mixed voices with piano or guitar (and optional oboe, flute, or violin). (Kittredge, Walter). *Schirmer. Unpriced* DW (B75-50443)
Smith, J. Ferguson. A trip to the circus : piano. *Forsyth. Unpriced* QPJ (B75-51254)
Smith, Lorna. Judy, with love : the story of 'Miss Show Business'. *Hale. £3.80* AKDW/GB/E(P) (B75-24859) ISBN 0-7091-5257-4
Smith, Michael, *b.1922.* 'His Master's Voice' recordings, plum label 'C' series (12 inch). (Gramophone Company). *Old School House, Tarrant Hinton, Blandford, Dorset : Oakwood Press. £4.50* A/FD(T/WT) (B75-08384) ISBN 0-85361-166-1
Smith, Michael J. The Lord is my shepherd : anthem for two sopranos, chorus and organ. (Wise, Michael). *Novello. £0.20* DK (B75-51010)
Smith, Peter Melville. Willowbrook suite : for treble, alto and tenor recorders. *Lengnick. Unpriced* VSNTG (B75-50863)
Smith, Ronald. Mazurka for piano, op.68, no.4, in F minor. Mazurka in F minor. Op.68, no.4, (The final composition). (Chopin, Frederic). *Hansen House. Unpriced* QPHQ (B75-50676)
Smith, Stevie. Who killed Lawless Lean? : for voices, 4 melody instruments, percussion and piano. (Pehkonen, Elis). *Universal. Unpriced* JFE/LNRPXDW (B75-51096)
Smith, William Joseph Thomas. The organ & organists. *Boreham Vicarage, Chelmsford, Essex CM3 3EG : The author. £0.25* AR/B(YDDB) (B75-21667) ISBN 0-9504312-0-6
Smith, Winifred Mary. Contemporary organ technique : 20 progressive studies and pieces. (Stoker, Richard). *Ashdown. £1.20* R/AF (B75-51266)
Smith-Masters, Stanley.
Joshua fought the battle of Jericho : traditional. *Studio Music. Unpriced* WMK/DW/LC (B75-50932)
A Texas lullaby : brass band. *Studio Music. Unpriced* WMJ (B75-51419)
Snowman of Kashmir : a workshop opera for children. (Kay, Peter). *Universal. Unpriced* CN (B75-50401)
Snowman of Kashmir : a workshop opera for children. (Kay, Peter). *Universal. Unpriced* CQN (B75-50995)
Snowman of Kashmir. *Vocal score.* The snowman of Kashmir : a workshop opera for children. (Kay, Peter). *Universal. Unpriced* CN (B75-50401)
Sobin, Linda. Deep the water, shallow the shore : three essays on shantying in the West Indies. (Abrahams, Roger David). *University of Texas Press for the American Folklore Society. £3.80* ADW/GMC(YUH) (B75-00739) ISBN 0-292-71502-1
Sociable songs
Book 3, part 1 : for unison or part-singing with optional instrumental parts. *Oxford University Press. Unpriced* JDW/AY (B75-51085) ISBN 0-19-330590-9
Book 3, part 2 : for unison or part-singing with optional instrumental parts. *Oxford University Press. Unpriced* JDW/AY (B75-51086) ISBN 0-19-330592-5
Solemn overture. Op.73. Festouverture = Solemn overture. Opus 73 : for orchestra. (Glazunov, Aleksandr Konstantinovich). *Belaieff : Peters. Unpriced* MMJ (B75-50144)
Soliloquy : for piano. (Del Tredici, David). *Boosey and Hawkes. £1.50* QPJ (B75-50696)
'Sollt ich meinem Gott nicht singen' : Choralkonzert für zwei Trompeten, zwei Posaunen und Orgel. (Wenzel, Eberhard). *Bärenreiter. Unpriced* NWXPNRF (B75-50646)
Some folks : for four-part chorus of mixed voices with guitar or piano accompaniment. (Foster, Stephen Collins). *Schirmer. Unpriced* ETSDW (B75-50455)
Somerset wassail. (Toplis, Gloria). *Ricordi. Unpriced* FE/XDP/LF (B75-51058)
Somewhere further north : a history of music in Sheffield. (Mackerness, Eric David). *Northend. £3.00* A(YDCGS/X) (B75-16404) ISBN 0-901100-13-7
Sommer, Jurgen.
Ballet : elektronische Orgel. *Nagel : Bärenreiter. Unpriced* RPVK/AHM/AY (B75-50222)
Festliche Stunden : elektronische Orgel. *Nagel : Bärenreiter. £2.00* RPVK/AAY (B75-50218)
Operette : elektronische Orgel. *Nagel : Bärenreiter. £2.00* RPVK/DW/AY (B75-50220)
Romantik : elektronische Orgel. *Nagel : Bärenreiter. £2.00* RPVK/AAY (B75-50219)
Tanz und Unterhaltung : elektronische Orgel. *Nagel : Bärenreiter. £2.00* RPVJ (B75-50217)
Sonata for oboe, cello & basso continuo in G major. Trio sonata in G major : for oboe (or flute, violin, descant or tenor recorder), violoncello or bassoon, and harpsichord (or piano), with a second violoncello or basson ad lib. (Quantz, Johann Joachim). *Schott. £2.00* NUTNTE (B75-50636)
Sondheim, Stephen.
Candide. *Selections: arr.* Candide : vocal selections. (Bernstein, Leonard). *Schirmer. Unpriced* KDW (B75-50550)
A little night music. A little night music. *arr.* A little night

music : piano. *Chappell. Unpriced* QPK/CM (B75-51260)
A little night music. *Selections : arr.* A little night music : souvenir song folio. *Chappell. Unpriced* KDW (B75-50559)
Song and dance man : the art of Bob Dylan. (Gray, Michael, *b.1946*). *Abacus. £0.75* AKDW/GB/E(P) (B75-18369) ISBN 0-349-11540-0
Song of joy. (Beethoven, Ludwig van). *Studio Music. Unpriced* WMK/DW (B75-51427)
Song of praise and prayer : children's hymn. (Binkerd, Gordon). *Boosey and Hawkes. Unpriced* KFDM (B75-50569)
Song of praise and prayer : children's hymn, unison, with organ or piano accompaniment. (Binkerd, Gordon). *Boosey and Hawkes. Unpriced* JFDM (B75-50530)
Songayllo, Raymond. Ten short piano pieces. *Oxford University Press. Unpriced* QPJ (B75-50710)
Songs, drones and refrains of death : a cycle of poems by Federico Garcia Lorca for baritone, electric guitar, electric contrabass, electric piano, (electric harpsichord), percussion (2 players). (Crumb, George). *Peters. Unpriced* KGNE/PVDW (B75-51136)
Song's eternity : part-song for unaccompanied female voices (SSA). (Short, Michael). *Roberton. £0.14* FEZDW (B75-50503)
Songs for Naomi : unison voices, glockenspiel and/or chime bars, xylophone, descant recorder, triangle, tambourine, wood blocks, piano (one stave). (Burnett, Michael). *Ricordi. Unpriced* JFE/NYFSRDW (B75-50099)
Songs from Frank Loesser's Hans Andersen. (Loesser, Frank). *Edwin H. Morris. Unpriced* VSRNRK/DW/JR (B75-50871)
Songs from Michelangelo : for baritone and piano. (Laderman, Ezra). *Oxford University Press. Unpriced* KGNDW (B75-51134)
Songs from the golden years of Gracie Fields. *Chappell. Unpriced* KDW/AY (B75-51114)
Songs of good counsel. Op.73 : for mezzo-soprano and pianoforte. (Cruft, Adrian). *Central Music Library : Chappell. Unpriced* KFQDW (B75-50579)
Songs. *Selections.* The land of lost content and other songs. (Ireland, John). *Stainer and Bell. Unpriced* KDW (B75-51104) ISBN 0-85249-320-7
Soon it will die : for orchestra. (Meale, Richard). *Universal. Unpriced* MMJ (B75-51155)
Sorrentino, Gilbert. Ballad 2 : music/theatre piece for voice and piano. (Rands, Bernard). *Universal. Unpriced* CB/J (B75-50986)
Soul book. *Eyre Methuen. £1.50* AKDW/GB/E(YTLD/M) (B75-29984) ISBN 0-413-32150-9
Sound structure in music. (Erickson, Robert). *University of California Press. £6.00* A/PU (B75-27354) ISBN 0-520-02376-5
Soundings : for orchestra. (Gould, Morton). *Chappell. Unpriced* MMJ (B75-50145)
Sounds I prefer. *arr.* Sounds I prefer : for mixed chorus (SATB). (Lombardo, Mario). *Chappell. Unpriced* DW (B75-51021)
Sounds like folk
No.4: Victorian tear jerkers. *E.F.D.S. Unpriced* JE/TSDW/G/AY (B75-50092)
No.5: Songs of faith and feeling. *EFDS. Unpriced* JE/TSDW/G/AY (B75-50093)
Sous, Alfred. Etüden für Oboe. *Litolff : Peters. Unpriced* VT/AF (B75-50340)
South, Harry. The Sweeney. Theme. *arr.* 'The Sweeney' : theme from the Thames television series, for piana. *Sparta Florida Music : Chappell. Unpriced* QPK/JS (B75-50199)
Souvenir d'Amérique, 'Yankee doodle'. *arr.* Souvenir d'Amérique, 'Yankee doodle' : variations burlesques. (Vieuxtemps, Henri). *Galaxy : Galliard. Unpriced* SPK/LT (B75-51298)
Souvenir : für Violine und Klavier. (Kupkovič, Ladislav). *Universal. Unpriced* SPJ (B75-50768)
Space play : a concerto for nine instruments. (Musgrave, Thea). *Novello. Unpriced* NVNMF (B75-51180)
Speaight, George. Bawdy songs of the early music hall. *David and Charles. £3.95* AKDW/K/G/KDX(XHK11) (B75-31191) ISBN 0-7153-7013-8
Spectra : for four recorders. (Alemann, Eduardo Armando). *Galaxy : Galliard. Unpriced* VSNS (B75-50859)
Spells : soprano solo, mixed chorus & orchestra. (Bennett, Richard Rodney). *Novello. £1.00* DX (B75-50448)
Spells. *Vocal score.* Spells : soprano solo, mixed chorus & orchestra. (Bennett, Richard Rodney). *Novello. £1.00* DX (B75-50448)
Spencer, Roderick. The zoo. *Vocal score.* The zoo : a musical folly. (Sullivan, *Sir* Arthur Seymour). *Cramer. Unpriced* CF (B75-50397)
Spes nostra : for two treble, two tenor and bass viols. (Parsley, Osbert). *Oxford University Press. £0.30* STNR (B75-50785) ISBN 0-19-341212-8
Spider monkey uncle king. *Vocal score.* The spider monkey uncle king : an opera pantomime for children. (Kelly, Bryan). *Novello. £1.10* CN (B75-50008)
Spielheft Klassik : für drei Gitarren. *Schott. Unpriced* TSNTK/AAY (B75-50799)
Spielheft Klassik : für zwei Gitarren. *Schott. Unpriced* TSNUK/AAY (B75-50801)
Spink, Ian. Songs. *Collections.* Ayres, songs and dialogues. (Johnson, Robert, *b.1582*). 2nd revised ed. *Stainer and Bell. Unpriced* KE/TWDW/AZ (B75-51123)
Spink, Peter. Rags. (Joplin, Scott). *Oxford University Press. £1.75* VVNSK/AHXJ (B75-50894) ISBN 0-19-357320-2
Spinner, Leopold.
Cantata on German folksong texts. Op. 20. *Choral score.* Cantata on German folksong texts. Op. 20 : for mezzo-soprano solo, chorus and chamber orchestra. *Boosey and Hawkes. £1.50* DADX (B75-50014)
Drei Lieder. Op.16 : für Sopran und Klavier. *Boosey and Hawkes. £1.50* KFLDW (B75-50571)
Spirit! : a musical. (Larsson, John). *Salvationist Publishing and Supplies. Unpriced* CM/LN (B75-50400)
Spirit of Christmas : for wind band and optional chorus. (Balent, Andrew). *Warner : Blossom. Unpriced* UM/LF (B75-51332)
Spirit of the Lord : SATB. (Barnes, Norman J). *Banks. Unpriced* DK (B75-50424)
Spirit!. *Vocal score.* Spirit! : a musical. (Larsson, John). *Salvationist Publishing and Supplies. Unpriced* CM/LN (B75-50400)
Spirituals : elektronische Orgel. *Nagel : Bärenreiter. £2.00* RPVK/DW/LC/AY (B75-50221)
Spotless rose : S.A. unacc. (Lane, Philip). *Banks. Unpriced* FEZDP/LF (B75-51062)
Spring dances : for pianoforte. (Judd, Margaret). *Bosworth. Unpriced* QPH (B75-50675)
Spruchmotten
3: Motetten. *Bärenreiter. £1.40* EZDJ/AYE (B75-50056)
Spurgin, Anthony. Sylvia. *arr.* Sylvia. (Fleming, Jimmy). *Studio Music. Unpriced* WMK/DW (B75-50926)
Stadler, Werner. Fünf Schlagzeugtrois. *Schott. £2.00* XNT (B75-51480)
Stadlmair, Hans. Drei Fantasien : für Viola. *Litolff : Peters. Unpriced* SQPMJ (B75-50772)
Staehelin, Dieter. Sonatas for two cellos. Op.2, nos. 1, 4, 3. Sonates. Op.2, pour 2 violoncelles basses de violes (Gamben) ou bassons (fagotti). (Guignon, Jean Pierre). 1st ed. *Kneusslin : Hinrichsen. Unpriced* SRNUE (B75-50260)
Stage parodies : piano suite for young players, for one piano, four hands. (Dello Joio, Norman). *Associated Music. £1.30* QNVG (B75-51216)
Stamaty, Camille. Chant et mécanisme. Op.37, 38. *Selections : arr.* Five Stamaty pieces from Op.37 and 38. *New Wind Music. £0.50* VVPK (B75-51405)
Stamitz, Anton.
8 Capricen für Flöte. *Litolff : Peters. Unpriced* VRPMJ (B75-50327)
Concerto for viola & string orchestra, no.4, in D major. Concerto no.4 in D major : for viola and strings. *Nagel Bärenreiter. £3.60* RXMPSQF (B75-50229)
Standford, Patric. Sonatina for treble recorder & harpsichord. Op.26. Sonatine for treble recorder and harpsichord. Op.26. *Stainer and Bell. Unpriced* VSSPEM (B75-50882)
Stanley, John. Voluntaries for organ. *Selections: arr.* Six voluntaries for 2 trumpets and organ. *Musica rara. Unpriced* WSNTRK (B75-51456)
Starobin, David.
Some folks : for four-part chorus of mixed voices with guitar or piano accompaniment. (Foster, Stephen Collins). *Schirmer. Unpriced* ETSDW (B75-50455)
Tenting on the old camp ground : for four-part mixed voices with piano or guitar (and optional oboe, flute, or violin). (Kittredge, Walter). *Schirmer. Unpriced* DW (B75-50443)
Steel, Christopher. Six pieces for organ. Opus 33. *Novello. £0.85* RJ (B75-50213)
Steglich, Rudolf. Keyboard works
Vol.1: First set of 1720, The eight great suites. (Handel, George Frideric). *Bärenreiter. £3.00* QRP/AZ (B75-50202)
Steigleder, Johann Ulrich. Recercares for organ, nos.1-4. Four recercars : for organ. New ed. *Bärenreiter. Unpriced* RJ (B75-50734)
Stein, Cathi. Elton John. *Futura Publications. £0.45* AKDW/GB/E(P) (B75-19733) ISBN 0-86007-201-0
Stein, Joseph. Johannes Brahms : his work and personality. (Gál, Hans). *Severn House. £4.50* BBT(N) (B75-30567) ISBN 0-7278-0078-7
Stein, Leonard. Style and idea : selected writings of Arnold Schoenberg. (Schoenberg, Arnold). *Faber. £17.50* A(D) (B75-11219) ISBN 0-571-09722-7
Stent, Keith. Sullivan at sea. *arr.* Sullivan at sea : a trip for trombones. *Paxton. £1.75* WMK (B75-50370)
Stephen Foster song book : original sheet music of 40 songs. (Foster, Stephen). *Dover : Constable. £2.40* KDW (B75-50553)
Stephens, Norris L. A recital for handbells : ten classical pieces. *Schirmer. Unpriced* XSQMK/AAY (B75-50972)
Stephenson, Elspeth. Mary Jones : a musical play for young people. (Warren, Norman). *Maplewell Press. Unpriced* CM/L (B75-50991) ISBN 0-9504473-0-7
Sterian, Raluca. Traité de naï roumain : methode de flûte de Pan. (Zamfir, Gheorghe). *Chappell. Unpriced* VSX/AC (B75-50886)
Stevens, John. Musica Britannica : a national collection of music
Vol.36: Early Tudor songs and carols; transcribed and edited by John Stevens. *Stainer and Bell. Unpriced* C/AYD (B75-50982)
Stevens, Susan. Help yourself to play the guitar. *Girl Guides Association. £0.35* ATS/E (B75-10255) ISBN 0-85260-002-x
Stewart, Harold. Five songs on Japanese haiku : soprano, clarinet, in A, violin, violoncello. (Riley, Dennis). *Peters. Unpriced* KFLE/NVVQNTDW (B75-51125)
Stierhof, Karl. Dreissig Estüden für Viola. (Uhl, Alfred). *Schott. £2.25* SQPMJ (B75-51304)
Stille Nacht. *arr.* Stille Nacht = Silent night. (Gruber, Franz). *Oxford University Press. Unpriced* EZDP/LF (B75-51042) ISBN 0-19-343053-3
Stimac, Anthony. Fashion : a musical comedy. (Mowatt, Anna Cora). *French. £1.10* BPIACM (B75-20393) ISBN 0-573-68065-5
Stockhausen, Karlheinz. Nr 17 = Mikrophonie 2 : für Chor, Hammondorgel und 4 Ringmodulatoren. *Universal. Unpriced* EPVDX (B75-50038)
Stockhausen serves imperialism, and other articles : with commentary and notes. (Cardew, Cornelius). *Latimer New Dimensions. £3.00* A(ZC/D) (B75-04503) ISBN 0-901539-29-5
'Stockholm sonatas' : for viola d'amore (viola) and basso continuo
1: Sonatas in F major, A minor, G major. (Ariosti, Attilio). *Bärenreiter. £2.80* SQQPE (B75-50259)
Stockmeier, Wolfgang.
Selected organ works
6. (Pachelbel, Johann). *Bärenreiter. £2.40* RJ (B75-50211)
Zwei Stücke : für Trompete und Orgel. *Bärenreiter. £3.20* WSPLR (B75-50382)
Stoker, Richard.
Contemporary organ technique : 20 progressive studies and pieces. *Ashdown. £1.20* R/AF (B75-51266)
Zodiac variations : twelve pieces of moderate difficulty for piano. *Ashdown. Unpriced* QP/T (B75-50183)
Stokowski, Leopold. Pictures at an exhibition. *arr.* Pictures at an exhibition. (Musorgsky, Modest). *Henmar Press : Peters. Unpriced* MMK (B75-50619)
Stone litany : runes from a House of the Dead, for mezzo-soprano and orchestra. (Davies, Peter Maxwell). *Boosey and Hawkes. £7.50* KFNE/MDX (B75-50577)
Stones Touring Party. *See* Greenfield, Robert.
Storm. Op.76. L'Orage : Ouverture für Orchester nach dem Drama von A.N. Ostrowsky. (Tchaikovsky, Peter). *Belaieff : Hinrichsen. £8.00* MMJ (B75-50147)
Story of the Handel Opera Society. (Handel Opera Society). *Flat 3, 26 Medway St., S.W.1 : The Society. £0.75* AC/E(YC/QB/X) (B75-08736) ISBN 0-901175-02-1
Story of the Royal Opera House, Covent Garden. (Goodwin, Noël). *Head Office, Poultry, EC2P 2BX : Midland Bank Ltd. Free* AC/E(YC/QB) (B75-50001) ISBN 0-9501576-2-7
Stout, Alan.
O altitudo : soprano solo, flute solo, violin, violoncello, harp, celesta, percussion, women's chorus. *Peters. Unpriced* FE/NYERNQDH (B75-50075)
Study in densities and durations : organ. *Peters. Unpriced* RJ (B75-50214)
STP. A journey through America with the Rolling Stones. (Greenfield, Robert). *Panther. £0.75* AKDW/GB/E)P/XQM) (B75-24849) ISBN 0-586-04195-8
Strauss, Johann, *b.1805.* Radetzky march. Op.228. *arr.* Radetzky march. Op.228. *Bosworth. Unpriced* MK/AGM (B75-50599)
Strauss, Johann, *b.1825.*
Annen-Polka. Op.117. *arr.* Annen-Polka. Op.117 : polka française. *Bosworth. Unpriced* MK/AHVH (B75-50129)
Operettas. *Selections : arr.* The Johann Strauss song book : containing twelve songs for solo voice and piano. *Weinberger. Unpriced* KDW (B75-51113)
Persischer Marsch. Op.289. *arr.* Persian march. Op.289. *Bosworth. Unpriced* MK/AGM (B75-50600)
Waltzes. *Selections: arr.* Waltz themes from Strauss. *British and Continental. Unpriced* NVPK/AHW (B75-51182)
Stravinsky, Igor. An autobiography. *Calder and Boyars. £5.95* BSV(N) (B75-25554) ISBN 0-7145-1063-7
Stravinsky, Igor. Chronicle of my life. *See* Stravinsky, Igor. An autobiography.
Stravinsky, Igor.
Scherzo for piano (1902). Scherzo (1902) : for piano. 1st ed. *Faber Music. Unpriced* QPJ (B75-50711)
Sonata for piano in F sharp minor. Sonata in F sharp minor (1903-4) for piano. *Faber Music. Unpriced* QPE (B75-50667)
Stravinsky, Soulima.
Music alphabet : piano, four hands
Vol.1. *Peters. Unpriced* QNV (B75-50179)
Vol.2. *Peters. Unpriced* QNV (B75-50180)
Stravinsky. (Routh, Francis). *Dent. £4.50* BSV (B75-24847) ISBN 0-460-03138-4
Street, Allan.
Concorde march. *arr.* Concorde march. (Farnon, Robert). *Chappell. Unpriced* WMK/AGM (B75-51425)
Swingalongamax. *arr.* Swingalongamax. (Back in my childhood days). (Bygraves, Max). *Boosey and Hawkes. £1.00* UMMK/DW (B75-51350)
Swingalongamax. *arr.* Swingalongamax. (Back in my childhood days). (Bygraves, Max). *Boosey and Hawkes. £0.85* WMK/DW (B75-51428)
The wonder march. *arr.* The wonder march. (Allen, Rod). *Boosey and Hawkes. Military band set, £1.00, Brass band set £0.85* UMMK/AGM (B75-50834)
Street corner overture. *arr.* Street corner overture. (Rawsthorne, Alan). *Oxford University Press. Unpriced* UMMJ (B75-51345)
Striggio, Alessandro.
Ecco ch'io lass'il core : SSATTB (unacc. or with lutes). *Oxford University Press. Unpriced* ETWNUDU (B75-50457) ISBN 0-19-341221-7
Opera. Air. Air : for soprano and orchestra. (Berio, Luciano). *Universal. Unpriced* KFLE/MDW (B75-50572)
Opera. Air. *arr.* Air : for soprano and 4 instruments. (Berio, Luciano). *Universal. Unpriced* KFLE/NXNSDW (B75-50573)
String along : 22 easy graded pieces for violin and piano. (Appleby, William). *Oxford University Press. £1.60* SPJ (B75-50766) ISBN 0-19-355204-3

String music in print. (Farish, Margaret K). 2nd ed. *Bowker. £18.00* ARXN(TC) (B75-25110) ISBN 0-8352-0596-7

Studies in Renaissance and baroque music in honour of Arthur Mendel. *32 Great Titchfield St., W.1 : Bärenreiter-Verlag etc.. £20.70* A(XD251/D)

Studies in the psychology of culture. *See* Holbrook, David. Studies in the psychology of culture.

Study in densities and durations : organ. (Stout, Alan). *Peters. Unpriced* RJ (B75-50214)

Study of Brindley and Foster, organ builders of Sheffield, 1854-1939. (Knott, Joshua Robert). *101 Highcroft Cres., Bognor Regis, Sussex PO22 8DT : The author. £1.15* AR/BC(Q/YDJGS) (B75-50002) ISBN 0-9503869-0-1

Stundenbuch : für 12 Stimmen und 12 Bläser. (Heider, Werner). *Litolff : Peters. Unpriced* EUMDX (B75-50041)

Sturm, Walther. Blüh nur mein Sommerkorn : songs aus der klingenden Saat. *Bärenreiter. £3.20* FEZDW/G/AY (B75-50078)

Stutschewsky, Joachim. Concertos for keyboard, nos.2, 5. S.1053, 1056. *Selections : arr.* Siciliano/Largo. (Bach, Johann Sebastian). *Schott. Unpriced* SRPK (B75-51307)

Style and idea : selected writings of Arnold Schoenberg. (Schoenberg, Arnold). *Faber. £17.50* A(D) (B75-11219) ISBN 0-571-09722-7

Suite caracteristique = Characteristic suite. Opus 9 : for orchestra. (Glazunov, Aleksandr Konstantinovich). *Belaieff : Peters. Unpriced* MMG (B75-50136)

Sullivan, *Sir* Arthur Seymour.
- The best of Gilbert and Sullivan : all organ. *Chappell. Unpriced* RK/DW (B75-50739)
- The best of Gilbert and Sullivan : SATB. *Chappell. Unpriced* DW (B75-50445)
- Four miniature string quartets, from the Sullivan operas. *Paxton. £1.25* RXNSK/DW (B75-50238)
- The Mikado. *Choral score : arr.* The Mikado, or, The Town of Titipu. *Cramer. £1.20* DACF (B75-50405)
- Ten tunes from Gilbert and Sullivan. *Novello. £1.00* VRPLTSK/DW (B75-50324)
- Twilight. *arr.* Twilight. *Emerson. Unpriced* VRNTQK (B75-51367)
- The zoo. *Vocal score.* The zoo : a musical folly. *Cramer. Unpriced* CF (B75-50397)

Sullivan at sea : a trip for trombones. (Stent, Keith). *Paxton. £1.75* WMK (B75-50370)

Sullivan at sea. *arr.* Sullivan at sea : a trip for trombones. (Stent, Keith). *Paxton. £1.75* WMK (B75-50370)

Sulyok, Imre. Dioclesian. *Selections.* Suite für Streicher. (Purcell, Henry). *Litolff : Peters. Unpriced* RXM/JM (B75-50225)

Sulyok, Imré. Piano works
- Vol.7: Années de pélerinage II. (Liszt, Franz). *Bärenreiter. Unpriced* QP/AZ (B75-50664)

Sulyok, Imre. Six fugues for organ. Op.7. Sechs Fugen für Orgel/Cembalo. Opus 7. (Albrechtsberger, Johann Georg). *Litolff : Peters. Unpriced* R/Y (B75-50203)

Summertime music. (Gershwin, George). *Chappell. Unpriced* UMK/DW (B75-50825)

Sumsion, Herbert.
- 50 hymns for band
  - Book I: General and Christmas. *Oxford University Press. Unpriced* UMK/DM/AY (B75-50823) ISBN 0-19-363060-5
- Les Troyens. Gloire, gloire à Didon. *Vocal score.* Hail all hail to the queen : SATB. (Berlioz, Hector). *Oxford University Press. £0.08* DW (B75-50028) ISBN 0-19-343046-0

Sunday songs for chord organs. *EMI Music. Unpriced* RPVCK/DM/AY (B75-50741)

Sundermann, Albert. Complete works for solo lute. (Johnson, Robert). *Oxford University Press. £2.75* TW/AZ (B75-50291) ISBN 0-19-357390-3

Sunny bank : carol, SATB. (Hurford, Peter). *Oxford University Press. £0.10* DP/LF (B75-50430) ISBN 0-19-343051-7

Surge, illuminare Jerusalem : a motet for two four-part choirs (SATB SATB for the feast of the Epiphany). (Palestrina, Giovanni Pierluigi da). *Chester. Unpriced* EZDJ/LFP (B75-51040)

Surinach, Carlos.
- Suite espagnole. Bolero de los picaros. *arr.* Bolero de los picaros. *Associated Music. Unpriced* TSPMK/AHJK (B75-50816)
- Las Trompetas de la serafines : overture for orchestra. *Associated Music. £3.90* MMJ (B75-51158)

Sutermeister, Heinrich. Modeste Mignon : d'après une valse d'Honoré de Balzac, i.e. par Daniel Auber, pour dix instruments à vent. *Schott. Unpriced* UMJ (B75-51335)

Sutherland's law. (MacCunn, Hamish). *Ambleside Music : EMI. Unpriced* WMK (B75-51422)

Sutton, Wadham.
- Six little marches for wind septet. Wq.195. *arr.* Six little marches. (Bach, Carl Philipp Emanuel). *Novello. £0.30* VVNTK/AGM (B75-50347)
- Six menuets for keyboard, nos. 1, 2, 3, 5. Perger 70. Four minuets. (Haydn, Michael). *Novello. £0.30* VNTK/AHR (B75-50313)

Swann, Donald. The Michael Flanders and Donald Swann song book. *Chappell. Unpriced* KDW (B75-50114)

Swansea town : folk song, theme and variations, for wind quintet. (Jacob, Gordon). *Emerson. Unpriced* UNR/T (B75-50840)

Swansea town : wind quintet. (Jacob, Gordon). *Emerson. Unpriced* UNR/T (B75-51358)

Swarsenski, H.
- Ballade : piano solo. (Debussy, Claude). *Peters. Unpriced* QPJ (B75-50688)
- Danse : piano solo. (Debussy, Claude). *Peters. Unpriced* QPH (B75-50674)
- Etudes : piano solo
  - Book 1. (Debussy, Claude). *Peters. Unpriced* QPJ (B75-51239)
  - Book 2. (Debussy, Claude). *Peters. Unpriced* QPJ (B75-51240)
- Hommage à Haydn : piano. (Debussy, Claude). *Peters. Unpriced* QPJ (B75-50689)
- Images : piano solo
  - Book I. (Debussy, Claude). *Peters. Unpriced* QPJ (B75-50690)
  - Book II. (Debussy, Claude). *Peters. Unpriced* QPJ (B75-50691)
- The little nigar. The little negro = Le petit Negre : piano solo. (Debussy, Claude). *Peters. Unpriced* QPJ (B75-50692)
- Masques : piano. (Debussy, Claude). *Peters. Unpriced* QPJ (B75-50693)
- Mazurka : piano solo. (Debussy, Claude). *Peters. Unpriced* QPHQ (B75-50677)
- Nocturne : piano solo. (Debussy, Claude). *Peters. Unpriced* QPJ (B75-50694)
- Pour le piano : piano solo. (Debussy, Claude). *Peters. Unpriced* QPG (B75-51230)
- Valse romantique : piano solo. (Debussy, Claude). *Peters. Unpriced* QPHW (B75-50681)

Sweeney. Theme. *arr.* 'The Sweeney' : theme from the Thames television series, for piana. (South, Harry). *Sparta Florida Music : Chappell. Unpriced* QPK/JS (B75-50199)

'Sweeney' : theme from the Thames television series, for piana. (South, Harry). *Sparta Florida Music : Chappell. Unpriced* QPK/JS (B75-50199)

Sweet Rosie O'Grady. (Nugent, Maud). *455 Brighton Rd, South Croydon : Paul. Unpriced* WUNSK/DW (B75-50958)

Sweet Rosie O'Grady. *arr.* Sweet Rosie O'Grady. (Nugent, Maud). *455 Brighton Rd, South Croydon : Paul. Unpriced* WUNSK/DW (B75-50958)

Swing low, sweet chariot. (Burt, James). *Chappell. Unpriced* KDW/LC (B75-50562)

Swingalongamax. *arr.* Swingalongamax. (Back in my childhood days). (Bygraves, Max). *Boosey and Hawkes. £1.00* UMMK/DW (B75-51350)

Swingalongamax. *arr.* Swingalongamax. (Back in my childhood days). (Bygraves, Max). *Boosey and Hawkes. £0.85* WMK/DW (B75-51428)

Swingalongamax. (Back in my childhood days). (Bygraves, Max). *Boosey and Hawkes. £1.00* UMMK/DW (B75-51350)

Swingalongamax. (Back in my childhood days). (Bygraves, Max). *Boosey and Hawkes. £0.85* WMK/DW (B75-51428)

Sykora, Vaclav Jan.
- 36 fugues for the piano. Op.36
  - Vol.1: Nos. 1-13. (Reicha, Anton). *Bärenreiter. £3.20* QP/Y (B75-50184)
  - Vol.2: Nos. 14-24. (Reicha, Anton). *Bärenreiter. £3.20* QP/Y (B75-50185)
  - Vol.3: Nos. 25-36. (Reicha, Anton). *Bärenreiter. £3.20* QP/Y (B75-50186)

Sylvia. (Fleming, Jimmy). *Studio Music. Unpriced* WMK/DW (B75-50926)

Sylvia. *arr.* Sylvia. (Fleming, Jimmy). *Studio Music. Unpriced* WMK/DW (B75-50926)

Syzygy : for soprano, French horn and chamber orchestra. (Del Tredici, David). *Boosey and Hawkes. £9.00* KFLE/MPWTDX (B75-50118)

Szervanszky, Endre. Funf Konzertüden : für Flöte. *Litolff : Peters. Unpriced* VRPMJ (B75-50328)

Szkolay, Sándor. Quartet for strings, no.1. Streichquartett Nr.1. *Litolff : Peters. Unpriced* RXNS (B75-50237)

Szokolay, Sándor. Concerto for violin. Konzert für Violine und Orchester. *Litolff : Peters. Unpriced* MPSF (B75-50151)

Szokolay, Sandor. Concerto for violin. *arr.* Konzert für Violine und Orchester. *Litolff : Peters. Unpriced* SPK/LF (B75-50253)

Szokolay, Sándor. Hungarian children's songs. *Boosey and Hawkes. £1.00* SNUK/DW/GJ/AYG (B75-51293)

Take me home : part-songs. (London Welsh Male Voice Choir). *Chappell. Unpriced* DW/AY (B75-51022)

'Talking Machine Review'. Numerical listing of Edison Bell 'Winner'. *19 Glendale Rd, Bournemouth BH6 4JA : 'Talking Machine Review'. £2.00* A/FD(T/WT) (B75-19333) ISBN 0-902338-17-x

Tamara : symphonic poem. (Balakirev, Mily). *Eulenburg. £2.50* MMJ (B75-50609)

Tango el Torro. *arr.* Tango el Torro : piano. (Smith, Bryan). *Swan. Unpriced* QPK/AHVR (B75-51258)

Tango el Torro : piano. (Smith, Bryan). *Swan. Unpriced* QPK/AHVR (B75-51258)

Tanz und Unterhaltung : elektronische Orgel. (Sommer, Jurgen). *Nagel : Bärenreiter. £2.00* RPVJ (B75-50217)

Taqsim : for two pianos. (Camilleri, Charles). *Fairfield. £1.50* QNU (B75-50659)

Tarr, Edward H.
- Sinfonia à 4 in C major. G.33. Sinfonia à 4 in C major. G.33 : for 4 trumpets, 4 oboes, 2 bassoons, strings (concertino and rip.) and basso continuo. (Torelli, Giuseppe). *Musica rara. Unpriced* MRE (B75-51166)
- Sinfonia avanti l'opera. G.14. *arr.* Sinfonia avanti l'opera, G.14 : for trumpet, strings and continuo. (Torelli, Giuseppe). *Musica rara. £1.50* WSPK/LE (B75-51462)
- Sinfonia avanti l'opera. G.14 : for trumpet, strings and continuo. (Torelli, Giuseppe). *Musica rara. £4.50* MRE (B75-51167)
- Sinfonia in D major. G.3. Sinfonia in D. G.3 : for trumpet, strings and continuo. (Torelli, Giuseppe). *Musica rara. Unpriced* MRE (B75-51168)
- Sinfonia in D major. G.3. *arr.* Sinfonia in D. G.3 : for trumpet, strings and continuo. (Torelli, Giuseppe). *Musica rara. £1.50* WSPK/LE (B75-51463)
- Sinfonia in D major. G.4. Sinfonia in D. G.4 : for trumpet, strings and continuo. (Torelli, Giuseppe). *Musica rara. Unpriced* MRE (B75-51169)
- Sinfonia in D major. G.4. *arr.* Sinfonia in D. G.4 : for trumpet, strings and continuo. (Torelli, Giuseppe). *Musica rara. £1.50* WSPK/LE (B75-51464)
- Sinfonia in D major. G.5. Sinfonia in D. G.5 : for trumpet, strings and continuo. (Torelli, Giuseppe). *Musica rara. £4.50* MRE (B75-51170)
- Sinfonia in D major. G.5. *arr.* Sinfonia in D. G.5 : for trumpet, strings and continuo. (Torelli, Giuseppe). *Musica rara. £1.50* WSPK/LE (B75-51465)
- Sinfonia no.10 for two trumpets & strings in D major. Sinfonia decima à 7 for 2 trumpets and strings. (Bononcini, Giovanni Battista). *Musica rara. Unpriced* RXMPWSNUE (B75-51290)
- Sinfonia no.10 for two trumpets & strings in D major. *arr.* Sinfonia decima à 7 for 2 trumpets and strings. (Bononcini, Giovanni Battista). *Musica rara. Unpriced* NUXSNSK/LE (B75-51178)
- Sonata for trumpet, two violins, viola & basso continuo in D major. G.6. Sonata in D.G.6 : for trumpet, strings and continuo. (Torelli, Giuseppe). *Musica rara. £4.50* NUXSNRE (B75-51177)
- Sonata for trumpet, two violins, viola & basso continuo in D major. G.6. *arr.* Sonata in D.G.6 : for trumpet, strings and continuo. (Torelli, Giuseppe). *Musica rara. £1.50* WSPK/LE (B75-51466)

Tate, Phyllis.
- Lyric suite : for piano duet. *Oxford University Press. £2.50* QNVG (B75-50661) ISBN 0-19-373807-4
- To words by Joseph Beaumont : three songs for soprano and alto voices (SSA) and piano. *Oxford University Press. £0.90* FDW (B75-50496) ISBN 0-19-338382-9
- Trois chansons tristes, from the late 19th century collection of old French songs by Theodore Botrel. *Oxford University Press. £0.90* KE/TSDW/G/AYH (B75-50566) ISBN 0-19-345828-4
- Two ballads : for mezzo-soprano and guitar. *Oxford University Press. £0.80* KFNE/TSDW (B75-50121) ISBN 0-19-345827-6

Tatlock, Richard. The providence of God : a sequence of readings, hymns and anthems to celebrate the harvest. *Novello. £0.60* DF/LP (B75-50409)

Taverner, John. Dum transisset Sabbatum : S.A.T. Bar. B. unacc. *Oxford University Press. Unpriced* EZDGKH/LL (B75-51031) ISBN 0-19-350350-6

Tchaikovsky, Peter.
- The sleeping beauty. *Eulenberg. Unpriced* MM/HM (B75-50601)
- The storm. Op.76. L'Orage : Ouverture für Orchester nach dem Drama von A.N. Ostrowsky. *Belaieff : Hinrichsen. £8.00* MMJ (B75-50147)

Tchaikovsky : a self portrait. (Volkoff, Vladimir). *Crescendo Publishing Co. : Hale. £5.50* BTD(N) (B75-21665) ISBN 0-7091-4976-x

Tchaikovsky symphonies and concertos. (Warrack, John). 2nd ed. *British Broadcasting Corporation. £0.45* BTDAMME (B75-00740) ISBN 0-563-12773-2

Tchaikowsky, André. Inventions for piano. Opus 2. *Novello. £1.00* QPJ (B75-50712)

Tcherepnin, Nikolai. Destiny. Op.59. Le Destin = Destiny. Opus 59 : three symphonic fragments on a ballad by Edgar Allan Poe. *Belaieff : Peters. Unpriced* MMJ (B75-50148)

Teach yourself books.
- Fradd, Dale. The guitar. *Teach Yourself Books. £1.50* ATS/E (B75-18373) ISBN 0-340-16197-3
- Harvey, Eddie. Jazz piano. *English Universities Press. £0.95* AQPHX/E (B75-09744) ISBN 0-340-12456-3

Teaching the cello to groups. (Horsfall, Jean). *Oxford University Press. £2.75* ASR/E(VC) (B75-01178) ISBN 0-19-318510-5

Teasdale, Sarah. The look, the kiss and joy : three madrigals with coda, SSA unaccompanied. (Kennedy, John Brodbin). *Boosey and Hawkes. Unpriced* FEZDW (B75-51065)

Technical exercises for the oboe. (East, Raina). *Schott. Unpriced* VT/AF (B75-50339)

Telemann, Georg Philipp.
- Sonata for bassoon & basso continuo in F minor. Sonata in F minor for bassoon and basso continuo. *Musica rara. Unpriced* VWPE (B75-51414)
- Sonata for flute, oboe & continuo in E minor. Sonata in E minor : for flute, oboe (violin) and basso continuo. 1st ed. *Bärenreiter. £2.40* NWPNTE (B75-50167)
- Sonatina for oboe, violin & basso continuo in E minor. Sonatine in E minor : for oboe, violin and basso continuo. First ed. *Bärenreiter. Unpriced* NUTNT (B75-50635)
- Sonatina for violin & harpsichord, no.6, in C major. *arr.* Sonatina no.3. *Boosey and Hawkes. £0.65* VVPK/AEM (B75-51408)

Tell me what month : an American Christmas folk song. (Bune, Robert). *Warner : Blossom. Unpriced* ENVSNRDW/LF (B75-50451)

Telyn y werin : harpCyfrol 1. *Adlais. Unpriced* TQPMK/DW/AYDK (B75-50793)

Templa quam dilecta. *Vocal score.* Templa quam dilecta : cantata for SATB and orchestra. (Drayton, Paul). *Novello. £0.95* DE (B75-50997)

Temporary diversion. *Vocal score.* A temporary diversion : (or the monumental photographic and zoological umbrella show). (Paynter, John). *Universal. Unpriced* CN (B75-50992)

Ten Scottish impressions : for guitar. (Daw, Stephen).

Stainer and Bell. Unpriced TSPMJ (B75-50808)

Ten tunes from Gilbert and Sullivan. (Sullivan, Sir Arthur Seymour). Novello. £1.00 VRPLTSK/DW (B75-50324)

Tenebrae : a song cycle for baritone and piano. (Bennett, Richard Rodney). Universal. Unpriced KGNDW (B75-51132)

Tennyson, Alfred, Lord. The poet's song : for four-part chorus of mixed voices with piano accompaniment. (Dello Joio, Norman). Associated Music. £0.25 DW (B75-51017)

Tennyson, Alfred, Lord Tennyson. Crossing the bar : anthem for solo quartet or mixed choir and organ. (Ives, Charles). Associated Music. Unpriced DH (B75-50419)

Tenor banjo chord coloring book : chords and how to use them. (Owen, Tom). Chappell. Unpriced TTV/RC (B75-51331)

Tentacles of the dark nebula : for tenor & strings. (Bedford, David). Universal. Unpriced KGHE/RXNNDX (B75-51129)

Tenting on the old camp ground : for four-part mixed voices with piano or guitar (and optional oboe, flute, or violin). (Kittredge, Walter). Schirmer. Unpriced DW (B75-50443)

Terpsichore. Selections: arr. Four dances
Set 1. (Praetorius, Michael). Ricordi. Unpriced WNRH (B75-50376)

Terpsichore. Selections: arr. Four dances
Set 2. (Praetorius, Michael). Ricordi. Unpriced WNRH (B75-50377)

Terzakis, Dimitri. Ikos. Ikos : für zwei Soprane, zwei Alte, zwei Tenore, zwei Basse, with Katawassia : für zwei Soprane, Alt, zwei Tenore, Bariton. Bärenreiter. Unpriced EZDW (B75-50482)

Terzetto : flute, viola and guitar. (Walker, Eldon). Thames. Unpriced NVRNT (B75-50644)

Terzi, Giovanni Antonio. Libro primo de canzoni da sonare. Canzona 'La Girella'. Canzona 'La Girella' : for four instruments. (Maschera, Florentio). Oxford University Press. £0.55 LNS (B75-51146)   ISBN 0-19-341206-3

Tesserae C : violoncello solo. (Connolly, Justin). Novello. £1.00 SRPMJ (B75-50775)

Tetrazzini, Luisa. Caruso and Tetrazzini on the art of singing. (Caruso, Enrico). Dover Publications : Constable. £0.84 AB/E (B75-22212)   ISBN 0-486-23140-2

Texas lullaby : brass band. (Smith-Masters, Stanley). Studio Music. Unpriced WMJ (B75-51419)

That's a very good sign. arr. That's a very good sign : for two-part chorus of treble voices and piano. (Williams, Phyllis). Frank Music. Unpriced FLDW (B75-51072)

That's entertainment : a musical and pictorial history of the MGM musical. Chappell. Unpriced KDW/JR/AY (B75-50115)

The best of Scott Joplin. (Joplin, Scott). Chappell. Unpriced WMK/AHXJ (B75-50371)

The Booke of Common Praier noted. The Lord's Praier. arr. The Lord's Prayer : for unison choir or solo voice and piano or organ. (Merbecke, John). Oxford University Press. Unpriced JDTF (B75-51084)

The inch worm : for mixed chorus (SATB) and piano with optional rhythm guitar, bass guitar and drums. (Loesser, Frank). Frank Music. Unpriced DW (B75-51020)

Theme from Godfather 2 : piano solo. (Rota, Nina). Famous Music : Chappell. Unpriced QPK/JR (B75-50197)

Theory and practice of piano construction, with a detailed practical method for tuning. (White, William Braid). Dover Publications etc. : Constable. £1.40 AQ/BC (B75-19735)   ISBN 0-486-23139-9

Theory and practice of pianoforte building. Theory and practice of piano construction, with a detailed practical method for tuning. (White, William Braid). Dover Publications etc. : Constable. £1.40 AQ/BC (B75-19735)   ISBN 0-486-23139-9

There is a garden in her face : TTB, unaccompanied. (Binkerd, Gordon). Boosey and Hawkes. Unpriced GEZDW (B75-50513)

There's a road (which leads from Jerusalem) : hymn. (Schneider, Martin Gotthard). Bosworth. Unpriced JDM (B75-50524)

Thibault, G. Eighteenth century musical instruments, France and Britain = Les Instruments de musique au XVIIIe Siecle, France et Grande-Bretagne : catalogue of an exhibition. Victoria and Albert Museum. £2.50 AL/B(YH/XF101) (B75-03646)   ISBN 0-901486-71-x

Thiman, Eric Harding.
Chatter box : piano solo. British and Continental. Unpriced QPJ (B75-50713)
The thrush in spring : two-part song. Roberton. £0.12 FDW (B75-50497)

Third man. (Karas, Anton). Chappell. Unpriced UMK/JR (B75-50826)

Third man. Harry Lime theme. arr. The third man. (Karas, Anton). Chappell. Unpriced UMK/JR (B75-50826)

Thirty selected duets. See 30 selected duets.

This worlde's joie : a cantata for soprano, tenor and baritone soloists, mixed chorus, boys' (or girls') choir, and orchestra. (Mathias, William). Oxford University Press. £3.95 DE (B75-50408)   ISBN 0-19-337437-4

This worlde's joie. Vocal score. This worlde's joie : a cantata for soprano, tenor and baritone soloists, mixed chorus, boys' (or girls') choir, and orchestra. (Mathias, William). Oxford University Press. £3.95 DE (B75-50408)   ISBN 0-19-337437-4

Thomas, Bernard.
Newe ausserlesene liebliche Branden, Intraden. Newe auserlesene Branden, Intraden, Mascheraden, Baletten, Allmanden, Couranten, Volten, Auffzuge und frembde Tantze (1617)
Volume 1 : for 2 cornetti (trumpets in C) and 3 trombones. Musica rara. £4.00 WNRH/AY (B75-51441)

Newe ausserlesene liebliche Branden, Intraden. Newe auserlesene Branden, Intraden, Mascheraden, Baletten, Allmanden, Couranten, Volten, Auffzuge und frembde Tantze (1617)
Volume 2 : for 2 cornetti (trumpets in C) and 3 trombones. Musica rara. £4.00 WNRH/AY (B75-51442)

Newe ausserlesene liebliche Branden, Intraden. Newe auserlesene Branden, Intraden, Mascheraden, Baletten, Allmanden, Couranten, Volten Auffzuge und frembde Tantze (1617)
Volume 3 : for 3 cornetti and 2 trombones. Musica rara. £4.00 WNRH/AY (B75-51443)

Opus newer Paduanen, Galliarden, Intraden, Canzonen (1617) : for 3 cornetti (trumpets in C) and 2 trombones
Volume 1. (Simpson, Thomas). Musica rara. Unpriced WNRH (B75-51439)
Volume 2. (Simpson, Thomas). Musica rara. Unpriced WNRH (B75-51440)

Two chansons for flutes. Oxford University Press. £0.12 EZDU (B75-50062)   ISBN 0-19-341220-9

Thomas, Dylan. Ceremony after a fire raid. Op.63 : for mixed voices (SATB Bar B), piano and percussion. (Mathias, William). Oxford University Press. £1.50 ENYLDX (B75-50452)   ISBN 0-19-337434-x

Thomas, Edward. Early one morning : five poems of Edward Thomas, for tenor and guitar. (Hold, Trevor). Thames Music. Unpriced KGHE/TSDW (B75-50590)

Thomas, Paul Lindsley.
Shout the glad tidings. Op.12 : for mixed choir and organ, with optional instruments. Oxford University Press. Unpriced DH (B75-51006)
Variations on the Welsh hymn tune 'Aberystwyth', Op.3 : for organ. Oxford University Press. Unpriced R/T (B75-51269)

Thomason, Charles Simson. Ceol mor notation : a new and abbreviated system of musical notation for the piobaireachd as played on the Highland bagpipe, with examples. EP Publishing etc.. £6.75 AVY/T(QU) (B75-22850)   ISBN 0-7158-1114-2

Thompson, Charles. Bing : the authorised biography. W.H. Allen. £3.95 AKDW/GB/E(P) (B75-25558)   ISBN 0-491-01715-4

Thomson, John Mansfield. Your book of the recorder. 2nd ed. Faber. £1.25 AVS/B (B75-08738)   ISBN 0-571-04873-0

Thou wert my purer mind : unaccompanied part song for SATB. (Dale, Mervyn). Ashdown. £0.15 EZDW (B75-50476)

Three carols for brass. British and Continental Music. Unpriced WMK/DP/LF/AYC (B75-50924)

Three choral songs from 'As you like it' : SATB. (Horovitz, Joseph). Novello. £0.50 EZDW (B75-51047)

Three etudes on themes of Gershwin : for unaccompanied clarinet. (Harvey, Paul). Chappell. Unpriced VVPMJ (B75-51410)

Three for Barton : for solo brass tuba. (Blank, Allan). Associated Music. £1.05 WVPMJ (B75-51473)

Three Herrick songs. Op.41 : medium voice and guitar. (Winters, Geoffrey). Thames. Unpriced KFVE/TSDW (B75-50587)

Three journeys : a carol. (Graves, Richard). Novello. £0.10 JDP/LFP (B75-50526)

Three Latin-American sketches : for orchestra. (Copland, Aaron). Boosey and Hawkes. £7.50 MMJ (B75-50613)

Three more songs for two-part choir. (Dale, Mervyn). Ashdown. £0.15 FDW (B75-50071)

Three piece suite : for four clarinets. (Lyons, Graham). British and Continental Music. Unpriced VVNSG (B75-50892)

Three pieces for 4. See Warren, Edward.

Three poems of Robert Frost : for voice and piano. (Carter, Elliott). Associated Music. £1.30 KDW (B75-51103)

Three Scottish folk tunes. Oxford University Press. Unpriced QNVK/DW/G/AYDL (B75-51220)   ISBN 0-19-372985-7

Threlfall, Robert John. Concerto for violin. Violin concerto. (Delius, Frederick). Stainer and Bell. Unpriced MPSF (B75-51164)   ISBN 0-85249-355-x

Thrush in spring : two-part song. (Thiman, Eric Harding). Roberton. £0.12 FDW (B75-50497)

Thy perfect love : SATB. (Rutter, John). Oxford University Press. £0.10 DH (B75-50420)   ISBN 0-19-351122-3

Tick-tock song : for SATB (or SA, SSA, TTB) with instrumental accompaniment. (Sansom, Clive A). Paterson. Unpriced ENYLDW (B75-50036)

Tidy, Bill. Kiss me goodnight, Sergeant Major : the songs and ballads of World War II. Panther. £0.60 ADW/KG(YC/XNU7) (B75-29320)   ISBN 0-586-04152-4

Tiempo para espacios : for harpsichord and string orchestra. (Halffter, Cristóbal). Universal. Unpriced RXMPQR (B75-50751)

Tillett, Beverley.
Jerry Silverman's folk song encyclopaedia : with over 1,000 favorite songs arranged for voice and guitar
Vol.1. Chappell. Unpriced KE/TSDW/G/AY (B75-50564)
Vol.2. Chappell. Unpriced KE/TSDW/G/AY (B75-50565)

Tillman, June. Music as stimulus in secondary assembly and RE ... 2 Chester House, Pages La., N10 1PR : Christian Education Movement, Religious Education Service. £0.40 A/FD(VK/WT) (B75-15228)   ISBN 0-905022-00-9

Tilmouth, Michael. Consort of four parts. (Locke, Matthew). Stainer and Bell. Unpriced STNSG (B75-51309)

Time to play : for piano. (King, Janet). M.S.M. Unpriced QPJ (B75-51248)

Tin Pan Alley : a pictorial history (1919-1939) with complete words and music of forty songs. EMI Music. £2.95 KDW/GB/AY (B75-50560)

Tinga layo : West Indian song. (Gillies, Douglas). Oxford University Press. Unpriced JFDW (B75-51093)   ISBN 0-19-342051-1

Tippett, Sir Michael. Sonata no.3 for piano. Schott. Unpriced QPE (B75-51226)

Tischler, Hans. Four centuries of song, from the troubadour to the Elizabethan age : for voice and guitar. Associated Music. Unpriced KE/TSDW/AY (B75-50563)

Tittel, Karl. Orgelwerke
Bd.2. (Krebs, Johann Ludwig). Litolff : Peters. Unpriced RJ (B75-50210)

Tjeknavorian, Loris. Armenian sketches : piano solo. Novello. £1.00 QPJ (B75-50714)

To a mountain stream : piano. (Da-Veena). Pandian Press Galliard. Unpriced QPJ (B75-51238)

To a young girl. (Rorem, Ned). Boosey and Hawkes. Unpriced KDW (B75-51111)

To words by Joseph Beaumont : three songs for soprano and alto voices (SSA) and piano. (Tate, Phyllis). Oxford University Press. £0.90 FDW (B75-50496)   ISBN 0-19-338382-9

Tomlinson, Ernest. English pageant : a suite for orchestra. Central Music Library : Belwin-Mills. Unpriced MMG (B75-50607)

Tomlinson, Geoffrey. Creature conforts : a fantasy for voices and percussion. Boosey and Hawkes. 2.50 JFE/NYLDX (B75-50542)

Tommy Thumb : ten songs for young singers and players, for unison voices with tuned and untuned percussion (and guitar symbols). Oxford University Press. £0.65 JFE/XMDW/AY (B75-50101)   ISBN 0-19-330558-5

Tomorrow the fox will come to town : mixed chorus, SATB. (Binkerd, Gordon). Boosey and Hawkes. Unpriced EZDW (B75-50064)

Top pop scene
1975. Purnell. £0.85 A/GB (B75-14332)   ISBN 0-361-03192-0

Toplis, Gloria.
The angel Gabriel : for S.S.A. Ricordi. Unpriced FEZDP/LF (B75-51063)
Now the holly bears a berry : unison song with descant. Ricordi. Unpriced FDP/LF (B75-51053)
Somerset wassail. Ricordi. Unpriced FE/XDP/LF (B75-51058)

Torchinsky, Abe. Suites for cello. S.1007-12. Selections: arr. Dance movements. (Bach, Johann Sebastian). Schirmer. Unpriced WVPMK/AH (B75-50963)

Torelli, Giuseppe.
Sinfonia à 4 in C major. G.33. Sinfonia à 4 in C major. G.33 : for 4 trumpets, 4 oboes, 2 bassoons, strings (concertino and rip.) and basso continuo. Musica rara. Unpriced MRE (B75-51166)
Sinfonia avanti l'opera. G.14. arr. Sinfonia avanti l'opera, G.14 : for trumpet, strings and continuo. Musica rara. £1.50 WSPK/LE (B75-51462)
Sinfonia avanti l'opera. G.14 : for trumpet, strings and continuo. Musica rara. £4.50 MRE (B75-51167)
Sinfonia in D major. G.3. Sinfonia in D. G.3 : for trumpet, strings and continuo. Musica rara. Unpriced MRE (B75-51168)
Sinfonia in D major. G.3. arr. Sinfonia in D. G.3 : for trumpet, strings and continuo. Musica rara. £1.50 WSPK/LE (B75-51463)
Sinfonia in D major. G.4. Sinfonia in D. G.4 : for trumpet, strings and continuo. Musica rara. Unpriced MRE (B75-51169)
Sinfonia in D major. G.4. arr. Sinfonia in D. G.4 : for trumpet, strings and continuo. Musica rara. £1.50 WSPK/LE (B75-51464)
Sinfonia in D major. G.5. Sinfonia in D. G.5 : for trumpet, strings and continuo. Musica rara. £4.50 MRE (B75-51170)
Sinfonia in D major. G.5. arr. Sinfonia in D. G.5 : for trumpet, strings and continuo. Musica rara. £1.50 WSPK/LE (B75-51465)
Sonata for trumpet, two violins, viola & basso continuo in D major. G.6. Sonata in D.G.6 : for trumpet, strings and continuo. Musica rara. £4.50 NUXSNRE (B75-51177)
Sonata for trumpet, two violins, viola & basso continuo in D major. G.6. arr. Sonata in D.G.6 : for trumpet, strings and continuo. Musica rara. £1.50 WSPK/LE (B75-51466)

Torres, Pedro Manuel. El Gallo : danza venezuelana per chitarra. Zanibon : Hinrichsen. Unpriced TSPMH (B75-50275)

Tortelier, Paul. Pishnetto : recital étude no.5, for cello and piano. Chester. Unpriced SRPJ (B75-51306)

Touchin, Colin M. A royal pageant. Op.11 : for recorder quartet, (2 descant treble tenor). Carne House, Parsons Lane, Bury, Lancs. : Tomus. Unpriced VSNS (B75-50861)

Townsend, Paul. A temporary diversion. Vocal score. A temporary diversion : (or the monumental photographic and zoological umbrella show). (Paynter, John). Universal. Unpriced CN (B75-50992)

Traditional Music
No.1- ; mid 1975-. 90 St Julian's Farm Rd, SE27 0RS : Traditional Music. £0.35(£1.20 yearly) A/G(YC/B)

Traditionen und Reforman in der Kirchenmusik : Festschrift für Konrad Ameln zum 75. Geburtstag am 6, Juli 1974. 32 Great Titchfield St., W.1 : Bärenreiter-Verlag. £13.80 AD/LD(YE/X)

Traité de nai roumain : methode de flûte de Pan. (Zamfir, Gheorghe). Chappell. Unpriced VSX/AC (B75-50886)

Transformations of 'Love bade me welcome' : for clarinet and piano. (Harvey, Jonathan). Novello. £3.00 VVPJ

(B75-51404)
Tranter, Eric.
Making electronic music : a course for schools
Book 1. (Dwyer, Terence). *Oxford University Press. £1.50* **APV(D) (B75-24850)** ISBN 0-19-321071-1
Book 2. (Dwyer, Terence). *Oxford University Press. £1.50* APV/D (B75-24851) ISBN 0-19-321072-x
Teacher's book. (Dwyer, Terence). *Oxford University Press. £2.50* APV/D (B75-24852) ISBN 0-19-321070-3
Trapp, Willy. Prince of Denmark's march. *arr.* Let the earth resound ('Lobt den Herrn der Welt'). (Clarke, Jeremiah). *Bosworth. Unpriced* JDH (B75-50522)
Treatise on the art of pianoforte construction. (Wolfenden, Samuel). *The Gresham Press, Old Woking, Surrey : Union Bros Ltd. £5.85* AQ/BC (B75-18372) ISBN 0-9502121-3-x
Tredici, David del. *See* Del Tredici, David.
Treemonisha. *Selections: arr.* Treemonisha. (Joplin, Scott). *Fanfare Press : Chappell : Chappell. Unpriced* KDW (B75-51105)
Tremlett, George.
The Cliff Richard story. *Futura Publications. £0.50* AKDW/GB/E(P) (B75-29318) ISBN 0-86007-232-0
The Gary Glitter story. *Futura Publications. £0.40* AKDW/GB/E(P) (B75-01177) ISBN 0-86007-094-8
The Paul McCartney story. *Futura Publications. £0.50* AKDW/GB/E(P) (B75-19734) ISBN 0-86007-200-2
The Slade story. *Futura Publications. £0.40* AKDW/GB/E(P) (B75-13167) ISBN 0-86007-193-6
The Who. *Futura Publications. £0.40* AKDW/GB/E(P) (B75-13168) ISBN 0-86007-069-7
Tremplins : voices and orchestra. (Miroglio, Francis). *Universal. Unpriced* JNCE/MDX (B75-50545)
Trevor, Caleb Henry.
Organ music for manuals
Book 5. *Oxford University Press. Unpriced* R/AY (B75-51267) ISBN 0-19-375852-0
Book 6. *Oxford University Press. Unpriced* R/AY (B75-51268) ISBN 0-19-375853-9
Short chorale preludes with and without pedals
Book 1. *Oxford University Press. £0.95* R/AY (B75-50726) ISBN 0-19-375843-1
Book 2. *Oxford University Press. £0.95* R/AY (B75-50727) ISBN 0-19-375844-x
Triad : for violin and piano. (Dorward, David). *Oxford University Press. Unpriced* SPJ (B75-51295) ISBN 0-19-356261-8
Triad Press bibliographical series.
MacDonald, Malcolm, *b.1948.* John Foulds : his life in music : with a detailed catalogue of his works, a discography, a bibliographical note, and with music examples and illustrations. *22 Pheasants Way, Rickmansworth, Herts. : Triad Press. £4.75* BFS(N) (B75-28637) ISBN 0-902070-15-0
Rapoport, Paul. Vagn Holmboe : a catalogue of his music, discography, bibliography, essays. *10E Prior Bolton St., N.1 : Triad Press. £2.50* BHO(N) (B75-04505) ISBN 0-902070-13-4
Trinity College, *Dublin. Library.* Ina Boyle : an appreciation : with a select list of her music. (Maconchy, Elizabeth). *Trinity College Dublin, Library. Unpriced* BBSL (B75-50003) ISBN 0-904720-00-4
Trip to the circus : piano. (Smith, J. Ferguson). *Forsyth. Unpriced* QPJ (B75-51254)
Triptych : for flute, clarinet, violin, cello, piano and percussion. (Johnson, Robert Sherlaw). *Oxford University Press. £2.50* NYDPNQ (B75-50650) ISBN 0-19-357331-8
Triumph of time : for orchestra. (Birtwistle, Harrison). *Universal. Unpriced* MMJ (B75-50142)
Trois biberons : pour accordeon symphonique. (Dubois, Pierre Max). *Chappell. Unpriced* RSPMJ (B75-50223)
Trois chansons tristes, from the late 19th century collection of old French songs by Theodore Botrel. *Oxford University Press. £0.90* KE/TSDW/G/AYH (B75-50566) ISBN 0-19-345828-4
Trois poèmes à crier et à danser
Chant 1. (Humble, Keith). *Universal. Unpriced* XNS (B75-50967)
Chant 2. (Humble, Keith). *Universal. Unpriced* XNS (B75-50968)
Chant 3. (Humble, Keith). *Universal. Unpriced* XNS (B75-50969)
Trojan, Jan. Festival chorus. Slavnostní sbor = Festlicher Chor = Festival chorus : for four male voices, women's and men's chorus and piano. (Janacek, Leos). *Bärenreiter. £1.20* DX (B75-50033)
Trombone rockanova. (Kenny, Terry). *Studio Music. Unpriced* WMJ (B75-50922)
Trombone rockanova : brass band. (Kenny, Terry). *Studio Music. Unpriced* WMH (B75-50918)
Trompetas de la serafines : overture for orchestra. (Surinach, Carlos). *Associated Music. £3.90* MMJ (B75-51158)
Troyens. (Berlioz, Hector). *Eulenburg. Unpriced* CQC (B75-50010)
Troyens. Gloire, gloire à Didon. *Vocal score.* Hail all hail to the queen : SATB. (Berlioz, Hector). *Oxford University Press. £0.08* DW (B75-50028) ISBN 0-19-343046-0
Trumpet voluntary. (Clarke, Jeremiah). *Chester. Unpriced* WMK/AGM (B75-51424)
Trumpets sound! (Elms, Albert). *Ambleside Music : EMI. Unpriced* WMPWRNSK (B75-51432)
Tschaikowsky, Peter. *See* Tchaikovsky, Peter.
Tull, Fisher. Reflections on Paris : symphonic band. *Boosey and Hawkes. £20.50* UMJ (B75-51336)
Tunnard, Thomas. Maker of man : plainsong melody, faburden verses SATB. *Banks. Unpriced* EZDH (B75-50461)
Turn it up! (I can't hear the words). (Sarlin, Bob). *Coronet. £0.50* ADW/GB(XQ14) (B75-07793) ISBN 0-340-17848-5
Turnbull, Michael.
Mortorium à 5. Sonata (Mortorium) à 5 (1737) : for trumpet, oboe, flute, violin and basso continuo. (Linike, Johann Georg). *Musica rara. Unpriced* NUNR (B75-51173)
Sonata for trumpet, oboe and basso continuo in C major. (Finger, Godfrey). *Musica rara. Unpriced* NWNTE (B75-51190)
Sonata for trumpet, violin, oboe and basso continuo in C major. (Finger, Godfrey). *Musica rara. Unpriced* NUNSE (B75-51174)
Turner, Michael R. Just a song at twilight : the second parlour song book. *Michael Joseph. £8.50* KDW/GB/AY(XHS64) (B75-51115) ISBN 0-7181-1339-x
Turpin hero, nos. 9-16. Flight, fight and romance : eight folk songs for voices and guitar. *Oxford University Press. £0.35* JE/TSDW/G/AY (B75-50094) ISBN 0-19-330628-x
Turpin hero, nos. 17-21. Good earth : five folk songs for voices and guitar. *Oxford University Press. £0.35* JE/TSDW/G/AY (B75-50095) ISBN 0-19-330629-8
Turpin hero, nos. 22-30. Bravado and travellers all : nine folk songs for voices and guitar. *Oxford University Press. £0.35* JE/TSDW/G/AY (B75-50096) ISBN 0-19-330630-1
Tusiani, Joseph. Songs from Michelangelo : for baritone and piano. (Laderman, Ezra). *Oxford University Press. Unpriced* KGNDW (B75-51134)
Twelve days of Christmas : traditional song. (Naylor, Frank). *Bosworth. Unpriced* QPK/DW/LF (B75-51263)

Twelve easy anthems. *Royal School of Church Music. Unpriced* DH/AY (B75-51007)
Twelve hours of sunset. (Bedford, David). *Universal. Unpriced* DADX (B75-50406)
Twelve hours of sunset. *Choral score.* Twelve hours of sunset. (Bedford, David). *Universal. Unpriced* DADX (B75-50406)
Twelve pieces for the musical clock (Flötenuhr, 1773). (Haydn, Joseph). *Universal. Unpriced* VRPK/B/FK (B75-51372)
Twentieth century carol : unison with optional 2nd part. (Graves, Richard). *Bosworth. Unpriced* JDP/LF (B75-51081)
Twenty-eight selected duets. *See* 28 selected duets.
Twenty great TV themes. *Essex Music. Unpriced* QPK/JS/AY (B75-50721)
Twenty-one Scots tunes from James Thomson's music book (1702). *Forsyth. Unpriced* VSSPMJ (B75-50884)
Twentyfive pages : for 1 to 25 pianos. (Brown, Earle). *Universal. Unpriced* QN (B75-51213)
Twilight. (Sullivan, *Sir* Arthur Seymour). *Emerson. Unpriced* VRNTQK (B75-51367)
Twilight. *arr.* Twilight. (Sullivan, *Sir* Arthur Seymour). *Emerson. Unpriced* VRNTQK (B75-51367)
Twinn, Sydney. Four miniature string quartets, from the Sullivan operas. (Sullivan, *Sir* Arthur Seymour). *Paxton. £1.25* RXNSK/DW (B75-50238)
Two ballads : for mezzo-soprano and guitar. (Tate, Phyllis). *Oxford University Press. £0.80* KFNE/TSDW (B75-50121) ISBN 0-19-345827-6
Two contrasts : oboe and piano. (Hanmer, Ronald). *Emerson. Unpriced* VTPJ (B75-50342)
Two in one : violin duets in the first finger position. (Nelson, Sheila M). *Boosey and Hawkes. £1.00* SNU (B75-50242)
Two lullaby carols : for 4-part female voices unaccompanied. (Copley, Ian Alfred). *Roberton. £0.10* FEZDP/LF (B75-51060)
Two of a kind : 8 short inventions, for piano, introducing contrapuntal style. (Last, Joan). *Forsyth. Unpriced* QP/RM (B75-51224)
Two of a kind : 8 short inventions introducing contrapuntal style. (Last, Joan). *Forsyth. Unpriced* QP/RM (B75-50665)
Two short Elizabethan anthems : for SATB unaccompanied or with organ. *Novello. Unpriced* EZDK (B75-50465)
Two studies for bassoon. Zwei Studien : für Fagott. (Goodman, Alfred). *Litolff : Peters. Unpriced* VWPMJ (B75-50352)
Two trebles : nine pieces arranged for two treble recorders and piano. *Oxford University Press. £1.20* VSSNTQK/AAY (B75-50879) ISBN 0-19-355202-7
Two-way pieces : twelve progressive miniatures, for descant recorder with optional piano accompaniment. (Duke, Henry). *British and Continental. Unpriced* VSRPMJ (B75-51382)
Two-way pieces : twelve progressive miniatures, for piano solo, with optional descant recorder. (Duke, Henry). *British and Continental. Unpriced* QPJ (B75-51241)
Tydeman, Richard. Sing mortals! : a sonnet for the festival of St Cecilia, for SATB and organ. (Bliss, *Sir* Arthur). *Novello. Unpriced* DH (B75-50021)
Tyler, Tony. The Beatles : an illustrated record. (Carr, Roy). *New English Library. £1.95* AKDW/GB/E(P) (B75-13736) ISBN 0-450-02626-4
Tympanorum musices : for four timpani and three bongos. (Jenni, Donald). *Associated Music. Unpriced* XQNP (B75-50971)
Tyree, Ronald.
Sonata for bassoon & basso continuo in F minor. Sonata in F minor for bassoon and basso continuo. (Telemann, Georg Philipp). *Musica rara. Unpriced* VWPE (B75-51414)
Sonata for bassoon & basso continuo, op.26, no.2, in A minor. Sonata no.2 in A minor : for bassoon and basso continuo. (Boismortier, Joseph Bodin de). *Musica rara. £2.00* VWPE (B75-51413)
Über die Orgelkunst der Gotik, der Renaissance und des Barock : Musik, Disposition, Mixturen, Mensuren, Registrierung, Gebrauch der Klaviere. (Klotz, Hans). 2., völlig neubearb. Aufl. *32 Great Titchfield St., W.1 : Bärenreiter. £31.50* AR/B(XCL431)
Ugly duckling : for two-part chorus of treble voices with piano. (Loesser, Frank). *Frank Music. Unpriced* FLDW (B75-51068)
Uhl, Alfred. Dreissig Estüden für Viola. *Schott. £2.25* SQPMJ (B75-51304)
Ungarisches Klavierbuchlein = Hungarian piano booklet. *Litolff : Peters. Unpriced* QP/AYG (B75-50182)
University of Bristol. *Department of Music.* Composers' catalogue. *Royal Fort House, Bristol BS8 1UJ : The Department. Free* A(YDHDB/TC) (B75-12885) ISBN 0-904877-00-0
University of Cambridge. *Fitzwilliam Museum. See* Fitzwilliam Museum.
University of Dublin. *See* Trinity College, *Dublin.*
University of East Anglia. Careers information sheets. Fortescue, Margaret. Careers with music ... *Careers Centre, University of East Anglia, University Plain, Norwich NR4 7TJ : University of East Anglia. £0.15(£0.10 to university and polytechnic careers services)* A(MN/YD) (B75-15001)
University of Exeter. *American Arts Documentation Centre.* American arts pamphlets. Elkus, Jonathan. Charles Ives and the American band tradition : a centennial tribute. *American Arts Documentation Centre, University of Exeter. £0.60* BIVUMM (B75-05796) ISBN 0-85989-005-8
University of Zambia. Zambian papers. *See* Zambian papers.
University of Zambia. *Institute for African Studies.* The Kachamba Brothers' Band : a study of neo-traditional music in Malaŵi. (Kubik, Gerhard). *Manchester University Press for University of Zambia Institute for African Studies. £2.25* BZNNALN(P) (B75-15002) ISBN 0-7190-1408-5
Vaccai, Nicolo. Metodo practico di canto italiano. Practical method of Italian singing. New ed. *Schirmer. Unpriced* K/AFH (B75-50547)
Vagn Holmboe : a catalogue of his music, discography, bibliography, essays. (Rapoport, Paul). *10E Prior Bolton St., N.1 : Triad Press. £2.50* BHO(N) (B75-04505) ISBN 0-902070-13-4
Valbonesi, Ruggero.
Aquarelles. Op.19, no.4. *arr.* Humoreske. Op.19, no.4. (Gade, Niels Vilhelm). *British and Continental Music. Unpriced* VVPK (B75-50902)
Capriccio. *arr.* Capriccio. *British and Continental, EMI Music. Unpriced* VVPK (B75-50903)
Vallier, Jacques. Fantasie for two trumpets & piano. Fantasie : pour 2 trompettes (ut ou si bémol) et piano. *Chappell. Unpriced* WSNTQ (B75-50381)
Valse romantique : piano solo. (Debussy, Claude). *Peters. Unpriced* QPHW (B75-50681)
Van Beethoven, Ludwig. *See* Beethoven, Ludwig van.
Van Camp, Leonard.
Christmas music from Colonial America : an anthology of Christmas psalms and anthems from the revolutionary and federal eras : for mixed chorus, organ and optional instruments. *Galaxy : Galliard. Unpriced* EZDH/AYT (B75-50463)
Hora novissima. Urbs Syon unica. City of high renown = Urbs Syon unica : unaccompanied mixed chorus. (Parker, Horatio). *Galaxy : Galliard. Unpriced* EZDH (B75-51035)
Judith. God. Jehovah. God, Jehovah : mixed chorus and keyboard. (Chadwick, George Whitfield). *Galaxy Galliard. Unpriced* DH (B75-51003)
Van Dresar, Mary. Christmas magic. *arr.* Christmas magic. *Warner : Blossom. Unpriced* DW/LF (B75-51024)
Van Dyke, Henry. Four things a man must learn to do : for mixed chorus and piano with optional bass and guitar. (Atkinson, Condit). *Galaxy : Galliard. Unpriced* DW (B75-50436)
Van Puijenbroeck, Victor. *See* Puijenbroeck, Victor van.
Van Vechten, Carl. My musical life. (Rimsky-Korsakoff, Nikolai). *48 Great Marlborough St., W.1 : Ernst Eulenberg Ltd. £6.25* BRI(N) (B75-24236) ISBN 0-903873-13-3
Variants on a madrigal by Gesualdo : for large chamber ensemble. (Schifrin, Lalo). *Associated Music. £3.25* MR/T (B75-50626)
Variations 2 : trio, violin, viola, violoncello. (Riley, Dennis). *Peters. Unpriced* RXNT/T (B75-50240)
Variations 3 : viola alone. (Riley, Dennis). *Peters. Unpriced* SQPMJ (B75-50258)
Variations in a mod mood : for concert band. (Lombardo, Mario). *Chappell. Unpriced* UM/T (B75-50294)
Variations on a theme of Paganini : for brass quartet, or saxophone quartet, or woodwind quartet. (Horovitz, Joseph). *R. Smith. Unpriced* WNS/T (B75-50379)
Variations on 'Jerusalem the golden'. *arr.* Variations on 'Jerusalem the golden'. (Ives, Charles). *Associated Music. £1.30* UMK (B75-51341)
Variations on the Welsh hymn tune 'Aberystwyth', Op.3 : for organ. (Thomas, Paul Lindsley). *Oxford University Press. Unpriced* R/T (B75-51269)
Vaughan Williams, Ralph.
Norfolk rhapsody. *arr.* Norfolk rhapsody. *Oxford University Press. Unpriced* UMMK (B75-51348)
O how amiable. *arr.* O how amiable : anthem for mixed chorus (SATB) and band or organ. *Oxford University Press. Unpriced* EUMDK (B75-51028)
Vêpres siciliennes. Overture. *arr.* Overture, Sicilian vespers. (Verdi, Giuseppe). *Studio Music. Unpriced* WMK

(B75-51423)
Verdi, Giuseppe. Les Vêpres siciliennes. Overture. *arr.* Overture, Sicilian vespers. *Studio Music. Unpriced* WMK (B75-51423)
Verlaine, Paul. Jeux-thème : for mezzo-soprano and chamber orchestra. (Hoyland, Vic). *Universal. Unpriced* KFNE/MRDW (B75-51127)
Verlieh uns Frieden : Variationen für Blechbläser und Orgel. (Ehmann, Heinrich). *Bärenreiter. £2.20* WNRR/T (B75-50378)
Vermeer, Hans Dieter.
Moderne Rhythmen : für Jazz-Gitarre. *Schott. £1.75* TSPMK (B75-51327)
Negro Spirituals für Gitarre solo. *Schott. £1.75* TSPMK/DW/LC (B75-51330)
Verrall, Pamela Motley.
Old English music : for oboe, clarinet and bassoon (or two clarinets and bassoon). *Oxford University Press. Unpriced* VNTK/AYD (B75-51364) ISBN 0-19-359203-7
Six dances for descant duets and piano. *Rahter. Unpriced* VSRPH (B75-50874)
Vester, Frans.
Duo concertant for flute and piano. Op.129. (Czerny, Carl). *Universal. Unpriced* VRPF (B75-51370)
Three fantasias. Opus 38 : for flute solo. (Kuhlau, Friedrich Daniel Rudolph). *Universal. Unpriced* VRPMJ (B75-50855)
Twelve pieces for the musical clock (Flötenuhr, 1773). (Haydn, Joseph). *Universal. Unpriced* VRPK/B/FK (B75-51372)
Victor Herbert memories. (Herbert, Victor). *Studio Music. Unpriced* WMK/DW (B75-50374)
Victoria and Albert Museum. Eighteenth century musical instruments, France and Britain = Les Instruments de musique au XVIIIe Siecle, France et Grande-Bretagne catalogue of an exhibition. (Thibault, G). *Victoria and Albert Museum. £2.50* AL/B(YH/XF101) (B75-03646) ISBN 0-901486-71-x
'Vie de matelot = A sailor's life : theme and variations for brass band. (Farnon, Robert). *R. Smith. Unpriced* WM/T (B75-50913)
Vier Choral-Motetten = Four chorale motets. Op.102 : for unaccompanied four-part chorus. (Herzogenberg, Heinrich von). *Bärenreiter. £1.20* EZDH (B75-50049)
Vier Collagen : für Klavier und Kammerchor nach Inventionen von J.S. Bach und Epigrammen von A.G. Kastner, J.W.L. Gleim, Fr. von Hagedorn und J.J. Ewald. (Zimmerman, Heinz Werner). *Bärenreiter. £2.40* DW (B75-50030)
Vieuxtemps, Henri. Souvenir d'Amérique, 'Yankee doodle'. *arr.* Souvenir d'Amérique, 'Yankee doodle' : variations burlesques. *Galaxy : Galliard. Unpriced* SPK/LT (B75-51298)
Village pictures : piano. (Last, Joan). *Forsyth. Unpriced* QPJ (B75-50704)
Village pictures : piano pieces. (Last, Joan). *Forsyth. Unpriced* QPJ (B75-51250)
Vining, Paul. Lord we beseech thee = The collect for the Annunciation of the Blessed Virgin Mary : verse anthem for alto and chorus (SAATB) with accompaniment for viols or organ. (Gibbons, Orlando). *Novello. £0.20* ESTNRDK (B75-50040)
Vintage Light Music : for the enthusiast of light music on 78 r.p.m. records
No.1- ; Jan. 1975-. *c/o Hon. Secretary, 4 Harvest Bank Rd, West Wickham, Kent : Vintage Light Music Society. £0.25(£1.00 yearly)* A/GB/FD(B) (B75-15703)
Vintage Light Music Society. Vintage Light Music : for the enthusiast of light music on 78 r.p.m. records
No.1- ; Jan. 1975-. *c/o Hon. Secretary, 4 Harvest Bank Rd, West Wickham, Kent : Vintage Light Music Society. £0.25(£1.00 yearly)* A/GB/FD(B) (B75-15703)
Viollier, Renée.
Sonatas for flute duet, nos.1-6. 6 Sonaten für zwei Querflöten
Heft 1: Sonatas 1-3. (Mouret, Jean Joseph). *Heinrichshofen : Hinrichsen. Unpriced* VRNUE (B75-50846)
Sonatas for flute duet, nos.1-6. 6 Sonaten für zwei Querflöten
Heft 2: Sonatas 4-6. (Mouret, Jean Joseph). *Heinrichshofen : Hinrichsen. Unpriced* VRNUE (B75-50847)
Viva Napoli. *See* Lopez, Francis.
Viva Napoli. (Lopez, Francis). *Chappell. Unpriced* TMK/DW (B75-51313)
Viva Napoli. La Mandoline a du bon. *arr.* La Mandoline a du bon. (Lopez, Francis). *Chappell. Unpriced* TMK/DW (B75-51311)
Viva Napoli. Ma sérénade. *arr.* Ma sérénade. (Lopez, Francis). *Chappell. Unpriced* TMK/DW (B75-51312)
Viva Napoli : operette à grand spectacle en 2 actes et 12 tableaux. (Lopez, Francis). *Chappell. Unpriced* CF (B75-50990)
Viva Napoli. Viva Napoli. *arr.* Viva Napoli. (Lopez, Francis). *Chappell. Unpriced* TMK/DW (B75-51313)
Viva Napoli. *Vocal score.* Viva Napoli : operette à grand spectacle en 2 actes et 12 tableaux. (Lopez, Francis). *Chappell. Unpriced* CF (B75-50990)
Vivaldi, Antonio.
Concerto for oboe, bassoon & string orchestra in G major. P.129. Concerto in G major for oboe, bassoon, strings and basso continuo. P.129. *Musica rara. £5.50* RXMPVTPLVWF (B75-51288)
Concerto for oboe, bassoon & string orchestra in G major. P.129. *arr.* Concerto in G major for oboe, bassoon, strings and basso continuo. P.129. *Musica rara. Unpriced* NWPNTK/LF (B75-51193)
Concerto for three violins & string orchestra in F major. P.278. *arr.* Concerto F-Dur. P.V.278 : für drei Violinen, Streichorchester und Basso continuo. *Schott. £3.00* SNSQK/LF (B75-51292)
Concerto for two horns & string orchestra in F major. P.320. *arr.* Concerto, F major, for two horns solo, strings, bassoon ad lib. and basso continuo. *Heinrichshofen : Hinrichsen. Unpriced* NUXTNSK/LF (B75-50638)
L'Estro armonico. Op.3, no.11. Largo, Allegro. *arr.* Sicilienne and finale. *Chappell. Unpriced* UMMK (B75-51349)
Vocalise-etude. *arr.* Vocalise : for flute and piano. (Copland, Aaron). *Boosey and Hawkes. £0.75* VRPK/DW (B75-50323)
Vocalise : for flute and piano. (Copland, Aaron). *Boosey and Hawkes. £0.75* VRPK/DW (B75-50323)
Voices of the past. Gramophone Company. 'His Master's Voice' recordings, plum label 'C' series (12 inch). *Old School House, Tarrant Hinton, Blandford, Dorset : Oakwood Press. £4.50* A/FD(T/WT) (B75-08384) ISBN 0-85361-166-1
Volcanic rock : for concert band. (Lombardo, Mario). *Chappell. Unpriced* UMMJ (B75-51344)
Volkoff, Vladimir. Tchaikovsky : a self portrait. *Crescendo Publishing Co. : Hale. £5.50* BTD(N) (B75-21665) ISBN 0-7091-4976-x
Volkskinderlieder. *Selections: arr.* Seven pieces. (Brahms, Johannes). *Oxford University Press. £1.00* RXMK (B75-50750) ISBN 0-19-361906-7
Vom Hönensagen : für Frauenstimmen und obligates Harmonium. (Kagel, Mauricio). *Universal. Unpriced* FDE (B75-50485)
Von der Freundlichkeit der Welt = The world's welcome (1930/1973) : choral settings on texts by Bert Brecht for mixed chorus, three pianos and percussion instruments. (Orff, Carl). *Schott. Unpriced* ENYLDW (B75-51027)
Von Dittersdorf, Carl Ditters. *See* Dittersdorf, Carl Ditters von.
Von Eichendorff, Joseph. *See* Eichendorff, Joseph von.
Von Einem, Gottfried. *See* Einem, Gottfried von.
Von Eschenbach, Wolfram. *See* Eschenbach, Wolfram von.
Von Goethe, Johann Wolfgang. *See* Goethe, Johann Wolfgang von.
Von Herzogenberg, Heinrich. *See* Herzogenberg, Heinrich von.
Von Hofmannsthal, Hugo. *See* Hofmannsthal, Hugo von.
Von Loeffelholz, Klaus. *See* Loeffelholz, Klaus von.
Von Schacht, Theodor. *See* Schacht, Theodor von.
Voss, Egon. Wagner : a documentary study. *Thames and Hudson. £12.00* BWC(N) (B75-30568) ISBN 0-500-01137-0
Voxman, Himie.
Concert and contest collection : for E flat or BB flat bass (tuba or sousaphone) with piano accompaniment. *Rubank. Unpriced* WVP/AY (B75-51472)
Introduction et rondeau écossais. Op.63. Duo. Op.63 : for horn and piano. (Moscheles, Ignaz). *Musica rara. £1.50* WTPJ (B75-51468)
Sextet for wind instruments in E flat major. Sextet in E flat major : for 2 clarinets, 2 bassoons and 2 horns. (Pleyel, Ignaz). *Musica rara. £6.50* UNQ (B75-51355)
Sonata for flute, oboe & basso continuo in G major. Trio sonata in G, for flute, oboe and basso continuo. (Platti, Giovanni). *Musica rara. Unpriced* NWPNTE (B75-51191)
Trio for two clarinets & bassoon, op.20, no.2, in E flat major. Trio in E flat. Op.20, no.2, for 2 clarinets and bassoon. (Pleyel, Ignaz *Musica rara. Unpriced* VNT (B75-51363)
Wade in the water : traditional. (Edmunds, John F). *Robbins. Unpriced* UMMJ (B75-50304)
Wadleigh, Richard. Beethoven : a documentary study. Abridged ed. *Thames and Hudson. £3.00* BBJ (B75-03644) ISBN 0-500-18146-2
Wagner, Lavern. Music. *Holt, Rinehart and Winston. £7.00* A (B75-29313) ISBN 0-03-012681-9
Wagner : a documentary study. *Thames and Hudson. £12.00* BWC(N) (B75-30568) ISBN 0-500-01137-0
Wainwright, David, *b.1929.* The piano makers. *Hutchinson. £6.00* AQ/B(K/X) (B75-50979) ISBN 0-09-122950-2
Waitzman, Daniel. Sonata for descant recorder & basso continuo in C minor. Sonata for alto recorder (or flute) and harpsichord (or piano) obbligato with cello (or bassoon) continuo. (Bach, Carl Philipp Emanuel). *Associated Music. Unpriced* VSRPE (B75-50873)
Wakeman, Rick. The myths and legends of King Arthur and the Knights of the Round Table. *Vocal score.* The myths and legends of King Arthur and the Knights of the Round Table : cantata. *Rondor Music. Unpriced* JDX (B75-51087)
Wale, Michael. The Bay City Rollers. (Paton, Tam). *Everest. £0.45* AKDW/GB/E(P) (B75-29316) ISBN 0-903925-60-5
Walker, Christopher. Cry out with joy : unison. *Oxford University Press. Unpriced* JDR (B75-51083) ISBN 0-19-351121-5
Walker, Eldon. Terzetto : flute, viola and guitar. *Thames. Unpriced* NVRNT (B75-50644)
Walker, James.
Sonatina for clarinet & piano. *Schirmer. Unpriced* VVPEM (B75-50899)
Sonatina for trumpet and piano. *Schirmer. Unpriced* WSPEM (B75-50946)
Walking to New Orleans : the story of New Orleans rhythm & blues. (Broven, John). *38a Sackville Rd, Bexhill-on-Sea, Sussex : Blues Unlimited. £3.75* AKDW/HHR(YTRN/XPF28) (B75-00201) ISBN 0-9500229-3-4
Wall, Elizabeth. Help yourself to play the guitar. (Stevens, Susan). *Girl Guides Association. £0.35* ATS/E (B75-10255) ISBN 0-85260-002-x
Walmisley, Thomas Attwood. Cathedral music. Morning and Evening Service in D major. Magnificat and Nunc dimittis : for SATB and organ. *Oxford University Press. £0.50* DGPP (B75-50414) ISBN 0-19-395316-1
Walsh, Colin. Mud songs and Blighty : a scarpbook of the first World War. *Hutchinson : EMI. £3.50* KDW/GB/AYC(XMP5) (B75-51116) ISBN 0-09-124421-8
Walter, Bruno. Gustav Mahler. *Severn House : Distributed by Hutchinson. £3.75* BME (B75-27349) ISBN 0-7278-0075-2
Walter, David. The elephant's gavotte : for double bass and piano. *Yorke. Unpriced* SSPHM (B75-50777)
Walter, Horst.
Symphony, no.99, in E flat major. Symphony in E flat major, (London Symphony no.7). (Haydn, Joseph). *Bärenreiter. £1.80* MME (B75-50131)
Symphony, no.100, in G major, 'Military'. Symphony in G major, 'Military' (London Symphony no.9). (Haydn, Joseph). *Bärenreiter. £2.40* MME (B75-50132)
Symphony, no.101, in D major, 'The clock'. Symphony in D major, 'The clock' (London Symphony no.8). (Haydn, Joseph). *Bärenreiter. £2.40* MME (B75-50133)
Walters, Edmund.
The bells : a carol for S.S.A. and piano. *Boosey and Hawkes. £0.15* FDP/LF (B75-51054)
Born in Bethlehem : a carol for treble voices with optional S.A. or S.A.T.B. chorus. *Boosey and Hawkes. £0.10* FDP/LF (B75-51055)
The cuckoo carol : a traditional Czech carol. *Boosey and Hawkes. £0.10* JFLDP/LF (B75-51100)
Walters, Harold L.
Bands around the world. (Yoder, Paul). *Rubank : Novello. Unpriced* UMMJ (B75-51347)
Country and westerns : military band. *Rubank : Novello. Unpriced* UMMJ (B75-50832)
The entertainer. *arr.* The entertainer. (Joplin, Scott). *Rubank : Novello. Unpriced* VQPK/AHXJ (B75-51365)
The entertainer. *arr.* The entertainer. (Joplin, Scott). *Rubank : Novello. Unpriced* VRNTK/AHXJ (B75-51366)
The entertainer. *arr.* The entertainer. (Joplin, Scott). *Rubank : Novello. Unpriced* VVNTK/AHXJ (B75-51402)
The entertainer. *arr.* The entertainer. (Joplin, Scott). *Rubank : Novello. Unpriced* VVRPK/AHXJ (B75-51411)
Walton, *Sir* William.
Anniversary fanfare : for trumpet, trombones and percussion. *Oxford University Press. Unpriced* WMGN (B75-50916) ISBN 0-19-368100-5
Duets for children. *arr.* Miniatures for wind band
Set 1, nos 1-5. *Oxford University Press. £2.50* UMK/AG (B75-50299) ISBN 0-19-368267-2
Duets for children. *arr.* Miniatures for wind band
Set 2, nos 6-10. *Oxford University Press. £3.00* UMK/AG (B75-50300) ISBN 0-19-368507-8
Wanek, Friedrich. Zehn Essays : für Gitarre solo. *Schott. £1.75* TSPMJ (B75-51326)
Warburton, K M. The thrush in spring : two-part song. (Thiman, Eric Harding). *Roberton. £0.12* FDW (B75-50497)
Ward, Robert. Invocation and toccata : orchestra. *Highgate Press : Galliard. Unpriced* MMJ (B75-50618)
Warlock, Peter. Rutterkin : an overture for recorders, (descant, 2 trebles, 2 tenors, 2 basses), after a song by Peter Warlock, (from 1st set of Peterisms). (Hold, Trevor). *Tomus. Unpriced* VSNP (B75-51376)
Warner, Alan. Celluloid rock : twenty years of movie rock. (Jenkinson, Philip). *Lorrimer. £1.95* A/GB/JR(XPP21) (B75-06416) ISBN 0-85647-046-5
Warrack, John. Tchaikovsky symphonies and concertos. 2nd ed. *British Broadcasting Corporation. £0.45* BTDAMME (B75-00740) ISBN 0-563-12773-2
Warren, Edward. 3 pieces for 4 : a suite of 3 movements for woodwind quartet, flute, oboe, clarinet in B flat, bassoon. *Camera Music. Unpriced* VNSG (B75-51362)
Warren, Norman. Mary Jones : a musical play for young people. *Maplewell Press. Unpriced* CM/L (B75-50991) ISBN 0-9504473-0-7
Warwick suite : for pianoforte solo. (Whittaker, Anthony F). *22 Waller St., Leamington Spa, Warwickshire : Anthony Music. £0.60* QPG (B75-50670)
Washburn, Robert.
Ceremonial music : military band. *Oxford University Press. Unpriced* UMMJ (B75-51346)
Concertino for wind and brass quintets. *Oxford University Press. Unpriced* UNRFL (B75-51359)
Earth song. *Vocal score.* Earth song : mixed voices with brass accompaniment and timpani, trumpets 1 and 2 in B flat, horns 1 and 2 in F, trombones 1 and 2, tuba, timpani (optional). *Boosey and Hawkes. Unpriced* EWNPDW (B75-50043)
Excursion : for orchestra. *Oxford University Press. Unpriced* MMJ (B75-51159)
Saturn V : wind band. *Boosey and Hawkes. £12.00* UMJ (B75-51337)
Symphony no.1. Allegro con spirito. Festive overture : for orchestra. *Oxford University Press. Unpriced* MMJ (B75-51160)
We hold these truths : bicentennial ode, for chorus and symphonic band with optional strings. *Boosey and Hawkes. £15.00* EUMDX (B75-51029)
Washington, Joe. Songs. *Selections : arr.* The Beatles for classical guitar. (Lennon, John). *Wise, Music Sales. Unpriced* TSPMK/DW (B75-50818)

Wastall, Peter.
Babylon's falling : a jazz spiritual for junior band and optional voices in two parts. *Boosey and Hawkes. £2.05* UMJ (B75-51338)
Didn't my Lord deliver Daniel? : a jazz spiritual for junior wind band and optional voices in two parts. *Boosey and Hawkes. £2.05* UMJ (B75-51339)
Joshua fought the battle of Jericho : a jazz spiritual for junior wind band and optional voices in two parts. *Boosey and Hawkes. £2.05* UMJ (B75-51340)
Sonatas for flute & piano. Op.99, nos.3, 2. *arr.* Two sonatas. (Hook, James). *Boosey and Hawkes. £1.25* WSPK/AE (B75-51461)
Sonatina for violin & harpsichord, no.6, in C major. *arr.* Sonatina no.3. (Telemann, Georg Philipp). *Boosey and Hawkes. £0.65* VVPK/AEM (B75-51408)
Watermill. (Binge, Ronald). *Inter-Art. £0.30* QPK (B75-50715)
Watermill. *arr.* The watermill. (Binge, Ronald). *Inter-Art. £0.30* QPK (B75-50715)
Watson, Derek. Bruckner. *Dent. £2.95* BBUE (B75-21066) ISBN 0-460-03144-9
Watson, Walter. Reflection : for organ. *Oxford University Press. Unpriced* RJ (B75-51275)
Watts, Isaac. An Easter introit : SATB. (Beechey, Gwilym). *Banks. Unpriced* EZDM (B75-50466)
Waxman, Donald.
A Christmas pageant : carols from around the world and classical Christmas excerpts. *Galaxy : Galliard. Unpriced* QPK/DP/LF/AY (B75-51262)
Nine carols or ballads. Lord of the dance. *arr.* Lord of the dance. (Carter, Sydney). *Galaxy : Galliard. Unpriced* DP (B75-50429)
Nine carols or ballads. Lord of the dance. *arr.* Lord of the dance. (Carter, Sydney). *Galaxy : Galliard. Unpriced* FLDP (B75-50506)
We hold these truths : bicentennial ode, for chorus and symphonic band with optional strings. (Washburn, Robert). *Boosey and Hawkes. £15.00* EUMDX (B75-51029)
Weaver, John. Rhapsody : for flute and organ. *Boosey and Hawkes. £2.25* VRPJ (B75-51371)
Webber, Andrew Lloyd. Joseph and the amazing technicolour dreamcoat. *Vocal score.* Joseph and the amazing technicolour dreamcoat. Revised and enlarged ed. *Novello. £2.00* CM/L (B75-50399)
Wedderburn, James. Balulalow : carol for SAATB with divisions unaccompanied. (Inness, Peter). *Novello. £0.10* EZDP/LF (B75-50061)
Wedderburn, John. Balulalow : carol for SAATB with divisions unaccompanied. (Inness, Peter). *Novello. £0.10* EZDP/LF (B75-50061)
Wedderburn, Robert. Balulalow : carol for SAATB with divisions unaccompanied. (Inness, Peter). *Novello. £0.10* EZDP/LF (B75-50061)
Wedding cantata. Set me as a seal. *arr.* Wedding song : high voice and organ. (Pinkham, Daniel). *Peters. Unpriced* KFTDH/KDD (B75-51128)
Wedding song : high voice and organ. (Pinkham, Daniel). *Peters. Unpriced* KFTDH/KDD (B75-51128)
Weg der Barmherzigkeit. There's a road (which leads from Jerusalem) : hymn. (Schneider, Martin Gotthard). *Bosworth. Unpriced* JDM (B75-50524)
Weihnachtsgesang : for four-part mixed choir. (Agricola, Martin). *Bärenreiter. £0.60* EZDP/LF (B75-50060)
Weir, Ronald. The composer in the market place. (Peacock, Alan). *Faber. £5.50* A(JC/K/YC/XM70) (B75-18726) ISBN 0-571-10011-2
Weiss, Gunther. Sonatas for viola d'amore & continuo, 'Stockholm'. 'Stockholm sonatas' : for viola d'amore (viola) and basso continuo
1: Sonatas in F major, A minor, G major. (Ariosti, Attilio). *Bärenreiter. £2.80* SQQPE (B75-50259)
Weiss, Sylvius Leopold.
Fantasia, fuga, tombeau, capriccio : per chitarra dalla intavolutura per liuto. *Zanibon : Hinrichsen. Unpriced* TSPMK (B75-50285)
Sonata for lute in B minor, London no.16. Sonate (London nr 16). *Uitgave Metropolis : Hinrichsen. Unpriced* TSPMK/AE (B75-50287)
Suite for lute, no.18, in A major. Suite in la maggiore : per chitarra dalla intavolatura per linto. *Zanibon : Hinrichsen. Unpriced* TSPMK/AG (B75-50289)
Welch, Marie de L. *See* De L Welch, Marie.
Welcome Yule : a Christmas fanfare, SATB. (Wills, Arthur). *Oxford University Press. Unpriced* DP/LF (B75-51014) ISBN 0-19-343052-5
Well-tuned fiddle : original compositions for violin and pianoforte by contemporary composers
Book 1. (Associated Board of the Royal Schools of Music). *Associated Board of the Royal Schools of Music. £0.70* SP/AY (B75-50243)
Book 2. (Associated Board of the Royal Schools of Music). *Associated Board of the Royal Schools of Music. £0.70* SP/AY (B75-50244)
Book 3. (Associated Board of the Royal Schools of Music). *Associated Board of the Royal Schools of Music. £0.70* SP/AY (B75-50245)
Wells Cathedral. *Friends of Wells Cathedral.* The organs and organists of Wells Cathedral. (Bowers, Roger). *22 Vicars' Close, Wells, Somerset BA5 2UJ : The Friends of Wells Cathedral. £0.20* AR/B(YDFGWB) (B75-00741) ISBN 0-902321-12-9
Welsh national music and dance. (Williams, William Sidney Gwynn). 4th ed. *Gwynn. £1.10* A/G(YDK) (B75-02368) ISBN 0-900426-01-2
Welshman can't help singing = Mae'r Cymro'n canu heunydd : chorus for male voices (TTBB) and piano. (Noble, Harold). *Bosworth. Unpriced* GDW (B75-50508)
Wenth, Johann. Divertimento for two oboes & cor anglais in B flat major. Divertimento, B-dur : für 2 Oboi und Corno inglese B-dur. 1st ed. *Kneusslin : Hinrichsen. Unpriced* VNT (B75-50312)
Wenzel, Eberhard.
Psalm-Tripychon : für gemischten Chor und Bläserchor. *Bärenreiter. £2.40* EWMDR (B75-50042)
'Sollt ich meinem Gott nicht singen' : Choralkonzert für zwei Trompeten, zwei Posaunen und Orgel. *Bärenreiter. Unpriced* NWXPNRF (B75-50646)
Westmore, Peter. Christ in competition. *Edwardian Music. Unpriced* JDM/AY (B75-51078) ISBN 0-551-05530-8
Westrup, *Sir* Jack. The works of Henry Purcell
Vol.2: Timon of Athens originally edited by Frederick Arthur Gore Ouseley ; revised by Jack Westrup ; words by Thomas Shadwell. (Purcell, Henry). 2nd ed. *Novello. £3.00* C/AZ (B75-50007)
Westrup, *Sir* Jack Allan. Purcell. 7th ed.. *Dent. £3.60* BPV (B75-24233) ISBN 0-460-03150-3
What instrument shall I play? (Ingman, Nicholas). *Ward Lock. £2.95* AL/B (B75-29314) ISBN 0-7063-1988-5
Wheeler, Tom. The guitar book : a handbook for electric and acoustic guitarists. *Macdonald and Jane's. £5.50* ATS/B (B75-25560) ISBN 0-356-08322-5
When I heard the learn'd astronomer : for tenor and wind band. (Bedford, David). *Universal. Unpriced* KGHE/UMDX (B75-51130)
When icicles hang : a cycle of choral settings (SATB) with small orchestra. (Rutter, John). *Oxford University Press. £1.50* DW (B75-50444) ISBN 0-19-338073-0
When icicles hang. *Vocal score.* When icicles hang : a cycle of choral settings (SATB) with small orchestra. (Rutter, John). *Oxford University Press. £1.50* DW (B75-50444) ISBN 0-19-338073-0
Whimsey for brass. (Butt, James). *British and Continental Music. Unpriced* WMG (B75-50915)
Whistling gypsy : Irish folk song, for four-part chorus of mixed voices with baritone solo, piano and guitar accompaniment. (De Cormier, Robert). *Roberton. £0.16* ETSPDW (B75-50456)
Whitcomb, Ian. Tin Pan Alley : a pictorial history (1919-1939) with complete words and music of forty songs. *EMI Music. £2.95* KDW/GB/AY (B75-50560)
White, Donald H. Lyric suite : for euphonium and piano with treble clef and bass clef parts. *Schirmer. Unpriced* WWPG (B75-51474)
White, Eric Walter.
Scherzo for piano (1902). Scherzo (1902) : for piano. (Stravinsky, Igor). 1st ed. *Faber Music. Unpriced* QPJ (B75-50711)
Sonata for piano in F sharp minor. Sonata in F sharp minor (1903-4) for piano. (Stravinsky, Igor). *Faber Music. Unpriced* QPE (B75-50667)
White, Jon Manchip. The silver swimmer. Opus 84 : for mixed chorus, SATB and piano duet. (Hoddinott, Alun). *Oxford University Press. £1.20* DX (B75-50032) ISBN 0-19-336840-4
White, William Braid. Theory and practice of piano construction, with a detailed practical method for tuning. *Dover Publications etc. : Constable. £1.40* AQ/BC (B75-19735) ISBN 0-486-23139-9
Whitlock, Percy. Five short pieces for organ. Folk tune. *arr.* Folk tune. *Emerson. Unpriced* UNNK (B75-50308)
Whitman, Walt. When I heard the learn'd astronomer : for tenor and wind band. (Bedford, David). *Universal. Unpriced* KGHE/UMDX (B75-51130)
Whitney, Maurice C. Dance suite for strings, with optional piano and string bass. *Warner : Blossom. Unpriced* RXNQHG (B75-50235)
Whittaker, Anthony F. Warwick suite : for pianoforte solo. *22 Waller St., Leamington Spa, Warwickshire : Anthony Music. £0.60* QPG (B75-50670)
Whittall, Mary. Wagner : a documentary study. *Thames and Hudson. £12.00* BWC(N) (B75-30568) ISBN 0-500-01137-0
Who. (Tremlett, George). *Futura Publications. £0.40* AKDW/GB/E(P) (B75-13168) ISBN 0-86007-069-7
Who killed Lawless Lean? : for voices, 4 melody instruments, percussion and piano. (Pehkonen, Elis). *Universal. Unpriced* JFE/LNRPXDW (B75-51096)
Who's who in music, and musicians' international directory. *For later issues of this publication see* International who's who in music and musicians' directory.
Wichmann, Russell G. Bell carol : based on the tune 'Puer nobis', for junior choir, mixed choir, and organ, with optional bells. *Oxford University Press. Unpriced* DP/LF (B75-51013)
Widow of Ephesus : chamber opera in one act. (Hurd, Michael). *Novello. £2.10* CC (B75-50395)
Widow of Ephesus. *Vocal score.* The widow of Ephesus : chamber opera in one act. (Hurd, Michael). *Novello. £2.10* CC (B75-50395)
Wiggins, Bram.
Duets for children. *arr.* Miniatures for wind band
Set 1, nos 1-5. (Walton, *Sir* William). *Oxford University Press. £2.50* UMK/AG (B75-50299) ISBN 0-19-368267-2
Duets for children. *arr.* Miniatures for wind band
Set 2, nos 6-10. (Walton, *Sir* William). *Oxford University Press. £3.00* UMK/AG (B75-50300) ISBN 0-19-368507-8
Wigness, Robert. Sonata à 3 for two violins, trombone & basso continuo, no.3, in A minor. Sonata à 3, no.3, in A minor for 2 violins, trombone and basso continuo. (Bertali, Antonio). *Musica rara. £4.50* NUXUNSE (B75-51179)
Wigransky, Dave. *See* Jay, Dave.
Wilbur, Richard. Candide. *Selections: arr.* Candide : vocal selections. (Bernstein, Leonard). *Schirmer. Unpriced* KDW (B75-50550)
Wilcock, Frank. Six monologues for boys. *Brown, Son and Ferguson. Unpriced* HYE/QP (B75-50520)
Wild wild west : an American medley for military band. (Hanmer, Ronald). *Studio Music. Unpriced* UMMJ (B75-50306)
Wild wild west. Conductor. The wild wild west : an American medley for military band. (Hanmer, Ronald). *Studio Music. Unpriced* UMMJ (B75-50306)
Wilder, Alec. American popular song : the great innovators, 1900-1950. *Oxford University Press. £3.25* ADW/GB(YT/XM51) (B75-18368) ISBN 0-19-284009-6
Wiliam, Urien. A Welshman can't help singing = Mae'r Cymro'n canu heunydd : chorus for male voices (TTBB) and piano. (Noble, Harold). *Bosworth. Unpriced* GDW (B75-50508)
Wilkinson, Anthony. Liszt. *Macmillan. £3.75* BLJ(N) (B75-14335) ISBN 0-333-15064-3
Willcocks, David.
Birthday carol : SATB. *Oxford University Press. £0.08* DP/LF (B75-50026) ISBN 0-19-343050-9
Five folk-songs. *Oxford University Press. £0.75* EZDW/AY (B75-50483) ISBN 0-19-343836-4
Stille Nacht. *arr.* Stille Nacht = Silent night. (Gruber, Franz). *Oxford University Press. Unpriced* EZDP/LF (B75-51042) ISBN 0-19-343053-3
William Billings of Boston : eighteenth-century composer. (McKay, David Phares). *Princeton University Press. £8.40* BBNS (B75-50980) ISBN 0-691-09118-8
William Crotch, 1775-1847 : composer, artist, teacher. (Rennert, Jonathan). *Dalton. £3.20* BCT(N) (B75-20390) ISBN 0-900963-61-1
Williams, Aaron. Lassus, Victoria, Palestrina : three-part vocal compositions. *Ricordi. Unpriced* VSNTK/CB/AY (B75-50865)
Williams, Allan. The man who gave the Beatles away. *Elm Tree Books. £3.50* AKDW/GB/E(P/XPU4) (B75-16094) ISBN 0-241-89204-x
Williams, Andrew H. The calculation of organ pipe scales from the middle ages to the mid-nineteenth century. (Mahrenholz, Christhard). *130 Southfield Rd, Oxford OX4 1PA : Positif Press. £2.50* AR/BPPG (B75-31193) ISBN 0-9503892-2-6
Williams, Grace. Ave maris stella : for unaccompanied mixed voices. *Oxford University Press. £0.50* EZDH (B75-50462) ISBN 0-19-338755-7
Williams, Patrick.
Easy album for the organ
4th. *Bosworth. Unpriced* RK/AAY (B75-50215)
Mr Squirrel : SSA. *Bosworth. Unpriced* FLDW (B75-50081)
Williams, Phyllis.
Friends, relatives, parents. *arr.* Friends, relatives, parents : a program opener for two-part chorus of treble voices with piano and optional guitar. *Frank Music. Unpriced* FLDW (B75-51070)
How do you open a show without a curtain?. *arr.* How do you open a show without a curtain? : a program opener, for two-part chorus of treble voices with piano and optional guitar. *Frank Music. Unpriced* FLDW (B75-51071)
That's a very good sign. *arr.* That's a very good sign : for two-part chorus of treble voices and piano. *Frank Music. Unpriced* FLDW (B75-51072)
Williams, Ralph Vaughan. *See* Vaughan Williams, Ralph.
Williams, Richard, *b.1947.* Out of his head : the sound of Phil Spector. *Abacus. £0.65* A/FD/E(P) (B75-22851) ISBN 0-349-13723-4
Williams, William Sidney Gwynn. Welsh national music and dance. 4th ed. *Gwynn. £1.10* A/G(YDK) (B75-02368) ISBN 0-900426-01-2
Williamson, Malcolm. The glitter gang. *Vocal score.* The glitter gang : a cassation for audience and orchestra (piano). *Weinberger. Unpriced* FDX (B75-50074)
Willow song. (Miller, Carl). *Chappell. Unpriced* FDW (B75-50494)
Willowbrook suite : for treble, alto and tenor recorders. (Smith, Peter Melville). *Lengnick. Unpriced* VSNTG (B75-50863)
Wills, Arthur.
Evening service (with verses) : SATB. *Oxford University Press. £0.35* DGPP (B75-50020) ISBN 0-19-351648-9
Homage to John Stanley : voluntary for organ manuals. *Chappell. Unpriced* RJ (B75-51276)
I hunger and I thirst : anthem for SATB with divisions and organ. *Novello. Unpriced* DH (B75-50421)
I sing of a Maiden : two-part. *Oxford University Press. £0.10* FLDP/LF (B75-50507) ISBN 0-19-341510-0
Sonata for guitar. *Oxford University Press. Unpriced* TSPME (B75-50804) ISBN 0-19-359531-1
Welcome Yule : a Christmas fanfare, SATB. *Oxford University Press. Unpriced* DP/LF (B75-51014) ISBN 0-19-343052-5
Wilson, Don. Rejoice ye pure in heart : for mixed chorus and keyboard, based on a hymn by Arthur Messiter. *Galaxy : Galliard. Unpriced* DH (B75-50023)
Wilson, Reg. The story of the Royal Opera House, Covent Garden. (Goodwin, Noël). *Head Office, Poultry, EC2P 2BX : Midland Bank Ltd. Free* AC/E(YC/QB) (B75-50001) ISBN 0-9501576-2-7
Wilson, Robert Barclay. Selected songs. (Arne, Thomas Augustine). *Cramer. Unpriced* KDW (B75-50548)
Wilson, Sandy. I could be happy : an autobiography. *Joseph. £6.00* BWNTM(N) (B75-50389) ISBN 0-7181-1370-5
Wilson, Thomas. Complementi : clarinet doubling bass clarinet, violin, cello, piano. *Central Music Library : Chappell. Unpriced* NUVNS (B75-50637)

Wilson-Dickson, Andrew. The word : SATB. *Banks.*
Unpriced DK (B75-50427)
Wind band book : seven pieces, for woodwind and brass
instruments with optional percussion. *Oxford University
Press.* £2.75 UMK/AAY (B75-50298)
ISBN 0-19-369800-5
Wind has blown the rain away : SATB and piano. (King,
Jeffrey). *Boosey and Hawkes. Unpriced* DW
(B75-51018)
Windmills : for orchestra. (Pavey, Sidney). *Bosworth.
Unpriced* MJ (B75-50596)
Winter fragments : SSA unacc. (Benger, Richard). *Banks
Music. Unpriced* FEZDW (B75-50501)
Winters, Geoffrey. Three Herrick songs. Op.41 : medium
voice and guitar. *Thames. Unpriced* KFVE/TSDW
(B75-50587)
Winters, Leslie.
Pleasure and practice music cards : songs
Set 1. *E.J. Arnold. Unpriced* LNK/DW/AY
(B75-51143)
ISBN 0-560-00487-7
Set 2. *E.J. Arnold. Unpriced* LNK/DW/AY (B75-51144)
ISBN 0-560-00488-5
Set 3. *E.J. Arnold. Unpriced* LNK/DW/AY (B75-51145)
ISBN 0-560-00489-3
Wise, Michael. The Lord is my shepherd : anthem for two
sopranos, chorus and organ. *Novello.* £0.20 DK
(B75-51010)
Wishart, Peter. Messiah. *Selections.* Messiah ornamented :
an ornamented edition of the solos from the oratorio.
(Handel, George Frideric). *Stainer and Bell. Unpriced*
DADD (B75-50013) ISBN 0-85249-318-5
Wishart, Trevor. Journey into space travelogue : an
antiscore. *2 Fareham St., W.1 : Distributed by Alfred A.
Kalmus. Unpriced* BWNVAPV (B75-31194)
ISBN 0-9504561-0-1
Witches : for piano. (Judd, Margaret). *Bosworth. Unpriced*
QPJ (B75-50702)
Witches : for piano. (Judd, Margaret). *Bosworth. Unpriced*
QPJ (B75-50703)
Witham, June. Music workshop : an approach to music for
the non-specialist teacher. *Macmillan.* £4.75 A/C(VG)
(B75-04501) ISBN 0-333-14455-4
Woehl, Waldemar. Zodiaci musici. Part 1. Nos 1, 2. Suites
for four parts (strings or wind instruments and basso
continuo). (Schmierer, Johann Abraham). *Bärenreiter.*
£4.80 NXNRG (B75-50168)
Wohltemperirte Clavier, Tl. 1. S.867. *arr.* Prelude and fugue.
(Bach, Johann Sebastian). *Oxford University Press. Score,*
£0.75 ; *Parts, Unpriced* SRNRK/Y (B75-50773)
ISBN 0-19-355238-8
Wolf, Hugo. Sechs geistliche Lieder = Six sacred songs : for
four-part chorus of mixed voices. *Bärenreiter.* £1.60
EZDH (B75-50053)
Wolfenden, Samuel. A treatise on the art of pianoforte
construction. *The Gresham Press, Old Woking, Surrey :
Union Bros Ltd.* £5.85 AQ/BC (B75-18372)
ISBN 0-9502121-3-x
Wolkenloses Christfest : Requiem für Bariton, Violoncello
und Orchester. (Reimann, Aribert). *Schott.* £11.00
KGNE/MPSRDE (B75-51135)
Wonder march. (Allen, Rod). *Boosey and Hawkes. Military
band set,* £1.00, *Brass band set* £0.85 UMMK/AGM
(B75-50834)
Wonder march. *arr.* The wonder march. (Allen, Rod).
Boosey and Hawkes. Military band set, £1.00, *Brass band
set* £0.85 UMMK/AGM (B75-50834)
Wonderful Copenhagen : for two-part chorus of treble voices
with piano. (Loesser, Frank). *Frank Music. Unpriced*
FLDW (B75-51069)
Wonderful thing : Easter carol, unison, piano (flute hand
bells optional). (Davis, Katherine Kennacott). *Warner :
Blossom. Unpriced* JDP/LL (B75-50090)
Wood, Adolf. Four simple songs : baritone and piano.
(Glasser, Stanley). *Piers Press.* £1.25 KGNDW
(B75-51133)
Woodfield, Ian. Five pieces for four viols. *Oxford University
Press. Unpriced* STNS/AY (B75-50786)
ISBN 0-19-343241-2
Woodfield, Ray.
The land of the mountain and the flood. *Selections : arr.*
Sutherland's law. (MacCunn, Hamish). *Ambleside Music
: EMI. Unpriced* WMK (B75-51422)
Trumpets sound! (Elms, Albert). *Ambleside Music : EMI.
Unpriced* WMPWRNSK (B75-51432)
Woodward, G R. Blessed be that maid Mary : Christmas
carol, SATB and organ. (Mario of the Cross, *Sister*).
Oxford University Press. Unpriced FDP/LF
(B75-51052)
Wooldridge, David. Charles Ives : a portrait. *Faber.* £6.00
BIV(N) (B75-15003) ISBN 0-571-10687-0
Wooldridge, David. From the steeples and mountains. *See*
Wooldridge, David. Charles Ives.
Woolf, Virginia. From the diary of Virginia Woolf : for
medium voice and piano. (Argento, Dominick). *Boosey
and Hawkes. Unpriced* KFVDW (B75-50582)
Word : SATB. (Wilson-Dickson, Andrew). *Banks. Unpriced*
DK (B75-50427)
Work, John W. A heritage of spirituals : a collection of
American spirituals, for mixed chorus and piano or
organ. *Galaxy : Galliard. Unpriced* DW/LC/AY
(B75-50447)
World of musical comedy : the story of the American
musical stage as told through the careers of its foremost
composers and lyricists. (Green, Stanley, *b.1923*). 3rd ed.
revised and enlarged. *Barnes : Yoseloff.* £7.00
ACM/E(YT/X) (B75-29315) ISBN 0-498-01409-6
World of sacred music : for all C or G chord organs.
Bobrich Music : Phoenix. Unpriced RPVCK/DM/AY
(B75-50742)

World War II songs. *See* Great songs of World War II.
World's favorite popular classics : for piano. *Ashley
Phoenix. Unpriced* QPK/AAY (B75-51257)
World's favorite pure and simple pieces for flute solos, duets
and trios : includes basic charts and playing principles
with chords for accompaniment by piano, guitar, etc.
Ashley : Phoenix. Unpriced VRPK/AAY (B75-50853)
World's favorite selected masterpieces for classic guitar
Vol.2. *Ashley : Phoenix. Unpriced* TSPMK/AAY
(B75-50286)
World's favourite more classic to contemporary piano music
: early grade piano music in its original form. *Ashley
Phoenix. Unpriced* QP/AY (B75-51221)
Wright, John. Missa brevis : for unaccompanied voices. *35
West St., Chipping Norton : Gray Jewitt Pritchard.
Unpriced* EZDGS (B75-50047)
Wuorinen, Charles.
Adapting to the times : violoncello and piano. *Peters.
Unpriced* SRPJ (B75-50262)
Sonata for piano. *Peters. Unpriced* QPE (B75-50187)
Wyatt, Geoffrey. At the mighty organ. *Oxford Illustrated
Press.* £3.75 ARPV/JR(X) (B75-12698)
ISBN 0-902280-22-8
Wyatt, *Sir* Thomas.
And will you leave me so? : SATB unaccompanied.
(Baksa, Robert F). *Boosey and Hawkes. Unpriced*
EZDW (B75-50474)
And wilt thou leave me thus? : SATB. (Brydson, John
Collis). *Cramer.* £0.12 EZDW (B75-50475)
Wye, Trevor. Twilight. *arr.* Twilight. (Sullivan, *Sir* Arthur
Seymour). *Emerson. Unpriced* VRNTQK (B75-51367)
Yeats, William Butler. To a young girl. (Rorem, Ned).
Boosey and Hawkes. Unpriced KDW (B75-51111)
Yoder, Paul. Bands around the world. *Rubank : Novello.
Unpriced* UMMJ (B75-51347)
You are the temple of God : for treble choir in two parts
and organ. (Hilty, Everett Jay). *Oxford University Press.
Unpriced* FLDK (B75-50079)
Young, Douglas. The listeners. *Vocal score.* The listeners : a
dramatic cantata for soprano solo, male speaker and
small soprano chorus, with chamber orchestra. *Faber
Music. Unpriced* FLDX (B75-51073)
Young, Percy Marshall. Handel. Revised ed.. *Dent.* £3.95
BHC (B75-13734) ISBN 0-460-03161-9
Young, Thomas McClelland-. *See* McClelland-Young,
Thomas.
Young man's song : TTBB unacc. (Clements, John). *Oxford
University Press.* £0.10 GEZDW (B75-50514)
ISBN 0-19-341020-6
Your book of the recorder. (Thomson, John Mansfield). 2nd
ed. *Faber.* £1.25 AVS/B (B75-08738)
ISBN 0-571-04873-0
Yuval : studies of the Jewish Music Research Centre
Vol.3. *Magnes Press : Distributed by Oxford University
Press.* £10.25 A(YBU/D) (B75-08735)
ISBN 0-19-647920-7
Zagreber Konzert : für Gitarre und Orchester. Op.19.
(Kelkel, Manfred). *Schott. Unpricd* TSPMK/LF
(B75-50290)
Zalzabar : a Christmas cantata for children, music for
voices, melodic instrument, percussion & piano.
(Coombes, Douglas). *28 Knolls Way, Clifton, Beds. :
Lindsay Music.* £0.49 JFE/NYLDE/LF (B75-50540)
Zambia University. *See* University of Zambia.
Zambian papers (ISSN 0084-5124). Kubik, Gerhard. The
Kachamba Brothers' Band : a study of neo-traditional
music in Malaŵi. *Manchester University Press for
University of Zambia Institute for African Studies.* £2.25
BZNNALN(P) (B75-15002) ISBN 0-7190-1408-5
Zamfir, Gheorghe.
L'Alouette : pour flûte de Pan. *Chappell. Unpriced*
VSXPMJ (B75-50887)
Traité de naï roumain : methode de flûte de Pan. *Chappell.
Unpriced* VSX/AC (B75-50886)
Zehn Essays : für Gitarre solo. (Wanek, Friedrich). *Schott.*
£1.75 TSPMJ (B75-51326)
Zehn Psalmspruche : für drei und vierstimmigen gemischten
Chor und Orgel. (Schweizer, Rolf). *Bärenreiter.* £2.00
DR (B75-50027)
Zelter, Carl.
Four songs for male voices
1: Saint Paul ; text from I Timothy 5. *Boosey and
Hawkes. Unpriced* GEZDW (B75-50516)
2: Ephiphanias. *Boosey and Hawkes. Unpriced* GEZDW
(B75-50517)
3 & 4: Master and journeyman ; and, Song of the flea.
Boosey and Hawkes. Unpriced GEZDW (B75-50518)
Zempléni, Kornel. Piano works
Vol.7: Années de pélerinage II. (Liszt, Franz). *Bärenreiter.
Unpriced* QP/AZ (B75-50664)
Zimmerman, Heinz Werner. Vier Collagen : für Klavier und
Kammerchor nach Inventionen von J.S. Bach und
Epigrammen von A.G. Kastner, J.W.L. Gleim, Fr. von
Hagedorn und J.J. Ewald. *Bärenreiter.* £2.40 DW
(B75-50030)
Zinovieff, Peter. Nenia. The death of Orpheus : for soprano
solo, crotales, two pianos and three clarinets. (Birtwistle,
Harrison). *Universal. Unpriced* KFLE/NYFVNQDX
(B75-50575)
Zodiac variations : twelve pieces of moderate difficulty for
piano. (Stoker, Richard). *Ashdown. Unpriced* QP/T
(B75-50183)
Zodiaci musici. Part 1. Nos 1, 2. Suites for four parts
(strings or wind instruments and basso continuo).

(Schmierer, Johann Abraham). *Bärenreiter.* £4.80
NXNRG (B75-50168)
Zohar : alto recorder (or flute). (Amram, David). *Peters.
Unpriced* VSSPMJ (B75-50338)
Zoo : a musical folly. (Sullivan, *Sir* Arthur Seymour).
Cramer. Unpriced CF (B75-50397)
Zoo. *Vocal score.* The zoo : a musical folly. (Sullivan, *Sir*
Arthur Seymour). *Cramer. Unpriced* CF (B75-50397)
Zwei Studien : für Fagott. (Goodman, Alfred). *Litolff :
Peters. Unpriced* VWPMJ (B75-50352)
Zweistimmige Orgelchorale : gemeinsame Lieder der
deutschsprachigen Kirchen. (Schade, Wernerfritz).
Schott. £4.50 RJ (B75-51274)
Zytowski, Carl.
Four songs for male voices
1: Saint Paul ; text from I Timothy 5. (Zelter, Carl).
Boosey and Hawkes. Unpriced GEFZDW (B75-50516)
2: Ephiphanias. (Zelter, Carl). *Boosey and Hawkes.
Unpriced* GEZDW (B75-50517)

SUBJECT INDEX

6

Quartets: Saxophone VUNS
Quartets: String ensemble RXNS
Quartets: String ensemble: Accompanying soprano voice KFLE/RXNS
Quartets: String ensemble: Beethoven, L. van: Books BBJARXNS
Quartets: String ensemble & orchestra MPRXNS
Quartets: Strings & keyboard NXNS
Quartets: Strings & keyboard: Accompanying soprano voice KFLE/NXNS
Quartets: Trombone WUNS
Quartets: Trombone, strings and keyboard NUXUNS
Quartets: Trumpet, strings & keyboard NUXSNS
Quartets: Viol STNS
Quartets: Vocal ensembles JNC
Quartets: Wind & keyboard NWNS
Quartets: Wind, strings, & keyboard NUNS
Quartets: Woodwind ensemble VNS
Quartets: Woodwind, strings, keyboard & percussion NYDPNS
Questions and answers: Books A(DE)
Quintets: Accordion RSNR
Quintets: Brass & keyboard NWXPNR
Quintets: Brass ensemble WNR
Quintets: Cello SRNR
Quintets: Clarinet & strings NVVNR
Quintets: Clarinet in A & strings NVVQNR
Quintets: Descant recorder VSRNR
Quintets: Flute, strings & keyboard NURNR
Quintets: Recorder VSNR
Quintets: Recorder & strings: Accompanying choral works ENVSNR
Quintets: String ensembles: Accompanying choral music ERXNR
Quintets: Strings & keyboard NXNR
Quintets: Strings & keyboard: Accompanying bass voice KGXE/NXNR
Quintets: Treble recorder VSSNR
Quintets: Trumpet, strings & keyboard NUXSNR
Quintets: Viol STNR
Quintets: Viol: Accompanying choral music ESTNR
Quintets: Wind instruments UNR
Quintets: Wind, strings & keyboard NUNR
Quintets: Woodwind & strings NVPNR

Radio: Recorded music: Books A/FD/JT
Ragtime: Arrangements for brass band WMK/AHXJ
Ragtime: Arrangements for clarinet quartet VVNSK/AHXJ
Ragtime: Arrangements for clarinet trio VVNTK/AHXJ
Ragtime: Arrangements for clarinet (E flat) & piano VVPK/AHXJ
Ragtime: Arrangements for flute trio VRNTK/AHXJ
Ragtime: Arrangements for guitar ensemble TSNK/AHXJ
Ragtime: Arrangements for organ solo RK/AHXJ
Ragtime: Arrangements for piccolo & piano VQPK/AHXJ
Ragtime: Piano solos QPHXJ
Recorded blues: Songs: Solo voice: Books AKDW/HHW/FD
Recorded jazz: Books AMT/FD
Recorded music: Books A/FD
Recorded music: Popular music: Books A/GB/FD
Recorded music: Popular songs: Books ADW/GB/FD
Recorded music: Smetana, B. BSIM/FD
Recorder VS
Recorder (bass) VSU
Recorder (descant) VSR
Recorder (tenor) VST
Recorder (treble) VSS
Recorder: Accompanying contralto voice KFQE/VS
Recorder: Accompanying female voice, Child's voice KFE/VS
Recorder: Books AVS
Recorder & guitar VSPLTS
Recorder & strings: Ensembles: Accompanying choral music ENVS
Recorder, keyboard & percussion: Ensembles: Accompanying female voices, children's voices: Unison JFE/NYFS
Recorder, strings, keyboard & percussion: Chamber music NYDS
Recorder, strings, keyboard & percussion: Ensembles: Accompanying female voices, children's voices: Unison JFE/NYDS
Recorders (3) & piano VSNSQ
Recording: Books A/F
Reels: Military band UMMHVJ
Regimental marches: Military band UMMGM/KH
Regimental music: Irish bagpipes VYT/KH
Religious cantatas DE

Religious cantatas: Accompanied by brass septet GE/WNPDE
Religious cantatas: Accompanied by orchestra EMDE
Religious cantatas: Baritone voice: Accompanied by cello & orchestra KGNE/MPSRDE
Religious cantatas: Female voices, Children's voices FDE
Religious cantatas: Female voices, Children's voices: Unison: Accompanied by percussion & keyboard JFE/NYLDE
Religious cantatas: Unaccompanied female voices, children's voices FEZDE
Religious choral music DC
Accompanied by brass septet GE/WNPDC
Accompanied by orchestra EMDC
Baritone voice: Accompanied by cello & orchestra KGNE/MPJRDC
Books AD/L
Contralto voice: Accompanied by cello & piano KFQE/SRPDC
Female voices, Children's voices: Unison: Accompanied by percussion & keyboard JFE/NYLDC
Unaccompanied female voices, children's voices FEZDC
Religious music: Motets, Anthems, Hymns, etc. DH
Accompanied by brass band EWMDH
Accompanied by string quintet ERXNRDH
Accompanied by trumpets (3) & organ EWSNSRDH
Accompanied by viol quintet ESTNRDH
Accompanied by violins (2) & keyboard ESNTPWDH
Accompanied by wind band EUMDH
Arrangements for brass band WMK/DH
Arrangements for chord organ RPVCK/DH
Arrangements for guitar solo TSPMK/DH
Arrangements for piano solo QPK/DH
Arrangements for wind band UMK/DH
Baritone voice KGNDH
Bass voice: Accompanied by strings & keyboard quintet KGXE/NXNRDH
Duets: Middle voices: Vocal ensembles JNFVEDH
Female voice, Child's voice KFDH
Female voices, Children's voices: Accompanied by flute, strings & percussion sextet FE/NYERNQDH
Female voices, Children's voices: Accompanied by percussion FE/XDH
Female voices, Children's voices: Accompanied by woodwind, keyboard & percussion FE/NYFPNTDH
Female voices, Children's voices: Unison JFDH
Female voices, Children's voices: Unison: Accompanied by wind & percussion JFE/NYHDH
High voice KFTDH
Male voices: Accompanied by brass & keyboard sextet GE/NWXPNQDH
Soprano voices: Unison JFLDH
Tenor voices: Unison: Accompanied by brass sextet JGHE/WNQDH
Unaccompanied female voices, children's voices FEZDH
Unaccompanied male voices GEZDH
Unaccompanied works EZDH
Unison JDH
Vocal duets JNEDH
Religious music: Popular music A/GB/L
Religious musical plays: Vocal scores CM/L
Religious vocal music CB/L
Requiem Masses: Roman liturgy DGKAV
Retford Centenary Exhibition ARXT/BC(P/WJ)
Rhythm 'n' blues: Books AKDW/HHR
Richard, Cliff: Books AKDW/GB/E(P)
Rigaudons: Piano solos QPHVK
Rimsky-Korsakoff, Nikolai: Books BRI
Ringing: Church bells: Books AXSR/E
Rock 'n' roll: Books A/HK
Rock 'n' roll—influenced by folk music A/HK(ZF)
Rock 'n' roll singers: Books AKDW/HK/E(M)
Rolling Stones: Books AKDW/GB/E(P)
Roman liturgy: Choral works DFF
Roman liturgy: Unaccompanied works EZDFF
Roman liturgy: Unison JDFF
Rondos: Arrangements for double bass & piano SSPK/W
Rondos: Arrangements for violin & piano STK/LW
Rondos: Brass septet WNP/W
Rondos: Horn & piano WTP/W

Rondos: Violin & piano SP/W
Rounds: Songs: Unaccompanied female voices: children's voices FEZDW/XC
Rounds: Songs: Unaccompanied male voices GEZDW/XC
Rounds: Unaccompanied works EZDW/XC
Royal College of Organists: Books AR(YC/VP/Q)
Royal Opera House, Covent Garden: Books AC/E(YC/QB)
Rudiments of music: Books A/M
Russia: Collections: Holy Week: Orthodox Eastern Church: Unaccompanied works EZDGTC/LH/AYM

St Andrew's Church, Boreham: Organ AR/B(YDDB)
Salvator mundi: Anglican liturgy DGMS
Sambas: Brass band WMHVKS
Satie, Erik: Books BSCT
Savoy operas: Sullivan, Sir A. S.: Books BSWACF
Saxophone VU
Saxophone (alto) VUS
Scaling: Pipes: Organ: Books AR/BPPG
Schools: Education: Books A(VF)
Schubert, Franz: Books BSF
Scotland: Collection: Folk songs: Arrangements for piano duet, 4 hands QNVK/DW/G/AYDL
Scotland: Folk songs: Collections: Arrangements for piano solo QPK/DW/G/AYDL
Sea: Shanties: Books ADW/GMC
Secondary schools: Recorded music A/FD(VK)
Sequences: Proper of the Mass: Unaccompanied works EZDGKADD
Serial music: Books A/PN
Secular cantatas DX
Secular cantatas: Accompanied by electronic instruments EPVDX
Secular cantatas: Accompanied by orchestra EMDX
Secular cantatas: Accompanied by wind band EUMDX
Secular cantatas: Accompanying choral music ENYLDX
Secular cantatas: Female voices, Children's voices FDX
Secular cantatas: Female voices, Children's voices: Unison: Accompanied by keyboard & percussion JFE/NYLDX
Secular cantatas: Female voices, Children's voices: Unison: Accompanied by recorder, strings, keyboard & percussion JFE/NYDSDX
Secular cantatas: Female voices, Children's voices: Unison: Accompanied by wind, strings & percussion JFE/NYEDX
Secular cantatas: Mezzo-soprano voice: Accompanied by orchestra KFNE/MDX
Secular cantatas: Mezzo-soprano voice: Accompanied by woodwind, strings, keyboard & percussion sextet KFNE/NYDNQDX
Secular cantatas: Soprano voice KFLDX
Secular cantatas: Soprano voice: Accompanied by horn & orchestra KFLE/MPWTDX
Secular cantatas: Soprano voice: Accompanied by string quartet KFLE/RXNSDX
Secular cantatas: Soprano voice: Accompanied by wind, strings & keyboard sextet KFLE/NUNQDX
Secular cantatas: Soprano voice: Accompanied by wind, strings, keyboard & percussion sextet KFLE/NYDNQDX
Secular cantatas: Soprano voices FLDX
Secular cantatas: Soprano voices: Accompanied by clarinet, keyboard & percussion sextet KFLE/NYFVNQDX
Secular cantatas: Tenor voice: Accompanied by horn & string orchestra KGHE/RXMPWTDX
Secular cantatas: Tenor voice: Accompanied by string octet KGHE/RXNNDX
Secular cantatas: Tenor voice: Accompanied by wind band KGHE/UMDX
Secular cantatas: Unaccompanied works EZDX
Secular cantatas: Unison JDX
Secular cantatas: Unison: Accompanied by wind band JE/UMDX
Secular cantatas: Vocal quartet: Accompanied by orchestra JNCE/MDX
Secular choral music DTZ
Accompanied by brass septet EWNPDTZ
Accompanied by chime bars EXTPRPDTZ
Accompanied by electronic instruments EPVDTZ
Accompanied by guitar ETSDTZ
Accompanied by guitar & piano ETSPDTZ
Accompanied by keyboard & percussion ENYLDTZ
Accompanied by keyboard & percussion trio ENYLNTDTZ
Accompanied by lute duet ETWNUDTZ

6

Accompanied by orchestra   EMDTZ
Accompanied by recorder & string quintet
    ENVSNRDTZ
Accompanied by violin   ESDTZ
Accompanied by wind band   EUMDTZ
Arrangements for brass band
    WMK/DTZ
Arrangements for brass quartet
    WNSK/DTZ
Arrangements for cello & piano
    SRPK/DTZ
Arrangements for cello duet
    SRNUK/DTZ
Arrangements for descant recorder & piano
    VSRPK/DTZ
Arrangements for descant recorder quintet
    VSRNRK/DTZ
Arrangements for descant recorder solo
    VSRPMK/DTZ
Arrangements for electronic organ
    RPVK/DTZ
Arrangements for flute & guitar
    VRPLTSK/DTZ
Arrangements for flute & piano
    VRPK/DTZ
Arrangements for guitar   TSPMK/DTZ
Arrangements for harp   TQPMK/DTZ
Arrangements for instrumental ensembles
    LNK/DTZ
Arrangements for military band
    UMMK/DTZ
Arrangements for organ   RK/DTZ
Arrangements for piano duet, 4 hands
    QNVK/DTZ
Arrangements for piano solo
    QPK/DTZ
Arrangements for plucked string instrument
    band   TMK/DTZ
Arrangements for recorder, strings, keyboard &
    percussion   NYDSK/DTZ
Arrangements for recorders (3) & piano
    VSNSQK/DTZ
Arrangements for string quartet
    RXNSK/DTZ
Arrangements for tenor recorder trio
    VSTNTK/DTZ
Arrangements for treble recorder quintet
    VSSNRK/DTZ
Arrangements for trombone quartet
    WUNSK/DTZ
Arrangements for violin duet
    SNUK/DTZ
Arrangements for wind band
    UMK/DTZ
Books   ADTZ
Choral scores   DADTZ
Cotton, R.: Books   BCMTADTZ
Female voices, Children's voices
    FDTZ
Female voices, Children's voices: Unison
    JFDTZ
Female voices, Children's voices: Unison:
    Accompanied by descant recorder,
    keyboard & percussion
    JFE/NYFSRDTZ
Female voices, Children's voices: Unison:
    Accompanied by guitar
    JFE/TSDTZ
Female voices, Children's voices: Unison:
    Accompanied by instruments (4) &
    percussion   JFE/LNRPXDJZ
Female voices, Children's voices: Unison:
    Accompanied by keyboard & percussion
    JFE/NYLDTZ
Female voices, Children's voices: Unison:
    Accompanied by percussion band
    JFE/XMDTZ
Female voices, Children's voices: Unison:
    Accompanied by recorder, keyboard &
    percussion   JFE/NYFSDTZ
Female voices, Children's voices: Unison:
    Accompanied by recorder, strings,
    keyboard & percussion
    JFE/NYDSDTZ
Female voices, Children's voices: Unison:
    Accompanied by strings & percussion
    JFE/NYJDTZ
Female voices, Children's voices: Unison:
    Accompanied by wind, strings &
    percussion   JFE/NYEDTZ
Male voices   GDTZ
Schubert, F.: Books   BSFADTZ
Soprano voice   FLDTZ
Unaccompanied female voices, children's
    voices   FEZDTZ
Unaccompanied female voices, children's
    voices: Unison   JFEZDTZ
Unaccompanied male voices   GEZDTZ
Unaccompanied works   EZDTZ
Unison   JDTZ
Unison: Accompanied by guitar
    JE/TSDTZ
Unison: Accompanied by wind band
    JE/UMDTZ
Secular vocal music: Accompanied by chamber
    orchestra   KE/MRDTZ
Baritone voice   KGNDTZ
Baritone voice: Accompanied by electronic
    instruments   KGNE/PVDTZ

Books   AKDTZ
Contralto voice   KFQDTZ
Contralto voice: Accompanied by recorder &
    piano   KFQE/VSPDTZ
Female voice, Child's voice: Accompanied by
    recorder & piano   KFE/VSPDTZ
Female voice, Child's voice duets: Vocal
    ensembles   JNFEDTZ
High voice   KFTDTZ
High voice: Accompanied by clarinet & piano
    KFTE/VVPDTZ
Low voice   KFXDTZ
Mezzo-soprano voice: Accompanied by
    chamber orchestra
    KFNE/MRDTZ
Mezzo-soprano voice: Accompanied by guitar
    KFNE/TSDTZ
Mezzo-soprano voice: Accompanied by
    orchestra   KFNE/MDTZ
Mezzo-soprano voice: Accompanied by wood-
    wind, strings, keyboard & percussion
    sextet   KFNE/NYDNQDTZ
Middle voice: Accompanied by guitar
    KFVE/TSDTZ
Solo voice: Accompanied by guitar
    KE/TSDTZ
Solo voice: Accompanied by guitar & piano
    KE/TSPDTZ
Solo voice: Accompanied by lute
    KE/TWDTZ
Solo voice: Accompanied by percussion
    KE/XDTZ
Solos   KDTZ
Soprano voice   KFLDTZ
Soprano voice: Accompanied by cello solo
    KFLE/SSPMDTZ
Soprano voice: Accompanied by clarinet (4)
    & string trio
    KFLE/NVVQNTDTZ
Soprano voice: Accompanied by clarinet,
    keyboard & percussion sextet
    KFLE/NYFVNQDTZ
Soprano voice: Accompanied by horn &
    orchestra   KFLE/DPWTDTZ
Soprano voice: Accompanied by orchestra
    KFLE/MDTZ
Soprano voice: Accompanied by string &
    keyboard quartet
    KFLE/NXNSDTZ
Soprano voice: Accompanied by string
    quartet   KFLE/RXNSDTZ
Soprano voice: Accompanied by violins (2)
    & keyboard   KFLE/SNTPWDTZ
Soprano voice: Accompanied by wind, strings
    & keyboard sextet
    KFLE/NUNQDTZ
Soprano voice: Accompanied by wind, strings,
    keyboard & percussion sextet
    KFLE/NYDNQDTZ
Tenor duets: Accompanied by orchestra
    JNGHE/MDTZ
Tenor voice   KGHDTZ
Tenor voice: Accompanied by guitar
    KGHE/TSDTZ
Tenor voice: Accompanied by horn & string
    orchestra   KGHE/RXMPWTDTZ
Tenor voice: Accompanied by string octet
    KGHE/RXNNDTZ
Tenor voice: Accompanied by wind band
    KGHE/UMDTZ
Vocal quartet: Accompanied by orchestra
    JNCE/MDTZ
Septets: Brass ensemble   WNP
Septets: Brass ensemble: Accompanying choral
    works   EWNP
Septets: Brass ensemble: Accompanying male
    voices   GE/WNP
Septets: Drums   XQNP
Septets: Recorder   VSNP
Septets: Woodwind instruments   VNP
Septets: Woodwind, keyboard & percussion
    NYFPNP
Sext: Divine Office: Roman liturgy:
    Unaccompanied works   EZDGKHL
Sextets: Brass & keyboards: Accompanying male
    voices   GE/NWXPNQ
Sextets: Brass instruments: Accompanying tenor
    voices: Unison   JGHE/WNQ
Sextets: Clarinet   VVNQ
Sextets: Clarinet, keyboard & percussion:
    Accompanying soprano voice
    KFLE/NYFVNQ
Sextets: Flute, strings & percussion: Accompanying
    female voices, children's voices
    FE/NYERNQ
Sextets: Percussion ensemble   XNQ
Sextets: String ensemble   RXNQ
Sextets: Wind ensemble   UNQ
Sextets: Wind, strings & keyboards   NUNQ
Sextets: Wind, strings & keyboard:
    Accompanying soprano voice
    KFLE/NUNQ
Sextets: Wind, strings, keyboard & percussion:
    Accompanying soprano voice
    KFLE/NYDNQ
Sextets: Wind, strings, keyboard & percussion:
    Accompanying speaking chorus
    HYE/NYDNQ
Sextets: Woodwind ensemble   VNQ

Sextets: Woodwind, strings, keyboard & percussion
    NYDPNQ
Sextets: Woodwind, strings, keyboard & percussion:
    Accompanying mezzo-soprano voice
    KFNE/NYDNQ
Shaw, Martin: Books   BSGP
Sheffield: Books   A(YDCGS)
Sicilianos: Flute & piano   VRPHVQ
Sight reading: Piano playing   Q/EG
Sinfoniettas: Symphony orchestra   MMEM
Singers: Blues: Solo voice: Books
    AKDW/HHW/E(M)
Singers: Castrato voice: Books
    AKGGC/E(M)
Singers: Popular music: Books
    AKDW/GB/E(M)
Singers: Rock'n' roll: Songs: Solo voice: Books
    AKDW/HK/E(M)
Singers: Tenor voice: Books   AKGH/E(M)
Singing: Books   AB/E
Sitar: Books   ATSX
Slade: Books   AKDW/GB/E(P)
Slovakia: Folk songs: Collections: Unaccompanied
    voices   GEZDW/G/AYFS
Smetana, Bedrich: Books   BSIM
Solos: Organ   R
Solos: Vocal music   K
Solos: Vocal music: Books   AK
Solos, Unaccompanied: Accordion   RSPM
Solos, Unaccompanied: Bassoon   VWPM
Solos, Unaccompanied: Cello   SRPM
Solos, Unaccompanied: Clarinet   VVPM
Solos, Unaccompanied: Descant recorder
    VSRPM
Solos, Unaccompanied: Double bass   SSPM
Solos, Unaccompanied: Flute   VRPM
Solos, Unaccompanied: Guitar   TSPM
Solos, Unaccompanied: Harp   TQPM
Solos, Unaccompanied: Lute   TWPM
Solos, Unaccompanied: Oboe   VTPM
Solos, Unaccompanied: Treble recorder
    VSSPM
Solos, Unaccompanied: Trombone   WUPM
Solos, Unaccompanied: Trumpet   WSPM
Solos, Unaccompanied: Tuba   WVPM
Solos, Unaccompanied: Viola   SQPM
Solos, Unaccompanied: Violin   SPM
Sonatas: Arrangements for recorder quintet
    VSNRK/AE
Sonatas: Arrangements for treble recorder & piano
    VSSPK/AE
Sonatas: Arrangements for trumpet & piano
    WSPK/AE
Sonatas: Arrangements for unaccompanied guitar
    TSPMK/AE
Sonatas: Arrangements for viola & piano
    SQPK/LE
Sonatas: Bassoon & piano   VWPE
Sonatas: Cello duet   SRNUE
Sonatas: Cello solos   SRPME
Sonatas: Clarinet & piano   VVPE
Sonatas: Descant recorder & piano   VSRPE
Sonatas: Flute & piano   VRPE
Sonatas: Flute duet   VRNUE
Sonatas: Flute, strings & keyboard trio
    NURNTE
Sonatas: Guitar solo   TSPME
Sonatas: Keyboard solos   PWPE
Sonatas: Oboe & keyboard trio   NWNTE
Sonatas: Oboe, string & keyboard trio
    NUTNTE
Sonatas: Organ   RE
Sonatas: Piano solos   QPE
Sonatas: Sextets: Wind, strings & keyboard
    NUNQE
Sonatas: Strings & keyboard trio   NXNTE
Sonatas: Treble recorder & piano   VSSPE
Sonatas: Treble recorders (2) & keyboard
    VSSNTPWE
Sonatas: Trombone, strings & keyboard quartet
    NUXUNSE
Sonatas: Trumpet, keyboard & percussion
    NYFXSNNE
Sonatas: Trumpet, strings & keyboard quintet
    NUXSNRE
Sonatas: Trumpets (2) & string orchestra
    RXMPWSNUE
Sonatas: Unaccompanied bassoon   VWTME
Sonatas: Viola d'amore & piano   SQQPE
Sonatas: Violin & piano   SPE
Sonatas: Violin solos   SPME
Sonatas: Wind, strings & keyboard quartet
    NUNSE
Sonatas: Woodwind & keyboard trio
    NWPNTE
Sonatinas: Arrangements for clarinet & piano
    VVPK/AEM
Sonatinas: Clarinet & piano   VVPEM
Sonatinas: Flute & piano   VRPEM
Sonatinas: Oboe & piano   VTPEM
Sonatinas: Treble recorder & piano
    VSSPEM
Sonatinas: Trumpet & piano   WSPEM
Sonatinas: Unaccompanied oboe   VTPMEM
Sonatinas: Viola duets   SQNUEM
Songs: Accompanied by brass septet
    EWNPDW
Songs: Accompanied by chime bars
    EXTPRPDW

Trios: Percussion ensemble XNT
Trios: Recorder VSNT
Trios: String ensembles RXNT
Trios: Strings & keyboard NXNT
Trios: Tenor recorder VSTNT
Trios: Wind & keyboard NWNT
Trios: Woodwind instruments VNT
Trios: Woodwind & keyboard NWPNT
Trios: Woodwind, keyboard & percussion: Accompanying female voices, children's voices FE/NYFPNT
Trombone WU
Trombone & brass band WMPWU
Trombone, strings, & keyboard: Chamber music NUXU
Trombone, strings, keyboard & percussion NYDXU
Trumpet WS
Trumpet & organ WSPLR
Trumpet & string orchestra RXMPWS
Trumpet & timpani WSPLXR
Trumpet & wind band UMPWS
Trumpet, keyboard & percussion: Chamber music NYFXS
Trumpet, strings & keyboard: Chamber music NUXS
Trumpets (2) & keyboard WSNTPW
Trumpets (2) & organ WSNTR
Trumpets (2) & piano WSNTQ
Trumpets (2) & string orchestra RXMPWSNU
Trumpets (3) & organ: Accompanying choral music EWSNSR
Tuba WV
Tuba & military band UMMPWV
Turkey: Books BZC
Tutors: Brass instruments W/AC
Tutors: Chord organ RPVC/AC
Tutors: Descant recorder VSR/AC
Tutors: Drum XQ/AC
Tutors: Oboe VT/AC
Tutors: Piano Q/AC
Tutors: Pipes VSX/AC
Tutors: Recorder VS/AC
Tutors: Tabla: Percussion instruments: North India: Books BZFLAXQ/AC
Tutors: Trombone WU/AC
Twelve tone music: Books A/PN

Unaccompanied accordion solos RSPM
Unaccompanied bassoon solos VWPM
Unaccompanied cello solos SRPM
Unaccompanied choral works EZ
Unaccompanied clarinet solos VVPM
Unaccompanied descant recorder solos VSRPM
Unaccompanied double bass: Accompanying soprano voice KFLE/SSPM
Unaccompanied double bass solos SSPM
Unaccompanied female voices, children's voices: Choral works FEZ
Unaccompanied female voices, children's voices: Unison JFEZ
Unaccompanied flute solos VRPM
Unaccompanied guitar TSPM
Unaccompanied harp solos TQPM
Unaccompanied lute solos TWPM
Unaccompanied male voices: Choral music GEZ
Unaccompanied oboe solos VTPM
Unaccompanied pipes VSXPM
Unaccompanied treble recorder VSSPM
Unaccompanied trombone solos WUPM
Unaccompanied trumpet solos WSPM
Unaccompanied tuba solos WVPM
Unaccompanied viola solos SQPM
Unaccompanied violin solos SPM
Unison choral works J
Unison songs JDW
United Reform Church: Hymns DM/LSG
United States: Books A(YT)
United States: Collections: Arrangements for piano solo QPK/AYT
United States: Collections: Hymns: Unaccompanied male voices GEZDM/AYT
United States: Collections: Motets, Anthems, Hymns, etc. DH/AYT
United States: Collections: Popular songs: Vocal solo KDW/GB/AYT
United States: Collections: Motets, Anthems, Hymns, etc.: Unaccompanied works EZDH/AYT

United States: Musical plays: Books ACM/E(YT)
United States: Organs AR/B(YT)
United States: Popular music: Books ADW/GB(YT)
United States: Recorded music: Popular songs: Books ADW/GB/FD(YT)

Variations: Arrangements for unaccompanied harp TQPMK/AT
Variations: Arrangements for violin & piano SPK/LT
Variations: Brass band WM/T
Variations: Brass quartet WNS/T
Variations: Brass & organ quintet WNRR/T
Variations: Chamber orchestra MR/T
Variations: Clarinet & piano VVP/T
Variations: Guitar solo TSPM/T
Variations: Organ R/T
Variations: Piano solos QP/T
Variations: String trio RXNT/T
Variations: Viola & piano SQP/T
Variations: Wind band UM/T
Variations: Wind quintet UNR/T
Verdi, Giuseppe: Books BVE
Vespers: Divine Office: Unaccompanied works EZDGKJ
Victoria, Tomàs Luis de: Books BVI
Viol ST
Viola SQ
Viola d'amore SQQ
Viola & orchestra MPSQ
Viola & string orchestra RXMPSQ
Violin S
Violin: Accompanying choral music ES
Violin & cello SPLSR
Violin & orchestra MPS
Violin, cello & orchestra MPSPLSR
Violin, flute & string orchestra RXMPVRPLS
Violin, piano & orchestra MPSP
Violins (2) & keyboard: Accompanying soprano voice KFLE/SNTPW
Violins (4) & string orchestra RXMPSNS
Violoncello SR
Violoncello: Books ASR
Violoncello & double bass SRPLSS
Violoncello & string orchestra RXMPSR
Violoncello, violin & orchestra MPSPLSR
Virginals QSQ
Vocalises CB/AFH
Vocalises K/AFH
Vocal music CB
Vocal music: Arrangements for recorder trio VSNTK/CB
Vocal music: Books AB
Vocal music: Choral scores DACB
Voice: Books AB

Wagner, Richard: Books BWC
Wales: Collections: Folk songs: Female voices, Children's voices: Unison JFDW/G/AYDK
Wales: Collections: Folk songs: Male voices GDW/G/AYDK
Wales: Collections: Songs, Arrangements for unaccompanied harp TQPMK/DW/AYDK
Wales: Folk music: Books A/G(YDK)
Waltzes: Accordion solos RSPMHW
Waltzes: Arrangements for woodwind & strings NVPK/AHW
Waltzes: Guitar solo TSPMHW
Waltzes: Piano solos QPHW
Weddings: Motets, Anthems, Hymns, etc.: High voice KFTDH/KDD
Wells Cathedral: Organ: Books AR/B(YDFGWB)
Wells: Somerset: Organ: Books AR/B(YDFGW)
West Indies: Collections: Folk songs: Arrangements for piano solo QPK/DW/G/AYULD
West Indies: Collections: Folk songs: Unaccompanied female voices, children's voices FEZDW/G/AYULD
Whitsun: Musical plays CM/LN
Who, The: Books AKDW/GB/E(P)
Wilson, Sandy: Books BWNTM

Wind & keyboard: Ensembles: Chamber music NW
Wind & percussion: Ensembles: Accompanying female voices, children's voices: Unison JFE/NYH
Wind & strings: Ensembles: Chamber music NV
Wind & strings: Ensembles: Accompanying choral music ENV
Wind band: Accompanying tenor voice KGHE/UM
Wind band: Accompanying unison voices JE/UM
Wind instruments U
Wind instruments: Accompanying choral music EU
Wind instruments: Accompanying tenor voice KGHE/U
Wind instruments: Accompanying unison choral works JE/U
Wind instruments: Books AU
Wind, keyboard & percussion: Ensembles: Accompanying female voices, children's voices FE/NYF
Wind, keyboard & percussion: Ensembles: Accompanying female voices, children's voices: Unison JFE/NYF
Wind, keyboard & percussion: Ensembles: Chamber music NYF
Wind, strings & keyboard: Ensembles: Accompanying soprano voice KFLE/NU
Wind, strings & keyboard: Ensembles: Chamber music NU
Wind, strings, keyboard & percussion: Ensembles: Accompanying female voices, children's voices: Unison JFE/NYD
Wind, strings, keyboard & percussion: Ensembles: Accompanying mezzo-soprano voice KFNE/NYD
Wind, strings, keyboard & percussion: Ensembles: Accompanying soprano voice KFLE/NYD
Wind, strings, keyboard & percussion: Ensembles: Accompanying speaking chorus HYE/NYD
Wind, strings, keyboard & percussion: Ensembles: Chamber music NYD
Wind, strings & percussion: Ensembles: Accompanying female voices, children's voices FE/NYE
Wind, strings & percussion: Ensembles: Accompanying female voices, children's voices: Unison JFE/NYE
Wind, strings & percussion: Ensembles: Chamber music NYE
Wishart, Trevor: Books BWNV
Woman's voice KF
Women's voices: Choral works F
Women's voices: Unison JF
Woodwind & keyboard: Ensembles: Chamber music NWP
Woodwind & strings: Ensembles: Chamber music NVP
Woodwind & strings: Ensembles: Accompanying choral music ENVP
Woodwind instrument & orchestra MPV
Woodwind instruments V
Woodwind instruments: Accompanying contralto voice KFQE/V
Woodwind instruments: Books AV
Woodwind, keyboard & percussion: Ensembles: Accompanying female voices, children's voices FE/NYFP
Woodwind, keyboard & percussion: Ensembles: Accompanying female voices, children's voices: Unison JFE/NYFP
Woodwind, keyboard & percussion: Ensembles: Chamber music NYFP
Woodwind, strings & keyboard: Ensembles: Chamber music NUP
Woodwind, strings & percussion: Ensembles: Accompanying female voices, children's voices FE/NYEP
Woodwind, strings, keyboard & percussion: Ensembles: Accompanying female voices, children's voices: Unison JFE/NYDP
Woodwind, strings, keyboard & percussion: Ensembles: Chamber music NYDP
Writers: Aesthetics & criticism: Books A/CC(M)

Yorkshire: Collections: Dances for dancing: Instrumental ensemble LH/H/G/AYDJG

LIST OF MUSIC PUBLISHERS

While every effort has been made to check the information given in this list with the publishers concerned, the British Library cannot hold itself responsible for any errors or omissions.

ACUFF-ROSE Music Ltd. 16 St George St., London W.1. *Tel:* 01-629-0392. *Grams:* Acufrose London.

AFFILIATED MUSIC Publishers Ltd. 138 Charing Cross Rd, London WC2H OLD. *Tel:* 01-836-9351.

AMERICAN UNIVERSITY PUBLISHERS Group, Ltd. 70 Great Russell St., London WC1B 3BY. *Tel:* 01-405-0182. *Grams:* Amunpress.

ANTICO Edition. North Harton, Lustleigh, Newton Abbot, Devon TQ13 9SG. *Tel:* Lustleigh (064 77) 260.

ARNOLD. E.J. Arnold & Son Ltd. Butterley St., Leeds LS10 1AX.

ARS VIVA. 48 Great Marlborough St., London W1V 2BN.

ASCHERBURG, HOPWOOD AND CREW Ltd. 50 New Bond St., London W1A 2BR. *Tel:* 01-629-7600. *Grams:* Symphony London.

ASHDOWN. Edwin Ashdown, Ltd. 275-281 Cricklewood Broadway, London NW2 6QR. *Tel:* 01-450-5237.

ASHLEY-FIELDS Music Ltd. 61 Frith St., London W1V 5TA. *Tel:* 01-734-7462. *Grams:* Fieldmus London.

ASSOCIATED BOARD OF THE ROYAL SCHOOLS OF MUSIC. (Publications Dept), 14 Bedford Sq., London WC1B 3JG. *Tel:* 01-636-6919. *Grams:* Musexam London WC1.

ASSOCIATED MUSIC Publishers Inc. c/o G. Schirmer Ltd, 140 Strand, London WC2R 1HH. *Tel:* 01-836-4011.

BANKS and Son (Music) Ltd. Stonegate, York.

BARENREITER Ltd. 32 Great Titchfield St., London W.1. *Tel:* 01-580-9008.

BAYLEY AND FERGUSON, Ltd. 65 Berkeley St., Glasgow C3. *Tel:* Central 7240. *Grams:* Bayley Glasgow.

B.B.C. *See* British Broadcasting Corporation.

BELWIN-MILLS Music, Ltd. 250 Purley Way, Croydon CR9 4QD. *Tel:* 01-681-0855. *Grams:* Belmilmus Croydon.

BERRY MUSIC Co. Ltd. 10 Denmark St., London WC2H 8LU. *Tel:* 01-836-1653.

BLOSSOM Music, Ltd. 139 Piccadilly, London W.1. *Tel:* 01-629-7211. *Grams:* Leedsmusik London W1.

BODLEY HEAD. The Bodley Head, Ltd. 9 Bow St., London WC2E 7AL. *Tel:* 01-836-9081. *Grams:* Bodleian London WC2.

BOOSEY AND HAWKES Music Publishers, Ltd. 295 Regent St., London W1A 1BR. *Tel:* 01-580-2060. *Grams:* Sonorous London W1. *Trade:* The Hyde, Edgware Rd, London NW9 6JN. *Tel:* 01-205-3861. *Grams:* Sonorous London NW9.

BOSWORTH and Co., Ltd. 14 Heddon St., London W1R 8DP. *Tel:* 01-734-0475. *Grams:* Bosedition London W1.

BOURNE MUSIC Ltd. 34/36 Maddox St., London W1R 9PD. *Tel:* 01-493-6412. *Grams:* Bournemusic London W1.

BREGMAN, VOCCO AND CONN, Ltd. 50 New Bond St., London W1A 1BR. *Tel:* 01-629-7600. *Grams:* Symphony London.

BREITKOPF AND HARTEL (London) Ltd. 8 Horse and Dolphin Yard, London W1V 7LG. *Tel:* 01-437-3342. *Grams:* Breitkopfs London W.1.

BRITISH AND CONTINENTAL Music Agencies, Ltd. 64 Dean St., London W.1. *Tel:* 01-437-7543.

BRITISH BROADCASTING CORPORATION. BBC Publications, 35 Marylebone High St., London W1M 4AA. *Tel:* 01-580-5577. *Grams:* Broadcasts London. *Telex:* 265781.

CAMBRIDGE UNIVERSITY PRESS. Bentley House, P.O. Box 92, 200 Euston Rd, London NW1 2DB. *Tel:* 01-387-5030. *Grams:* Cantabrigia London NW1. *Telex:* 27335. *Editorial and Production:* The Pitt Building, Trumpington St., Cambridge CB2 1RP. *Tel:* Cambridge 58331. *Grams:* Unipress Cambs. *Telex:* 817256.

CAMPBELL CONNELLY and Co., Ltd. 10 Denmark St., London W.C.2. *Tel:* 01-836-1653.

CARY. L.J. Cary and Co., Ltd. 50 New Bond St., London W1A 2BR. *Tel:* 01-629-7600. *Grams:* Symphony London W1.

CENTRAL COUNCIL OF CHURCH BELL RINGERS. c/o 'Monsal', Bredon, Tewkesbury, Glos. GL20 7LY.

CHAPPELL and Co., Ltd. 50 New Bond St., London W1A 1DR. *Tel:* 01-629-7600. *Grams:* Symphony London. *Telex:* 268403.

CHARNWOOD MUSIC Publishing Co. 5 University Rd, Leicester.

CHESTER. J. and W. Chester/Edition Wilhelm Hansen London Ltd. Eagle Court, London EC1M 5QD. *Tel:* 01-253-6947. *Grams:* Guarnerius London EC1.

CLIFFORD ESSEX Music Co. Ltd. 20 Earlham St., London W.C.2. *Tel:* 01-836-2810. *Grams:* Triomphe London WC2.

COLLIER MACMILLAN Publishers. Division of Cassell and Collier Macmillan Publishers Ltd, 35 Red Lion Sq., London WC1R 4SG. *Tel:* 01-242-6281.

Connelly, Campbell and Co., Ltd. *See* Campbell Connelly.

CONSTABLE and Co., Ltd. 10 Orange St., London WC2H 7EG. *Tel:* 01-930-0801. *Grams:* Dhagoba London WC2. *Trade:* Tiptree, Essex. *Tel:* 0621-81-6362.

CRAMER. J.B. Cramer and Co., Ltd. 99 St Martin's Lane, London WC2N 4AZ. *Tel:* 01-240-1612.

CRANZ and Co. Ltd. Alderman's House, Bishopsgate, London E.C.2. *Tel:* 01-283-4266. *Grams:* Cranz Usually London.

Curwen. J. Curwen and Sons, Ltd. *See* Faber Music.

DANIEL. The C.W. Daniel Co. Ltd. 60 Muswell Rd, London N.10. *Tel:* 01-444-8650.

DAVID AND CHARLES (Publishers), Ltd. South Devon House, Railway Station, Newton Abbot, Devon TQ12 2BP. *Tel:* 0626-3521. *Telex:* 42904.

DE WOLFE, Ltd. 80-82 Wardour St., London W1V 3LF. *Tel:* 01-437-4933. *Grams:* Musicall London.

DICK JAMES MUSIC Ltd. 71 New Oxford St., London WC1A 1DP. *Tel:* 01-836-4864.

EFDS. *See* English Folk Dance and Song Society.

EGRET HOUSE. 93 Chancery La., London W.C.2.

ELKIN and Co., Ltd. Borough Green, Sevenoaks, Kent. *Tel:* 0732-88-3261. *Grams:* Novellos Sevenoaks.

EMERSON. June Emerson Wind Music. Windmill Farm, Ampleforth, York.

EMI MUSIC. 20 Manchester Sq., London W.1. *Tel:* 01-486-4488.

ENGLISH FOLK DANCE AND SONG SOCIETY. Cecil Sharp House, 2 Regent's Park Rd, London NW1 7AY. *Tel:* 01-485-2206.

EP PUBLISHING. EP Group of Companies. Bradford Rd, East Ardsley, Wakefield, Yorkshire. *Tel:* Wakefield 823971 (0924). *Grams:* Edpro Wakefield. *London Office:* 27 Maunsel St., London SW1P 2QS. *Tel:* 01-834-1067.

Essex, C. Clifford Essex Music Co. Ltd. *See* Clifford Essex.

ESSEX MUSIC Group. Essex House, 19/20 Poland St., London W1V 3DD. *Tel:* 01-734-8121. *Grams:* Sexmus London. *Trade:* Music Sales Ltd, 78 Newman St., London W.1.

EULENBURG. Ernst Eulenburg, Ltd. 48 Great Marlborough St., London W1V 2BN. *Tel:* 01-437-1246.

FABER MUSIC, Ltd. 38 Russell Sq., London WC1B 5DA. *Tel:* 01-636-1344. *Grams:* Fabbaf London WC1.

FAMOUS CHAPPELL, Ltd. 50 New Bond St., London W1A 2BR. *Tel:* 01-629-7600. *Grams:* Symphony London.

FELDMAN. B. Feldman and Co., Ltd. 1-6 Denmark Place, London WC2H 8NL. *Tel:* 01-836-6699. *Grams:* Humfriv London WC2.

FENETTE MUSIC. 138-140 Charing Cross Rd, London WC2H OLD.

FORSYTH Brothers, Ltd. 190 Grays Inn Rd, London WC1X 8EW. *Tel:* 01-837-4768.

Fox. Sam Fox Publishing Co. (London) Ltd. *See* Sam Fox.

FRANCIS, DAY AND HUNTER, Ltd. 138 Charing Cross Rd, London WC2H OLD. *Tel:* 01-836-6699. *Grams:* Arpeggio London WC2.

FRANK MUSIC Co, Ltd. 50 New Bond St., London W1A 2BR. *Tel:* 01-629-7600. *Grams:* Symphony London.

FREEMAN. H. Freeman, Ltd. 138 Charing Cross Rd, London WC2H OLD. *Tel:* 01-836-6699.

GALLIARD, Ltd. 82 High Rd, London N2 9PW.

GLOCKEN Verlag, Ltd. 10-16 Rathbone St., London W1P 2BJ. *Tel:* 01-580-2827. *Grams:* Operetta London W1.

GOOD NEWS CRUSADE. 32a Fore St., St Austell, Cornwall PL25 5EP. *Tel:* St Austell 2716.

GRAHAM. Frank Graham. 6 Queen's Terrace, Newcastle upon Tyne 2. *Tel:* Newcastle upon Tyne 813067.

GWASG PRIFYSGOL CYMRU. *See* University of Wales Press.

Hansen. Edition Wilhelm Hansen London Ltd. *See* Chester.

HANSEN Publications Ltd. 218 Great Portland St., London W1N 6JH. *Tel:* 01-387-0851.

Hart. F. Pitman Hart and Co., Ltd. *See* Pitman Hart.

HINRICHSEN Edition Ltd. 10 Baches St., London N1 6DN. *Tel:* 01-253-1638. *Grams:* Musipeters London.

HORTON TRUST. 1 Sherbourne Rd, Great Horton, Bradford, West Yorkshire BD7 1RB. *Tel:* Bradford (0274) 26975. *Grams:* Hortrust Bradford.

HUGHES A'I FAB. (Hughes and Son) Publishers, Ltd. 29 Rivulet Rd, Wrexham, Clwyd. *Tel:* Wrexham 4340.

IMPERIA MUSIC Co. Ltd. 21 Denmark St., London W.C.2. *Tel:* 01-836-6699. *Grams:* Mauritunes London WC2.

INTER-ART Music Publishers. 10-16 Rathbone St., London W1P 2BJ. *Tel:* 01-580-2827. *Grams:* Operetta London W1.

James. Dick James Music Ltd. *See* Dick James Music.

KALMUS. Alfred A. Kalmus, Ltd. 2-3 Fareham St., London W1V 4DU. *Tel:* 01-437-5203. *Grams:* Alkamus London W1.

KEITH PROWSE MUSIC Publishing Co., Ltd. 21 Denmark St., London WC2H 8NE. *Tel:* 01-836-6699.

LEEDS MUSIC, Ltd. 230 Purley Way, Croydon CR9 4QD. *Tel:* 01-681-0855. *Grams:* Leedsmusik London.

LENGNICK. Alfred Lengnick and Co., Ltd. Purley Oaks Studios, 421a Brighton Rd, South Croydon, Surrey CR2 6YR. *Tel:* 01-660-7646.

LEONARD, GOULD AND BOLTTLER. 99 St Martin's Lane, London WC2N 4AZ. *Tel:* 01-240-1612.

LONDON PRO MUSICA. 42 Christchurch Ave., London N.W.6.

LONGMAN Group Ltd. Longman House, Burnt Mill, Harlow, Essex. *Tel:* Harlow 26721. *Trade:* Pinnacles, Harlow, Essex. *Tel:* Harlow 29655. *Grams:* 81259.

MORRIS. Edwin H. Morris and Co., Ltd. 50 New Bond St., London W1Y 9HA. *Tel:* 01-629-0576.

MOZART EDITION (Great Britain) Ltd. 199 Wardour St., London W1V 3FA. *Tel:* 01-734-3711.

MUSIC SALES Ltd. 78 Newman St., London W.1. *Tel:* 01-636-9033.

MUSICA RARA. 2 Great Marlborough St., London W.1. *Tel:* 01-437-1576.

MUSICA VIVA. 558 Galleywood Rd, Chelmsford, Essex CM2 8BX.

NATIONAL FEDERATION OF WOMEN'S INSTITUTES. 39 Eccleston St., London SW1W 9NT. *Tel:* 01-730-7212. *Grams:* Fedinsti London SW1.

NOVELLO and Co., Ltd. Borough Green, Sevenoaks, Kent TN15 8DT. *Tel:* 0732-88-3261. *Grams:* Novellos Sevenoaks.

OCTAVA Music Co., Ltd. *See* Weinberger.

OXFORD UNIVERSITY PRESS (Music Department). 44 Conduit St., London W1R ODE. *Tel:* 01-734-5364. *Grams:* Fulscore London W1.

PATERSON. Paterson's Publications, Ltd. 38 Wigmore St., London W1H OEX. *Tel:* 01-935-3551. *Grams:* Paterwia London W1.

PAXTON. Borough Green, Sevenoaks, Kent TN15 8DT.

PENGUIN Books, Ltd. Bath Rd, Harmondsworth, Middx. *Tel:* 01-759-1984. *Grams:* Penguinook West Drayton. *Telex:* 263130. *London office:* 17 Grosvenor Gardens, London S.W.1.

PETERS Edition. 10 Baches St., London N1 6DN. *Tel:* 01-253-1638. *Grams:* Musipeters London.

PHOENIX. 61 Frith St., London W1V 5TA.

PITMAN HART. F. Pitman Hart, and Co., Ltd. 99 St Martin's Lane, London WC2N 4AZ. *Tel:* 01-240-1612.

Pro Musica. *See* London Pro Musica.

Prowse. Keith Prowse Music Publishing Co. Ltd. *See* Keith Prowse Music.

R. SMITH and Co. Ltd. 210 Strand, London WC2R 1AP. *Tel:* 01-353-1166.

RAHTER. D. Rahter. Lyra House, 67 Belsize La., London N.W.3. *Tel:* 01-794-8038.

REGINA MUSIC Publishing Co., Ltd. Old Run Rd, Leeds LS10 2AA. *Tel:* Leeds 700527.

RICORDI. G. Ricordi and Co. (London), Ltd. The Bury, Church St., Chesham, Bucks HP5 1JG. *Tel:* Chesham 3311. *Grams:* Ricordi Chesham.

ROBBINS Music Corporation, Ltd. 138 Charing Cross Rd, London WC2H 0LD. *Tel:* 01-836-6699.

ROBERTON Publications. The Windmill, Wendover, Aylesbury, Bucks. HP22 6JJ. *Tel:* Wendover (0296) 623107.

ROYAL SCHOOL OF CHURCH MUSIC. Addington Palace, Croydon CR9 5AD. *Tel:* 01-654-7676. *Grams:* Cantoris Croydon.

ROYAL SCOTTISH COUNTRY DANCE SOCIETY. 12 Coates Cres., Edinburgh EH3 7AF. *Tel:* 031-225-3854.

SALVATIONIST PUBLISHING AND SUPPLIES, Ltd. 117 Judd St., London WC1H 9NN. *Tel:* 01-387-1656. *Grams:* Savingly London WC1.

SAM FOX Publishing Co. (London) Ltd. 21 Denmark St., London WC2H 8NE. *Tel:* 01-836-6699.

SCHAUER AND MAY. 67 Belsize La., London N.W.3. *Tel:* 01-794-8038.

SCHIRMER. G. Schirmer Ltd, (Music Publishers). 140 Strand, London WC2R 1HH. *Tel:* 01-836-4011.

SCHOFIELD AND SIMS, Ltd. 35 St John's Rd, Huddersfield, Yorkshire HD1 5DT. *Tel:* Huddersfield 30684. *Grams:* Schosims Huddersfield.

SCHOOLMASTER PUBLISHING Co. Ltd. Derbyshire House, Lower St., Kettering, Northants. NN16 8BB. *Tel:* 053687-3407.

SCHOTT and Co. Ltd. 48 Great Marlborough St., London W1V 2BN. *Tel:* 01-437-1246. *Grams:* Shotanco London.

SCHROEDER, A. A. Schroeder Music Publishing Co., Ltd. 15 Berkeley St., London W.1. *Tel:* 01-493-2506.

SCHROEDER AND GUNTHER Inc. c/o G. Schirmer Ltd., 140 Strand, London WC2R 1HH. *Tel:* 01-836-4011.

SIMROCK. N. Simrock. Lyra House, 67 Belsize Lane, London NW3 5AX. *Tel:* 01-794-8038.

Smith. R. Smith and Co. Ltd. *See* R. Smith.

SPARTA FLORIDA MUSIC Group Ltd. Suite 4, Carlton Tower Place, London S.W.1. *Tel:* 01-245-9339.

ST GREGORY PUBLISHING Co. 4 West Hill Rd, Hoddesdon, Herts. *Tel:* Hoddesdon 64483.

ST MARTINS PUBLICATIONS, Ltd. *No longer publishing.*

STAINER AND BELL Ltd. 82 High Rd, London N2 9PW. *Tel:* 01-444-9135.

STOCKWELL. Arthur H. Stockwell, Ltd. Elms Court, Ilfracombe, Devon EX34 8BA. *Tel:* 02716-2557. *Grams:* Stockwell, Ilfracombe.

STUDIO MUSIC Co. 89-91 Vicarage Rd, London NW10 2UA. *Tel:* 01-459-6194.

THAMES MUSIC. 39-41 New Bond St., London W.1. *Tel:* 01-499-5961.

THAMES Publishing. 14 Barlby Rd, London W10 6AR. *Tel:* 01-969-3579.

TOMUS Publications. Carne House, Parsons La., Bury, Lancs. BL9 0JT. *Tel:* 061-764-1099.

UNITED MUSIC Publishers Ltd. 1 Montague St., London WC1B 5BS. *Tel:* 01-636-5171.

UNIVERSAL Edition (London), Ltd. 2 Fareham St., Dean St., London W1V 4DU. *Tel:* 01-437-5203. *Grams:* Alkamus London W1.

UNIVERSITY OF ILLINOIS PRESS. *See* American University Publishers.

UNIVERSITY OF TEXAS PRESS, Ltd. *See* American University Publishers.

UNIVERSITY OF WALES PRESS. Merthyr House, James St., Cardiff CF1 6EU. *Tel:* Cardiff 31919.

VANGUARD MUSIC Ltd. 19 Charing Cross Rd, London W.C.2. *Tel:* 01-839-3655.

WARREN AND PHILLIPS. 196 Grays Inn Rd, London WC1X 8EW.

WEINBERGER. Joseph Weinberger Ltd. 10-16 Rathbone St., London W1P 2BJ. *Tel:* 01-580-2827. *Grams:* Operetta London W1.

WISE Publications. 78 Newman St., London W.1. *Tel:* 01-636-0933.

WOLFE Publishing, Ltd. 10 Earlham St., London WC2H 9LP. *Tel:* 01-240-2935.

YORKE Edition. 8 Cecil Rd, London W3 ODA. *Tel:* 01-992-1068.